MORE HUMOROUS STORIES

MORE HUMOROUS STORIES

INTRODUCED BY
RONNIE BARKER

This edition published in Great Britain in 1986 by

Octopus Books Limited
59 Grosvenor Street
London W1

Copyright © 1986 Introduction and arrangement
Octopus Books Limited

ISBN 0 86273 353 7

Printed and bound in Great Britain by Collins, Glasgow

CONTENTS

Contents

Contents

Contents

Introduction

Sequels are brave men's territory. There's always a risk in going back for more of a good thing: perhaps the lights won't twinkle as brightly the second time around, the beer is flatter, the conversation flags. But who could pass up this opportunity to include all the side-splitting sagas and witty snippets that had to be left out last time because the book was already a wrist-spraining weight and anyway, the pages ran out!

These days, every runaway success must have a follow-up, whether it's *Grandson of Rocky* or *Jaws meets 0072*. So here goes with another generous helping of tickling tales. It's just as well that comedy is the one addiction you can enjoy with a clear conscience because by the time you reach the back cover you'll be well and truly hooked on humour and once that happens you'll always be wanting more. I've been a dedicated finder of funnies for years and it never palls; there's always another laugh around the corner.

Old friends joining for another ride on the merry-go-round will find as choice a mix of buffoonery, whimsy and downright absurdity as before. You can relish the urbane humour of David Niven, oiling his braces with hair lotion before meeting royalty in *Gentlemen Cadets*, gloat over the waspish gossip of Kenneth Williams' *Pages From a Private Diary* or surrender to hysteria with Bernard Levin in *The Luck of the Irish* as the stars of the Wexford Operatic Society slither across the slippery stage like jellyfish on ice.

If this is your first go, hold on tight because there's a whole witty world to savour. One of the joys of comedy is that there are no fences; anything is possible. Toto, the gorilla with theatrical ambitions in John Shepley's *The Gorilla Suit* is just as believable as Mutt the motoring mongrel in Farley Mowat's *Vignettes of Travel*. Bizarre characters like Victoria Wood's unwashed lady novelist offering her visitors instant dysentery, Damon Runyon's safecracking babyminders and Nancy Mitford's horrendous Uncle Matthew, hunting his children with bloodhounds, seem almost lovable once you start laughing over them.

Anthologies are books for sharing; keep this book to yourself and you aren't getting your money's worth. A sense of humour is just about as individual as fingerprints, so the story that leaves you helpless with hilarity leaves the fellow next door wondering what the joke was. Meanwhile, he'll laugh his socks off at the bit you thought was there because the author gave the editor a slap-up lunch. So share this collection with your husband/wife/lover – or all three if you've had a colourful life – so that you don't waste a word.

Tomes have been written on tragedy but no sensible soul tries to analyze humour. It's like prodding a spider's web – the whole sparkling, intricate fabric turns to grey gunge on your finger. Comedy is for chuckling, not dissection. So take my tip: don't think – enjoy!

If there are sober folk out there (the sort who research the eating preferences of the woodworm or send out tax demands) who shrug off humour as trivial and think that any book worth its print must educate and inform, just think what this collection has to offer. Where else could you learn that ladies' underwear makes the best manure for sprouts, that hot buttered muffins are an essential prelude to enjoying a love story, or that a goose is far more useful than an electric typewriter in a transatlantic boat race? With knowledge like that, who knows how far you could go – or if there's any point in coming back. (Incidentally, if you want to know exactly *where* all this information is, then I'm not at all sorry to say that I'm not going to tell you – you'll just have to read the stories and find out.)

If you still aren't convinced that this is a useful book, consider the testimonials from readers of the first volume. There's the man who says it stopped his wife nagging for a whole week: that was how long it took her to come round after he threw it at her. A titled lady bought it for her coffee table: said it was just the thing to prop up the broken leg. It even did its bit to warm up the Cold War. A businessman bound for Moscow took it along to cheer himself up and had it confiscated in customs. The KGB spent three weeks trying to crack the codes in P. G. Wodehouse's *The Rummy Affair of Old Biffy* and *Pig Hoo-e-y*. There were even reports that two of them were seen to smile, but *Pravda* issued an immediate denial.

If none of these arguments can woo you, think what it can do for your health. I wouldn't think of telling you that laughter is a tonic because that's a cliché. But then, what is a cliché? Some bit of indisputable fact that's been repeated a couple of times too often. There's no denying the benefits: laughing aerates the lungs, exercises the cheek muscles, puffs out the wrinkles and vibrates the pot-belly. In fact, if you go in for it wholeheartedly, it's just as effective as any jogging machine.

Now, I've never gone in that much for Health – anyway, not the sort with a capital H, that means getting yourself up in a tracksuit like some wilted ballet dancer. However much they dress it up with sexy sylphs in leotards on the cover, it always adds up to discomfort and deprivation by the time you get to the small print. My specs steam up in the sauna, all those fibre-full seeds get stuck in my fillings and jogging seems an exhausting way of not going anywhere. But I think there's a fortune to be made turning health farms into humour farms. Think of it: a few quick jokes before breakfast, a round of laughter before lunch, three lengths of funnies in the afternoon and a brisk session of wisecracks before bed. You'd go home a new man (substitute woman or person, to taste). It would kill the carrot juice sales.

It makes you wonder why this book doesn't come on prescription: take ten pages every time you feel your spirits dropping. So far, thousands have felt better for it, so carry on with the treatment!

The Hitch-hiker

Roald Dahl

I had a new car. It was an exciting toy, a big B.M.W. 3.3 Li, which means 3.3 litre, long wheelbase, fuel injection. It had a top speed of 129 m.p.h. and terrific acceleration. The body was pale blue. The seats inside were darker blue and they were made of leather, genuine soft leather of the finest quality. The windows were electrically operated and so was the sun-roof. The radio aerial popped up when I switched on the radio, and disappeared when I switched it off. The powerful engine growled and grunted impatiently at slow speeds, but at sixty miles an hour the growling stopped and the motor began to purr with pleasure.

I was driving up to London by myself. It was a lovely June day. They were haymaking in the fields and there were buttercups along both sides of the road. I was whispering along at seventy miles an hour, leaning back comfortably in my seat, with no more than a couple of fingers resting lightly on the wheel to keep her steady. Ahead of me I saw a man thumbing a lift. I touched the footbrake and brought the car to a stop beside him. I always stopped for hitch-hikers. I knew just how it used to feel to be standing on the side of a country road watching the cars go by. I hated the drivers for pretending they didn't see me, especially the ones in big cars with three empty seats. The large expensive cars seldom stopped. It was always the smaller ones that offered you a lift, or the old rusty ones, or the ones that were already crammed full of children and the driver would say, 'I think we can squeeze in one more.'

The hitch-hiker poked his head through the open window and said, 'Going to London, guv'nor?'

'Yes,' I said, 'Jump in.'

He got in and I drove on.

He was a small ratty-faced man with grey teeth. His eyes were dark and quick and clever, like a rat's eyes, and his ears were slightly pointed at the

top. He had a cloth cap on his head and he was wearing a greyish-coloured
jacket with enormous pockets. The grey jacket, together with the quick eyes
and the pointed ears, made him look more than anything like some sort of
a huge human rat.

'What part of London are you headed for?' I asked him.

'I'm goin' right through London and out the other side,' he said. 'I'm
goin' to Epsom, for the races. It's Derby Day today.'

'So it is,' I said. 'I wish I were going with you. I love betting on horses.'

'I never bet on horses,' he said. 'I don't even watch 'em run. That's a
stupid silly business.'

'Then why do you go?' I asked.

He didn't seem to like that question. His little ratty face went absolutely
blank and he sat there staring straight ahead at the road, saying nothing.

'I expect you help to work the betting machines or something like that,'
I said.

'That's even sillier,' he answered. 'There's no fun working them lousy
machines and selling tickets to mugs. Any fool could do that.'

There was a long silence. I decided not to question him any more. I
remembered how irritated I used to get in my hitch-hiking days when drivers
kept asking *me* questions. Where are you going? Why are you going there?
What's your job? Are you married? Do you have a girl-friend? What's her
name? How old are you? And so on and so forth. I used to hate it.

'I'm sorry,' I said. 'It's none of my business what you do. The trouble is,
I'm a writer, and most writers are terrible nosey parkers.'

'You write books?' he asked.

'Yes.'

'Writin' books is okay,' he said. 'It's what I call a skilled trade. I'm in a
skilled trade too. The folks I despise is them that spend all their lives doin'
crummy old routine jobs with no skill in 'em at all. You see what I mean?'

'Yes.'

'The secret of life,' he said, 'is to become very very good at somethin' that's
very very 'ard to do.'

'Like you,' I said.

'Exactly. You and me both.'

'What makes you think that *I'm* any good at my job?' I asked. 'There's
an awful lot of bad writers around.'

'You wouldn't be drivin' about in a car like this if you weren't no good
at it,' he answered. 'It must've cost a tidy packet, this little job.'

'It wasn't cheap.'

'What can she do flat out?' he asked.

'One hundred and twenty-nine miles an hour,' I told him.

'I'll bet she won't do it.'

'I'll bet she will.'

'All car makers is liars,' he said. 'You can buy any car you like and it'll never do what the makers say it will in the ads.'

'This one will.'

'Open 'er up then and prove it,' he said. 'Go on, guv'nor, open 'er right up and let's see what she'll do.'

There is a roundabout at Chalfont St Peter and immediately beyond it there's a long straight section of dual carriageway. We came out of the roundabout on to the carriageway and I pressed my foot down on the accelerator. The big car leaped forward as though she'd been stung. In ten seconds or so, we were doing ninety.

'Lovely!' he cried. 'Beautiful! Keep goin'!'

I had the accelerator jammed right down against the floor and I held it there.

'One hundred!' he shouted ... 'A hundred and five! ... A hundred and ten! ... A hundred and fifteen! Go on! Don't slack off!'

I was in the outside lane and we flashed past several cars as though they were standing still – a green Mini, a big cream-coloured Citroën, a white Land-Rover, a huge truck with a container on the back, an orange-coloured Volkswagen Minibus ...

'A hundred and twenty!' my passenger shouted, jumping up and down. 'Go on! Go on! Get 'er up to one-two-nine!'

At that moment, I heard the scream of a police siren. It was so loud it seemed to be right inside the car, and then a policeman on a motor-cycle loomed up alongside us on the inside lane and went past us and raised a hand for us to stop.

'Oh, my sainted aunt!' I said. 'That's torn it!'

The policeman must have been doing about a hundred and thirty when he passed us, and he took plenty of time slowing down. Finally, he pulled into the side of the road and I pulled in behind him. 'I didn't know police motor-cycles could go as fast as that,' I said rather lamely.

'That one can,' my passenger said, 'It's the same make as yours. It's a B.M.W. R90S. Fastest bike on the road. That's what they're usin' nowadays.'

The policeman got off his motor-cycle and leaned the machine sideways on to its prop stand. Then he took off his gloves and placed them carefully on the seat. He was in no hurry now. He had us where he wanted us and he knew it.

'This is real trouble,' I said. 'I don't like it one bit.'

'Don't talk to 'im any more than is necessary, you understand,' my companion said. 'Just sit tight and keep mum.'

Like an executioner approaching his victim, the policeman came strolling slowly towards us. He was a big meaty man with a belly, and his blue breeches were skintight around his enormous thighs. His goggles were pulled up on the helmet, showing a smouldering red face with wide cheeks.

We sat there like guilty schoolboys, waiting for him to arrive.

'Watch out for this man,' my passenger whispered. ''Ee looks mean as the devil.'

The policeman came round to my open window and placed one meaty hand on the sill. 'What's the hurry?' he said.

'No hurry, officer,' I answered.

'Perhaps there's a woman in the back having a baby and you're rushing her to hospital? Is that it?'

'No, officer.'

'Or perhaps your house is on fire and you're dashing home to rescue the family from upstairs?' His voice was dangerously soft and mocking.

'My house isn't on fire, officer.'

'In that case,' he said, 'you've got yourself into a nasty mess, haven't you? Do you know what the speed limit is in this country?'

'Seventy,' I said.

'And do you mind telling me exactly what speed you were doing just now?' I shrugged and didn't say anything.

When he spoke next, he raised his voice so loud that I jumped. *'One hundred and twenty miles per hour!'* he barked. 'That's *fifty* miles an hour over the limit!'

He turned his head and spat out a big gob of spit. It landed on the wing of my car and started sliding down over my beautiful blue paint. Then he turned back again and stared hard at my passenger. 'And who are you?' he asked sharply.

'He's a hitch-hiker,' I said. 'I'm giving him a lift.'

'I didn't ask you,' he said. 'I asked him.'

''Ave I done somethin' wrong?' my passenger asked. His voice was as soft and oily as haircream.

'That's more than likely,' the policeman answered. 'Anyway, you're a witness. I'll deal with you in a minute. Driving-licence,' he snapped, holding out his hand.

I gave him my driving-licence.

He unbuttoned the left-hand breast-pocket of his tunic and brought out the dreaded books of tickets. Carefully, he copied the name and address from my licence. Then he gave it back to me. He strolled round to the front of the car and read the number from the number-plate and wrote that down as well. He filled in the date, the time and the details of my offence. Then he tore out the top copy of the ticket. But before handing it to me, he checked that all the information had come through clearly on his own carbon copy. Finally, he replaced the book in his tunic pocket and fastened the button.

'Now you,' he said to my passenger, and he walked around to the other side of the car. From the other breast-pocket he produced a small black notebook. 'Name?' he snapped.

'Michael Fish,' my passenger said.

'Address?'

'Fourteen, Windsor Lane, Luton.'

'Show me something to prove this is your real name and address,' the policeman said.

My passenger fished in his pockets and came out with a driving-licence of his own. The policeman checked the name and address and handed it back to him. 'What's your job?' he asked sharply.

'I'm an 'od carrier.'

'A *what?*'

'An 'od carrier.'

'Spell it.'

'H-O-D C-A- ...'

'That'll do. And what's a hod carrier, may I ask?'

'An 'od carrier, officer, is a person 'oo carries the cement up the ladder to the bricklayer. And the 'od is what 'ee carries it in. It's got a long 'andle, and on the top you've got two bits of wood set at an angle ...'

'All right, all right. Who's your employer?'

'Don't 'ave one. I'm unemployed.'

The policeman wrote all this down in the black notebook. Then he returned the book to its pocket and did up the button.

'When I get back to the station I'm going to do a little checking up on you,' he said to my passenger.

'Me? What've I done wrong?' the rat-faced man asked.

'I don't like your face, that's all,' the policeman said. 'And we just might have a picture of it somewhere in our files.' He strolled round the car and returned to my window.

'I suppose you know you're in serious trouble,' he said to me.

'Yes, officer.'

'You won't be driving this fancy car of yours again for a very long time, not after *we've* finished with you. You won't be driving *any* car again come to that for several years. And a good thing, too. I hope they lock you up for a spell into the bargain.'

'You mean prison?' I asked, alarmed.

'Absolutely,' he said, smacking his lips. 'In the clink. Behind bars. Along with all the other criminals who break the law. *And* a hefty fine into the bargain. Nobody will be more pleased about that than me. I'll see you in court, both of you. You'll be getting a summons to appear.'

He turned away and walked over to his motor-cycle. He flipped the prop stand back into position with his foot and swung his leg over the saddle. Then he kicked the starter and roared off up the road out of sight.

'Phew!' I gasped. 'That's done it.'

'We was caught,' my passenger said. 'We was caught good and proper.'

'I was caught, you mean.'

'That's right,' he said. 'What you goin' to do now, guv'nor?'

'I'm going straight up to London to talk to my solicitor,' I said. I started the car and drove on.

'You mustn't believe what 'ee said to you about goin' to prison,' my passenger said. 'They don't put nobody in the clink just for speedin'.'

'Are you sure of that?' I asked.

'I'm positive,' he answered. 'They can take your licence away and they can give you a whoopin' big fine, but that'll be the end of it.'

I felt tremendously relieved.

'By the way,' I said, 'why did you lie to him?'

'Who, me?' he said. 'What makes you think I lied?'

'You told him you were an unemployed hod carrier. But you told *me* you were in a highly-skilled trade.'

'So I am,' he said. 'But it don't pay to tell everythin' to a copper.'

'So what *do* you do?' I asked him.

'Ah,' he said slyly. 'That'd be tellin', wouldn't it?'

'Is it something you're ashamed of?'

'Ashamed?' he cried. 'Me, ashamed of my job? I'm about as proud of it as anybody could be in the entire world!'

'Then why won't you tell me?'

'You writers really is nosey parkers, aren't you?' he said. 'And you ain't goin' to be 'appy, I don't think, until you've found out exactly what the answer is?'

'I don't really care one way or the other,' I told him, lying.

He gave me a crafty little ratty look out of the sides of his eyes. 'I think you do care,' he said. 'I can see it in your face that you think I'm in some kind of a very peculiar trade and you're just achin' to know what it is.'

I didn't like the way he read my thoughts. I kept quiet and stared at the road ahead.

'You'd be right, too,' he went on. 'I *am* in a very peculiar trade. I'm in the queerest peculiar trade of 'em all.'

I waited for him to go on.

'That's why I 'as to be extra careful 'oo I'm talkin' to, you see. 'Ow am I to know, for instance, you're not another copper in plain clothes?'

'Do I look like a copper?'

'No,' he said. 'You don't. And you ain't. Any fool could tell that.'

He took from his pocket a tin of tobacco and a packet of cigarette papers and started to roll a cigarette. I was watching him out of the corner of one eye, and the speed with which he performed this rather difficult operation was incredible. The cigarette was rolled and ready in about five seconds. He ran his tongue along the edge of the paper, stuck it down and popped the cigarette between his lips. Then, as if from nowhere, a lighter appeared in his hand. The lighter flamed. The cigarette was lit. The lighter disappeared. It was altogether a remarkable performance.

'I've never seen anyone roll a cigarette as fast as that,' I said.

'Ah,' he said, taking a deep suck of smoke. 'So you noticed.'

'Of course I noticed. It was quite fantastic.'

He sat back and smiled. It pleased him very much that I had noticed how quickly he could roll a cigarette. 'You want to know what makes me able to do it?' he asked.

'Go on then.'

'It's because I've got fantastic fingers. These fingers of mine,' he said, holding up both hands high in front of him, 'are quicker and cleverer than the fingers of the best piano player in the world!'

'Are you a piano player?'

'Don't be daft,' he said. 'Do I look like a piano player?'

I glanced at his fingers. They were so beautifully shaped, so slim and long and elegant, they didn't seem to belong to the rest of him at all. They looked more like the fingers of a brain surgeon or a watchmaker.

'My job,' he went on, 'is a hundred times more difficult than playin' the piano. Any twerp can learn to do that. There's titchy little kids learnin' to play the piano in almost any 'ouse you go into these days. That's right, ain't it?'

'More or less,' I said.

'Of course it's right. But there's not one person in ten million can learn to do what I do. Not one in ten million! 'Ow about that?'

'Amazing,' I said.

'You're darn right it's amazin',' he said.

'I think I know what you do,' I said. 'You do conjuring tricks. You're a conjurer.'

'Me?' he snorted. 'A conjurer? Can you picture me goin' round crummy kids' parties makin' rabbits come out of top 'ats?'

'Then you're a card player. You get people into card games and deal yourself marvellous hands.'

'Me! A rotten card-sharper!' he cried. 'That's a miserable racket if ever there was one.'

'All right. I give up.'

I was taking the car along slowly now, at no more than forty miles an hour, to make quite sure I wasn't stopped again. We had come on to the main London–Oxford road and were running down the hill towards Denham.

Suddenly, my passenger was holding up a black leather belt in his hand. 'Ever seen this before?' he asked. The belt had a brass buckle of unusual design.

'Hey!' I said. 'That's mine, isn't it? It *is* mine! Where did you get it?'

He grinned and waved the belt gently from side to side. 'Where d'you think I got it?' he said. 'Off the top of your trousers, of course.'

I reached down and felt for my belt. It was gone.

'You mean you took it off me while we've been driving along?' I asked, flabbergasted.

He nodded, watching me all the time with those little black ratty eyes.

'That's impossible,' I said. 'You'd have to undo the buckle and slide the whole thing out through the loops all the way round. I'd have seen you doing it. And even if I hadn't seen you, I'd have felt it.'

'Ah, but you didn't, did you?' he said, triumphant. He dropped the belt on his lap, and now all at once there was a brown shoelace dangling from his fingers. 'And what about this, then?' he exclaimed, waving the shoelace.

'What about it?' I said.

'Anyone round 'ere missin' a shoelace?' he asked, grinning.

I glanced down at my shoes. The lace of one of them was missing. 'Good grief!' I said. 'How did you do that? I never saw you bending down.'

'You never saw nothin',' he said proudly. 'You never even saw me move an inch. And you know why?'

'Yes,' I said. 'Because you've got fantastic fingers.'

'Exactly right!' he cried. 'You catch on pretty quick, don't you?' He sat back and sucked away at his home-made cigarette, blowing the smoke out in a thin stream against the windshield. He knew he had impressed me greatly with those two tricks, and this made him very happy. 'I don't want to be late,' he said. 'What time is it?'

'There's a clock in front of you,' I told him.

'I don't trust car clocks,' he said. 'What does your watch say?'

I hitched up my sleeve to look at the watch on my wrist. It wasn't there. I looked at the man. He looked back at me, grinning.

'You've taken that, too,' I said.

He held out his hand and there was my watch lying in his palm. 'Nice bit of stuff, this,' he said. 'Superior quality. Eighteen-carat gold. Easy to flog, too. It's never any trouble gettin' rid of quality goods.'

'I'd like it back, if you don't mind,' I said rather huffily.

He placed the watch carefully on the leather tray in front of him. 'I wouldn't nick anything from you, guv'nor,' he said. 'You're my pal. You're giving me a lift.'

'I'm glad to hear it,' I said.

'All I'm doin' is answerin' your questions,' he went on. 'You asked me what I did for a livin' and I'm showin' you.'

'What else have you got of mine?'

He smiled again, and now he started to take from the pocket of his jacket one thing after another that belonged to me – my driving-licence, a key-ring with four keys on it, some pound notes, a few coins, a letter from my publishers, my diary, a stubby old pencil, a cigarette-lighter, and last of all, a beautiful old sapphire ring with pearls around it belonging to my wife. I was taking the ring up to the jeweller in London because one of the pearls was missing.

'Now *there's* another lovely piece of goods,' he said, turning the ring over in his fingers. 'That's eighteenth century, if I'm not mistaken, from the reign of King George the Third.'

'You're right,' I said, impressed. 'You're absolutely right.'

He put the ring on the leather tray with the other items.

'So you're a pickpocket,' I said.

'I don't like that word,' he answered. 'It's a coarse and vulgar word. Pickpockets is coarse and vulgar people who only do easy little amateur jobs. They lift money from blind old ladies.'

'What do you call yourself, then?'

'Me? I'm a fingersmith. I'm a professional fingersmith.' He spoke the words solemnly and proudly, as though he were telling me he was the President of the Royal College of Surgeons or the Archbishop of Canterbury.

'I've never heard that word before,' I said. 'Did you invent it?'

'Of course I didn't invent it,' he replied. 'It's the name given to them who's risen to the very top of the profession. You've 'eard of a goldsmith and a silversmith, for instance. They're experts with gold and silver. I'm an expert with my fingers, so I'm a fingersmith.'

'It must be an interesting job.'

'It's a marvellous job,' he answered. 'It's lovely.'

'And that's why you go to the races?'

'Race meetings is easy meat,' he said. 'You just stand around after the race, watchin' for the lucky ones to queue up and draw their money. And when you see someone collectin' a big bundle of notes, you simply follows after 'im and 'elps yourself. But don't get me wrong, guv'nor. I never takes nothin' from a loser. Nor from poor people neither. I only go after them as can afford it, the winners and the rich.'

'That's very thoughtful of you.' I said. 'How often do you get caught?'

'Caught?' he cried, disgusted. '*Me* get caught! It's only pickpockets get caught. Fingersmiths never. Listen, I could take the false teeth out of your mouth if I wanted to and you wouldn't even catch me!'

'I don't have false teeth,' I said.

'I know you don't,' he answered. 'Otherwise I'd 'ave 'ad 'em out long ago!'

I believed him. Those long slim fingers of his seemed able to do anything.

We drove on for a while without talking.

'That policeman's going to check up on you pretty thoroughly,' I said. 'Doesn't that worry you a bit?'

'Nobody's checkin' up on me,' he said.

'Of course they are. He's got your name and address written down most carefully in his black book.'

The man gave me another of his sly, ratty little smiles. 'Ah,' he said. 'So 'ee 'as. But I'll bet 'ee ain't got it all written down in 'is memory as well. I've never known a copper yet with a decent memory. Some of 'em can't even remember their own names.'

'What's memory got to do with it?' I asked. 'It's written down in his book, isn't it?'

'Yes, guv'nor, it is. But the trouble is, 'ee's lost the book. 'Ee's lost both books, the one with my name in it *and* the one with yours.'

In the long delicate fingers of his right hand, the man was holding up in triumph the two books he had taken from the policeman's pockets. 'Easiest job I ever done,' he announced proudly.

I nearly swerved the car into a milk-truck, I was so excited.

'That copper's got nothin' on either of us now,' he said.

'You're a genius!' I cried.

''Ee's got no names, no addresses, no car number, no nothin',' he said.

'You're brilliant!'

'I think you'd better pull in off this main road as soon as possible,' he said. 'Then we'd better build a little bonfire and burn these books.'

'You're a fantastic fellow,' I exclaimed.

'Thank you, guv'nor,' he said. 'It's alway nice to be appreciated.'

Postcard from Biarritz

Clive James

The weekly Air France Caravelle to Biarritz took off from Heathrow only an hour late. The French air-traffic controllers must have slipped up. Most other flights routed over French air-space were being delayed for days on end, with passengers eating one another in airports. But by some miracle we had been allowed through.

Nor were we intercepted en route. I was fully expecting a squadron of Mirage jet fighters to come screaming out of the sun and shoot us down. Not a bit of it. Popping the odd rivet, our ageing but trusty Caravelle made a gallant left turn over the Coast of Silver and alighted with its characteristic hot landing speed – none of that reverse thrust nonsense, just turn off all the power and wait until she stops rolling – on the mini-golf course that Biarritz calls an airport.

Biarritz receives you like a clapped-out Disneyland with brains. In the days when the place was an amusement park for the rich, they outdid one another building holiday homes that would express their high spirits. The high spirits were mainly induced by the fact that they were not obliged to share the bracing ozone with the low orders. Nowadays anybody is allowed in. When anybody arrives, he finds the enchanted playground looking pretty much as its upper-crust habitués left it. He also finds the ozone as bracing as it ever was, the beaches just as long, the water just as warm, the sunsets just as gorgeous, and the young ladies wearing far fewer clothes. The great days of Biarritz are over, but the nice days might just be beginning.

This was my second visit to Biarritz. Last year at about the same date I went down there to work on a film script with my compatriot, the theatre director Michael Blakemore, who owns a house on the Rue Gambetta, right in the middle of town. Most of Biarritz is in the middle of town. The beaches are endless, with real sand on them, but the town itself is quite small. Turning some of his iffy West End earnings into a tangible asset. Blakemore bought the house seven years ago. The purchase cleaned him out, but the climate, cliffs and waves reminded him of home. They did the same to me. We spent two weeks not writing a film. This year we planned to spend another two weeks not writing a play.

Biarritz is on the Atlantic coast of France, just north of the Spanish border, which puts it in the Basque country. It used to be a fishing village before it became the most fashionable resort of the nineteenth century. With the end of the *belle époque* it went into a long decline, until by now the place is so far out that it's almost on its way back in. People are starting to recognize the name again, even if they can't say exactly where it is, or even tell the Côte d'Argent from the Côte d'Azur. Biarritz is starting to revive. But there are ways in which the prospect of renewed vitality is a pity as well as a blessing.

In the twelfth century the Basque fishermen of the Biarritz used to hunt whales with deadly efficiency. When the whales sensibly moved away, the Basques chased them further and further, with the consequence that the fishermen of Biarritz discovered America before Columbus did. (This is a matter for local pride but on a larger view it is not quite so stunning, since with the possible exception of the Swiss everybody discovered America before Columbus did.)

Having too small a port for deep-sea trading, Biarritz became a backwater and stayed that way until a certain Spanish noblewoman started sending her daughter there for the annual holidays. The daughter married Napoleon III of France, became the Empress Eugénie, and persuaded her husband that Biarritz was the ideal place for the Second Empire to set up its summer headquarters. Together, in the late 1850s, they built the Résidence Eugénie. Biarritz rapidly became the Beach of the Kings – a title it kept in good repair until the last spasm of the *belle époque*.

They all turned up. Reigning monarchs from all over Europe headed for Biarritz in special trains. Deposed monarchs went into exile there. Maharajahs moved in. There was a commingling of crowns, a tangling of tiaras. Even after the Empire fell, the season didn't slow down for a minute. In fact it lasted the whole year round. The English, a hardy breed, were there all winter. The Russians were there in the autumn, the French and Spanish in the spring and summer. The Empress Elizabeth of Austria was a regular. So, eventually, was the Prince of Wales, who acquired much of his girth in the Biarritz pastry shops and as Edward VII continued to favour the town with his massive presence, thereby laying the foundations of its lasting fondness for the English.

Why did the princes of the blood and all their parasites like Biarritz so much and for so long? Part of the answer was that it cost so much to get there. The train fare from Paris to the Normandy beaches was only twenty-five francs. From Paris to Biarritz was 125. So the commonalty couldn't afford to make the trip. That left the nobs free to hob with each other. The word democracy was probably never mentioned except in jest.

Yet paradoxically the nobility and the high bourgeoisie gave more to Biarritz than they ever took away. Private patronage resulted in an astonishing array of public works. On Eugénie's orders, a tunnel was driven through the rocks to give access from the Grande Plage in the north to the Côte des Basques in the south. Miles of walkways appeared, all lined with tamarisks and hydrangeas. Casinos and grand hotels duly materialized. Everyone who was anyone built a château or a villa. Architecture was encouraged to reflect the festive mood by running riot. Turrets, gables, gazebos and similar ridiculosities proliferated, forming a pop-up picture-book skyline against the pink extravaganza of the sunset.

Mad with enthusiasm, some of the more adventurous spirits even dared to immerse themselves in the sea. Previously the idea had not occurred to anyone. Eugénie had not been the only illustrious name to admire the onrushing ocean of Biarritz and environs. Stendhal, Taine, Flaubert, Victor Hugo and other great romantics had all, at one time or another, pronounced themselves awed by the remorseless waves. But it was a long step from admiring them to actually getting in amongst them. Eventually the fad caught on, but like every other nineteenth-century diversion it was accompanied by a lot of ritualized fuss and elaborate machinery.

Even in the closing years of the *belle époque*, a fashionable lady in full walking-out regalia needed a moving staircase, or *trottoir roulant*, to get her and her various attendants down to the beach. Once there, she disappeared into *la cabine de l'établissement* and spent three-quarters of an hour getting changed for an encounter with the waters that was never allowed to exceed more than a few minutes, lest death intervene.

Having approached the water's edge, she was divested of her *peignoir* by a *guide-baigneur* and stood provokingly revealed – still fully dressed from neck to knee, but marginally less voluminously. The *guides-baigneurs*, most of them Basques, were themselves fully dressed, including straw hat: only their hands, feet and that part of the face not covered by a handlebar moustache could be regarded as bare.

While one *guide-baigneur* alertly held the *peignoir*, another *guide-baigneur*, or in the case of more exalted clients two other *guides-baigneurs*, accompanied the lady a few inches into the pitiless torrent. Supported by her muscular champions, the lady gave herself up to the mercy of the deep. What went on beneath the waves must remain forever unknown, but one trusts that class barriers were suitably eroded. Ankles must have touched. Knees must have collided. Surely the occasional rendezvous was made, as it is today in the winter resorts, where fine ladies sometimes invite their ski instructors to bed, although never to dinner.

Upon her retreat from the pounding *vagues*, the lady was once again enveloped in her *peignoir* and escorted back up the beach for another three-quarters of an hour in *la cabine*, after which the *trottoir roulant* was ready to hoist her back to civilization. The rest of the day could be spent discussing her adventure with other ladies of her own rank.

The whole routine went without a hitch until the day in 1908 when the Comtesse de Madron put her foot in it. She got one of her buttoned boots caught in the mechanism of the *trottoir roulant*. Minus four toes, she sued everyone, and the offending device, like so much else, was closed down for keeps in 1914.

Sealed in a bubble of indifference, Biarritz was preserved by neglect. Two World Wars with a Depression in between left it looking pretty much as it had been when life was still sweet. Art deco was added to the conglomerate of styles; another Prince of Wales, thinner this time, was added to the aggregate of princely visitors; but the old confidence was gone. The fashionable action moved to the Mediterranean. Biarritz still served the turn as a plush funk-hole, but as a display case it was past tense. The postcards on sale from year to year showed little that was altered, still less that was new. During the Second World War the Germans installed concrete gun emplacements to enfilade the beaches in case the Allies tried a right hook. The Allies never came and the gun emplacements, too solid to blow up, were turned into flower-beds.

To put it cruelly, Biarritz became a ghost town – a magnificent but dispirited relic of the old Europe. After the Second World War the high-born and well-placed still came for the season, but only if they were of a certain age. Their sons and daughters went to St Tropez, where the waves were very flat but there was a chance of seeing Brigitte Bardot's behind.

Nobody thought of the big waves at Biarritz with any special fondness until 1956, when Richard Zanuck and Peter Viertel arrived on the coast to scout locations for *The Sun Also Rises*.

Zanuck was the producer of the movie and Viertel was the writer. The minute they clapped eyes on the surf at Biarritz they started producing and not writing. They had their surfboards shipped over from California. These were Malibu, or hot-dog, surfboards, the ancestors of the potato-chip surfboards in use today. When Zanuck and Viertel stood up on the waves, the locals were variously outraged and enchanted. Some of the village elders said it was against the laws of both God and gravity. But the younger men couldn't wait to join in.

Few Frenchmen had ever gone in for body-surfing, and you still don't see much of it even now. As a direct result of the long season Zanuck and Viertel spent not working on *The Sun Also Rises*, the French think of surfing as an activity carried out exclusively on surfboards. Old Australian crocks like Blakemore and myself can occasionally be seen shooting the breakers on all our bare chests – all right, bare stomachs – but for the natives surfing is something you do standing up.

The awful truth is that young people all over the world think the same way. My generation has been bypassed. On the Sydney beaches when I was young, a surfboard was something only a weightlifter could ride: built of wood, it went straight for the beach like a large landing barge while the rider crouching on top of it pretended to be in control. The first Malibu boards arrived at about the time I left, so I never learned to ride one. In fact I never even touched one until I met Peter Viertel in Biarritz. Viertel has white hair by now but his way of life – which includes being married to Deborah Kerr – keeps him young. He can still stand on the waves like a boy on a dolphin. Under his tuition I finally got to stand up on a surfboard, if only for a few seconds. It feels great.

Surfing has helped to revive the energies of Biarritz. Surfers come there from all over Europe and indeed the world: a new, penniless royalty. There are elegant French surfers with degrees in science, stunning wives or husbands, and surfboards with sails on them. There are German surfers who look as if they took up the sport because terrorism was too much like work. You see van-loads of Australians with John Newcombe moustaches and countersunk eyes like tacks in a carpet. Half my age and not even sure which country they are in, the Australians climb into their Rip Curl wet-suits and sit for hours half a mile off the Côte des Basques, patiently waiting for a wave worthy of their steel. Last year, on a flat day, I heard one of them say: 'Shit, this is no good. Let's go to Spain.'

Usually it is good enough. You can see why a generation brought up on skateboards, surfboards and *Crystal Voyager* should want to make Biarritz one of their summer stopovers. Unfortunately, from the viewpoint of the municipality, the surfing boom is not enough by itself to generate prosperity. Too many surfers are bums. They sleep in a van, dry their clothes on top of it, eat off the pavement and don't even tip the lady in the WC. Most of the cash is brought to town by ordinary people who wouldn't mind if the surf disappeared tomorrow, so long as the sand was still there.

Wealth resides not in the few hundred surfers but in the thousands of ordinary paddlers who bring their children. As the old hotels continue to rot away, it looks like common sense to replace them with the kind of modern building that will pack the punters in more efficiently. Alas, the results are horrible to behold. Rearing up out of Biarritz's otherwise dinky eclecticism, the typical new hotels look like a cross between a typewriter and a toilet. So far there are only about a dozen of them, but they point the way that things might go. By now the original buildings are falling down of their own accord. To restore and maintain so many bizarre old edifices would seem quixotic even supposing it were technically possible. The temptation to let them all collapse is reinforced by the suspicion that most holidaymakers wouldn't care. What they want is hot showers that work. Yet a compromise ought to be possible. Perhaps the interiors could be gutted and the façades kept – apart from people in the social swim, nobody ever saw what was behind them anyway.

Biarritz is a jumble of a town and no single solution to its problems can possibly be right. The Basques being a fiery lot, they might easily talk themselves into a ruinous snap decision concerning the town's most immediate problem, which is what to do about the advancing sea. On the Côte des Basques the beach is reputedly getting smaller year by year, while the cliffs show a disconcerting tendency to cave in, with detrimental effects on property values. The mayor is in favour of a scheme by which piers would be built at regular intervals, thereby producing a string of bijou beachettes with plenty of sand in them but no surf. This is a notch better than an earlier scheme to turn the whole beach into a marina, but it still ranks as a catastrophe, since even the non-surfing Basque elders are well aware that the unbroken line of *sable d'or* on the Côte des Basques is the chief glory of Biarritz.

I went to a public meeting at which the mayor proposed his scheme at enormous length. A spoke was put in his wheel by a prodigiously ancient Basque who got to his feet – this process in itself consuming a good proportion of the evening – and announced that the Côte des Basques was exactly the same now as it had been when he was a boy. The meeting erupted. People were screaming at one another. Suddenly it was easy to see why successive Spanish Governments, whether of the Left or the Right, have always found it hard to keep the Basques in line.

If you drive down to San Sebastian the Spanish Basques will serve you a dish of prawns cooked in salt that taste better than anything else you have ever eaten. Unfortunately they might also blow up your car. The Basques are simply an explosive people. They play half a dozen different versions of *pelote*. One version is played with the bare hand, which comes to resemble a catcher's mitt. The fastest version, *cesta punta*, is played with a long basket strapped to the right wrist. The venue is a sort of giant squash court and the ball travels fast enough to kill. The players wear crash helmets and spend a lot of time falling on their heads.

The chummiest version of *pelote* is called *grande chistera*. It is played with the long basket but in the open air and against only one wall. The game is not quite as sensational as *cesta punta* but it involves the spectators in a big way, since there is no net between them and the action. If you take your eyes off the ball you can end up with a bad headache. A girl sitting only a few feet away from me got absorbed in conversation with her boyfriend. They had only just arrived. He was watching the ball and she wasn't. It hit her in the right temple. He had to take her home. Having just blown 30 francs in a matter of seconds, he was one very embittered Basque.

The Basques were in Biarritz before the whales went away and will probably be there when they come back. But in the mean time they are willing to make the rest of us feel welcome. There has probably never been a better time in Biarritz than now. The old days had a lot of style but little substance. Think of all those elegantly turned-out gentlemen lined up on the esplanade and searching the beach for the glimpse of an ankle. Nowadays you can see some of the most heartbreakingly pretty girls in the world springing around with hardly anything on at all. Sucking in our paunches, Blakemore and I stride seawards in a masterful manner. Can anyone doubt that life today is better, now that the gap between those who lie about and those who work for a living has narrowed to the point that they are often the same people? Anyway, as a place in which not to do something, Biarritz is unbeatable. Already we have not written a film and a play. Next year we might not write a musical.

Travel Hints

Fran Lebowitz

These hints are the result of exhaustive and painstaking research conducted during a recently completed fourteen-city promotional book tour. This does not mean that if your own travel plans do not include a fourteen-city promotional book tour you should disregard this information. Simply adjust the hints to fit your personal needs, allow for a certain amount of pilot error and you will benefit enormously.

1. It is imperative when flying coach that you restrain any tendency toward the vividly imaginative. For although it may momentarily appear to be the case, it is not at all likely that the cabin is entirely inhabited by crying babies smoking inexpensive domestic cigars.

2. When flying first class, you may frequently need to be reminded of this fact, for it all too often seems that the only discernible difference is that the babies have connections in Cuba. You will, however, be finally reassured when the stewardess drops your drink and the glass breaks.

3. Airplanes are invariably scheduled to depart at such times as 7:54, 9:21 or 11:37. This extreme specificity has the effect on the novice of instilling in him the twin beliefs that he will be *arriving* at 10:08, 1:43 or 4:22, and that he should get to the airport on time. These beliefs are not only erroneous but actually unhealthy, and could easily be dispelled by an attempt on the part of the airlines toward greater realism. Understandably, they may be reluctant to make such a radical change all at once. In an effort to make the transition easier I offer the following graduated alternatives to 'Flight 477 to Minneapolis will depart at 8:03 P.M.':

   a. Flight 477 to Minneapolis will depart oh, let's say, eightish.

    b. Flight 477 to Minneapolis with depart around eight, eight-thirty.

    c. Flight 477 to Minneapolis will depart while it's still dark.

    d. Flight 477 to Minneapolis will depart before the paperback is out.

4. Stewardesses are not crazy about girls.

5. Neither are stewards.

6. You *can* change planes in Omaha, Nebraska.

7. You are advised to do so.

8. Whether or not you yourself indulge in the habit, always sit in the smoking section of an airplane. The coughing will break up the trip.

9. Whenever possible, fly with someone who is color-blind. Explaining to him the impact of rust, orange and yellow stripes against a background of aquamarine florals will fill the time you have left over from coughing.

10. When making bookstore appearances in areas heavily populated by artistic types, limit your signing of books 'For Douglas and Michael' or 'Joseph and Edward' or 'Diane and Katy' to under ten copies. It will take you approximately that amount of time to be struck by the realization that you are losing sales. Announce pleasantly but firmly that it is common knowledge that homosexual liaisons are notoriously short-lived, and that eventually there will be a fight over your book. If this fails to have an immediate effect, remind them gently of the number of French whisks they've lost through the years.

11. It's not that it's three hours earlier in California; it's that the days are three hours longer.

12. Room-service menus that don't charge extra for cheese on hamburgers are trying to tell you something.

13. Fleeting romantic alliances in strange cities are acceptable, especially if you've already seen the movie. Just make sure that your companion has gotten the name of your publisher wrong.

14. Local television talk-show hosts are not interested in the information that the *Today* show uses more than one camera.

15. Twenty-four-hour room service generally refers to the length of time that it takes for the club sandwich to arrive. This is indeed disheartening, particularly when you've ordered scrambled eggs.

16. Never relinquish clothing to a hotel valet without first specifically telling him that you want it back.

17. Leaving a wake-up call for four P.M. is certain to result in a loss of respect from the front desk and overfamiliarity on the part of bellboys and room-service waiters.

18. If you're going to America, bring your own food.

19. If while staying at a stupendously expensive hotel in Northern California you observe that one of your fellow guests has left his sneakers in front of his door, try to behave yourself.

20. Under no circumstances order from room service an item entitled 'The Cheese Festival' unless you are prepared to have your dream of colorfully costumed girls of all nations rolling enormous wheels of Gruyère and Jarlsberg replaced by three Kraft slices and a lot of toothpicks dressed in red cellophane hats.

21. Calling a taxi in Texas is like calling a rabbi in Iraq.

22. Local television talk shows do not, in general, supply make-up artists. The exception to this is Los Angeles, an unusually generous city in this regard, since they also provide this service for radio appearances.

23. Do not approach with anything even resembling assurance a restaurant that moves.

24. When a newspaper photographer suggests artistically interesting props, risk being impolite.

25. Absolutely, positively, and no matter what, wait until you get back to New York to have your hair cut.

26. Carry cash.

27. Stay inside.

28. Call collect.

29. Forget to write.

Kington's Book of Lists

Miles Kington

Ten Misleading Remarks Heard in Everyday Conversation.
'Things are fine, thanks.'
'... and it's the only drink I know which never gives you a hangover.'
'I don't think it's actually going to rain.'
'I know you're going to like him.'
'We only watch when there's something really good on.'
'We must keep in touch.'
'Gosh, no, I'm not very good at the game at all.'
'I have nothing against him personally, but ...'
'Apparently it has aphrodisiac qualities.'
'I'll just come in for coffee, then.'

Ten Most Read Magazines in Britain
Caravan and Yacht Owner
Motorbike and Caravan Owner
Yacht and Penthouse Owner
Yachtmen Only
Skate, Bike and Yacht Monthly
Skaters' Digest
The Times Boating Supplement
The Incredible Hulk Meets Yachtsman
Ms Yachtperson

Ten Objects Rarely Found in the Average Household
String
Spare can-opener
Fuses
Unused stamps

The newspaper with that article you were going to cut out
A pencil within twenty feet of the telephone
Parsley
The drink your guest asks for
An umbrella

Ten Very Common Objects in the Average Household
Dead parsley
An empty ice tray
Last week's *Time Out*
A phone number on a piece of paper, with no name
A match box, with one match in it, dead
A screw lying on the floor, without any apparent origin
Gin but not tonic, or tonic, but not gin
A pile of records and empty sleeves; ten records, nine sleeves
A pair of underpants disclaimed by all residents
A tube of toothpaste, started yesterday, almost empty today

Ten Extremely Annoying Sounds
The sniffing of a human being
The singing of a sparrow
The raving of a motor bike radio
The chimes of an ice cream van
The clapping of a rock audience recognizing a tune
The singing at the Last Prom
The poetry voices on Radio 3
The noises in the empty flat upstairs
The ringing of a phone after bedtime
The sound of brown envelopes coming through the letter box

Ten Very Boring Conversationalists
Jazz enthusiasts
Motorists with good short cuts
People who are reminded of stories
Those who do not own TV sets or cars
People who have just given up something
People who have just been burgled
People who can still remember their dreams in detail

Those who would rather talk about wine than drink it
People who have seen a good film or programme that you haven't
People who tell long boring stories about events that happened to you and
them twenty years ago (inevitably parents or spouses)

Ten Absolutely Vital Things to know about Taking a Bath
Spiders can run round baths faster than you can.
When you leave a bath to run by itself, the plug jumps out just as you
leave the bathroom, and you return to an empty bath just as the hot water
runs out.
If you run a bath too hot and then add some cold water, the cold water
stays at the tap end. You never realize this until you sit in the other end
and burn your bottom.
When you lie back in a bath, your right foot slides forward until it is
positioned exactly beneath the dripping tap.
It is physically impossible to turn a tap on or off with your foot.
Lost soap is always behind you.
The odd flannel you are using to wash yourself is not a flannel at all; it is
a sock which has just fallen from the clothes line above.
The dirt which you wash off yourself gathers on the surface of the water
and then reattaches itself to you as you rise to leave.
When you get out of the bath, the first bit you dry is the one bit you
suddenly realize you forgot to wash.
However hard you dry yourself, you are still wet when you put your clothes
on.

Growing Pains

Miles Kington

The care, maintenance and decent burial of house and office plants is made far too complicated by the amount of books about them. Especially as all the books list about 200 of them, none of which looks like the one you've been given. So, to help you, I have devised an entirely new classification of indoor plants which reduces their number to ten and enables you to identify any one at a glance.

1. The Last Minute Birthday Present, or African Violet
This is instantly recognizable for its masses of green leaves and small coloured bloom. The bloom dies the next day but the leaves go on for ever.

2. The Architect's Drawing Plant, or Pseudoplasticus
You know those tall, lifeless green monsters that architects stick in their ideal drawings to make a place look lived in? They have now managed to breed them in real life. You can spot them at once; they look as if they are made from green plastic. They should be polished once a day, and sandpapered once a month. (Experiments are also under way to breed the *people* seen in architect's drawings, who never drop litter and have no faces.)

3. The Shrinking Violet, or Anorexia Nervosa
This spindly, sad, skeletal plant starts out quite tall and gradually gets smaller and smaller, by dropping leaves and branches, until it vanishes completely. It doesn't much like heat, cold, dark, light, food or water.

4. The Nut Tree, or Palmus Miniaturus
These are generally grown from pips or seeds left over from fruit salads or steak and avocado lunches, and can be spotted instantly through their

complete inability to produce nuts, fruits, or indeed flowers. If ignored for
several years, they may grow into Architect's Drawing Plants.

5. Last Year's Bulb
This non-flowering plant is the only one in nature which grows bent over
with a rubber band round it. The leaves eventually turn a beautiful yellow,
which is a sign that it is asking to be thrown away.

6. The Incredible Creeping Ivy
Any plant which grows down rather than up can be classed as an ivy. It
grows out as well, spreading fast when you're not looking but staying
absolutely still when you've got your eye on it. It likes to spread over
unanswered letters, vital missing files and out-of-date cheques. Its leaves are
highly poisonous, though nobody knows how this was discovered.

7. The Travelling Flower Arrangement
A colourful, attractive, mixed growth which appears mysteriously in many
offices on Monday morning and vanishes again the next weekend, if it's still
alive by then.

8. The Climbing Office Plant
Anything which climbs up a stick in a pot is one of these. Many of them
seem to suffer from vertigo or oxygen starvation or something and peg out
at about two feet above sea level, which is why you see so many pots in
offices with just a stick in them. Unless, of course, people are taking the easy
way out and just planting sticks.

9. The Yoghurt Pot Plant
A pleasant, light green growth exactly the same size as a yoghurt pot, though
there is a larger version called The Double Cream Pint Pot Plant, which is
much rarer owing to the price of double cream. They both thrive on crumbs,
biscuits and elevenses.

10. The Temp Secretary Bloom
Any plant which does not come into the first nine categories can safely be
classed as one of these, no matter what shape, size or colour they are. They
are always left behind by that girl who came in for three weeks, remember,
and then vanished to Spain and we found she hadn't been doing any of her

letters, just hiding them in her desk, goodness, Mr Whitgift was angry, but we hadn't the heart to throw the plant away.

Why Your Plant Isn't Looking Well
It was thought until recently that plants were damaged by either over-watering or under-watering. It is now known that plants can be simultaneously over-watered *and* under-watered. Most pots are boggy and swampy for the first two inches down, then bone-dry underneath. The plants are suffering because they are puzzled and do not know what is expected of them.

If you are giving your plants plant food, stop. If you are not feeding them, start immediately. This is based on the theory that whatever you are doing, it is bound to be the wrong treatment. Basically, what house plants like is *neglect*; this may kill a few weaker growths, but many house plants will emerge from a bout of fruitfulness and starvation even tougher and more determined to outlive you.

Three Men on the Bummel

Jerome K. Jerome

Harris, George and the narrator decide to tour the Black
Forest by bicycle. But even before they begin they encounter
complications ...

On Monday afternoon Harris came round; he had a cycling paper in his
hand.

I said: 'If you take my advice, you will leave it alone.'

Harris said: 'Leave what alone?'

I said: 'That brand-new, patent, revolution in cycling, record-breaking,
tomfoolishness, whatever it may be, the advertisement of which you have
there in your hand.'

He said: 'Well, I don't know; there will be some steep hills for us to
negotiate; I guess we shall want a good brake.'

I said: 'We shall want a brake, I agree; what we shall not want is a
mechanical surprise that we don't understand, and that never acts when it
is wanted.'

'This thing,' he said, 'acts automatically.'

'You needn't tell me,' I said. 'I know exactly what it will do, by instinct.
Going uphill it will jamb the wheel so effectively that we shall have to carry
the machine bodily. The air at the top of the hill will do it good, and it will
suddenly come right again. Going downhill it will start reflecting what a
nuisance it has been. This will lead to remorse, and finally to despair. It will
say to itself: "I'm not fit to be a brake. I don't help these fellows; I only
hinder them. I'm a curse, that's what I am"; and, without a word of warning,
it will "chuck" the whole business. That is what that brake will do. Leave
it alone. You are a good fellow,' I continued, 'but you have one fault.'

'What?' he asked indignantly.

'You have too much faith,' I answered. 'If you read an advertisement, you go away and believe it. Every experiment that every fool has thought of in connection with cycling you have tried. Your guardian angel appears to be a capable and conscientious spirit, and hitherto she has seen you through; take my advice and don't try her too far. She must have had a busy time since you started cycling. Don't go on till you make her mad.'

He said: 'If every man talked like that there would be no advancement made in any department of life. If nobody ever tried a new thing the world would come to a standstill. It is by –'

'I know all that can be said on that side of the argument,' I interrupted. 'I agree in trying new experiments up to thirty-five; *after* thirty-five I consider a man is entitled to think of himself. You and I have done our duty in this direction, you especially. You have been blown up by a patent gas lamp –'

He said: 'I really think, you know, that was my fault; I think I must have screwed it up too tight.'

I said: 'I am quite willing to believe that if there was a wrong way of handling the thing that is the way you handle it. You should take that tendency of yours into consideration; it bears upon the argument. Myself, I did not notice what you did; I only know we were riding peacefully and pleasantly along the Whitby Road, discussing the Thirty Years War, when your lamp went off like a pistol shot. The start sent me into the ditch; and your wife's face, when I told her there was nothing the matter and that she was not to worry, because the two men would carry you upstairs, and the doctor would be round in a minute bringing the nurse with him, still lingers in my memory.'

He said: 'I wish you had thought to pick up the lamp. I should like to have found out what was the cause of its going off like that.'

I said: 'There was not time to pick up the lamp. I calculate it would have taken two hours to have collected it. As to its "going off", the mere fact of its being advertised as the safest lamp ever invented would of itself, to anyone but you, have suggested accident. Then there was that electric lamp,' I continued.

'Well, that really did give a fine light,' he replied; 'you said so yourself.'

I said: 'It gave a brilliant light in the King's Road, Brighton, and frightened a horse. The moment we got into the dark beyond Kemp Town it went out, and you were summoned for riding without a light. You may remember that on sunny afternoons you used to ride about with that lamp shining for all it was worth. When lighting-up time came it was naturally tired, and wanted a rest.'

'It was a bit irritating, that lamp,' he murmured; 'I remember it.'

I said: 'It irritated me; it must have been worse for you. Then, there are saddles,' I went on – I wished to get this lesson home to him. 'Can you think of any saddle ever advertised that you have *not* tried?'

He said: 'It has been an idea of mine that the right saddle is to be found.'

I said: 'You give up that idea; this is an imperfect world of joy and sorrow mingled. There may be a better land where bicycle saddles are made out of rainbow, stuffed with cloud; in this world the simplest thing is to get used to something hard. There was that saddle you bought in Birmingham; it was divided in the middle, and looked like a pair of kidneys.'

He said: 'You mean that one constructed on anatomical principles.'

'Very likely,' I replied. 'The box you bought it in had a picture on the cover, representing a sitting skeleton – or rather that part of a skeleton which does sit.'

He said: 'It was quite correct; it showed you the true position of the –'

I said: 'We will not go into details; the picture always seemed to me indelicate.'

He said: 'Medically speaking, it was right.'

'Possibly,' I said, 'for a man who rode in nothing but his bones. I only know that I tried it myself, and that to a man who wore flesh it was agony. Every time you went over a stone or a rut it nipped you; it was like riding on an irritable lobster. You rode that for a month.'

'I thought it only right to give it a fair trial,' he answered.

I said: 'You gave your family a fair trial also; if you will allow me the use of slang. Your wife told me that never in the whole course of your married life had she known you so bad tempered, so unchristian-like, as you were that month. Then you remember that other saddle, the one with the spring under it.'

He said: 'You mean "the Spiral".'

I said: 'I mean the one that jerked you up and down like a jack-in-the-box; sometimes you came down again in the right place, and sometimes you didn't. I am not referring to these matters merely to recall painful memories, but I want to impress you with the folly of trying experiments at your time of life.'

He said: 'I wish you wouldn't harp so much on my age. A man at thirty-four –'

'A man at what?'

He said: 'If you don't want the thing, don't have it. If your machine runs away with you down a mountain, and you and George get flung through a church roof, don't blame me.'

'I cannot promise for George,' I said; 'a little thing will sometimes irritate him, as you know. If such an accident as you suggest happens, he may be cross, but I will undertake to explain to him that it was not your fault.'

'Is the thing all right?' he asked.

'The tandem,' I replied, 'is well.'

He said: 'Have you overhauled it?'

I said: 'I have not, nor is anyone else going to overhaul it. The thing is now in working order, and it is going to remain in working order till we start.'

I have had experience of this 'overhauling'. There was a man at Folkestone; I used to meet him on the Lees. He proposed one evening we should go for a long bicycle ride together on the following day, and I agreed. I got up early, for me; I made an effort, and was pleased with myself. He came half an hour late: I was waiting for him in the garden. It was a lovely day. He said:

'That's a good-looking machine of yours. How does it run?'

'Oh, like most of them!' I answered; 'easily enough in the morning; goes a little stiffly after lunch.'

He caught hold of it by the front wheel and the fork, and shook it violently. I said: 'Don't do that; you'll hurt it.'

I did not see why he should shake it; it had not done anything to him. Besides, if it wanted shaking, I was the proper person to shake it. I felt much as I should had he started whacking my dog.

He said: 'This front wheel wobbles.'

I said: 'It doesn't if you don't wobble it.' It didn't wobble, as a matter of fact – nothing worth calling a wobble.

He said: 'This is dangerous; have you got a screw-hammer?'

I ought to have been firm, but I thought that perhaps he really did know something about the business. I went to the tool shed to see what I could find. When I came back he was sitting on the ground with the front wheel between his legs. He was playing with it, twiddling it round between his fingers; the remnant of the machine was lying on the gravel path beside him.

He said: 'Something has happened to this front wheel of yours.'

'It looks like it, doesn't it?' I answered. But he was the sort of man that never understand satire.

He said: 'It looks to me as if the bearings were all wrong.'

I said: 'Don't you trouble about it any more; you will make yourself tired. Let us put it back and get off.'

He said: 'We may as well see what is the matter with it, now it is out.' He talked as though it had dropped out by accident.

Before I could stop him he had unscrewed something somewhere, and out rolled all over the path some dozen or so little balls.

'Catch 'em!' he shouted; 'catch 'em! We mustn't lose any of them.' He was quite excited about them.

We grovelled round for half an hour, and found sixteen. He said he hoped we had got them all, because, if not, it would make a serious difference to the machine. He said there was nothing you should be more careful about in taking a bicycle to pieces than seeing you did not lose any of the balls. He explained that you ought to count them as you took them out, and see that exactly the same number went back in each place. I promised, if ever I took a bicycle to pieces I would remember his advice.

I put the balls for safety in my hat, and I put my hat upon the doorstep. It was not a sensible thing to do, I admit. As a matter of fact, it was a silly thing to do. I am not as a rule addle-headed; his influence must have affected me.

He then said that while he was about it he would see to the chain for me, and at once began taking off the gear-case. I did try to persuade him from that. I told him what an experienced friend of mine once said to me solemnly:

'If anything goes wrong with your gear-case, sell the machine and buy a new one; it comes cheaper.'

He said: 'People talk like that who understand nothing about machines. Nothing is easier than taking off a gear-case.'

I had to confess he was right. In less than five minutes he had the gear-case in two pieces, lying on the path, and was grovelling for screws. He said it was always a mystery to him the way screws disappeared.

We were still looking for the screws when Ethelbertha came out. She seemed surprised to find us there; she said she thought we had started hours ago.

He said: 'We shan't be long now. I'm just helping your husband to overhaul this machine of his. It's a good machine; but they all want going over occasionally.'

Ethelbertha said: 'If you want to wash yourselves when you have done you might go into the back kitchen, if you don't mind; the girls have just finished the bedrooms.'

She told me that if she met Kate they would probably go for a sail; but that in any case she would be back to lunch. I would have given a sovereign to be going with her. I was getting heartily sick of standing about watching this fool breaking up my bicycle.

Common sense continued to whisper to me: 'Stop him, before he does any more mischief. You have a right to protect your own property from the ravages of a lunatic. Take him by the scruff of the neck, and kick him out of the gate!'

But I am weak when it comes to hurting other people's feelings, and I let him muddle on.

He gave up looking for the rest of the screws. He said screws had a knack of turning up when you least expected them, and that now he would see to the chain. He tightened it till it would not move; next he loosened it until it was twice as loose as it was before. Then he said we had better think about getting the front wheel back into its place again.

I held the fork open, and he worried with the wheel. At the end of ten minutes I suggested he should hold the forks, and that I should handle the wheel; and we changed places. At the end of his first minute he dropped the machine, and took a short walk round the croquet lawn, with his hands pressed together between his thighs. He explained as he walked that the thing to be careful about was to avoid getting your fingers pinched between the forks and the spokes of the wheel. I replied I was convinced, from my own experience, that there was much truth in what he said. He wrapped himself up in a couple of dusters, and we commenced again. At length we did get the thing into position; and the moment it was in position he burst out laughing.

I said: 'What's the joke?'

He said: 'Well, I am an ass!'

It was the first thing he had said that made me respect him. I asked him what had led him to the discovery.

He said: 'We've forgotten the balls!'

I looked for my hat; it was lying topsyturvy in the middle of the path, and Ethelbertha's favourite hound was swallowing the balls as fast as he could pick them up.

'He will kill himself,' said Ebbson – I have never met him since that day, thank the Lord; but I think his name was Ebbson – 'they are solid steel.'

I said: 'I am not troubling about the dog. He has had a bootlace and a packet of needles already this week. Nature's the best guide; puppies seem to require this kind of stimulant. What I am thinking about is my bicycle.'

He was of a cheerful disposition. He said: 'Well, we must put back all we can find, and trust to providence.'

We found eleven. We fixed six on one side and five on the other, and half an hour later the wheel was in its place again. It need hardly be added that it really did wobble now; a child might have noticed it. Ebbson said it would do for the present. He appeared to be getting a bit tired himself. If I had let him, he would, I believe, at this point have gone home. I was determined now, however, that he should stop and finish; I had abandoned all thoughts of a ride. My pride in the machine he had killed. My only interest lay now in seeing him scratch and bump and pinch himself. I revived his drooping spirits with a glass of beer and some judicious praise. I said:

'Watching you do this is of real use to me. It is not only your skill and dexterity that fascinates me, it is your cheery confidence in yourself, your inexplicable hopefulness, that does me good.'

Thus encouraged, he set to work to refix the gear-case. He stood the bicycle against the house, and worked from the off side. Then he stood it against a tree, and worked from the near side. Then I held it for him, while he lay on the ground with his head between the wheels, and worked at it from below, and dropped oil upon himself. Then he took it away from me, and doubled himself across it like a pack-saddle, till he lost his balance and slid over on to his head. Three times he said:

'Thank heaven, that's right at last!'

And twice he said:

'No, I'm damned if it is after all!'

What he said the third time I try to forget.

Then he lost his temper and tired bullying the thing. The bicycle, I was glad to see, showed spirit; and the subsequent proceedings degenerated into little else than a rough-and-tumble fight between him and the machine. One moment the bicycle would be on the gravel path, and he on top of it; the next, the position would be reversed – he on the gravel path, the bicycle on him. Now he would be standing flushed with victory, the bicycle firmly fixed between his legs. But his triumph would be short-lived. By a sudden, quick movement it would free itself, and, turning upon him, hit him sharply over the head with one of its handles.

At a quarter to one, dirty and dishevelled, cut and bleeding, he said: 'I think that will do'; and rose and wiped his brow.

The bicycle looked as if it also had had enough of it. Which had received most punishment it would have been difficult to say. I took him into the back kitchen, where, so far as was possible without soda and proper tools, he cleaned himself, and sent him home.

The bicycle I put into a cab and took round to the nearest repairing shop. The foreman of the works came up and looked at it.

'What do you want me to do with that?' said he.

'I want you,' I said, 'so far as is possible, to restore it.'

'It's a bit far gone,' said he; 'but I'll do my best.'

He did his best, which came to two pounds ten. But it was never the same machine again; and at the end of the season I left it in an agent's hands to sell. I wished to deceive nobody; I instructed the man to advertise it as a last year's machine. The agent advised me not to mention any date. He said:

'In this business it isn't a question of what is true and what isn't; it's a question of what you can get people to believe. Now, between you and me, it don't look like a last year's machine; so far as looks are concerned, it might be a ten-year-old. We'll say nothing about date; we'll just get what we can.'

I left the matter to him, and he got me five pounds, which he said was more than he had expected.

There are two ways you can get exercise out of a bicycle: you can 'overhaul' it, or you can ride it. On the whole, I am not sure that a man who takes his pleasure overhauling does not have the best of the bargain. He is independent of the weather and the wind; the state of the roads troubles him not. Give him a screw-hammer, a bundle of rags, an oil-can, and something to sit down upon, and he is happy for the day. He has to put up with certain disadvantages, of course; there is no joy without alloy. He himself always looke like a tinker, and his machine always suggests the idea that, having stolen it, he has tried to disguise it; but as he rarely gets beyond the first milestone with it, this, perhaps, does not much matter. The mistake some people make is in thinking they can get both forms of sport out of the same machine. This is impossible; no machine will stand the double strain. You must make up your mind whether you are going to be an 'overhauler' or a rider. Personally, I prefer to ride, therefore I take care to have near me nothing that can tempt me to overhaul. When anything happens to my machine I wheel it to the nearest repairing shop. If I am too far from the town or village to walk, I sit by the roadside and wait till a cart comes along. My chief danger, I always find, is from the wandering overhauler. The sight of a broken-down machine is to the overhauler as a wayside corpse to a crow; he swoops down upon it with a friendly yell of triumph. At first I used to try politeness. I would say:

'It is nothing; don't you trouble. You ride on, and enjoy yourself, I beg it of you as a favour; please go away.'

Experience has taught me, however, that courtesy is of no use in such an extremity. Now I say:

'You go away and leave the thing alone, or I will knock your silly head off.'

And if you look determined, and have a good stout cudgel in your hand, you can generally drive him off.

George came in later in the day. He said:

'Well, do you think everything will be ready?'

I said: 'Everything will be ready by Wednesday, except, perhaps, you and Harris.'

He said: 'Is the tandem all right?'

'The tandem,' I said, 'is well.'

He said: 'You don't think it wants overhauling?'

I replied: 'Age and experience have taught me that there are few matters concerning which a man does well to be positive. Consequently, there remain to me now but a limited number of questions upon which I feel any degree of certainty. Among such still-unshaken beliefs, however, is the conviction that that tandem does not want overhauling. I also feel a presentiment that, provided my life is spared, no human being between now and Wednesday morning is going to overhaul it.'

George said: 'I should not show temper over the matter, if I were you. There will come a day, perhaps not far distant, when that bicycle, with a couple of mountains between it and the nearest repairing shop, will, in spite of your chronic desire for rest, *have* to be overhauled. Then you will clamour for people to tell you where you put the oil-can, and what you have done with the screw-hammer. Then, while you exert yourself holding the thing steady against a tree, you will suggest that somebody else should clean the chain and pump the back wheel.'

I felt there was justice in George's rebuke – also a certain amount of prophetic wisdom. I said:

'Forgive me if I seemed unresponsive. The truth is, Harris was round here this morning –'

George said: 'Say no more; I understand. Besides, what I came to talk to you about was another matter. Look at that.'

He handed me a small book bound in red cloth. It was a guide to English conversation for the use of German travellers. It commenced 'On a Steamboat', and terminated 'At the Doctor's'; its longest chapter being devoted to conversation in a railway carriage, among, apparently, a compartment load of quarrelsome and ill-mannered lunatics: 'Can you not get farther away from me, sir?' – 'It is impossible, madam; my neighbour, here, is very stout' – 'Shall we not endeavour to arrange our legs?' – 'Please have the goodness to keep your elbows down' – 'Pray do not inconvenience yourself, madam, if my shoulder is of any accomodation to you,' whether intended to be said sarcastically or not, there was nothing to indicate – 'I really must request you to move a little, madam, I can hardly breathe,' the author's idea being, presumably, that by this time the whole party was mixed up together on the floor. The chapter concluded with the phrase: 'Here we are at our destination, God be thanked! (*Gott sei dank!*)' a pious exclamation, which under the circumstances must have taken the form of a chorus.

At the end of the book was an appendix, giving the German traveller hints concerning the preservation of his health and comfort during his sojourn in English towns; chief among such hints being advice to him to always travel with a supply of disinfectant powder, to always lock his bedroom door at night, and to always carefully count his small change.

'It is not a brilliant publication,' I remarked, handing the book back to George; 'it is not a book that personally I would recommend to any German about to visit England; I think it would get him disliked. But I have read books published in London for the use of English travellers abroad every whit as foolish. Some educated idiot, misunderstanding seven languages, would appear to go about writing these books for the misinformation and false guidance of modern Europe.'

'You cannot deny,' said George, 'that these books are in large request. They are bought by the thousand, I know. In every town in Europe there must be people going about talking this sort of thing.'

'Maybe,' I replied; 'but fortunately, nobody understands them. I have noticed, myself, men standing on railway platforms and at street corners reading aloud from such books. Nobody knows what language they are speaking; nobody has the slightest knowledge of what they are saying. This is, perhaps, as well; were they understood they would probably be assaulted.'

George said: 'Maybe you are right; my idea is to see what would happen if they were understood. My proposal is to get to London early on Wednesday morning, and spend an hour or two going about and shopping with the aid of this book. There are one or two little things I want – a hat and a pair of bedroom slippers, among other articles. Our boat does not leave Tilbury till twelve, and that just gives us time. I want to try this sort of talk where I can properly judge of its effect. I want to see how the foreigner feels when he is talked to in this way.'

It struck me as a sporting idea. In my enthusiasm I offered to accompany him, and wait outside the shop. I said I thought that Harris would like to be in it, too – or rather outside.

George said that was not quite his scheme. His proposal was that Harris and I should accompany him into the shop. With Harris, who looks formidable, to support him, and myself at the door to call the police if necessary, he said he was willing to adventure the thing.

We walked round to Harris's, and put the proposal before him. He examined the book, especially the chapters dealing with the purchase of shoes and hats. He said:

'If George talks to any bookmaker or any hatter the things that are put down here, it is not support he will want; it is carrying to the hospital that he will need.'

That made George angry.

'You talk,' said George, 'as though I were a foolhardy boy without any sense. I shall select from the more polite and less irritating speeches; the grosser insults I shall avoid.'

This being clearly understood, Harris gave in his adhesion; and our start was fixed for early Wednesday morning.

The Moon's a Balloon

David Niven

David Niven, popular film star and raconteur, wrote of his early life with humour and perception in *The Moon's a Balloon*. The excerpt which follows begins with the young Niven facing up to the consequences of cheating in his School Certificate.

Ratings of the Royal Navy have always prided themselves on the fact that without any official signals being made, news and gossip passes between ships at anchor with a rapidity that makes African tribesmen blush over their tom-toms. The ratings themselves would have blushed that day: ten minutes after chapel, the whole school knew who were the two culprits. Perhaps like being attacked by dogs or run away with on horses, Archie and I smelled of fear.

Poor Archie was the first to be summoned to the Headmaster's study – he went off like Sydney Carton at the end of *A Tale of Two Cities*. A quarter of an hour later, I was located near the lavatories where I had been spending the interim.

No smile on J.F.'s face this time, just a single terse question, 'Have you anything to say for yourself?'

For the lack of any flash of genius that might have saved me, I told him the truth – that I had failed the exam anyway and wanted to get out early. I also added that Archie was completely guiltless and stood to gain nothing by helping me.

J.F. stared at me in silence for a long time, then he crossed the quiet, beautifully furnished room and stood looking out of the open french windows into the flower garden where he had first interviewed me. Cheating in a public examination is a heinous crime and it seemed inevitable that I would be expelled. I braced myself for the news as he turned towards me.

'Montgomery-Campbell made a stupid mistake in helping you with your Latin translation and I have given him six strokes of the cane. Until you stood there and told me the truth, I had every intention of expelling you from the school. However, in spite of your very gross misbehaviour, I still have faith in you and I shall keep you at Stowe. Now, I propose to give you twelve strokes with the cane.'

My joy at not being thrown out was quickly erased by the thought of my short-term prospect ... Twelve! that was terrifying! J.F. was a powerfully built man and his beatings, though rare, were legendary.

'Go next door into the Gothic Library. Lift your coat, bend over and hold on to the bookcase by the door. It will hurt you very much indeed. When it is over, and I expect you to make no noise, go through the door as quickly as you wish. When you feel like it, go back to your house.'

The first three or four strokes hurt so much that the shock somehow cushioned the next three or four, but the last strokes of my punishment were unforgettable. I don't believe I did make any noise, not because I was told to avoid doing so, or because I was brave or anything like that – it hurt so much, I just couldn't get my breath.

When the bombardment finally stopped, I flung open the door and shot out into the passage. Holding my behind and trumpeting like a rogue elephant, down the stone passage, past the boiler rooms I went, out into the summer evening and headed for the woods.

After the pain subsided, the mortification set it. How was I going to face the other boys – a cheat? Obviously, my promised promotion to monitor would be cancelled and my remaining time at Stowe would be spent as an outcast.

Eventually, about bedtime, I crept up to my dormitory. It was a large room that accommodated twenty-five boys. The usual pillow fights and shouting and larking about were in full swing. They died away to an embarrassed silence as I came in. I took off my clothes, watched by the entire room. My underpants stuck to me and reminded me of my physical pain. Carrying my pyjamas I slunk off to the bathroom next door. An ominous murmur followed my exit.

In the bathroom mirror, I inspected the damage. It was heavy to say the least. Suddenly, Major Haworth's cheery voice made me turn, 'Pretty good shooting I'd call that ... looks like a two inch group'. He was his usual smiling, kindly self. 'When you've finished in here, get into bed. I'm going to read out a message the Headmaster has sent round the School ... nothing to worry about.'

When everyone was in bed and quiet, the Major stood by the dormitory door and read from a piece of paper.

'I have interviewed the two boys connected with the School Certificate irregularities. Their explanations have been accepted by me and the boys have been punished. The incident is now closed and will not be referred to again by anyone.'

'Good night, everybody,' said the Major, and then with a wink at me – 'When that sort of thing happened to me I used to sleep on my stomach and have my breakfast off the mantelshelf.'

In the darkness, the whispers started – 'How many did you get?' ... 'Did you blub' ... 'What sort of cane is it?' ... 'Promise to show us in the morning.' All friendly whispers. In the darkness, I buried my face in my pillow.

I determined there and then that, somehow, I would repay J.F. I never could, of course, but I became, I think, a good and responsible monitor the next term and, in due course, after squeaking past a mathematical barrier, I passed into the Royal Military College, Sandhurst, and became one of the first three Stowe boys to gain commissions in the Regular Army.

Summer holiday at Bembridge followed immediately after ten days of Officers' Training Corps camp on Salisbury Plain. It was at one such camp that I first smelled success in front of an audience. Several hundred boys from many different schools were attending the camp concert in a huge circus tent. Someone had told Major Haworth that as Stowe was a new school, it would be a good thing if we were part of the programme and he had asked me to do something about it.

There was at that time in England a monologuist named Milton Hayes. I had one of his records at school and had memorized some of his stuff for the benefit of my friends. I must now belatedly apologize to Milton Hayes for stealing from his material, which is what in part I did, adding topical touches of my own to fit the situation at the camp.

His monologue was a take-off of a half-witted politician electioneering. I made mine a half-witted General inspecting the camp. On the night of the concert, I sat outside the tent, waiting for my turn to go on. The boys were a rowdy audience and the noise from inside was deafening. There were a lot of boos. I experienced, for the first time, that delicious terror that has never left me – stage fright, and with rubbery knees, dry lips and sweating palms, I fought against the urge to dash madly away, grow a beard and emigrate to the Seychelles. At last I was called and I heard the Master of Ceremonies announce – 'Niven of Stowe'.

Miserably, I mounted the steps on to the stage, wearing the baggy General's uniform which Major Haworth had concocted for me. In my eye was a monocle and on my upper lip, a huge grey moustache.

Scattered applause and some laughter greeted my appearance.

The MC put up his hand – 'Major General Sir Useless Eunuch!' More laughter.

I gulped and prayed that the stage would open and swallow me up. Hundreds of boys in khaki filled the benches. The first three rows were occupied by officers in red Mess kit. I screwed my monocle into my eye and gazed at the officers....

'Sergeant-Major, why is it that these members of the band have no instruments?' I asked. A roar of delighted laughter filled the tent and suddenly, it was easy. Then lapsing into pilfered Milton Hayes –

'What we must do with this camp, Sergeant-Major, is find out where we stand, then get behind ourselves and push ourselves forward. We must get right down to the very roots, right down to rock bottom, then bring the whole thing up into one common pool ... and looking around here at Salisbury Plain – and how very plain it looks – we should keep the ships at sea ... the harbours will be much cleaner for one thing ...' and so on for about ten minutes.

Milton Hayes and I were a riotous success that night and the harpoon of craving success as a performer was planted deep inside me.

Sailing entered my life about this time. My mother bought Grizel and me a twenty-five-year-old 14 ft sailing dinghy for £12. She was called *Merlin* and is still being sailed by children at Bembridge.

I became a good 'hand' and the pinnacle of my sailing career came later while I was still at Sandhurst and was chosen as a member of Great Britain's International Crew in the Cumberland Cup, a race for 8-metre yachts, during Ryde Week. With Sir Ralph Gore, the famous helmsman, in command, we in *Severn* easily defeated the French challenger *L'Etoile* in a best of three final.

First, however, Brian Franks and I formed the Bembridge Sailing Dinghy Club for children between twelve and eighteen. I was the first Secretary, Brian the first Captain. At the end of the first year, the Club showed a profit of £2 12s 6d which Brian and I transferred into liqueur brandy. We were both found next morning, face down in some nettles.

*

When you are a senior boy in an English Public School, you perhaps reach the pinnacle of your self-importance. Given hitherto undreamed of responsibilities and privileges, often receiving the acclaim, even the adulation, of your juniors and sometimes served by 'fags', it is very easy to get carried away.

The Royal Military College, Sandhurst, soon took care of that ... it is never pleasant to be treated like mud but Sandhurst, at least, did it with style and no malice aforethought: it just came naturally.

We were called 'Gentlemen Cadets'. The officers and non-commissioned officer instructors were the pick of the whole British Army and the drill instructors were exclusively, the pick of the Brigade of Guards. Knowing you were due to become an officer in eighteen months' time, the NCOs could call you anything they liked provided they prefaced it with a 'Mr So-and-So, Sir.'

There were about one thousand cadets at Sandhurst divided into Seniors, Intermediates and Juniors. The course was eighteen months so one spent six months in each category.

The Commandant was Major-General Sir Eric Girdwood, DSO, etc., etc.; the Adjutant was the famous Major 'Boy' Browning, Grenadier Guards, DSO etc., later to command all British Airborne troops in World War II.

In No. I Company my Company Commander was Major Godwin Austen, South Wales Borderers, MC; my Chief Instructor was Major 'Babe' Alexander, Irish Guards, DSO, and the Company Sergeant Major was 'Robbo' Robinson, Grenadier Guards.

All these were completely splendid soldiers, with impeccable and gallant records, and however tough they may sometimes have been, they always had a deep understanding and sympathy for the cadets under their command.

The Cadet under-officer in charge of the Junior platoon to which I was assigned, was a shifty-looking customer with a broken nose named Wright – a singularly unattractive piece of work. It was small wonder to any of us who knew him at Sandhurst that later, after changing his name to Baillie-Stewart and joining the Seaforth Highlanders he was caught selling military secrets to the Germans, court-martialled and imprisoned in the Tower of London.

The 'mud treatment' started on the first day of our ten weeks of concentrated drill 'on the square'. We were paraded in the civilian clothes in which we had arrived the day before. A strange assortment wearing suits, tweed jackets, plus-fours, hats, caps, boots, shoes and some with umbrellas, we smiled nervously at each other as we awaited the ministrations of 'Robbo'.

Rapidly and with the minimum of trimmings, Robbo explained that although it looked unlikely at the moment, we were supposed to be officer material and it had fallen to his unfortunate lot to try, within eighteen months, to transform this ''orrible shower' into being worthy of the King's commission.

'I shall address you as "Sir" because that's orders but when you speak to me you'll stand at attention, look me right in the eye and call me Staff ... got it?'

Scattered murmurs of 'yes', 'right-ho' and 'jolly good' were silenced by one of the mightiest roars in the British Army.

'GOT IT !!!! ??? Now let me hear the answer, Gentlemen ... ONE, TWO, THREE' ... 'GOT IT STAFF,' we roared back.

Quickly and efficiently we were stripped of umbrellas and walking sticks and shown how to come to attention, how to march and how to halt. Then, at a hair-raising speed we were marched one and a half miles to be issued with boots and canvas uniforms. Round and round the College we whizzed, sweating and apprehensive beneath the patronizing glances of beautifully turned out older cadets to the barbers to be shorn like sheep, to the gym to be fitted with physical training outfits, to the stables for breeches, brown boots and leggings, to the laundry 'because I don't want to see a speck of dirt for the next year an' 'arf mind' and finally to the Chapel 'because 'ere, gentlemen, you can thank Almighty Gawd at the end of each week if you are still breathin'. Got it?' 'GOT IT STAFF!'

It was very hard and very exhausting – for the ten weeks on the square, we never stopped running, saluting, marching, drilling, climbing ropes, riding unmanageable charges and polishing and burnishing everything in sight ... boots, belts, chinstraps, buttons, bayonets and above all our rifles ... 'the soldier's best friend, mind.'

Normally, there were about fifteen minutes between being dismissed from one parade and being inspected for the next in a totally different and spotless outfit. The slightest lapse, a finger mark on a brass button, a cap at the wrong angle or hair not mown like a convict was rewarded with 'Defaulters' – a particularly gruelling extra drill in full battle order at the end of the day when everyone else was resting.

A rifle barrel imperfectly cleaned invariably meant 'Pack Drill' at the hands of the dreaded Wright – full battle order but with a difference: the Pack was filled with sand and in place of normal drill movements, it was a case of being forced after supper to run up and down several flights of stairs with the offending rifle at arm's length above the head, shouting at the top of our lungs 'Parade, Parade.'

The cadets incarcerated in their rooms, cleaning their equipment, made bets on how long each individual could stand the punishment. Many defaulters found it a matter of honour to prolong their agony in order to impress their listening friends. I was a firm supporter of the doctrine of another group which sought kudos by pretending to pass out long before they would normally have collapsed.

In the riding school, the rough riding Sergeant Majors were particularly heartless. We had a beauty, an Irishman from the Inniskilling Dragoons called McMyn. At 6.30 on a Monday morning, winter and summer, he would be waiting for us with the same grisly joke ... 'Now then, gentlemen, I'm supposed to make mounted officers of all of you so let's see how many dismounted showers we can have here on this lovely morning ... Knot your reins. Cross your stirrups. Fold your bleedin' arms and split ass over the jumps ... go!' Carnage, of course, but in those strange days all officers, even in infantry regiments, had to know how to ride, and ride well.

The great thing about those first ten weeks was that although one was being treated like mud, it was at least grown-up mud. We were treated like men for the first time in our lives and as men we were expected to react.

Those weeks 'on the square' were sheer, undiluted hell. At weekends we were allowed no dining-out passes but by Saturday night we were so exhausted anyway that all we wanted to do was to fall into bed, underneath which was a dreadful receptacle described in Military Stores as 'one pot, chamber, china with handle, Gentlemen Cadets for the use of.'

At the end of the purgatory, we 'passed off the square' and settled down to learning other things in addition to physical training, drill, riding, bayonet fighting and more drill. Instruction was given us in organization and administration, in the manual of military law and of course in tactics and man management.

Of the two hundred and fifty 'Juniors' who passed off the square and still remained in one piece, four in each Company were promoted to Lance-Corporal. I was one of the lucky four in No. 1 Company and as there was now a little more time for leisure, I managed also to get a Rugger 'Blue' and played regularly for two seasons with the 1st XV.

I furthermore performed in a couple of College concerts, writing my own sketches, and played the lead opposite Mrs Barcus, the wife of one of our company officers, in *It Pays to Advertise*.

Nessie came down one Saturday to see the show which opened after a particularly gruelling afternoon's rugger battle against the RAF College, Cranwell.

'Yew looked ever so nice up there on that stage, dear, but the sport's better for yew isn't it? – more balls, if yew know what I mean.'

My liaison with Nessie continued more or less full time all through my year and a half at Sandhurst. She still insisted that 'pretty soon I'm goin' to find that nice feller and – off to the Fiji Islands'. In the summer term, she came down for the June Ball, the big social event of the year. For the occasion she borrowed a magenta-coloured taffeta ball gown from a friend who danced in competitions on the outer London circuit. Her very great beauty and again, I say, her freshness overcame this extraordinary garment and I basked in her success as we waltzed and fox-trotted round the dusty gymnasium to the fluctuating rhythms of the Royal Military College Band.

Nessie was very specific about my seeing other girls – 'We're just together for the larfs and the –, dear, so don't go gettin' serious wiv me or yew'll spoil it.'

In her wisdom she encouraged my friendships and listened apparently with enthusiasm when I told her I had met a beautiful young actress playing in a naval comedy in London by Ian Hay and Stephen King-Hall – *The Middle Watch* – Ann Todd.

Ann had a tiny part and was infinitely glamorous. I had never been backstage in my life before and she was single-handedly responsible for my becoming incurably stage-struck. I had an allowance of five pounds a month so I was not exactly a well-heeled 'stage door Johnny' but Ann was often sent free tickets for the opening of restaurants or night clubs which helped enormously.

Cadets in their Intermediate and Senior terms were allowed cars. Obviously, I did not own one but the wheels of friends were always available and Saturday night in London on a late pass became the focal point of the week.

In the Intermediate Term, I was promoted to full Corporal and received the ultimate accolade for that rank. Along with one other Corporal, Dick Hobson of No. 3 Company, I was appointed Commandant's Orderly for six months. This post was highly coveted and besides announcing to all and sundry that the holder of it was practically bound to become an Under Officer in his senior term, it also carried various 'perks'. One was excused Saturday morning Drill Parade, which meant early to London, and on

Sunday, came the big moment ... breakfast with the General, Sir Eric Girdwood.

Those breakfasts must have been pure hell for this splendid officer but week after week, he toyed with toast and coffee while Dick and I ploughed through acres of scrambled eggs and miles of sausages. Afterwards, while the General was being dressed in highly polished riding boots, Sam Browne belt and sword, Dick and I waited in the garden proudly holding silver sticks, on which were engraved the names of a hundred years of Commandants' Orderlies. Across our chests were white pipe-clayed belts to which, between our shoulder blades, very beautiful and heavily embossed silver Victorian message boxes were attached. Upon the appearance of the General, we formed up on either side of him and escorted him on to the parade, slow marching together ahead of him up the front rank and down the rear as he inspected his battalion of one thousand spotless cadets: then into chapel, trying not to skate with our hobnailed boots on the black marble of the nave and, afterwards, leading his Sunday morning inspection of the College buildings, gymnasium, hospital, stables and so on.

The General was a most imposing and awe-inspiring figure with his chest full of medals and his bristling white moustache. He was also God. A creature so far above the lowly cadet as to make his every word and gesture seem, to us, divine. Of the thousand at that moment under his command, perhaps one would ultimately attain his exalted position.

The silver message box nearly proved to be my undoing. So many cadets asked me what was in it that I decided to give them a little food for thought, and I filled it with various commodities. Thereafter upon being asked the usual question I would reply, 'Commandant's personal supplies – take a look.' Inside they were delighted to find a packet of Woodbines, a box of Swan Vestas matches, a roll of toilet paper and a dozen French letters. I believe my purchases went a long way towards relieving the tedium of those Sunday mornings, and cadets, kept standing to attention far too long in all weathers, were deeply appreciative of the fact that visiting dignitaries, Kings, Presidents, Prime Ministers and Archbishops were invariably preceded in their inspection of the ranks by the pompous passing of this curious cargo.

One cloudless Sunday morning after breakfast, Dick Hobson and I were waiting for the General amidst the rhododendrons of his garden when he suddenly changed his routine. Normally, he would issue from the house, booted, spurred, shining like a new pin and we would fall into step on either side of him, listening to his extremely engaging and relaxed small talk as he headed towards the barrack square where the battalion would be drawn up ready for inspection by him and on occasion by his VIP guests.

Some five hundred yards from his house and just out of sight of the parade it was taken for granted that all informality would melt away and Dick and I would put our silver-headed orderly sticks under our left armpits and start our slow march for the tour of the ranks.

This beautiful June morning, however, he came out of the garden door and stopped in front of us.

'I think I'd better inspect you two fellers today,' he said.

We immediately sprang to attention secure and relaxed in the knowledge that we, too, were faultlessly turned out. I was on Dick's right, so the General looked first at my cap, chin, my buttons, my belt, my creases and my boots. Then, with a pace to the side and in the usual army fashion, he started on Dick from his boots up to his cap. Round the back he went, inspecting Dick from the rear when Christ! I heard a little click as he opened Dick's Message Box.

The joke of what mine contained had long since been over, hardly anybody bothered to ask me any more what was in it – everyone knew – in fact I had forgotten all about it myself. The few seconds that it took the Commander to inspect Dick's rear view seemed to me to take until autumn. Finally, I heard his breathing directly behind me. I prayed he would move round to the front again without looking into my Box. I promised God all sorts of rash things if he would arrange this for me, but he failed me. I felt rather than heard the General open my Box and sensed him rustling about among its horrible contents – Woodbines, matches, lavatory paper and French letters! My military career was obviously over before it had even started and I toyed with the idea of falling on my bayonet among the rhododendron petals. Dick too had realized the full possibilities of the situation and started to vibrate like a harp string on my left, a condition brought about by a mixture of concern for his partner, suppressed laughter and keen anticipation of impending doom.

After an eternity, Major-General Sir Eric Girdwood stood before me. He looked for a long time at my sea-green face without saying a word. Staring blankly ahead, I waited for the axe to fall.

'Niven', he said, 'I had heard about that … thank you very much … you are very considerate….'

It was never referred to again, but immediately after Church Parade that day I cleared out my Message Box.

*

Life at Sandhurst was tough but it was exhilarating and the cadets were a dedicated corps d'élite. Some went on to command Divisions and even armies. Several among the dignified Sikhs and Pathans became leaders in their countries but a heartbreakingly high percentage were destined in little more than ten years' time to meet death on the beaches, deserts and hillsides of World War II, for this was the vintage of professional soldiers that suffered most heavily when the holocaust came.

Led by Major Godwin Austen and goaded almost beyond endurance by the much loved Robbo Robinson, No. 1 Company became champion Company and for the eighteen months I was at Sandhurst, I was one of the privileged, proudly wearing the red lanyard of the Champions.

If the work was hard, so was the play. Cadets in their senior term were allowed motor cars and a few well-heeled young men could be seen whizzing up the Great West Road, London-bound for weekends in an assortment of jalopies. Jimmy Gresham in my platoon owned a Hillman Huskie and was most generous about giving his friends lifts. A very bright fellow destined for the Welsh Guards, he was highly resilient when it came to contretemps. For some misdemeanour he was not allowed to use his car for several weeks but he solved this temporary inconvenience by keeping a chauffeur's uniform and a false moustache at White's Garage in Camberley and our weekly forays to the capital continued without missing a beat.

Reggie Hodgkinson, an old Bembridge friend, also headed for the Welsh Guards, was a member of No. 3 Company housed across the Barrack Square in the new buildings. One night, having persuaded some kind friend to sign in for him before midnight, he was almost caught by the watchful Robbo crossing our Parade ground at 3 a.m. wearing a dinner jacket. Reggie arrived beating at my door, breathless – 'Give me a pair of pyjamas for Chirst's sake, that bloody Robbo nearly nabbed me.' He quickly donned the pyjamas over his dinner jacket and dashed out again.

From the window, I watched, fascinated, as Reggie, with closed eyes, gave it the full 'I come from haunts of coot and hern' treatment; arms stretched out before him, he ambled in the bright moonlight, straight across the Barrack Square towards No. 3 Company.

He soon realized that Robbo was walking beside him.

'Wot d'you think you're doin', Mr 'Odgkinson, Sir?'

'Sleep walking, Staff.'

'Then sleep walk into the bleedin' Guard Room. Lef rite, lef rite . . . smartly now, swing the arms, Sir,' and my pyjamas disappeared at high speed in the direction of 'the cooler'.

It had long been decided that no stone would be left unturned for me to be commissioned in the Argyll and Sutherland Highlanders once I had successfully passed out of Sandhurst. When I say it had been decided, I really mean that my mother had gone to a great deal of trouble to raise old influential friends of my father's from the days when we had lived in Argyllshire. For my part I was delighted at the prospect of joining such a glamorous regiment and revelled in the meetings that were arranged by one of my mother's advisers, the Colonel of the Regiment. The McClean of Loch Buie.

The McClean, three times during my days at Sandhurst, took me, all spruced up, to visit Princess Louise, sister of King George V, who was the honorary Colonel of the Regiment and who took a great interest in all things pertaining to that famous outfit.

The first time I was taken to visit her, I was instructed to meet the McClean at his London club so that he could check me over and among other things, teach me how to bow properly to Royalty – never, but never, any arching of the back or movement from the waist – that he informed me was strictly for headwaiters.

'Stand upright, my boy, look 'em right in the eye, then, with a completely stiff back, a sharp, very definite inclination of the head, bringing the chin almost to the chest.'

I tried this rather painful manocuvre several times and each time a peculiar squeaking sound issued from my undergarments. A minute inspection disclosed the fact that the new braces which I had purchased for the occasion, complete with a very complicated gadget – a sort of pulley effect ... little wheels over which passed elastic straps – had been delivered with a faulty wheel and this was complaining bitterly at the unusual strain that was being placed upon it. The McClean solved the problem by oiling the offending part with a dab of hair lotion.

The elderly Princess became a great ally and it was at her suggestion that I was invited to spend the day with the officers of the Regiment just before they embarked for service in the West Indies where I hoped to be joining them later. They were a gay and friendly group and Colonel and subalterns alike all made me feel confident of a warm welcome in about one year's time.

All I had to do, they assured me, was to pass the final Sandhurst exams and I would be with them for sure.

Before I returned to Sandhurst for my last term and final exams, I spent what was to be my last holiday at Bembridge. The whole family, minus Tommy, was there. My mother, whom I had finally grown to love and to appreciate, presided over the gathering. 'Max' was back from India, having become disenchanted with soldiering. He had resigned his commission and gone to work as the Starter on the Bombay Race Course. This, too, had palled and his adventurous spirit had taken him to Australia, where for the past five years he had been working as a jackaroo (cowboy) on a cattle station near Yarra Weir. Now he was having a last long look at England before sailing away to take a job as manager of a banana plantation on Norfolk Island in the South Pacific.

Looking back on that period, I now realize that at eighteen I must, by today's standards, have been a very square member of a very square group. There seems to have been the minimum of rebellion against the Establishment. There was mass unemployment; conditions in the mines and shipyards were appalling. There were hunger marches and general strikes but my generation of students remained shamefully aloof. We did little or nothing in protest. Perhaps we were still very much in shock from realizing that the cream of the generation immediately before ours had been wiped out. Perhaps there was no one left worth rebelling against and in my case, discipline was being pumped and bashed into me to such an extent that any sort of organized student revolt against authority, such as has now become the norm, was unthinkable. We drank a great deal, it is true, but we were immensely physically fit. Pot, speed, hashish and LSD were as yet unheard of so instead of sitting around looking inwards, we rushed about noisily and happily extroverted.

My final term at Sandhurst was a breeze. I had never had it so good. By now promoted to Under-Officer, I was also for the second season running a rugger blue and even found time to produce a couple of concerts and to play the juvenile lead in *The Speckled Band*. I had also discovered girls in a big way and although Nessie might with certain justification have been called 'the head mistress', I had a heart like a hotel with every room booked.

Nessie, as always describing herself as 'an 'ore wiv an 'eart of – gold', was staying with a gentleman friend on a yacht for Cowes week but managed a few clandestine meetings with me in Seaview. She was still the same, as funny and forthright and as beautiful as ever and, as always, most solicitous as to my sexual wellbeing. 'Gettin' plenty, dear?'

When I sat for the final exams I discovered with pleasure mixed with surprise that they came quite easily to me and as I had also accumulated a very nice bonus of marks for being an Under-Officer, my entry into the Argylls seemed purely a formality. Everything in the garden was beautiful – a fatal situation for me.

Just before the end of term, all cadets who were graduating were given a War Office form to fill in:

'Name in order of preference three regiments into which you desire to be commissioned.'

I wrote as follows:

1. The Argyll and Sutherland Highlanders
2. The Black Watch

and then for some reason which I never fully understood, possibly because it was the only one of the six Highland Regiments that wore trews instead of the kilt, I wrote

3. Anything but the Highland Light Infantry.

Somebody at the War Office was funnier than I was and I was promptly commissioned into the Highland Light Infantry.

Let Us Now Phone Famous Men

Alan Coren

A child's game, at root, like all good things. After all, could anything match that first fine discovery of the telephone and all it stood for? That first realization that, contained within ten simple digits, lay the infinitely possible? Out there – the information seeped into the infant brain in all its diabolical clarity – lay six billion ears, all the people in the world, available for contact and mystery and insult, unable to resist the beckoning of one small and villainous forefinger. We used, my tiny evil friends and I, to congregate at the nearest parentless house, and dial into the void, and innocent mouths would answer, and gullible ears would wait. Ah, to be only eight and wield such limitless power over adults! To fell a vicar with a practised oath, to turn bass breathing on a solitary spinster, to order fourteen tons of coal from Rickett Cockerell and have it delivered to the schoolmaster of ones choice – what could match this for delirious joy? Only the pièce de résistance of scouring the phone-book for a citizen called Dumm or Barmie and phoning him to inquire if he was. What nights we spent in illicit spinnings of the dial, tottering helplessly about our living-rooms, gasping at our own wit and ingenuity and smashing our milk-teeth on the fender in the thrashing thoes brought on by such hilarity!

I wonder, sometimes, if the men who were boys when I was a boy still do it. It's not a question you can ask of bald, august solicitors, of doctors nursing kids and mortgages, of paunched executives: but do they, a quarter of a century on, creep down, perhaps, at 4 a.m. and ring their enemies to offer six free foxtrot lessons, or scream indecencies at subscribers doomed to names like Bott and Hoare?

I thought of them last week, those tiny swine who helped mis-spend my youth. Because it suddenly occurred to me to crank the whole game up to a more sophisticated notch: perhaps it was the opening of direct dialling to New York, perhaps it was the acreage of puerile posters by which the Post

Office whips us on to take advantage of their miracle offers, but, whatever the spur, I decided to spend the day trying to telephone the leaders of the world. Why not? After all, they had ears like anyone else, they had desks with phones on, they were put in power, more or less, by insignificant souls like me: surely they could set aside a few seconds for a chat, an exchange of gossip, an acknowledgement that the silent majority had a right, occasionally, to speak? So I phoned Mao Tse-Tung.

'Who?' said the girl on 108 (International Directory Enquiries).

'He's the Chairman of the Chinese People's Republic,' I said. 'It's probably a Peking number.'

There was a long silence. I could see her there, repolishing an immaculate nail, shoving a wayward curl back beneath her head-set, sucking a Polo, wondering whether she should go on the pill.

'I'll get the Supervisor,' she said, finally.

'Nobody ever phones China,' said the Supervisor.

'Why not?'

'I don't know,' she said. Her voice was diamantine. 'I only know why people phone places, I don't know why they don't, do I?'

Ruined by syntax, I pled help.

'You could phone the Chinese Chargé d'Affaires in London,' she said. 'The number is 580 7509.'

580 7509 yielded a high-pitched moan. My Chinese may be less than flawless, but even I could tell that no human larynx was involved.

I phoned the Operator.

Who phoned the Engineer.

Whose Supervisor phoned me.

'It's NU,' he said. For a moment, I felt excitingly privy to some piece of inside dope about Post Office/Chinese Legation affairs: clearly, from the man's weary voice, it was old Enn-Yu up to his tricks again, Enn-Yu the phone-bugger (I don't mean that the way it looks), the tamperer, the Red Guard saboteur; Enn-Yu, the man who had plagued the GPO for years with his intercepted calls and weird Oriental devices fitted out in the Legation basement.

'Who's Enn-Yu?' I said.

'Not In Use,' he said, and a small world crashed. 'They're always switching their lines down there. Every six weeks, they want a new phone number. Hang on,' he said, and voices muttered in the background, and far bells rang. He came back. 'It's 636 9756 this week,' he said.

'Harro!' shouted a voice at 636 9756.

'Hallo,' I said. 'I want to know how I can telephone China.'

'Why?'

'I want to speak to Chairman Mao.'

'Why?'

'I have a personal message to deliver.'

Breathing. Whispering. A new, more senior voice.

'Not possible terrephone China!' it shrieked. 'Not possible terrephone Chairman! What you want?'

I explained again. It turned out that there were no lines between England and China. Nobody ever telephoned China. Nobody *would* ever telephone China.

'How do *you* speak to China?' I asked.

A third voice came on.

'GET OFF RINE!' it screamed. 'GET OFF RINE QUICK NOW!'

And rang off. The whole thing had taken forty-seven minutes. More than enough time for thermonuclear gee-gaws to have wiped both Asia and Europe off the map. I knew the PM didn't have a hot line to Mao, and it bothered me.

I dialled again.

'Yes?' said 108.

'I'd like,' I said, 'to speak to Mr Kosygin.'

She muffled the phone inadequately.

'I think it's him again,' I heard, distant and woolly. There was giggling. I waited. The Supervisor came on.

'Are you, she said, and the syllables fell like needles, 'the gentleman who just wanted to speak to Mao Tse-Tung?'

'Yes,' I said.

I sympathized. She had, I knew, a vision of this solitary loonie who had let himself loose on the telephonic world, prior, no doubt, to rape or suicide. I wondered if they were playing for time with their long, reflective pauses, trying to trace the call, trying to dispatch a van-load of GPO male nurses to my gate. But all she said was:

'Russian Inquiries are on 104.'

'Have you got his address and phone number?' said 104.

'No,' I said, 'I thought you'd have it.'

'They never send us directories,' she said. 'It's only them and the Rumanians that don't. Everyone else sends us their directories.'

'Then how do you phone Russians?'

'You have to have their number. We keep,' she grew confidential, 'a list of hotels and factories, a few things like that. We're not supposed to, but we do. I've got the Kremlin number. Do you think that would do?'

'Yes, that sounds very good.'

'There's an hour's delay to Moscow. I'll get them to ring you back, and he might come to the phone. That'd be nice, wouldn't it?'

'That would be very nice,' I said. 'In the meantime, as you're European Directory, could you get the Pope for me?'

'Oooh, you are *awful!*' she shrieked. Her voice faded, and I could just catch it explaining the situation to the other girls. Time passed. She came back.

'You're not going to say nothing dirty to them, are you?' she said. 'Excuse me for asking, but we have to.'

I reassured her.

'I'll have to keep your number by me,' she said, 'in case there's complaints, you know, afterwards, like. No offence meant, but you'd be surprised how many people ring up foreigners and swear at them.'

I agreed, wondering who. Insights were bursting in on every hand. It clearly wasn't all beer and skittles, being a world leader, trying to keep up the balance of payments and build new schools and hold back the opposition, with Englishmen phoning you up all hours of the day and night, shouting 'Eff off!'

She gave me the Pope's residential number. I dialled direct, 01039 6 6982. It was engaged. Odd. Was he, perhaps, on The Other Line? Or just on the balcony, waving? I tried again, trembling slightly at his proximity – five hundred million subjects under his thumb, and that thumb about to curl over the receiver in response to a far, agnostic call.

'Allo.'

'Your Holiness?'

Pause.

'Wod?'

'Am I speaking to the Pope? *Il Papa?*'

Scuffling.

'Allo, allo. Can I 'elp you?'

'May I speak to the Pope?'

A long, soft sigh, one of those very Italian sighs that express so much, that say *Ah, signor, if only this world were an ideal world, what would I not give to be able to do as you ask, we should sit together in the Tuscan sunshine, you and I, just two men together, and we should drink a bottle of the good red wine, and we should sing, ah, how we should sing, but God in His infinite wisdom has, alas, not seen fit to . . .*

'Can the Pope,' I said, determined, 'come to the phone?'

'The Bobe never gum to the delephone, signor. Nod for you, nod for me, nod for Italians, nod for nobody. Is not bozzible, many regrets, 'Is 'Oliness never spig on delephone. You give me your name, I give mezzage to 'Is 'Oliness, 'e give you blezzing, okay?'

'Okay,' I said. A blessing, albeit proxied, was something.

'Don menshnit,' he said, kindly, and clicked off.

By great good fortune (or even the grace of God: who knows how quickly a Pope's blessing might work?), there was a different operator on 108 when I tried to reach Richard Nixon. He put me on to 107, who got me the White House in three minutes flat, which gave tricky Dicky a thick edge over Mao, Kosygin and Il Papa when it came to accessibility. I thought you'd like to know that, Dick, since I didn't get the chance to tell you myself. Accessibility, as Harry Truman might have said, stops here. Or almost here. The lady secretary at the White House was extremely kind, incredibly helpful and understanding; doubtless because, given America's readiness to empty magazines at those in power, you can't be too careful with nuts who phone up to speak to the President. Fob them off with a 'Get lost!' one minute, and the next they're crouched on a nearby roof and pumping away with a mail-order Winchester. The President, she said, was down in Florida, at Key Biscayne, where his number was 305 358 2380; someone there would speak to me. They did, and they were just as syrupy and sympathetic, and who knows but that I mightn't have got into the Great Ear if I hadn't played one card utterly wrong? What happened was, the call from the Kremlin, booked, you'll remember, an hour before, suddenly came through on my other phone, and I was mug enough, drunk with bogus eminence, to say to the American voice:

'Sorry, can you hold on a sec, I've got Kosygin on the other line?'

It was a nice moment, of course, but that's as long as it lasted. America hung up. Tread carefully when you step among the great, friends, their corns are sensitive.

I rather liked the Kremlin.

'Is that Mister Coren?' they said.

It's no small thrill to think one's name has echoed down the corridors of

Soviet power, from room to room, while nervous men, fearful of the punishment that follows bureaucratic cock-ups, have tried to find out who one is, and what one wants with the Prime Minister. After all, so much is secret, so much unknown. I might have been anybody, even the sort of Anybody whose whisper in a top ear could send whole switchboardsful of comrades to the stake. Who was this Coren, this cool, curt international voice who seemed to be on such good terms with Alexi N. Kosygin that he thought nothing of phoning him person-to-person? For men who remembered Lavrenti Beria, no kindness to strangers was too much. Which is no doubt why I actually got to Kosygin's private secretary, who was himself extremely civil.

'I merely want to present the Prime Minister with my good wishes,' I told him.

He was heartbroken that the Prime Minister was inextricably involved at present, but swore to me that my message would be passed on immediately. And I have not the slightest doubt that it was. It's a long way to Siberia, after all, and the cattle-trains leave every hour, on the hour.

Which left me with just two numbers in my little black book: Havana 305 031 and Cairo 768944. It took me a day to get through to one, and three days to reach the other (all calls to Egypt are subject to censorship), and when I finally did make contact, Fidel and Anwar were, needless to say, busy elsewhere. Both, however, promised faithfully to ring me back, which is why I leave them till last. Courtesy I like. Not, though, that they actually *have* rung back, but who knows? Even now, the dark, dependable forefingers may be poised over their respective dials, groping along the cables for a chance to chew the fat and swop a joke or two. If not, and if they read this first, don't worry about it, lads. It's nothing urgent.

I just wanted to say hello.

Tobermory

Saki (H. H. Munro)

It was a chill, rain-washed afternoon of a late August day, that indefinite season when partridges are still in security or cold storage, and there is nothing to hunt – unless one is bounded on the north by the Bristol Channel, in which case one may lawfully gallop after fat red stags. Lady Blemley's house-party was not bounded on the north by the Bristol Channel, hence there was a full gathering of her guests round the tea-table on this particular afternoon. And, in spite of the blankness of the season and the triteness of the occasion, there was no trace in the company of that fatigued restlessness which means a dread of the pianola and a subdued hankering for auction bridge. The undisguised open-mouthed attention of the entire party was fixed on the homely negative personality of Mr Cornelius Appin. Of all her guests, he was the one who had come to Lady Blemley with the vaguest reputation. Someone had said he was 'clever', and he had got his invitation in the moderate expectation, on the part of his hostess, that some portion at least of his cleverness would be contributed to the general entertainment. Until tea-time that day she had been unable to discover in what direction, if any, his cleverness lay. He was neither a wit nor a croquet champion, a hypnotic force nor a begetter of amatuer theatricals. Neither did his exterior suggest the sort of man in whom women are willing to pardon a generous measure of mental deficiency. He had subsided into mere Mr Appin, and the Cornelius seemed a piece of transparent baptismal bluff. And now he was claiming to have launched on the world a discovery beside which the invention of gunpowder, of the printing-press, and of steam locomotion were inconsiderable trifles. Science had made bewildering strides in many directions during recent decades, but this thing seemed to belong to the domain of miracle rather than to scientific achievement.

'And do you really ask us to believe,' Sir Wilfrid was saying, 'that you have discovered a means for instructing animals in the art of human speech, and that dear old Tobermory has proved your first successful pupil?'

'It is a problem at which I have worked for the last seventeen years,' said Mr Appin, 'but only during the last eight or nine months have I been rewarded with glimmerings of success. Of course I have experimented with thousands of animals, but latterly only with cats, those wonderful creatures which have assimilated themselves so marvellously with our civilization while retaining all their highly developed feral instincts. Here and there among cats one comes across an outstanding superior intellect, just as one does among the ruck of human beings, and when I made the acquaintance of Tobermory a week ago I saw at once that I was in contact with a "Beyond-cat" of extraordinary intelligence. I had gone far along the road to success in recent experiments; with Tobermory, as you call him, I have reached the goal.'

Mr Appin concluded his remarkable statement in a voice which he strove to divest of a triumphant inflection. No one said 'Rats,' though Clovis's lips moved in a monosyllabic contortion which probably invoked those rodents of disbelief.

'And do you mean to say,' asked Miss Resker, after a slight pause, 'that you have taught Tobermory to say and understand easy sentences of one syllable?'

'My dear Miss Resker,' said the wonder-worker patiently, 'one teaches little children and savages and backward adults in that piecemeal fashion; when one has once solved the problem of making a beginning with an animal of highly developed intelligence one has no need for those halting methods. Tobermory can speak our language with perfect correctness.'

This time Clovis very distinctly said, 'Beyond-rats!' Sir Wilfrid was more polite, but equally sceptical.

'Hadn't we better have the cat in and judge for ourselves?' suggested Lady Blemley.

Sir Wilfred went in search of the animal, and the company settled themselves down to the languid expectation of witnessing some more or less adroit drawing-room ventriloquism.

In a minute Sir Wilfrid was back in the room, his face white beneath its tan and his eyes dilated with excitement.

'By Gad, it's true!'

His agitation was unmistakably genuine, and his hearers started forward in a thrill of awakened interest.

Collapsing into an armchair he continued breathlessly: 'I found him dozing in the smoking-room, and called out to him to come for his tea. He blinked at me in his usual way, and I said, "Come on, Toby; don't keep us waiting"; and, by Gad! he drawled out in a most horribly natural voice that he'd come when he dashed well pleased! I nearly jumped out of my skin!'

Appin had preached to absolutely incredulous hearers; Sir Wilfrid's statement carried instant conviction. A Babel-like chorus of startled exclamation arose, amid which the scientist sat mutely enjoying the first fruit of his stupendous discovery.

In the midst of the clamour Tobermory entered the room and made his way with velvet tread and studied unconcern across to the group seated round the tea-table.

A sudden hush of awkwardness and constraint fell on the company. Somehow there seemed an element of embarrassment in addressing on equal terms a domestic cat of acknowledged dental ability.

'Will you have some milk, Tobermory?' asked Lady Blemley in a rather strained voice.

'I don't mind if I do,' was the response, couched in a tone of even indifference. A shiver of suppressed excitement went through the listeners, and Lady Blemley might be excused for pouring out the sauceful of milk rather unsteadily.

'I'm afraid I've spilt a good deal of it,' she said apologetically.

'After all, it's not my Axminster,' was Tobermory's rejoinder.

Another silence fell on the group, and then Miss Resker, in her best district-visitor manner, asked if the human language had been difficult to learn. Tobermory looked squarely at her for a moment and then fixed his gaze serenely on the middle distance. It was obvious that boring questions lay outside his scheme of life.

'What do you think of human intelligence?' asked Mavis Pellington lamely.

'Of whose intelligence in particular?' asked Tobermory coldly.

'Oh, well, mine for instance,' said Mavis, with a feeble laugh.

'You put me in an embarrassing position,' said Tobermory, whose tone and attitude certainly did not suggest a shred of embarrassment. 'When your inclusion in this house-party was suggested Sir Wilfrid protested that you were the most brainless woman of his acquaintance, and that there was a wide distinction between hospitality and the care of the feeble-minded. Lady Blemley replied that your lack of brain-power was the precise quality which had earned you your invitation, as you were the only person she could think of who might be idiotic enough to buy their old car. You know, the one they call "The Envy of Sisyphus", because it goes quite nicely uphill if you push it.'

Lady Blemley's protestations would have had a greater effect if she had not casually suggested to Mavis only that morning that the car in question would be just the thing for her down at her Devonshire home.

Major Barfield plunged in heavily to effect a diversion.

'How about your carryings-on with the tortoise-shell puss up at the stables, eh?'

The moment he had said it every one realized the blunder.

'One does not usually discuss these matters in public,' said Tobermory frigidly. 'From a slight observation of your ways since you've been in this house I should imagine you'd find it inconvenient if I were to shift the conversation on to your own little affairs.'

The panic which ensued was not confined to the Major.

'Would you like to go and see if cook has got your dinner ready?' suggested Lady Blemley hurriedly, affecting to ignore the fact that it wanted at least two hours to Tobermory's dinner-time.

'Thanks,' said Tobermory, 'not quite so soon after my tea. I don't want to die of indigestion.'

'Cats have nine lives, you know,' said Sir Wilfrid heartily.

'Possibly,' answered Tobermory; 'but only one liver.'

'Adelaide!' said Mrs Cornett, 'do you mean to encourage that cat to go out and gossip about us in the servants' hall?'

The panic had indeed become general. A narrow ornamental balustrade ran in front of most of the bedroom windows at the Towers, and it was recalled with dismay that this had formed a favourite promenade for Tobermory at all hours, whence he could watch the pigeons – and heaven knew what else besides. If he intended to become reminiscent in his present outspoken strain the effect would be something more than disconcerting. Mrs Cornett, who spent much time at her toilet table, and whose complexion was reputed to be of a nomadic though punctual disposition, looked as ill at ease as the Major. Miss Scrawen, who wrote fiercely sensuous poetry and led a blameless life, merely displayed irritation; if you are methodical and virtuous in private you don't necessarily want every one to know it. Bertie van Tahn, who was so depraved at seventeen that he had long ago given up trying to be any worse, turned a dull shade of gardenia white, but he did not commit the error of dashing out of the room like Odo Finsberry, a young gentleman who was understood to be reading for the Church and who was possibly disturbed at the thought of scandals he might hear concerning other people. Clovis had the presence of mind to maintain a composed exterior; privately he was calculating how long it would take to procure a box of fancy mice through the agency of the *Exchange and Mart* as a species of hush money.

Even in a delicate situation like the present, Agnes Resker could not endure to remain too long in the background.

'Why did I ever come down here?' she asked dramatically.

Tobermory immediately accepted the opening.

'Judging by what you said to Mrs Cornett on the croquet-lawn yesterday, you were out for food. You described the Blemleys as the dullest people to stay with that you knew, but said they were clever enough to employ a first-rate cook; otherwise they'd find it difficult to get any one to come down a second time.'

'There's not a word of truth in it! I appeal to Mrs Cornett –' exclaimed the discomfited Agnes.

'Mrs Cornett repeated your remark afterwards to Bertie van Tahn,' continued Tobermory, 'and said, "That woman is a regular Hunger Marcher; she'd go anywhere for four square meals a day," and Bertie van Tahn said –'

At this point the chronicle mercifully ceased. Tobermory had caught a glimpse of the big yellow Tom from the Rectory working his way through the shrubbery towards the stable wing. In a flash he had vanished through the open French window.

With the disappearance of his too brilliant pupil Cornelius Appin found himself beset by a hurricane of bitter upbraiding, anxious inquiry, and frightened entreaty. The responsibility for the situation lay with him, and he must prevent matters from becoming worse. Could Tobermory impart his dangerous gift to other cats? was the first question he had to answer. It was possible, he replied, that he might have initiated his intimate friend the stable puss into his new accomplishment, but it was unlikely that his teaching could have taken a wider range as yet.

'Then,' said Mrs Cornett, 'Tobermory may be a valuable cat and a great pet; but I'm sure you'll agree, Adelaide, that both he and the stable cat must be done away with without delay.'

'You don't suppose I've enjoyed the last quarter of an hour, do you?' said Lady Blemley bitterly. 'My husband and I are very fond of Tobermory – at

least, we were before this horrible accomplishment was infused into him; but
now, of course, the only thing is to have him destroyed as soon as possible.'

'We can put some strychnine in the scraps he always gets at dinnertime,'
said Sir Wilfrid, 'and I will go and drown the stable cat myself. The coachman
will be very sore at losing his pet, but I'll say a very catching form of mange
has broken out in both cats and we're afraid of it spreading to the kennels.'

'But my great discovery!' expostulated Mr Appin; 'after all my years of
research and experiment –'

'You can go and experiment on the short-horns at the farm, who are under
proper control,' said Mrs Cornett, 'or the elephants at the Zoological Gardens.
They're said to be highly intelligent, and they have this recommendation,
that they don't come creeping about our bedrooms and under chairs, and so
forth.'

An archangel ecstatically proclaiming the Millennium, and then finding
that it clashed unpardonably with Henley and would have to be indefinitely
postponed, could hardly have felt more crestfallen than Cornelius Appin at
the reception of his wonderful achievement. Public opinion, however, was
against him – in fact, had the general voice been consulted on the subject it
is probable that a strong minority vote would have been in favour of including
him in the strychnine diet.

Defective train arrangements and a nervous desire to see matters brought
to a finish prevented an immediate dispersal of the party, but dinner that
evening was not a social success. Sir Wilfrid had had rather a trying time
with the stable cat and subsequently with the coachman. Agnes Resker
ostentatiously limited her repast to a morsel of dry toast, which she bit as
though it were a personal enemy; while Mavis Pellington maintained a
vindictive silence throughout the meal. Lady Blemley kept up a flow of what
she hoped was conversation, but her attention was fixed on the doorway. A
plateful of carefully dosed fish scraps was in readiness on the sideboard, but
sweets and savoury and dessert went their way, and no Tobermory appeared
either in the dining-room or kitchen.

The sepulchral dinner was cheerful compared with the subsequent vigil in
the smoking-room. Eating and drinking had at least supplied a distraction
and cloak to the prevailing embarrassment. Bridge was out of the question
in the general tension of nerves and tempers, and after Odo Finsberry had
given a lugubrious rendering of 'Mélisande in the Wood' to a frigid audience,
music was tacitly avoided. At eleven the servants went to bed, announcing
that the small window in the pantry had been left open as usual for

Tobermory's private use. The guests read steadily through the current batch of magazines, and fell back gradually on the 'Badminton Library' and bound volumes of *Punch*. Lady Blemley made periodic visits to the pantry, returning each time with an expression of listless depression which forestalled questioning.

At two o'clock Clovis broke the dominating silence.

'He won't turn up tonight. He's probably in the local newspaper office at the present moment, dictating the first instalment of his reminiscences. Lady What's-her-name's book won't be in it. It will be the event of the day.'

Having made this contribution to the general cheerfulness, Clovis went to bed. At long intervals the various members of the houseparty followed his example.

The servants taking round the early tea made a uniform announcement in reply to a uniform question. Tobermory had not returned.

Breakfast was, if anything, a more unpleasant function than dinner had been, but before its conclusion the situation was relieved. Tobermory's corpse was brought in from the shrubbery, where a gardener had just discovered it. From the bites on his throat and the yellow fur which coated his claws it was evident that he had fallen in unequal combat with the big Tom from the Rectory.

By midday most of the guests had quitted the Towers, and after lunch Lady Blemley had sufficiently recovered her spirits to write an extremely nasty letter to the Rectory about the loss of her valuable pet.

Tobermory had been Appin's one successful pupil, and he was destined to have no successor. A few weeks later an elephant in the Dresden Zoological Garden, which had shown no previous signs of irritability, broke loose and killed an Englishman who had apparently been teasing it. The victim's name was variously reported in the papers as Oppin and Eppelin, but his front name was faithfully rendered Cornelius.

'If he was trying German irregular verbs on the poor beast,' said Clovis, 'he deserved all he got.'

Round the Horne

Transmission: Sunday 13th March 1966

Hugh Paddick　(*cockney*) I see Round the Horne's on in a minute, Dad.

Kenneth Williams　(*very very old*) Muck that is. Muck. I wouldn't pollute me ears with it.

Hugh Paddick　I think it's quite clever, the way they do them voices – that Kenneth Williams –

Kenneth Williams　Muck he is. Downright muck. They're all muck, every one of them.

Hugh Paddick　That Kenneth Horne isn't. He's educated.

Kenneth Williams　Well he ought to know better, consorting with that other muck. It's all double entendres, incinuendoes and catchpenny horseplay.

Hugh Paddick　So you're not going to have it on?

Kenneth Williams　No. I shall just sit here and polish me boots with the cat.

Hugh Paddick　Alright dad, but I think you should listen to it.

Kenneth Williams　Why? Give me one good reason?

Hugh Paddick　Well, you are the Head of Broadcasting.

Kenneth Williams　Alright – switch it on – but it's a load of muck.

ORCHESTRA　SIGNATURE TUNE
(*applause*)

Hugh Paddick　Ladies and Gentlemen – the programme that contains ninety-nine percent of all known jokes – Round The Horne.

ORCHESTRA SIGNATURE TUNE UP

Douglas Smith The story so far – the Japs were getting nearer. Brutal drill-pig sergeant Hugh Paddick – a regular now for the last twenty-one years (thanks to Boggis's Fruit Salts) crouched in a fox hole. Nearby, a fox, played by nimble Betty Marsden in a skin, crouched in a Hugh Paddick hole which she'd just dug. The Sergeant looked at his two companions – second lieutenant Bill Pertwee, he of the apple cheeks and pear-shaped body, and boyish, wistful Kenneth Williams, bent as always under the weight of the Vickers machine gun he'd borrowed from the Vicar.
'Would relief never come' thought Paddick. Suddenly Williams leapt to his feet, and unbuckling the Sam Browne belt that held up Sam Browne's trousers and brandishing them above his head, he cried, 'I'm going over the top'. The censor got him before he'd gone two yards. The two survivors crouched there – then suddenly when all seemed lost, they heard the cry that told them that the long awaited succour was on its way –

Kenneth Horne Good evening. This is the long awaited sucker – Kenneth Horne.

ORCHESTRA MUSIC
(*applause over*)

Kenneth Horne That was Douglas Smith, England's only nudist Kosher butcher and man-about-town. The town, of course being West Hartlepools. Well now, as this is the first of a brand new series, here are the answers to last week's questions. The answer to question one – complete the first lines of the following songs – 'If I were a blackbird I'd. . . .' The answer is 'I'd whistle and sing', and I positively will not accept any other suggestions. The second song was 'There's a rainbow round my. . . .' Now we got an amazing number of replies to this. We haven't had so many since we asked you to complete 'Over My Shoulder Goes. . . .' Really it makes it very difficult for us to keep up the high reputation for sophisticated comedy that we've never had. And now back again hot foot from his thick army socks comes that debonair yobbo, Douglas Smith.

Douglas Smith Hello again fans. And now the further adventures of Kenneth Horne – Master Spy.

ORCHESTRA   MUSIC

Kenneth Horne   I sat at the gaming table of my club – The White Orang
Utan in Jermyn Street. I'd been losing heavily at chemmy – and not for
the first time the thought crossed my mind – 'I wish I could chemmy like
my sister Kate'. I was in trouble and I knew it. Opposite me sat my
adversary – The Head of Stench, whose initials stood for 'Special Executive
for Terrorism, Extortion, Nuclear Counter Espionage and Hand Laundry'.
So this was Kronkmeyer, the arch criminal. He spoke –

KRONKMEYER (Kenneth Williams)   Come on Mr Horne, ducky, your
deal –

Kenneth Horne   I beg your pardon? Where does 'ducky' come in?

Kenneth Williams   I interpolated it. After all you *said* arch. If you wanted
a butch criminal you only had to say so. I can be as butch as the next
man, can't I?

Hugh Paddick   (*fey*) Course you can.

Kenneth Williams   See? I'm not limited, am I. I've got range – I'm
versatile.

Hugh Paddick   Bottomless, his versatility is. He can run the gamut. Run
your gamut for him. Do your act. The one you do in the clubs up North.

Kenneth Williams   (*as north country impersonator*) Alright. Ladies and
Gentlemen of Greaseborough – I went to a Hollywood party the other
night with my roving microphone. Well here I am at a Hollywood party
and who's that over there? Why it's Tom Mix talking to lovely Theda
Bara.
(*American voice*) Hello lovely Theda Bara. (*deep gruff voice*) Hello Tom Mix.

Kenneth Horne   Did Theda Bara really sound like that?

Kenneth Williams   Yes. That's what ruined her when talkies came in.
Don't interrupt. Pushing my way through the throngs of celebrities –
Excuse me Fatty Arbuckle, pardon me D. W. Griffiths – why who is that
I see now deep in conversation in the corner – why it's the late great
George Arliss talking to the late great Al Jolson. (*Arliss*) Hello late great
Al Jolson. Why don't you sing us a song in your inimitable way. (*Jolson*)

Alright late great George Arliss. (*sings*) Mammy, Mammy, I'd walk a million miles if I had your –

Kenneth Horne Excuse me – I don't want to appear stuffy but we're in the middle of a James Bond parody. I don't quite see a place for the late great Al Jolson – unless we play the sketch as a seance. I mean, you've only got one line – no need to make a meal of it.

URIAH HEAP (Bill Pertwee) I'll do it Mr Horne. I'm very humble. I'm grateful for anything. Please Mr Horne please – however menial it is, I'll do it – I'm humble you see, humble.

Hugh Paddick Oh here we go – the welcome return of Uriah Pertwee.

URIAH HEAP (*slipping into yokel or vice versa*) Did you hear that, Mr Horne. The way they sneer at me cos I'm a provincial. That Hugh Paddick with his glib London ways – and that Mr Williams. He's a Piccadilly Johnny he is. They look down on me – they laugh at my rude moleskin trousers and my clumsy manners. They mock me cos I'm not one of the fancy, but who would fancy anyone in rude moleskin trousers –

Kenneth Williams A rude mole.

URIAH HEAP (*dropping further into appalling rural accent*) Yes – you hates me Master Kenneth, you always did. Cos Miss Sibling up the hall preferred me to you. Ay, she spurned thee for oi – Ar – Aha – ar ahar.
(*Suddenly switching to breezy compere voice*)
And now ladies and gentlemen – The Hunchback of Notre Dame – (*guttural voice*) Why am I so ugly – why am I so ugly?

Betty Marsden Answers please on a postcard to Round the Horne – Care of the BBC, Ghana.

Kenneth Horne Please, Betty, don't start. I thought I could rely on you.

Betty Marsden (*as Duchess of Malfi*) Yes, you thought you'd bought my loyalty – with a plate of oysters and a bottle of milk stout. (*starts to shout*) I was a good girl till I met him. Selling flowers in Covent Garden I was. Then 'e come along. 'E had a wager with his fine gen'lman friend, Colonel Edwin Braden –

Kenneth Williams Great hairy fool!

Betty Marsden   He said I'd never be a lydy while I kept dropping me aspirates – he said he'd pass me off as a duchess.

Hugh Paddick   He promised me the same thing –

Kenneth Williams   Any luck?

Hugh Paddick   Well – so-so, but between ourselves I think the Duke's beginning to suspect something.

ORCHESTRA   CYMBAL CRASH – INTO VARIETY TYPE PAYOFF MUSIC IN FAST TWO

Betty Marsden   Mike and Bernie Winters are now appearing in 'Bareskins and Frolics' at the Opera House, Glyndebourne.

Douglas Smith   Meanwhile, back at the plot –

Kenneth Horne   Kronkmeyer and I stared across the gaming table at each other. His eyes smouldered fiercely. I stubbed them out in an ashtray. My losses were heavy. I pulled out my bankbook – my adversary smiled –

KRONKMEYER (Kenneth Williams)   You are acquainted with the game of chess I believe, Mr Horne –

Kenneth Horne   Yes.

KRONKMEYER   Then of course you understand the term 'checkmate'.

Kenneth Horne   Then you meant ...

KRONKMEYER   Yes. You know what you can do with your cheque mate.

Kenneth Horne   Kronkmeyer's hand snaked under his jacket and re-emerged holding something small, black and shiny that I recognized with a tremor of fear.

KRONKMEYER   You know what this is, Mr Horne?

Kenneth Horne   Yes, a pickled walnut.

KRONKMEYER   Precisely. And I'm not afraid to use it.

Kenneth Horne   There was only one thing could save me now. I had to go for my gun. Excuse me Kronkmeyer, I have to go for my gun.

KRONKMEYER Well hurry back. I can't hang about here all night clutching a soggy pickled walnut.

Kenneth Horne I slipped out into the bar. It had been a close call. I knew that the next time we met, Kronkmeyer and I would have to have a reckoning. I propped my long lean form against the bar, and sat on a stool next to it. The swarthy barman smiled and showed me his gold teeth –

Hugh Paddick (*gummy*) Here you are – have a look at my gold teeth.

Kenneth Horne Very nice. Now just slip them back and get me a drink – I'll have my usual – a small glass of Parrish's Chemical Food – stirred but not shaken. I drank it in one gulp — I was shaken but not stirred. At that moment a waiter sidled over, sneezed discreetly into my drink and whispered up my nose. It was the message I had been expecting. 'M' wanted to see me – at once. I hailed a passing announcer and told him to step on it. Smith?

Douglas Smith Yes sir?

Kenneth Horne Step on it will you.

Douglas Smith Very good sir.

F/X SOMETHING NASTY BEING CRUNCHED UNDERFOOT

Douglas Smith There – I've stepped on it – it's quite dead now.

Kenneth Horne Good – then announce me to the Headquarters of M.I.5.

Douglas Smith Certainly sir. Five minutes later – outside a small back room in the top security wing of Whitehall.

F/X KNOCK ON DOOR

Betty Marsden (*Russian off mike*) Come in Comrade.

F/X DOOR OPENS

Kenneth Horne 'M's' new secretary sat behind the desk. I surveyed her briefly and recommended immediate possession. She had everything a tough virile man could want – big biceps, a huge black beard – not formally good looking but interesting to a certain kind of man – Bertram Mills, Billy Smart, Barnum and Bailey. She spoke again –

Betty Marsden   (*Russian*) If you wish to see the decadent Imperialist Capitalist hyena, I'll tell him you're here.

Kenneth Horne   She waved me in the direction of the office with her Communist Party membership card – there was something wrong – what was she doing here? I would have to ask 'M'. I strode into his office. He was bent over his work, but off duty, straight as a die.

'M' (Hugh Paddick)   Ah Horne – glad you've come. I've just had these plates sent over from the lab. What do you make of them?

Kenneth Horne   Mmm. Baked beans I'd say.

'M'   Just as I thought. The food in the canteen gets worse every day.

Kenneth Horne   That girl outside, your new secretary –

'M'   You mean Gladys?

Kenneth Horne   Yes. Has she defected recently?

'M'   Well none of us is perfect. No. She's a double agent for SMERSH and WHOOSH.

Kenneth Horne   WHOOSH?

'M'   A new detergent. But we've got something more important to worry about. Here – take these binoculars – look out of this window at the Houses of Parliament – what do you see?

Kenneth Horne   I see the Earl of Arran's at it again –

'M'   No. Look at Big Ben.

Kenneth Horne   That's not Big Ben. What is it?

'M'   It's just coming up to twelve o'clock – Listen.

F/X   LOUD WHIRRING OF CLOCK MACHINERY – INCLUDING VERY LOUD TICKING AND THEN – HUGE DEEP 'CUCKOO – CUCKOO'.

Kenneth Horne   Good heavens – a fifty-foot high cuckoo.

'M'   Yes. Someone's stolen Big Ben and substituted a mechanical cuckoo –

at least we hope it's mechanical. You realize what this means to the Empire – No Big Ben!

Kenneth Horne Yes. The end of the Big Ben Banjo Band as we know it.

'M' Precisely. So far we've managed to cover it up. The BBC have been very cooperative. Before the nine o'clock news, Sir Hugh Greene himself comes into the studio and shouts 'Bong Bong' but if the poor chap gets laryngitis, it'll be civil war.

Kenneth Horne Who would have taken Big Ben? I mean it'd be very difficult to get it out of the country.

'M' Yes – we've alerted the police and customs officials to be on the look out for a very tall man with an enormous bulge in his waistcoat pocket. We have one slight clue to the identify of the thief – a visiting card left at the scene of the crime. Here –

Kenneth Horne (*reading*) 'Doctor Chou En Ginsberg, International Clock Thief – 14 Station Parade, Switzerland.' Hm – not much to go on. But why Switzerland?

'M' I think the scriptwriters are planning some dreadful joke about the Matterhorn. Be on your guard against it. Now you'll need some special equipment – Colonel Haverstrap of stores will be glad to fill you in – he's never liked you.

Kenneth Horne The interview was over. 'M' smiled at me wryly – I smiled at his O'Hara – then together the two Irishmen, Riley and O'Hara swaggered off arm in arm in the direction of Kilburn. I hurried to the bottom of the page where Colonel Haverstrap was waiting for me, disguised as a greasy thumbprint.

COLONEL HAVERSTRAP (Bill Pertwee) (*gruff army N.C.O. type*) Alright Horne – here's your equipment. These are your small arms, these are your puny hairy legs and this is your tiny bald head – you know how to use them I take it. Here's a plastic Japanese junior spy kit, comprising a small plastic dagger, the egg in bag trick, a revolving bow tie, nail through finger trick, an exploding banjo – and this . . .

Kenneth Horne Good heavens – what is it?

COLONEL HAVERSTRAP   Ah well, the trade name is – Naughty Doggie – Fido Gets The Blame. Only use it if you're in a tight corner.

Kenneth Horne   How does it help me escape?

COLONEL HAVERSTRAP   While they're beating the daylights out of the dog, you can slip out unnoticed. But if there's no other way out – use this card – but remember, you can only use it once.

Kenneth Horne   (*reads*) Get out of jail free.

COLONEL HAVERSTRAP   That's all then Horne, except for these – a gun that looks like a transistor radio – a transistor radio that looks like a gun – and ...

ORCHESTRA   DRAMATIC MUSIC

COLONEL HAVERSTRAP   .... this umbrella.

Kenneth Horne   Mmm. A cunning device. What's it for?

COLONEL HAVERSTRAP   To keep the rain off, you bald-headed fool! Right. Good luck Horne. There's a plane leaving London Airport for Switzerland in eight bars time – Be on it.

ORCHESTRA   FAST MUSIC LINK

Kenneth Horne   I relaxed in the luxury first class compartment of the Super Constellation Pan World Airways Swept Wing Sopwith Camel that was to take me to my rendezvous with fate. The hostess bent over me.

AIR HOSTESS (Betty Marsden)   We're about to take off sir. Would you like a boiled sweet or cotton wool?

Kenneth Horne   I won't have the boiled sweets. They just fall out of my ears. I'll just have some cotton wool?

AIR HOSTESS   Here you are, sir.

Kenneth Horne   Thank you. (*sound of munching*) Delicious. Then suddenly I realized, too late, the cotton wool had been impregnated with a sleep inducing drug manufactured from a blend of poppy seed, liquorice and senna pods. Well to be honest, it didn't induce sleep, but it seemed the safest thing to do. My head spun and then blackness engulfed me.

GRAMS   SHORT DRAMATIC SWEEP OF STRINGS

Kenneth Horne   When I came to, I found myself in a bare room strapped to an operating table. A face swam into focus – an evil yellow face that I knew to be that of my adversary – the inscrutable Doctor Chou En Ginsberg.

CHOU EN GINSBERG (Kenneth Williams)   Ah Mr Horne – so we meet again – etcetera blah blah blah –

Kenneth Horne   Why do you say that Ginsberg?

CHOU EN GINSBERG   While you were unconscious we cut twelve pages. You are being kept plisoner in underglound seclet labolatoly. Yes, Mr Horne – I lead the question in your eyes –

Kenneth Horne   Thank heavens, I thought, he hasn't spotted the one up my nose.

CHOU EN GINSBERG   Yes, Mr Horne – I stole Blig Blen.

Kenneth Horne   But why? Why?

CHOU EN GINSBERG   (*screams*) Because I wanted to undermine foundations of Blitish Empire – because I wanted to show I am most powerful man in whole universe! (*snide*) Besides, my Mickey mouse wrist watch has broken. But you will never live to tell Horne – you are going to die – but before you die you will be tortured. Aha – aha – oho – aha. (*snide*) There's about another half dozen of those but I think we can take it as read. Alright, Mr Horne, I clap hands (*claps hands*) and here comes Charlie.

LOTUS BLOSSOM (Hugh Paddick)   Yers guv?

Kenneth Horne   Good heavens – isn't that your concubine, Lotus Blossom?

CHOU EN GINSBERG   Yes. But changed name by deed poll. Neighbours starting to talk. Now known as Charlie Girl, from hit musical of same name ... 'I laughed till my sides ached' Halold Hobson, Sunday Times. Now my little bamboo ... shoot – my little Tsai double Tchin ...

LOTUS BLOSSOM   Yers oh mighty mandarin – what is your bidding – I await your behest.

CHOU EN GINSBERG   I'm never at my behest at this time of the morning. Go my little nightingale and prepare the torture.

LOTUS BLOSSOM   Yes oh warlord. I run like a fleet gazelle.

F/X   HEAVY CLUMPING OF BOOTS RUNNING INTO DISTANCE

CHOU EN GINSBERG   If you can imagine a fleet gazelle with hobnailed boots on. Now Mr Horne, I shall leave you to await my little friend on whom no man has looked and lived. Goodbye Mr Horne – we'll meet again, don't know where, don't know when (*sings in nasal Vera Lynn tones*) – but I know we'll meet again some sunny day.

F/X   DOOR CLOSES

Kenneth Horne   I was alone. I thought 'Horne – this is it'. I started to saw through my bonds – somewhere in Pinewood, Bond started to saw through his Hornes. When you're in Show Business you help each other. Then the door creaked open – a strange wild haired creature with insane staring eyes and great … fangs stood there. It opened its huge ravenous maw and from its throat issued a spine chilling sound which made my blood turn cold …

Bill Pertwee   (*as Ken Dodd, sings*) Tears have been my only consolation …

ORCHESTRA   MUSIC UP TO CLIMAX
(*applause over music*)

ORCHESTRA   'KENNETH HORNE MASTER SPY' THEME – UNDER FOLLOWING ANNOUNCEMENT …

Douglas Smith   (*over music*) That was Episode One of Kenneth Horne – Master Spy. Will his reason snap under the strain of Ken Dodd's singing – or will he escape and continue his pursuit of Big Ben? Will Chou En Ginsberg triumph over Justice? Will Arkle win the Cheltenham Gold Cup and Will ye no come back again. Tune in next week when we bring you Episode Two of Kenneth Horne – Master Spy.

The Luncheon

W. Somerset Maugham

I caught sight of her at the play and in answer to her beckoning I went over during the interval and sat down beside her. It was long since I had last seen her and if someone had not mentioned her name I hardly think I would have recognized her. She addressed me brightly.

'Well, it's many years since we first met. How time does fly! We're none of us getting any younger. Do you remember the first time I saw you? You asked me to luncheon.'

Did I remember?

It was twenty years ago and I was living in Paris. I had a tiny apartment in the Latin Quarter overlooking a cemetery and I was earning barely enough money to keep body and soul together. She had read a book of mine and had written to me about it. I answered, thanking her, and presently I received from her another letter saying that she was passing through Paris and would like to have a chat with me; but her time was limited and the only free moment she had was on the following Thursday; she was spending the morning at the Luxembourg and would I give her a little luncheon at Foyot's afterwards? Foyot's is a restaurant at which the French senators eat and it was so far beyond my means that I had never even thought of going there. But I was flattered and I was too young to have learned to say no to a woman. (Few men, I may add, learn this until they are too old to make it of any consequence to a woman what they say.) I had eighty francs (gold francs) to last me the rest of the month and a modest luncheon should not cost more than fifteen. If I cut out coffee for the next two weeks I could manage well enough.

I answered that I would meet my friend – by correspondence – at Foyot's on Thursday at half-past twelve. She was not so young as I expected and in appearance imposing rather than attractive. She was in fact a woman of forty (a charming age, but not one that excites a sudden and devastating passion at first sight), and she gave me the impression of having more teeth, white and large and even, than were necessary for any practical purpose. She was talkative, but since she seemed inclined to talk about me I was prepared to be an attentive listener.

I was startled when the bill of fare was brought, for the prices were a great deal higher than I had anticipated. But she reassured me.

'I never eat anything for luncheon,' she said.

'Oh, don't say that!' I answered generously.

'I never eat more than one thing. I think people eat far too much nowadays. A little fish, perhaps. I wonder if they have any salmon.'

Well, it was early in the year for salmon and it was not on the bill of fare, but I asked the waiter if there was any. Yes, a beautiful salmon had just come in, it was the first they had had. I ordered it for my guest. The waiter asked her if she would have something while it was being cooked.

'No,' she answered, 'I never eat more than one thing. Unless you had a little caviare. I never mind caviare.'

My heart sank a little. I knew I could not afford caviare, but I could not very well tell her that. I told the waiter by all means to bring caviare. For myself I chose the cheapest dish on the menu and that was a mutton chop.

'I think you're unwise to eat meat,' she said. 'I don't know how you can expect to work after eating heavy things like chops. I don't believe in overloading my stomach.'

Then came the question of drink.

'I never drink anything for luncheon,' she said.

'Neither do I,' I answered promptly.

'Except white wine,' she proceeded as though I had not spoken. 'These French white wines are so light. They're wonderful for the digestion.'

'What would you like?' I asked, hospitable still, but not exactly effusive.

She gave me a bright and amicable flash of her white teeth.

'My doctor won't let me drink anything but champagne.'

I fancy I turned a trifle pale. I ordered half a bottle. I mentioned casually that my doctor had absolutely forbidden me to drink champagne.

'What are you going to drink, then?'

'Water.'

She ate the caviare and she ate the salmon. She talked gaily of art and literature and music. But I wondered what the bill would come to. When my mutton chop arrived she took me quite seriously to task.

'I see that you're in the habit of eating a heavy luncheon. I'm sure it's a mistake. Why don't you follow my example and just eat one thing? I'm sure you'd feel ever so much better for it.'

'I *am* only going to eat one thing,' I said, as the waiter came again with the bill of fare.

She waved him aside with an airy gesture.

'No, no, I never eat anything for luncheon. Just a bite, I never want more than that, and I eat that more as an excuse for conversation than anything else. I couldn't possibly eat anything more – unless they had some of those giant asparagus. I should be sorry to leave Paris without having some of them.'

My heart sank. I had seen them in the shops and I knew that they were horribly expensive. My mouth had often watered at the sight of them.

'Madame wants to know if you have any of those giant asparagus,' I asked the waiter.

I tried with all my might to will him to say no. A happy smile spread over his broad, priest-like face, and he assured me that they had some so large, so splendid, so tender, that it was a marvel.

'I'm not in the least hungry,' my guest sighed, 'but if you insist I don't mind having some asparagus.'

I ordered them.

'Aren't you going to have any?'

'No, I never eat asparagus.'

'I know there are people who don't like them. The fact is, you ruin your palate by all the meat you eat.'

We waited for the asparagus to be cooked. Panic seized me. It was not a question now how much money I should have left over for the rest of the month, but whether I had enough to pay the bill. It would be mortifying to find myself ten francs short and be obliged to borrow from my guest. I could not bring myself to do that. I knew exactly how much I had and if the bill came to more I made up my mind that I would put my hand in my pocket and with a dramatic cry start up and say it had been picked. Of course it would be awkward if she had not money enough either to pay the bill. Then the only thing would be to leave my watch and say I would come back and pay later.

The asparagus appeared. They were enormous, succulent and appetising. The smell of the melted butter tickled my nostrils as the nostrils of Jehovah were tickled by the burned offerings of the virtuous Semites. I watched the abandoned woman thrust them down her throat in large voluptuous mouthfuls

and in my polite way I discoursed on the condition of the drama in the
Balkans. At last she finished.

'Coffee?' I said.

'Yes, just an ice-cream and coffee,' she answered.

I was past caring now, so I ordered coffee for myself and an ice-cream
and coffee for her.

'You know, there's one thing I thoroughly believe in,' she said, as she ate
the ice-cream. 'One should always get up from a meal feeling one could eat
a little more.'

'Are you still hungry?' I asked faintly.

'Oh, no, I'm not hungry; you see, I don't eat luncheon. I have a cup of
coffee in the morning and then dinner, but I never eat more than one thing
for luncheon. I was speaking for you.'

'Oh, I see!'

Then a terrible thing happened. While we were waiting for the coffee, the
head waiter, with an ingratiating smile on his false face, came up to us
bearing a large basket full of huge peaches. They had the blush of an innocent
girl; they had the rich tone of an Italian landscape. But surely peaches were
not in season then? Lord knew what they cost. I knew too – a little later, for
my guest, going on with her conversation, absentmindedly took one.

'You see, you've filled your stomach with a lot of meat' – my one miserable
little chop – 'and you can't eat any more. But I've just had a snack and I
shall enjoy a peach.'

The bill came and when I paid it I found that I had only enough for a
quite inadequate tip. Her eyes rested for an instant on the three francs I left
for the waiter and I knew that she thought me mean. But when I walked
out of the restaurant I had the whole month before me and not a penny in
my pocket.

'Follow my example,' she said as we shook hands, 'and never eat more
than one thing for luncheon.'

'I'll do better than that,' I retorted. 'I'll eat nothing for dinner tonight.'

'Humorist!' she cried gaily, jumping into a cab. 'You're quite a humorist!'

But I have had my revenge at last. I do not believe that I am a vindictive
man, but when the immortal gods take a hand in the matter it is pardonable
to observe the result with complacency. Today she weighs twenty-one stone.

Life at Boulton Wynfevers

Beachcomber (J. B. Morton)

When I was head aquarium keeper at Boulton Wynfevers, the commodious Tudor residence of the seventeenth Baron Shortcake, we had goldfish in every room. 'Travers,' my master would say to me, 'have you changed the fish-water in Lady Katharine's room?' or 'Travers,' he would call from the minstrels' gallery, 'are the fish in the Hon. Guy Clobbock's room eating well?' or, 'Travers,' he would yell from the gunroom, 'the fish in Lady Muriel's boudoir are making so much damned noise I can't hear myself eat.'

We had one fish that snored, and we always put it in Lord Thwacker's room, and told him it was the ghost of the ninth baron.

It was my duty as head aquarium keeper to keep an eye on all the different kinds of fish in our aquarium, and every night, before retiring to bed, Baron Shortcake expected me to report that all was well. The men under me had to count the fish, and then I would hand a slip of paper to my master, with the figure written on it. He always feared that some might escape – an impossible contingency, since the fish were in tanks and were watched night and day. I once ventured to ask the Baron where the fish could go to if they escaped. He answered: 'Travers, fish are queer customers. They might break out. I wish to run no risks.' One night he roused the household saying he had dreamed that a China Sea pterolotl had escaped, and was not satisfied until I had shown him the little beast asleep among weeds in his tank.

Towards his eightieth year my dear old master became an even greater goldfish-addict than before. He filled the house and grounds with goldfish, and I, as head aquarium keeper, was often called to flick the fish off people's clothes, or to drive them from the dining-hall table.

One evening, when sprats Melba were on the menu, Lady Thrashurst ate six sleeping goldfish by mistake. They had crept on to her plate. The consciousness of her error brought her to her feet with a roar of shame and anguish, and so energetically did she wriggle and squirm as the rudely awakened fish struggled in her throat that my master, recalling the Eastern dances of his youth, shouted an Oriental oath and clapped his hands.

On the morning after my old master had lost £73,000 in IOU's to a guest, we sold the entire Boulton Wynfevers collection of goldfish to a lonely old lady who had just cut her niece out of her will. From that day the Baron changed. He would wander listlessly from room to room, calling the absent fish by name and starting guiltily if he thought he saw a movement in the empty bowls.

He would sit late at his dinner, and would often call for me to repeat some story of the fish, saying, 'Travers, tell them about that time when two Burmese Rovers got down the back of Lady Felspar's dress,' or, 'Travers, do you recall how that little devil Silver Slipper drank a glass of my Meursault on the night of the fire?' or, 'Travers, I do not think Sir Arthur knows the story of how Tiny and his gang got into the Bishop's hot-water bottle and tickled his feet.' And he would sigh and say, 'Those were the days.'

They were, indeed, the days. Once a year the grounds were thrown open to the villagers and their friends, and the London papers would send photographers and reporters. The Baron was usually photographed standing between two of the biggest bowls, and little girls dressed as goldfish would curtsey to him and present him with an album in which to stick snapshots of his favourites and prizewinners.

Twelve years running we won the Shires Cup for the smartest turn-out, and the fish always got fresh water and an extra meal – not to mention a playful flip on the back from the beaming owner.

I still treasure the photograph of myself standing between my master and Lady Mockett and holding up Jellaby Wonder II by the tail.

Deafness troubled my old master considerably towards the end of his life. I remember an occasion on which he was entertaining the Lord Lieutenant of the County to dinner. He, also, was deaf. He suggested to Lord Shortcake that the craze for tropical fish was dying out.

'By topical,' said my master, 'I presume you mean fashionable.' 'I don't agree,' rejoined the Lord Lieutenant. 'I think they are unfashionable. They are aliens in any aquarium.' 'Who are aliens?' asked my master. 'No, no,' said the Lord Lieutenant. 'Not us. I said the fish.' 'Damn it,' hotly retorted Shortcake, 'what fish are you talking of?' 'No, no,' said the Lord Lieutenant, 'not us. I said the fish.' 'What?' roared my master. 'Do you mean *all* fish?' 'Well, they *are* all fish, aren't they?' said the Lord Lieutenant angrily.

As the evening wore on and the port in the decanter sank lower and lower, the two deaf men groped for an understanding. When the Lord Lieutenant spoke of flying fish, my master thought he had said 'frying fish'. He grew enraged at the idea of frying valuable specimens of his collection. 'But surely,' said the Lord Lieutenant, 'you keep flying fish?' 'I do no such thing,' replied Shortcake, 'and if I did I should do it in the kitchen, not in the aquarium.' 'That's the first time,' said the Lord Lieutenant, 'I ever heard of anybody with an aquarium in his kitchen.' 'Besides,' said my master, 'you couldn't eat most of them, even if you fried them.' 'There you are!' said the Lord Lieutenant, 'what's the good of flying fish?'

Nothing annoyed Lord Shortcake more than an obvious indifference to his goldfish. He would say to a guest before retiring: 'You will find your bowl in your room. Don't disturb the fish more than is necessary.'

The tactless guest would sometimes grin and say nothing or even show surprise, as though he were unused to such a thing. But what my dear master liked was to get some such reply as: 'Oh, but how very thoughtful of you! What breed are they? How many? What age? Certainly I will not disturb them.'

On one occasion a young lady of title, on receiving the parting information and admonition went into screaming hysterics, which infuriated my master. 'Does she think they are mice?' he asked me several times.

On another occasion a stupid dowager cried: 'What! Real goldfish?' 'Have you ever seen goldfish that weren't real?' snapped my master. 'But, do you mean *real* goldfish, like the ones in bowls?' she continued. 'Damn it all, madam,' said my master, 'I don't know what kind of goldfish you have been used to, but there's no nonsense about mine.'

'But why in the bedroom?' asked the dowager. 'Why on earth not?' countered Lord Shortcake. 'What odds is it to them what room they are in?' 'Well, I shall put them outside the door,' said the dowager. 'You can do that with your boots, but not with my fish,' said my master. 'Why not,' he added, 'fill your boots with water and put them in the bowl with the fish instead?' The dowager considered this for a while, and then left the room in high dudgeon.

I would not like my readers to have the idea that life at Boulton Wynfevers was all goldfish. There were days when my master became profoundly dissatisfied with his hobby. 'Travers,' he would say to me, 'these damned fish never *do* anything. They roam round their bowls, but anybody can do that.'

It was my task on such occasions to comfort him by referring to the sheen on their coats, or their efforts to look intelligent when shouted at, or their value as ornaments. 'Bah,' he would say, 'I prefer a good bloater. You can, at any rate, *eat* a bloater.' I would then point out that you can't keep bloaters in bowls all over a house. 'Quite right, Travers,' he would say, 'one must make allowances.' And he woud add: 'It takes all sorts to make a world.'

Curiously enough, my old master was always afraid of fire destroying his fish. An Indian law student had once told him that goldfish are terrified of fire. That is why, during the winter, their bowls were always placed as far from the fires as possible. And he even asked the chief of the local fire brigade to submit a plan for dealing with an outbreak of fire among the fish. This gentleman said: 'Oh, but they're safe enough. They're in water.' 'So are ships,' said the Baron, 'but they catch fire.' There was a fire-alarm in every room, and I, as head aquarium keeper, had to wear a fireman's helmet and carry an axe on windy days.

My dear old master, in spite of the immense wealth which enabled him to own the largest private aquarium in the shires, was a simple gentleman at heart.

Though he had a first-class chef he would never eat fish. He said to me one day: 'If I collected cows, and kept on eating beef, I should feel like a murderer. Same with fish. That is why I never shoot pheasants.'

But he was very fond of a plain boiled egg, and always kept the shells. Out of these he would make what he jestingly called 'Small porcelain bric-à-brac'. These were so fragile that no maid was allowed to dust them. They were kept on a mantelshelf in his dressing-room. And if he broke one, he would glue the pieces together again. I remember one ornament which he called a frigate in full sail. He used matches for the masts and calico for the sails. One day it disintegrated in the bath and disappeared with the bath water, to his chagrin.

Lord Shortcake collected stamps as well as goldfish – but only English twopenny stamps. He had no interest in foreign stamps, which, he said, should be left to foreigners. He had many albums filled with twopenny stamps, for he said that no two stamps were the same. Often a bored guest would be forced to admire the contents of these albums, and if he said: 'But they all look the same to me,' my dear old master would reply, 'That is because you don't study them enough. All Chinamen look the same to many Westerners, but they are really all different.'

It was the duty of my master's secretary, Aubyn Spicecraft, to keep every twopenny stamp which arrived with each day's post. Lord Shortcake showed no interest in the contents of his letters. He would ask, at breakfast, 'How

many of our well-known twopennies today, Spicecraft?' And, according to
the answer, he would smile or frown. Sometimes Spicecraft would venture
to remark that there was a letter from a relative or a dear friend. My master
would then reply, 'Well, what odds, so long as it's got the jolly old twopenny
stuck to it, eh? Give me the stamp, I always say, and anybody can have the
letter, eh?'

My dear old master was of so kindly a nature that he was easily victimized.
He was asked once to stand for Parliament, the member for the constituency
having died. On his inquiring what they would like him to stand as, a go-
ahead member of the local football club said, 'Why not the Goldfish
candidate? Better treatment for our dumb friends, and all that. Good publicity
value.'

My old master replied that goldfish were not dumb. He said they mewed
very faintly, at certain seasons. Otherwise, he said, he was prepared to present
the case for better treatment for all fish to the representatives of the nation.

Lord Shortcake was actually preparing his election literature when a friend
told him that if he got up in the House and talked about goldfish he would
be laughed at. 'Through me, then,' he said, 'they would be laughing at the
fish. I will not do it, eh?'

The newspapers, of course, ran the Goldfish candidate for all they were
worth, but my dear old master could be stubborn when he wanted to be. In
a final interview he said, 'I think I can best serve the interests of fish by
abstaining from the rostrum of public life, eh?'

Among my duties at Boulton Wynfevers, as I have stated, was the counting
of the goldfish. Every night, before the household retired to bed, I had to
hand to my dear old master a slip of paper with the total figure written on
it.

The figure was always 13,874, since every dead fish was replaced at once,
from a reserve tank, by a living one. But Shortcake always took the thing
seriously. He would say, 'Hum! 13,874. Not bad, Travers, not at all bad,
eh?'; or 'By George, Travers, 13,874, did you say? Pretty sound figure, eh?';
or 'Bravo, Travers, we're keeping it up, eh?'

Once I wrote 13,847 by mistake, and my dear old master made me count
them all over again. 'Slippery little devils,' he kept on saying. 'Can't be too
careful.'

When the house was full of guests the counting had to be done while they
were out of their rooms. I had to hang about the corridors and seize my
chance. And I well remember going into the Queen Elizabeth room in the

east wing to tot up the denizens of that particular bowl and hearing a scream. A young lady was arranging her hair at a mirror, and when I had explained my intrusion she said, 'It doesn't ring true, my man,' and, turning to her maid, she said, 'Germaine, lock up my jewels and give me the key.' Such base talk made me hang my head in shame, and under my breath I cursed the day those goldfish were born.

What struck me as so silly was that I had no need to count them. I knew the figure by heart, as the shrewd reader will have guessed.

My master's own personal bowl, in his bedroom, was stocked with the best of the fish, and I shall not be likely to forget the night when the lights fused and a certain bishop blundered into the room, mistaking it for his own, and plunged his right foot into the bowl. Candles were brought, but one big beauty was missing. My master surprised the bishop by saying, 'I think Wonder of Arden is hiding in your gaiter.' The bishop had to remove his gaiter, and out jumped the fish and slithered into a corner of the room. Lord Shortcake and I rounded it up and replaced it in the bowl. But it was an anxious night, and at two a.m. my dear old master beat on my door, shouting, 'I think I hear a stray fish in Sir Arthur's room.' It was a false alarm.

During the summer months it was Lord Shortcake's custom to entertain on a large scale. But the younger among his guests resented the lack of swimming pools, since every possible piece of water, ornamental or otherwise, was reserved for the goldfish.

One cocksure young lady said one day, 'Shorty, old hog, why not clear out these fish and give us a break?' My dear old master flushed with anger. 'Those fish,' he said, 'can do nothing but swim. You, my dear Poppy, have other accomplishments – or haven't you?'

I had strict orders to see that nobody dived into the main pond, and a large notice warned human beings to respect the privacy of the fish.

I remember the ghastly silence when, at dinner one night, a jovial young peer said, 'Any fishing down here, Shorty?' After a moment my dear old master replied, 'What would you say, Flinge, if while you were lying in your bath, a beast came and fixed a hook in your throat and hauled you out?' Young Mr Flinge gaped. 'Don't sort of get the idea,' he said. 'What are you talking about?' 'A parable,' said Lord Shortcake, 'a mere parable. If the cap fits shove it on.' 'What cap?' asked Mr Flinge. 'I say, I don't know what you're talking about.' But my master had summoned me from my place next to the third butler, and now shouted loudly, 'Keep him from the fish, eh?'

When I announced to my dear old master that Polly Cragge, one of the parlourmaids at Chealvercote Grange, the residence of Lord and Lady Hoopoe, had promised to marry me, he at once asked, 'Does she understand about goldfish?' I said that we had not discussed that subject much. To which he replied that marriage with a head aquarium keeper meant something more than a passive interest in his work.

He even sent Lord Hoopoe a bowl of fish, in the hope that Polly might become fond of them. He received in return a note from Lord Hoopoe which said, 'I take it that the present of goldfish was meant for someone else. I return them herewith.' They were at once sent back to Chealvercote, where a groom fed them to an Irish wolfhound.

Our engagement dragged on, because Polly took a violent dislike to the goldfish at Boulton Wynfevers. Every time we were together, my dear old master would track us down and get us into the aquarium. He kept on asking us to guess what he was going to give us for a wedding present. We would pretend not to know, and he would chuckle and say, 'Why, six dozen spankin' fine goldfish, eh?' And one day he gave Polly one of his Golden Marvels. To humour him she took it back to Chealvercote, where it escaped and was found half-dead in Lord Hoopoe's tobacco pouch, which he had offered to the rural dean. Polly was sacked and broke off our engagement. For a while I found it difficult not to hate the fish.

Among frequent visitors was a cunning lady in straitened circumstances, the handsome widow of a ne'er-do-well. How she wheedled my dear old master in order to get into his will! She who did not know a whale from a lobster, would simulate a deep interest in goldfish, crooming over them, stroking them, and pretending to recognize each individual fish. It was only when she mistook an Orange Wonder for a Tawny Perfection that Lord Shortcake smelt a rat. But she even went so far as to crowd her bedside table with books about goldfish and once wrote a poem about King Sam, one of our prize specimens, which began: 'Round and round and round and round, he swims without a human sound, sparkling here and sparkling there, what does he know of carking care?' My old master had this framed and hung in the aquarium.

My late lamented mistress, Lady Shortcake, who died in 1938, had often been accused of feigning interest in goldfish in order to keep my old master in good humour. But is it likely that any lady of her attainments could have stooped for sixty-one years to such deceit? The only member of the family who actively disliked the fish was the third son, Stanley. 'There must be some bad streak in the boy,' my old master would say. 'It isn't natural. He's not a Shortcake.' His own excuse, that he was bitten by a Yellow Peril in boyhood was never taken seriously at Boulton Wynfevers. 'Pah,' my master said once. 'If they were only bigger I'd put my head in their mouths without a tremor.'

The thought of Lord Shortcake with his head in a goldfish's mouth was too much for one of the young butlers. His chest heaved with inward laughter, and an entire dish of peas, about to be offered to Lord Hoopoe, slithered down the ear-trumpet of the Dowager Lady Garment, who had just placed the instrument in position in anticipation of some outrageous compliment from her neighbour. The cascade of peas against her leathery old ear drew from her an eldritch shriek. 'She might have awakened the fish,' said my master calmly, when it was all over, and she had apologized to Lord Hoopoe for smacking his face.

Aubyn Spicecraft, my dear old master's secretary, was one of those secretaries who must fold a newspaper before handing it to anybody, so that it has to be unfolded again before being read. This, he said, gives an employer the idea that he is independent and can look after himself. That is why, he would say, employers always unfold newspapers so pompously.

Lord Shortcake was interested only in stories about goldfish. If there were none in the papers, he sent them out to the servants' hall. It was Mr Spicecraft's task to mark with a blue pencil any such stories, and then to cut them out and file them after my master had read them. In addition to this, we subscribed to a press-cutting agency, which sent us all references to goldfish.

It was Spicecraft, of course, who took down at dictation and typed my dear old master's monumental work, *A History of Japanese Crossbreeds*, in eight volumes, with coloured plates of every kind of odd goldfish known to mankind. I cannot resist quoting its closing words, which hang above my Aquarium-Keeper's Diploma as I write. 'And so, reader, we say farewell to goldfish. May everybody find such constant companions upon life's thoroughfare as I have found. For this world is a bowl, where we poor mortals blunder round and round until our brief day is done. Nor, with all man's boasted brains, can he rival in beauty the little fish which has been the subject of my humble work. Gentlemen, I give you the toast: Goldfish!'

Here is another anecdote which shows the lovable simplicity of my master's character. One Christmas there was a party for all the children of the neighbourhood at Boulton Wynfevers. A Chinese conjurer (a Mr Sam Thickett) was engaged. His first trick was to make a bowl of goldfish disappear. This so annoyed Lord Shortcake that he stopped the performance, crying, 'Find them at once.' The conjurer began to produce the missing fish from the ears and pockets of the children. My master beckoned me from the room and said, 'Travers, this must be stopped.' So the magic lantern was brought in, and we had 'Glimpses of Jamaica' (Miss Grabbing at the piano).

It was for some time my dear old master's ambition to have a film made about the life of a goldfish. But he always fell out with the film people over the question of a plot. He said that no plot was needed, and that no human beings should appear.

He told one producer, 'I know what you mean by human interest, eh? Thousands of Hawaiian dancing girls.' 'What's wrong with Hawaiian dancing girls?' asked the producer. 'I want an English picture of animal life,' replied my master, 'and no jungle stuff, with mad escapes.' He insisted that the title should be 'Goldfish', and not 'Little Wonders of the Deep', which, he said, suggested a lot of dwarfs diving for pearls. Nor would he have any incidental music. 'The picture itself must hold the attention,' he said.

Finally the film was made by a week-end guest at Boulton Wynfevers, and was always shown after dinner. It was simple and beautiful. It showed the fish swimming round and round in the bowl, without any commentary. there was one tense moment when it looked as though the fish might turn and swim round in the opposite direction. At this point my master would grip the arms of his chair until his knuckles were white. But the fish, after a moment's hesitation, decided to go on as before. Then Lord Shortcake would give a contented sigh, and say loudly to the guests, 'You see? The little begger didn't reverse after all, eh?'

My dear old master was very forthright in his views on art. When a famous portrait-painter came to Boulton Wynfevers to paint him, he said bluntly, in my hearing, 'Mark this, sir, none of your confounded cubist portraits. I'm not a three-cornered tomato on a yellow banjo, even if I look like that to you.'

The artist, who painted the conventional glossy portraits at £2,000 a go, was taken aback. 'And,' continued Lord Shortcake, 'I want a background of goldfish in bowls. Bring the fish out strong. Idealize 'em, if you like. But don't call the thing "Sunset on a Dead Horse".'

Once a year Lord Shortcake's team of house-party guests played a cricket match against the village. My master himself captained his side, and showed those qualities of gay absent-mindedness and *laissez-faire* which were the despair of his friends. While fielding, he could not resist talking to the ladies, and often sat down among them, or took the arm of one of them and paced

up and down with her. When he bowled, he never would admit that he had
had a complete over. 'Now, Umpire,' he would say, 'can't you *count* eh?' And
he never yielded up the ball without a laughing protest. 'Oh, well,' he would
say loudly, 'if *that's* your idea of six balls, eh?' One young and timid umpire
once let him have his fling. He bowled fourteen balls, and then said, 'Come,
Umpire, I've had my six balls. You may call "Over", eh?'

Lady Shortcake, though not sharing her husband's passion for goldfish,
was a handsome and stately lady of the old world. Her main interest was
her rose garden.

But there came a clash when a rose was called after her. Her lord and
master had already called a goldfish after her, and though she assured him
that nobody could ever mistake the one for the other, he implored her,
for the sake of appearances, to write to the authorities and get the name
of the rose changed. This was done, and the bloom in question is now Mrs
Hufnagle.

My mistress also liked to play the harp, which instrument she never
mastered sufficiently to play a melody. But very beautiful she looked as
she allowed her fingers to roam at will over the golden wires, humming an
air the while.

Lord Shortcake was nothing if not unmusical. But that did not prevent
him from singing 'Asleep in the Deep', in a very loud and raucous baritone,
whenever he was bored. Sometimes, in his absent-minded way, he would
commence this lugubrious ditty at the crowded dinner-table, without warning.
It was then his helpmeet's task to recall him to reality by making some such
observation as 'Ernest, your tie is very nearly back to front', or 'My dear,
no Albert Hall stuff, I beg', or 'Shorty, don't break out yet'.

Once, when he was a young man, he went to a concert. A lady had just
begun to sing when my master shouted, 'We don't want any coal today.' He
always referred to that as his best joke.

Lord Shortcake's widowed sister, Lady Bursting, was a frequent visitor.
She had a singing mouse given to her by a friend and we had to be very
careful of it. It was fed on the choicest morsels of cheese, which so amused
my master that one night he gave it some port. That night the singing was
distinctly husky and out of tune, and when put out for its run before being
shut up for the night, the mouse staggered along the terrace and finally fell
down the steps into the rose garden. There a stray cat got it.

To console his sister, my master wrote an epitaph for the mouse.

Alas for Henrietta's mouse!
It was the pet of everyone in the house.
But the cat pounced like a couple of retrievers,
And that was the end of the pride of Boulton Wynfevers.

Lady Bursting's attitude to the ubiquitous goldfish was very peculiar. She affected to be unaware of their presence in the house. When her attention was called to them, she would say, non-committally, Oh, *those*. Yes.' Nothing would induce her to talk about them, or even to look at them. My master used to say, 'That woman goes through life with her eyes shut. Anybody would think there were no fish in the place.' As aquarium-keeper I felt myself included in her lack of interest, and once, when she found my peaked hat on a table, she picked it up between finger and thumb as though it had been a putrid rat. Doubtless she had some deep-seated hatred of goldfish which she cloaked with a veneer of apathy.

Lady Shortcake was deeply interested in folk-dancing, and we always had a village team in her lifetime. The only time my master became aware of this was when, returning one early spring morning from bird-watching on the banks of the Bottlemere, and about to let himself in by the back door, he ran into Angelica, one of the parlourmaids. She was dressed up as Queen of the May. He asked for an explanation. On being told that she was on her way to the Maypole, he thought she was referring to a local inn. 'How long have you had this dreadful habit?' he asked. 'I only began it last year,' said Angelica, 'to please her ladyship.' 'What on earth do you mean?' roared my master, so loudly that one of the guests, a Miss Fowler, opened her bedroom window, and cried, 'Can't you two make less noise?'

At breakfast, Lord Shortcake said to my mistress, 'My dear, I met Angelica going to the Maypole. She had the impudence to say she did it to please you.' 'Of course,' said Lady Shortcake. 'She's one of my most promising pupils.' 'Pupils?' bellowed my master. 'Am I mad? Since when have you been giving lessons in drinking?' Lady Shortcake drew herself up frigidly. 'Who said anything about drinking?' she asked. 'What else is there to do at the Maypole?' asked my master. 'They dance round it, you oaf,' was the reply. Lord Shortcake blinked unhappily, and murmured, 'I give it up.'

Ah, the old days at Boulton Wynfevers!

In a can of freshwater fleas intended as food for our fish, my master found one large flea, which he kept in a matchbox. He called it Polyphemus, because he said it had one large eye in the middle of its forehead. Nobody ever verified this, as the box was kept in a cupboard in the gun-room.

The flea died there, and Lord Shortcake said, somewhat inconsequently, that if only people would mind their own business these things would not keep on happening. Pressed by her ladyship for an explanation of so strange a saying, he replied, 'Shut up there in its box in the gun-room, it stood no chance.' 'Well, who shut it up?' asked Lady Shortcake. 'Somebody had to,' answered my master, 'to stop everybody peering and fussing.'

'I believe,' said Lady Shortcake, 'that it was just an ordinary flea.' 'I trust, my love,' replied her husband, with an old-world inclination of the head, 'I trust that my Lady Shortcake experience of ordinary fleas is so negligible as to preclude the possibility of her being a competent arbiter in the matter.'

'Vulgarity,' retorted my lady, 'cannot be cloaked by a spate of words.'

On one occasion a facetious young man, when the salmon was being served at dinner, said loudly to Lady Trowell, 'What next? Ho! Goldfish and chips.' Lord Shortcake gave him a look in which pain and anger fought for mastery. 'I was only joking, sir,' said the young fool. 'Had I believed you to be speaking seriously,' replied my master, 'I should have shown you the door.' An awkward silence fell, and then sillly old Mrs Fotherick-Dowler said heartily, 'And a very fine door it is, Shorty, if I may say so.' 'Jolly good show!' said a man's voice lower down the table. For everybody was trying to tide things over. 'Did you see Hobbs at the Oval in 1924?' came from a gaunt man. 'That was the year Myra married that gadget Helmsley,' screamed a woman's voice. But Shortcake sat glumly listening to jokes about his fish.

When the house was empty of guests, my master and mistress would often play a game of billiards after dinner. If the fish were quiet, I generally acted as marker. And a gloomy occasion it was. Lord Shortcake's bad eyesight and lack of skill prevented him from scoring any points, save by an occasional fluke. Lady Shortcake's eyesight was good, but she was an even worse player. And nothing less than a hundred up would suit them. Most of the scoring was done by misses, and towards the end of the game the cloth was nearly always torn by some savage and despairing stroke of my master's. What made things worse was that my master would tender advice to her ladyship before each stroke. After the stroke he would rebuke her, and outline her faults. And always, when the game ended he would say, 'I wasn't on top of my game tonight, Henrietta.'

I seem to hear their voices now.... Travers, the jigger for her ladyship.... Travers, I'll trouble you to chalk this damnable cue.... Shorty, keep quiet

while I aim.... Henrietta, my love, can't you manage a bit more spin?...
You aimed at the wrong ball, Henrietta.... Travers, kindly read out the
score as it stands at the moment.... There, Henrietta, I've left you a perfect
sitter, all you have to do.... My dear girl, you're playing putridly tonight....
Take your hands off the table, Shorty. I can't see the pocket.... Travers,
you aren't chalking my cue enough.... Women are no good at billards ...
RRRRRP.... Curse the cloth, it's always tearing!

Do It Yourself

Douglas Dunn

'Wait for it,' Bryan Harris told himself as he stood behind his front door. 'Wait for it.' Empty bottles chinked as the milkman put them into his wire crate. A dull, glassy thud followed as two full milk bottles were placed on Harris's doorstep. He cocked an ear towards the stairs.

'Bryan! I think that's the milkman!' his wife shouted from bed, surrounded by the Sundays which Harris had affectionately taken up to her ten minutes before.

'Yes, dear,' he said, making a face, 'I think it is.'

Ashamed of his inelegant dressing-gown and the Technicolored pyjamas which did not fit him, Harris swiped the bottles from the doorstep in the crouch of a man who does not want to be seen.

'Usual Sunday breakfast, darling?' he shouted up the stairs. He listened; he wondered if Georgina's silence was deliberate. 'I said, usual Sunday breakfast?'

'Do I have to write you a menu?' she shouted back.

Sunday breakfast meant two boiled eggs, instead of one; it meant butter on Georgina's toast instead of polyunsaturated marge; and it meant top-of-the-milk on her cereal instead of skimmed. It also meant the second instalment of their twice-weekly how's-your-father.

'Truly,' Harris said to the cat, 'it's Sunday morning. Next thing I know, she'll decide to have hard toilet paper six days a week, and soft on Sundays.'

Harris looked out at his back garden while the coffee filtered. On Wednesday, his goldfish pond had dried up in mysterious circumstances. He came home from work to find a hollow of grey, drying concrete with, in the middle, a single fish the cat had left for Mr Manners. Harris scratched his uncombed hair with foreboding. He had married into a clan of DIY experts; four of them were coming for Sunday lunch. They'd have plenty to say about his evaporated waterhole. The decorative heron that stood at its edge seemed to be staring at the parched concrete hole with one leg raised in livid frustration.

On his way upstairs with Georgina's tray the toe of his loose slipper caught the inside of his drooping pyjama trouser-leg. He slid downstairs on his belly and knees, trying to hold the tray steady.

'Bryan!'

'Sorry, dear,' he whimpered, picking a slice of toast from the wall.

Harris's in-laws and all their progeny were dissatisfied with him. 'Put the light on, Bryan, would you? You do this with the switch,' it was gestured, 'ha ha ha.' Harris was radically displeased with them but their practical, dexterous piety was unassailable. His father-in-law was the sort of man who could put in a new window before breakfast, mow the lawn, go to church, repair the vacuum cleaner while his Sunday lunch was being cooked, take a nap, and then repair the roof.

Once inside his house, Harris's restless father-in-law and his deceptively jovial in-law uncle subjected it to what looked like a systematic survey conducted in a series of fidgets.

'Fitted carpets,' said the uncle, 'hide a multitude of sins.' For a moment Harris feared that the carpets were coming up. 'I hope you had a good look at the boards before you laid that.' Harris assured them he had; in fact, the carpets had been laid by a fitter from the shop where he bought them.

'Are you a member,' his father-in-law asked, picking up the new *AA Members' Handbook*, 'of this?' Harris was a member of both motoring organizations. He dreaded a breakdown. In his opinion, the number of wayside emergency telephones was distressingly inadequate. He had nightmares about having to open the natty toolbox, his motorist's repair kit – a Christmas present from Georgina – and discover what was inside that might be of use to whatever hearty, interfering benefactor stopped to ask if he needed any help. 'I'll take a look at your car.'

'It's in for its service,' Harris said.

'What?' his father-in-law said. He seemed sincerely upset that a son-in-law of his resorted to garages.

'In all my years of motoring,' said Arthur, disappointed in Harris as much as he was proud of himself, 'I've never, never allowed these garage mechanics to touch, to so much as look at, any of my cars.' Harris shrugged.

'Arthur,' said Uncle Ted, 'Bryan wouldn't know where to start.'

Uncle Ted could make anything, including turnip wine: he had a complexion to prove it. He smelled of aftershave suppressed by an aroma of industrial fluid used to clean grease from the hands. Bored, he switched on the TV set. As both he and Arthur suspected, its controls were crying out for adjustment.

'Too much green,' said Arthur, as earnest as an art critic, his eyes narrowing, and his face screwed up as if on a sour taste.

'Too much blue?' Uncle Ted suggested. More delicate movements of the switches followed.

'You're back to green, Ted,' Taking a suitable screwdriver from his jacket pocket, Harris's father-in-law removed the protective grille at the back of the set. In spite of all warnings to the contrary, the set remained on; a programme for Pakistani viewers was in progress. Relishing the prospect of his father-in-law done to a crisp in front of the jabbering objects of his casual bigotry, Harris sat back with a newspaper. Both Uncle Ted and Arthur charred into one mutual, human, sizzling flake was too much to hope for: but he did not want that, because he knew it would leave him the man of the family.

'Spot on, Ted!' They rubbed their hands and screwed the grille back into place.

'Nig-nogs! Look, Arthur, nig-nogs!' Arthur switched it off; he looked for something else to fix.

'Oh, God, no, not now, please, please,' Harris lamented inwardly, like bad mental wind. Arthur, sniffing out things to occupy him, had reached the French doors that opened into the garden. It was a mess compared to his own; Harris's inexpert but conscientious gardening almost made Arthur weep. Uncle Ted wet his lips, winked, and wet his lips again.

'Drink, Ted?'

'I wouldn't say no, Bryan.'

Harris had observed Uncle Ted in his natural habitat. Among perfect workmanship lavished on bad taste, Uncle Ted would sit in his armchair within ordering distance of the black leatherette bar with gold studs which he had built into a corner of his living room. At the side was a hand-made bookcase containing volumes of adventure stories in what Ted believed were fine bindings and bought by mail order.

'Arthur? What about you?'

'What's wrong with this door?' Arthur asked, indignant, and puzzled; he was not used to door-handles that did not work without coaxing.

'You lift it a bit, and then push,' Harris said. Lifting more than was necessary and pushing harder than he needed to, Arthur barged his way into the garden. Uncle Ted downed his Scotch and scuttled after his brother.

'What's Daddy doing?' his mother-in-law asked in the overstaffed kitchen.

'Daddy's doing his nut,' said Harris, clearing the steamed windows to reveal two pond inspectors. He was always sure of sympathy from his mother-in-law and his in-law aunt. Georgina said, 'I told you, you should have asked Daddy to help you instead of trying to do it yourself. And look what happened.'

'Act of God,' said Harris. Georgina had offered to dig the pond herself when Harris tried to abort the operation half-way through. It had goaded him on, that imagined moment of his neighbours watching from their upstairs windows as his wife dug a large hole in the garden and mixed the cement to fill it.

'Arthur!' his mother-in-law shouted from the window. 'Dinner!' It was like tapping a spoon on a plate before a hungry cat. It was like a dinner gong struck in a seaside boarding-house. Uncle Ted dropped the hose he had been unwinding, preparing it for an experiment to find out where the leak was. 'Arthur!' said Harris's mother-in-law, and Arthur wiped his feet, then washed his hands obediently at the sink. Uncle Ted stood behind him like a small queue.

'Now go through it again.' Harris thought he might have a chance to eat something, but he was obliged to withhold his fork as, once more, he went through each stage of his pond-building process. 'Now,' said Uncle Ted, 'what did you forget to do?' He winked at Arthur.

'Leave Bryan alone,' said his in-law aunt. Arthur passed over the bit that Bryan was supposed to have missed out. Harris suspected that Arthur didn't know a pond from a hole in the ground.

'Do you have a pick?' Uncle Ted asked.

'A pick? No, of course I don't have a pick.'

'It'll have to be broken up,' Arthur said with his mouth full, 'dug up, chipped out, and removed.'

'You'll need a wheelbarrow,' said Ted, savouring his turnip wine.

'I've got a barrow,' said Harris. 'At least, I've got a barrow.'

'That's a diddy-barrow. You'll need a man's barrow.'

'And planks,' said his father-in-law.

'Planks?'

'Planks,' said Uncle Ted, 'to run the barrow on, or you'll rut your lawn.'

'I wouldn't call that a lawn, Ted. Of course, you'd save time with a pneumatic drill,' said his father-in-law. Harris shuddered pneumatically at the very thought. It was bad, imagining his neighbours watch him as he

undid two week's labour with a pick; but it was worse, much worse, picturing
them with their upturned noses and whispered remarks behind their bedroom curtains as he jumped up and down at the mercy of a pneumatic drill.
Arthur washed down his advice with a gulp of Ted's Hock-type turnip
wine.

After dinner, Uncle Ted ran the hose on the pond.

'A very slow seepage,' Arthur said, 'very slow.' To Harris it looked as if
it wasn't leaking at all.

'It must have been one of those things,' he said. 'It isn't leaking.'

'The birds,' said Uncle Ted, with a punishing command of the facts, 'didn't
drink it. Oh, it's leaking all right.'

'There's no swirl on the water,' said Harris desperately.

'Not at the moment,' said Arthur, with the deep, melancholy voice of a
born handyman passing judgement on a mistake, 'but there will be.'

Leaving Harris to roll up the hose, Arthur and Uncle Ted began to repair
the lock and handle on the French windows. These were one of the reasons
why the Harrises had bought the house.

'Oh, look, Bryan, French windows!'

'I've always known it,' Harris said to himself as he watched Arthur and
Uncle Ted at work, 'these blasted doors have been a downer on me ever
since I bought the place.'

It took a long time before his father-in-law and his in-law uncle were ready
to re-fit the several component parts of the locking mechanism and the door-
handle.

'Tea's up!' shouted his mother-in-law. Both workers straightened their
backs and seemed to put their jackets on in one movement while also taking
the first unhesitating step towards tea.

'Tea,' said Arthur.

'Tea,' said Uncle Ted.

'What about the doors?' Harris asked, fearing the worst.

'You'll have that back together in no time,' said Uncle Ted.

'You do it,' said his father-in-law.

'Do it yourself,' said Arthur, not unkindly, but with a hint that he felt he
had done enough for one day. After the goodbye ritual at the door, Georgina
said, 'I've been asking you about these doors for months.'

'Have you seen them? Have you seen the state they've left them in? Well,
have you?'

'You watched them take that lock apart, so surely you know how to put it together again, Bryan.'

'It looks like the insides of a Swiss watch!'

'I know, dear,' she said, 'they're trying, and the doors weren't all that bad, but I don't know how to fix a lock.' Harris nodded with gratitude for Georgina's sympathy. He sat down for a rest on the assumption that if he had one now he wouldn't need one later on.

'Daddy thought we'd made a very good job of the bathroom,' she said.

'Really?'

'And he asked what the marks were on the stair carpet.' Harris frowned.

'I rubbed, and rubbed,' he said. 'I hoped they'd dry out. Have we any stain remover?' he asked, getting to his feet.

'Not now, darling. I told him it was me. I didn't want him getting on at you.'

'You'd think it was his house.'

'I know, dear.'

Harris worked at the French doors until it got dark. He took up one screwdriver, put it down, took up another, and still the infernal object would not fit together, or, when it did, it would not match the space in the door it had been taken from.

'People shouldn't leave jobs unfinished,' he shouted to Georgina who was watching television at the other end of the room. 'If they have the cheek to chop up other people's houses, then they might have the decency to finish what they start.'

Lamps were rearranged to illuminate his work. The cat stole across the lit green of the lawn, followed by another. Georgina said she was going to bed.

'There were two of them, you know. And there's only one of me.'

'Is it tricky?'

'Good God, woman, it's midnight, and you ask, Is it tricky?'

'There's no need to shout.'

At two in the morning, Harris stood back and appraised his work. The paintwork was chipped and scored around the handle and the metal covering which surrounded the hole into which the tongue of the lock fitted. It looked unsightly. At least, you no longer had to lift and push. It worked perfectly. Time and again he opened the door, closed the door. The cat ran in; he patted it and it wanted out again: he opened the door and let it out. One gentle movement of the wrist was all it took. There was a click, soft, precise

and deeply satisfying. He turned the key. He reached up and slid the top
bolt; he bent down and slid the lower bolt.

'A pick,' he mused, 'or a pneumatic drill?' He drew the curtains. 'A pick
shouldn't be difficult to get.'

The Secret Life of Walter Mitty

James Thurber

'We're going through!' The Commander's voice was like thin ice breaking. He wore his full-dress uniform, with the heavily braided white cap pulled down rakishly over one cold gray eye. 'We can't make it, sir. It's spoiling for a hurricane, if you ask me.' 'I'm not asking you, Lieutenant Berg,' said the Commander. 'Throw on the power lights! Rev her up to 8,500! We're going through!' The pounding of the cylinders increased: ta-pocketa-pocketa-pocketa-*pocketa-pocketa*. The Commander stared at the ice forming on the pilot window. He walked over and twisted a row of complicated dials. 'Switch on No. 8 auxiliary!' he shouted. 'Switch on No. 8 auxiliary!' repeated Lieutenant Berg. 'Full strength in No. 3 turret!' shouted the Commander. 'Full strength in No. 3 turret!' The crew, bending to their various tasks in the huge, hurtling eight-engined Navy hydroplane, looked at each other and grinned. 'The Old Man'll get us through,' they said to one another. 'The Old Man ain't afraid of Hell!' ...

'Not so fast! You're driving too fast!' said Mrs Mitty. 'What are you driving so fast for?'

'Hmm?' said Walter Mitty. He looked at his wife, in the seat beside him, with shocked astonishment. She seemed grossly unfamiliar, like a strange woman who had yelled at him in a crowd. 'You were up to fifty-five,' she said. 'You know I don't like to go more than forty. You were up to fifty-five.' Walter Mitty drove on toward Waterbury in silence, the roaring of the SN202 through the worst storm in twenty years of Navy flying fading in the remote, intimate airways of his mind. 'You're tensed up again,' said Mrs Mitty. 'It's one of your days. I wish you'd let Dr Renshaw look you over.'

Walter Mitty stopped the car in front of the building where his wife went to have her hair done. 'Remember to get those overshoes while I'm having my hair done,' she said. 'I don't need overshoes,' said Mitty. She put her mirror back into her bag. 'We've been all through that,' she said, getting out of the car. 'You're not a young man any longer.' He raced the engine a little. 'Why don't you wear your gloves? Have you lost your gloves?' Walter Mitty reached in a pocket and brought out the gloves. He put them on, but after she had turned and gone into the building and he had driven on to a red light, he took them off again. 'Pick it up, brother!' snapped a cop as the light changed, and Mitty hastily pulled on his gloves and lurched ahead. He drove around the streets aimlessly for a time, and then he drove past the hospital on his way to the parking lot.

... 'It's the millionaire banker, Wellington McMillan,' said the pretty nurse. 'Yes?' said Walter Mitty, removing his gloves slowly. 'Who has the case?' 'Dr Renshaw and Dr Benbow, but there are two specialists here, Dr Remington from New York and Mr Pritchard-Mitford from London. He flew over.' A door opened down a long, cool corridor and Dr Renshaw came out. He looked distraught and haggard. 'Hello, Mitty,' he said. 'We're having the devil's own time with McMillan, the millionaire banker and close personal friend of Roosevelt. Obstreosis of the ductal tract. Tertiary. Wish you'd take a look at him.' 'Glad to,' said Mitty.

In the operating room there were whispered introductions: 'Dr Remington, Dr Mitty. Mr Pritchard-Mitford, Dr Mitty.' 'I've read your book on streptothricosis,' said Pritchard-Mitford, shaking hands.'A brilliant performance, sir.' 'Thank you,' said Walter Mitty. 'Didn't know you were in the States, Mitty,' grumbled Remington. 'Coals to Newcastle, bringing Mitford and me up here for a tertiary.' 'You are very kind,' said Mitty. A huge, complicated machine, connected to the operating table, with many tubes and wires, began at this moment to go pocketa-pocketa-pocketa. 'The new anesthetizer is giving way!' shouted an interne. 'There is no one in the East who knows how to fix it!' 'Quiet, man!' said Mitty, in a low, cool voice. He sprang to the machine, which was now going pocketa-pocketa-queep-pocketa-queep. He began fingering delicately a row of glistening dials. 'Give me a fountain pen!' he snapped. Someone handed him a fountain pen. He pulled a faulty piston out of the machine and inserted the pen in its place. 'That will hold for ten minutes,' he said. 'Get on with the operation.' A nurse hurried over and whispered to Renshaw, and Mitty saw the man turn pale. 'Coreopsis has set in,' said Renshaw nervously. 'If you would take over, Mitty?' Mitty looked at him and at the craven figure of Benbow, who drank, and at the grave, uncertain faces of the two great specialists. 'If you wish,' he said. They slipped a white gown on him; he adjusted a mask and drew on thin gloves; nurses handed him shining ...

'Back it up, Mac! Look out for that Buick!' Walter Mitty jammed on the brakes. 'Wrong lane, Mac,' said the parking-lot attendant, looking at Mitty closely. 'Gee. Yeh,' muttered Mitty. He began cautiously to back out of the lane marked 'Exit Only.' 'Leave her sit there,' said the attendant. 'I'll put her away.' Mitty got out of the car. 'Hey, better leave the key.' 'Oh,' said Mitty, handing the man the ignition key. The attendant vaulted into the car, backed it up with insolent skill, and put it where it belonged.

They're so damn cocky, thought Walter Mitty, walking along Main Street; they think they knew everything. Once he had tried to take his chains off, outside New Milford, and he had got them wound around the axles. A man had had to come out in a wrecking car and unwind them, a young, grinning garageman. Since then Mrs Mitty always made him drive to a garage to have the chains taken off. The next time, he thought, I'll wear my right arm in a sling; they won't grin at me then. I'll have my right arm in a sling and they'll see I couldn't possibly take the chains off myself. He kicked at the slush on the sidewalk. 'Overshoes,' he said to himself, and he began looking for a shoe store.

When he came out into the street again, with the overshoes in a box under his arm, Walter Mitty began to wonder what the other thing was his wife had told him to get. She had told him twice, before they set out from their house for Waterbury. In a way he hated these weekly trips to town – he was always getting something wrong. Kleenex, he thought, Squibb's, razor blades? No. Toothpaste, toothbrush, bicarbonate, carborundum, initiative and referendum? He gave it up. But she would remember it. 'Where's the what's-its-name?' she would ask. 'Don't tell me you forgot the what's-its-name.' A newsboy went by shouting something about the Waterbury trial.

. . . 'Perhaps this will refresh your memory.' The District Attorney suddenly thrust a heavy automatic at the quiet figure on the witness stand. 'Have you ever seen this before?' Walter Mitty took the gun and examined it expertly. 'This is my Webley-Vickers 50.80,' he said calmly. An excited buzz ran around the courtroom. The judge rapped for order. 'You are a crack shot with any sort of firearms, I believe?' said the District Attorney, insinuatingly. 'Objection!' shouted Mitty's attorney. 'We have shown that the defendant could not have fired the shot. We have shown that he wore his right arm in a sling on the night of the fourteenth of July.' Walter Mitty raised his hand briefly and the bickering attorneys were stilled. 'With any known make of gun,' he said evenly, 'I could have killed Gregory Fitzhurst at three hundred feet *with my left hand*.' Pandemonium broke loose in the courtroom. A woman's

scream rose above the bedlam and suddenly a lovely, dark-haired girl was
in Walter Mitty's arms. The District Attorney struck at her savagely. Without
rising from his chair, Mitty let the man have it on the point of the chin.
'You miserable cur!' ...

'Puppy biscuit,' said Walter Mitty. He stopped walking and the buildings
of Waterbury rose up out of the misty courtroom and surrounded him again.
A woman who was passing laughed. 'He said "Puppy biscuit,"' she said to
her companion. 'That man said "Puppy biscuit" to himself.' Walter Mitty
hurried on. He went into an A & P, not the first one he came to but a
smaller one farther up the street. 'I want some biscuit for small, young dogs,'
he said to the clerk. 'Any special brand, sir?' The greatest pistol shot in the
world thought a moment. 'It says "Puppies Bark for It" on the box,' said
Walter Mitty.

His wife would be through at the hairdresser's in fifteen minutes, Mitty saw
in looking at his watch, unless they had trouble drying it; sometimes they
had trouble drying it. She didn't like to get to the hotel first; she would want
him to be there waiting for her as usual. He found a big leather chair in the
lobby, facing a window, and he put the overshoes and the puppy biscuit on
the floor beside it. He picked up an old copy of *Liberty* and sank down into
the chair. 'Can Germany Conquer the World Through the Air?' Walter
Mitty looked at the pictures of bombing planes and of ruined streets.

... 'The cannonading has got the wind up in young Raleigh, sir,' said the
sergeant. Captain Mitty looked up at him through tousled hair. 'Get him to
bed,' he said wearily. 'With the others. I'll fly alone.' 'But you can't, sir,'
said the sergeant anxiously. 'It takes two men to handle that bomber and
the Archies are pounding hell out of the air. Von Richtman's circus is between
here and Saulier.' 'Somebody's got to get that ammunition dump,' said
Mitty. 'I'm going over. Spot of brandy?' He poured a drink for the sergeant
and one for himself. War thundered and whined around the dugout and
battered at the door. There was a rending of wood and splinters flew through
the room. 'A bit of a near thing,' said Captain Mitty carelessly. 'The box
barrage is closing in,' said the sergeant. 'We only live once, Sergeant,' said
Mitty, with his faint, fleeting smile. 'Or do we?' He poured another brandy
and tossed it off. 'I never see a man could hold his brandy like you, sir,' said
the sergeant. 'Begging your pardon, sir.' Captain Mitty stood up and strapped
on his huge Webley-Vickers automatic. 'It's forty kilometers through hell,
sir,' said the sergeant. Mitty finished one last brandy. 'After all,' he said

softly, 'what isn't?' The pounding of the cannon increased; there was the rat-tat-tatting of machine guns, and from somewhere came the menacing pocketa-pocketa-pocketa of the new flame-throwers. Walter Mitty walked to the door of the dugout humming 'Auprès de Ma Blonde.' He turned and waved to the sergeant. 'Cheerio!' he said....

Something struck his shoulder. 'I've been looking all over this hotel for you,' said Mrs Mitty. 'Why do you have to hide in this old chair? How did you expect me to find you?' 'Things close in,' said Walter Mitty vaguely. 'What?' Mrs Mitty said. 'Did you get the what's-its-name? The puppy biscuit? What's in that box?' 'Overshoes,' said Mitty. 'Couldn't you have put them on in the store?' 'I was thinking,' said Walter Mitty. 'Does it ever occur to you that I am sometimes thinking?' She looked at him. 'I'm going to take your temperature when I get you home,' she said.

They went out through the revolving doors that made a faintly derisive whistling sound when you pushed them. It was two blocks to the parking lot. At the drugstore on the corner she said, 'Wait here for me. I forgot something. I won't be a minute.' She was more than a minute. Walter Mitty lighted a cigarette. It began to rain, rain with sleet in it. He stood up against the wall of the drugstore, smoking.... He put his shoulders back and his heels together. 'To hell with the handkerchief,' said Walter Mitty scornfully. He took one last drag on his cigarette and snapped it away. Then, with that faint, fleeting smile playing about his lips, he faced the firing squad; erect and motionless, proud and disdainful, Walter Mitty the Undefeated, inscrutable to the last.

The Dog That Bit People

James Thurber

Probably no one man should have as many dogs in his life as I have had, but there was more pleasure than distress in them for me except in the case of an Airedale named Muggs. He gave me more trouble than all the other fifty-four or -five put together, although my moment of keenest embarrassment was the time a Scotch terrier named Jeannie, who had just had six puppies in the clothes closet of a fourth floor apartment in New York, had the unexpected seventh and last at the corner of Eleventh Street and Fifth Avenue during a walk she had insisted on taking. Then, too, there was the prize winning French poodle, a great big black poodle – none of your little, untroublesome white miniatures – who got sick riding in the rumble seat of a car with me on her way to the Greenwich Dog Show. She had a red rubber bib tucked around her throat and, since a rain storm came up when we were half way through the Bronx, I had to hold over her a small green umbrella, really more of a parasol. The rain beat down fearfully and suddenly the driver of the car drove into a big garage, filled with mechanics. It happened so quickly that I forgot to put the umbrella down and I will always remember, with sickening distress, the look of incredulity mixed with hatred that came over the face of the particular hardened garage man that came over to see what we wanted, when he took a look at me and the poodle. All garage men, and people of that intolerant stripe, hate poodles with their curious haircut, especially the pom-poms that you got to leave on their hips if you expect the dogs to win a prize.

But the Airedale, as I have said, was the worst of all my dogs. He really wasn't my dog, as a matter of fact: I came home from a vacation one summer to find that my brother Roy had bought him while I was away. A big, burly, choleric dog, he always acted as if he thought I wasn't one of the family. There was a slight advantage in being one of the family, for he didn't bite the family as often as he bit strangers. Still, in the years that we had him he bit everybody but mother, and he made a pass at her once but missed. That was during the month when we suddenly had mice, and Muggs refused to do anything about them. Nobody ever had mice exactly like the mice we had that month. They acted like pet mice, almost like mice somebody had trained. They were so friendly that one night when mother entertained at dinner the Friraliras, a club she and my father had belonged to for twenty years, she put down a lot of little dishes with food in them on the pantry floor so that the mice would be satisfied with that and wouldn't come into the dining room. Muggs stayed out in the pantry with the mice, lying on the floor, growling to himself – not at the mice, but about all the people in the next room that he would have liked to get at. Mother slipped out into the pantry once to see how everything was going. Everything was going fine. It made her so mad to see Muggs lying there, oblivious of the mice – they came running up to her – that she slapped him and he slashed at her, but didn't make it. He was sorry immediately, mother said. He was always sorry, she said, after he bit someone, but we could not understand how she figured this out. He didn't act sorry.

Mother used to send a box of candy every Christmas to the people the Airedale bit. The list finally contained forty or more names. Nobody could understand why we didn't get rid of the dog. I didn't understand it very well myself, but we didn't get rid of him. I think that one or two people tried to poison Muggs – he acted poisoned once in a while – and old Major Moberly fired at him once with his service revolver near the Seneca Hotel in East Broad Street – but Muggs lived to be almost eleven years old and even when he could hardly get around he bit a Congressman who had called to see my father on business. My mother had never liked the Congressman – she said the signs of his horoscope showed he couldn't be trusted (he was Saturn with the moon in Virgo) – but she sent him a box of candy that Christmas. He sent it right back, probably because he suspected it was trick candy. Mother persuaded herself it was all for the best that the dog had bitten him, even though father lost an important business association because of it. 'I wouldn't be associated with such a man,' mother said, 'Muggs could read him like a book.'

We used to take turns feeding Muggs to be on his good side, but that didn't always work. He was never in a very good humour, even after a meal. Nobody knew exactly what was the matter with him, but whatever it was it made him irascible, especially in the mornings. Roy never felt very well in the morning, either, especially before breakfast, and once when he came downstairs and found that Muggs had moodily chewed up the morning paper he hit him in the face with a grapefruit and then jumped up on the dining room table, scattering dishes and silverware and spilling the coffee. Muggs' first free leap carried him all the way across the table and into a brass fire screen in front of the gas grate but he was back on his feet in a moment and in the end he got Roy and gave him a pretty vicious bite in the leg. Then he was all over it; he never bit anyone more than once at a time. Mother always mentioned that as an argument in his favor; she said he had a quick temper but that he didn't hold a grudge. She was forever defending him. I think she liked him because he wasn't well. 'He's not strong,' she would say, pityingly, but that was inaccurate; he may not have been well but he was terribly strong.

One time my mother went to the Chittenden Hotel to call on a woman mental healer who was lecturing in Columbus on the subject of 'Harmonious Vibrations'. She wanted to find out if it was possible to get harmonious vibrations into a dog. 'He's a large tan-colored Airdale,' mother explained. The woman said that she had never treated a dog but she advised my mother to hold the thought that he did not bite and would not bite. Mother was holding the thought the very next morning when Muggs got the iceman but she blamed that slip-up on the iceman. 'If you didn't think he would bite you, he wouldn't,' mother told him. He stomped out of the house in a terrible jangle of vibrations.

One morning when Muggs bit me slightly, more or less in passing, I reached down and grabbed his short stumpy tail and hoisted him into the air. It was a foolhardy thing to do and the last time I saw my mother, about six months ago, she said she didn't know what possessed me. I don't either, except that I was pretty mad. As long as I held the dog off the floor by his tail he couldn't get at me, but he twisted and jerked so, snarling all the time, that I realized I couldn't hold him that way very long. I carried him to the kitchen and flung him onto the floor and shut the door on him just as he crashed against it. But I forgot about the backstairs. Muggs went up the backstairs and down the frontstairs and had me cornered in the living room. I managed to get up onto the mantelpiece above the fireplace, but it gave way and came down with a tremendous crash throwing a large marble clock, several vases, and myself heavily to the floor. Muggs was so alarmed by the racket that when I picked myself up he had disappeared. We couldn't find him anywhere, although we whistled and shouted, until old Mrs Detweiler called after dinner that night. Muggs had bitten her once, in the leg, and she came into the living room only after we assured her that Muggs had run away. She had just seated herself when, with a great growling and scratching of claws, Muggs emerged from under a davenport where he had been quietly hiding all the time, and bit her again. Mother examined the bite and put arnica on it and told Mrs Detweiler that it was only a bruise. 'He just bumped you,' she said. But Mrs Detweiler left the house in a nasty state of mind.

Lots of people reported our Airedale to the police but my father held a municipal office at the time and was on friendly terms with the police. Even so, the cops had been out a couple of times – once when Muggs bit Mrs Rufus Sturtevant and again when he bit Lieutenant-Governor Malloy – but mother told them that it hadn't been Muggs' fault but the fault of the people who were bitten. 'When he starts for them, they scream,' she explained, 'and that excites him.' The cops suggested that it might be a good idea to tie the dog up, but mother said that it mortified him to be tied up and that he wouldn't eat when he was tied up.

Muggs at his meals was an unusual sight. Because of the fact that if you reached toward the floor he would bite you, we usually put his food plate on top of an old kitchen table with a bench alongside the table. Muggs would stand on the bench and eat. I remember that my mother's Uncle Horatio, who boasted that he was the third man up Missionary Ridge, was splutteringly indignant when he found out that we fed the dog on a table because we were afraid to put his plate on the floor. He said he wasn't afraid of any dog that ever lived and that he would put the dog's plate on the floor if we would give it to him. Roy said that if Uncle Horatio had fed Muggs on the ground just before the battle he would have been the first man up Missionary Ridge. Uncle Horatio was furious. 'Bring him in! Bring him in now!' he shouted. 'I'll feed the – on the floor!' Roy was all for giving him a chance, but my father wouldn't hear of it. He said that Muggs had already been fed. 'I'll feed him again!' bawled Uncle Horatio. We had quite a time quieting him.

In his last year Muggs used to spend practically all of his time outdoors. He didn't like to stay in the house for some reason or other – perhaps it held too many unpleasant memories for him. Anyway, it was hard to get him to come in and as a result the garbage man, the iceman, and the laundryman wouldn't come near the house. We had to haul the garbage down to the corner, take the laundry out and bring it back, and meet the iceman a block from home. After this had gone on for some time we hit on an ingenious arrangement for getting the dog in the house so that we could lock him up while the gas meter was read, and so on. Muggs was afraid of only one thing, an electrical storm. Thunder and lightning frightened him out of his senses (I think he thought a storm had broken the day the mantelpiece fell). He would rush into the house and hide under a bed or in a clothes closet. So we fixed up a thunder machine out of a long narrow piece of sheet iron with a wooden handle on one end. Mother would shake this vigorously when she wanted to get Muggs into the house. It made an excellent imitation of thunder, but I suppose it was the most roundabout system for running a household that was ever devised. It took a lot out of mother.

A few months before Muggs died, he got to 'seeing things.' He would rise slowly from the floor, growling low, and stalk stiff-legged and menacing toward nothing at all. Sometimes the Thing would be just a little to the right or left of a visitor. Once a Fuller Brush salesman got hysterics. Muggs came wandering into the room like Hamlet following his father's ghost. His eyes were fixed on a spot just to the left of the Fuller Brush man, who stood it until Muggs was about three slow, creeping paces from him. Then he shouted. Muggs wavered on past him into the hallway grumbling to himself but the Fuller man went on shouting. I think mother had to throw a pan of cold water on him before he stopped. That was the way she used to stop us boys when we got into fights.

Muggs died quite suddenly one night. Mother wanted to bury him in the family lot under a marble stone with some such inscription as 'Flights of angels sing thee to thy rest' but we persuaded her it was against the law. In the end we just put up a smooth board above his grave along a lonely road. On the board I wrote with an indelible pencil '*Cave Canem*'. Mother was quite pleased with the simple classic dignity of the old Latin epitaph.

Showing Round

Alan Melville

You wouldn't like to see round the garden, would you?

Well ...

Because, though I says it as shouldn't, it really is beginning to look rather nice. I mean, considering. And it's practically left off raining, I mean it's only a sort of drizzle, and you can borrow Arthur's wellies, they're bound to fit you, they're just about your size; only you mustn't get those divine new shoes – they're Gucci, aren't they? Well, they *look* Gucci, which I always think is what matters – you mustn't get them covered in mud, and the far end of the lawn where Arthur had the men in to fix the drainage is inclined to be a bit swampy and in any case now Arthur's developed this fetish for croquet he has a bit of a Thing about stiletto marks anywhere near his hoops. Now you're sure you want to? – or would you rather just stay here by the fire and have another gin? I mean, do *say*.

Well ...

Good. Splendid. Super. We can go through this way and out the back; Arthur usually dumps his wellies in the cupboard under the stairs. You'd better slip on a cardie or something; we're rather exposed up here and when the wind's in the east or the north, or whatever it is, it's inclined to be breezy but of course madly healthy; if you're just getting over the flu it'll blow away all those cobwebs. Through here, dear – oops: I should have warned you, they *are* low, aren't they, the beams, and old Jacko in the village swears they're riddled with woodworm but both Arthur and I feel they give the place *character* and it's amazing how quickly one gets the knack of stooping automatically. That, of course, is typical: Arthur must have left his wellies in the toolshed, but not to worry, we can collect them on our way to the fruit-cage down at the foot of the garden through that gap in the hedge down there – you must have a grope through the fruit-cage, you never know, you might find a goosegog ripe enough to get your

teeth into – only try not to walk on the grass, just stick to the crazy paving
but dodge the cracks because we've just put in alyssum and aubrietia and
Heaven knows how many different varieties of saxifrage and little miniature
heathers and things, and we must give the poor darlings a chance. I'm
sorry about the mess out here on the verandah, but last night Arthur was
mixing peat with John Innes No 2 (you know, for potting up) and he had
to do it here because it was absolutely *pelting* down, and *both* bags burst.
You should have heard the language, *and* the woman who comes from the
village and 'does' said she knew she was thought of as a sort of two-legged
washing-machine but she'd no intention of starting up as a bulldozer as
well, so perhaps on our way back from the fruit-cage you could hold one
of those black plastic bags while I sweep up – or we could do it the other
way round, because you don't really have to catch the 6.20, do you?
– Well ...
– Of course you don't. Put your chiffon scarf over your head, dear, because
your hair's getting blown all over the place and it looked so nice when
you came off the train I hardly recognized you. Well, now, this, as if I
needed to tell you, is the herbaceous border. We copied it exactly, clump
for clump and plant for plant, from one of those chart things you see in
the papers when the Ideal Home Exhibition's on, you know, with everything
graded so the tall things like hollyhocks and red-hot pokers are at the back
and the lupins and Michaelmas daisies and so on are in the middle and
at the front you've all the small things like hellebore and Mrs Sinkin's
pinks and whatever, giving what the gardening man in the *Mail* called 'a
carefully graduated bank-like effect of glorious summer-long colour'. Only
Arthur insisted on doing the whole thing one evening when he'd been to
a Rotary lunch that had gone on a bit, so the red-hot pokers and the
hollyhocks are down here at the front, but if you come a little further up
here and kneel down and peer through all that digitalis there's the most
gorgeous little clump of campanula right at the back there up against the
wall. Careful, dear – oops: you've stepped in it, I'm afraid that's Bimbo –
he's next-door's Great Dane and he's an absolute poppet but sometimes I
think they train him to jump over the wall and do his jobs on this side.
Not to worry, when we get down to the veg garden you can take a cabbage
leaf or something and it'll come off in a sec. Now *these*, as if again you
needed telling, are the rose-beds and if only you'd come last week (it was
Joyce Grenfell or Ruth Draper or one of those people who used to do
other people who kept saying that, wasn't it?) if only you'd come last week,

well, one doesn't want to boast, but they were an absolute *picture*, but they've got a bit battered with all the gales we've had these last few days. Arthur thought it might be rather fun – you know what a sense of humour he has – to have what he calls 'incompatible bedfellows', so across there there's Fred Loads in the same bed as Minnehaha and in the middle bed we've Ralph Tizard and Wendy Cussons as cosy together and here we've Grandpa Dickson, of all people, bedded down with the Duchess of – *damn*: run, dear, it'll only be a passing plump and we can shelter in the toolshed, *no*, not across the grass, dear, up that path and round through the veg, there's a sort of beaten track between the runner beans, only for Heaven's sake jump over the marrows at the end of the row. Isn't it *maddening*, Trev the Wev – he's the met man on Television South, you don't get him in Town, you get that sawn-off little one with the moustache, Trev the Wev said occasional showers, sometimes heavy and prolonged, spreading from the West and for once he seems to have been right but, still, it's all part of Life's rich tapestry and it *is* rather fun, isn't it?

– Well ...

– There we are: we made it. This is Arthur's pride and joy, the toolshed, and where he's put those wellies I cannot imagine, but it *is* rather snug, isn't it? Arthur spends hours out here just sitting thinking; he's not what you'd call a born conversationalist, bless his cotton socks. Sit on that bag of Chichester grit, dear, and if it's damp put that old sacking under you; those up there are the nails for Arthur's tools, you know, spade, rake, hoe, fork, trowel, secateurs, and so on; and those are Arthur's tools on the floor, spade, rake, hoe, fork, trowel, secateurs and what have you. If you move nearer the door – d'you know, we've been trying for months to get old Jacko from the village to put in a new pane: that was Bimbo, or rather Bimbo's ballie – but if you move nearer the door you'll be out of the way of those drips from the roof, though of course what you should have done was grab Arthur's oil-skins when we were hunting for those wellies in the cupboard under the stairs, because that moiré silk twin-set is absolutely divine but it's rather more Sloane Square than Sussex, isn't it? No, panic ye not, it's practically stopped; I'd a feeling in my water it'd be one of those short sharp shock things that Willie Whitelaw keeps on about, so let's press on regardless with the conducted tour, shall we?

– Well ...

– There you are, hardly raining at all, it's only drips from the trees. Through the gap in the hedge, dear, that's it to your left; it *was* quite a sizeable gap

like Falaise or the one in Jilly Cooper's teeth, only Arthur keeps saying
he'll get the shears out and never does, so the best thing is to go through
it backwards and just keep nudging, it's perfectly all right, it's only privet.
And *this*, as if you didn't know, is the fruit-cage which really is rather our
pride and joy; I'll hold the netting up for you and you crawl under, just
a minute, it's got caught in your hair, you'll have to crouch much lower,
dear, because the netting's fixed on to these pole things to keep the sparrows
out and mind you don't skid because you'd never believe it but Arthur
put fresh straw down only three weeks ago but with all the rain we've
been having it's gone a bit soggy. D'you know, we picked very nearly
eleven pounds of rasps this year, you can see for yourself what a crop we
had, all those rather indecent little white knob things where the fruit were,
but of course if it's goosegogs you're after go for the lower branches right
at the bottom of each bush, there's bound to be one or two if you just get
right down on your – *Bimbo*! . . . now how in God's name did you get in?
It's all right, dear, he only wants to be friendly, he may not look it but
he's the soppiest date ever, if you tickle him under the chin he absolutely
adores it and he'll lick you all over – Bimbo, *down*: she's a very dear friend
of mine and we were at Roedean together and she's come all the way from
Knightsbridge to spend a lovely day in the country – Bimbo, *no*, she's not
playing hard to get, she just missed her footing and slipped backwards and
there's no need to pin her down in the straw with those ridiculous great
paw-paws – Bimbo, *scram*. Get the hell out of it. Honestly, if next-door
wasn't on the Planning Committee and we weren't thinking of adding on
a granny wing (where you'll always be welcome, dear) I think Arthur
would write him one of his letters. You're all right, are you?
– Well . . .
– Next time you come down you really *must* wear slacks. Everyone does
down here, we had the WI AGM in the Hall last Thursday and there
wasn't a skirt in sight except the vicar, I don't mean he's at all that way,
I mean he came to give the blessing in his cassock or hassock or whatever
it's called. You did say you found loganberries too acid for your flatulence
condition, didn't you, because there are two over here just starting to turn
pink, however, not to worry, we'll get out by the escape route at the other
end of the cage; I'll hold up the netting for you again, hang on a sec,
you've your heel caught in it this time, never mind, dear, very good for
the figure, all this stooping, get that tum of yours back to what it was in
the Vth at Roedean. Well, now, *this*, which will come as no surprise to

you, is the vegetable garden; take one of those rather droopy outside leaves off that cabbage, dear, and wipe your Guccis ... it doesn't matter now? You are a sport. These are the peas: those early ones are over, this row is the middle crop which we're eating now, and those are the last sowing which aren't quite ready yet. Otherwise we could have given you some to take back to Knightsbridge. These *were* the early potatoes, they're called Ulster Chieftain and they're quite delicious, not a bit like Ian Paisley, but of course we finished them weeks ago; these are the Catrionas which we're having now; and *those* are the late ones – Desirée – which won't be ready for digging for at least another three weeks, otherwise you could have taken some of *them* back home with you. But I tell you what you *are* going to take back as un *p'tit souvenir du jardin*. D'you like chives?
Well ...
You shall have a lovely clump of chives, by now they've masses of these rather attractive purple flowers all over them, remember to cut them off before you sprinkle the Vichysoisse, there you are, careful, it's rather damp, but you can wrap a tissue or something round the root and shove it in your handbag. Now if you can manoeuvre your way round the compost heap and I'll give you a hoist up over this heap, grass cuttings, dear, very good for manure mixed with rape and sewage sludge, and we'll go back through the gap in the hedge if we can find it and down to that other bed in the corner and I'm going to cut you an enormous armful of those gorgeous Madonna lilies. They're rather late this year but they've spread like mad and they all suddenly came out at the same time and we've so many we don't know how to get rid of them; if you *have* to catch the 6.20, after Haywards Heath it only stops at Gatwick and then all those Balhams and Claphams and Streathams and places, so if any football hooligans get in and see you looking rather pre-Raphaelite with that lovely delicate pale complexion of yours and all these lilies, you'll be perfectly safe, dear, sacrosanct, really. Hold them well away from you, dear, they're dripping a bit but we'll find an old copy of *Popular Gardening* to wrap them in. Oops ... it was a pigeon, dear. You know it's considered terribly lucky; it's on your shoulder, no, the other shoulder, don't rub it off in case you rub it in. Oh, well, take another leaf; not one of those, that's the magnolia stellata and rather special. Last August we were in the Dordogne and Arthur left the car under some trees outside the hotel we were staying in and in the morning you couldn't recognize the bonnet for droppings and you'll never believe this but he won fifteen francs in the *Loterie Nationale*. We had to go

all the way back to Limoges to collect the money at the *tabac* where he'd
bought the ticket; it cost a fortune in petrol but it does show you there's
something in it. Bless you, dear; that's the fourth time you've sneezed since
we came out of the toolshed; it's the pollen. You don't really have to catch
the 6.20, do you, because it's almost six, isn't it amazing how time flies
when you're just meandering round a garden; because naturally I'd adore
to run you to the station, only Tarquin's taking his latest steady, she's an
absolute poppet but just the teensiest bit slanty-eyed, to a disco in
Hurstpierpoint and I did say he could have the car and he's in one of his
parents-are-the-end moods, so you'll have to rush but you must come in
and dry off in front of the fire and have another gin if there's time which
I don't think there's going to be. We'll go in by the side door and do
remember to duck, that's the idea, you see how quickly you get into the
way of it – oops: yes, that's the other one, it's just a few inches lower than
this one. Now that clock says five past, either it's fast and I'm slow or I'm
slow and it's fast, but there's a short cut through Lady Hesketh's paddock,
if you nip over the stile at the end of the lane and then go across the
ploughed field when you get to the top of Poacher's Beacon you can see
the station at the bottom of the hill on the other side. You didn't have a
mack, did you, no, you said it was lovely and sunny in London, and you've
got the chives and the Madonnas; Arthur – (I don't believe it: do you see
what I see? ... the wellies, on top of the telly) – Arthur will be livid at
missing you, I warned him you were coming down but he's got this seminar
thing in Ipswich and God knows when he'll get back. Now you will come
back in the autumn, won't you, because though I says it as shouldn't the
chrysanths are really out of this world and I really think in a place like
this, with the sea fret drifting in and mixing with the low cloud over the
Downs, the 'season of mists and mellow fruitfulness' is the best time of the
year and we can warn next-door because I know they'd love to show you
round *their* garden after you've seen round ours again, theirs is *much* bigger
than ours and all terraced, quite steep, really, and you can get to know
Bimbo properly. I don't know why, but somehow I get the feeling that
the way the pair of you hit it off in the fruit-cage, it's going to be the start
of a beautiful friendship. So you will, won't you? I mean, you *promise* –
faithfully ...
– Well ...

The Pope's Mule

Alphonse Daudet

Of all the striking sayings, proverbs and adages with which our peasants of Provence flavour with their talk, I know none more picturesque and unusual than this one. For fifteen leagues around my mill, when they speak of a spiteful, vindictive person, they say: 'Beware of that man! He's like the Pope's mule who saved up her kick for seven years.'

For a long time I searched for the source of this proverb about a papal mule who kept a kick for somebody for seven years. Nobody here could enlighten me, not even Francet Mamai, my fife-player, who has all the legends of Provence at his finger tips. Francet thought, as I did, that it must be based on some ancient tale of the people of Avignon, but he had never heard of anything except the proverb.

'You'll only find out about that one from the cicadas' library,' the old fife-player said, with a laugh.

The suggestion seemed a good one, and as the cicadas' library is at my door, I went and browsed in it for a week.

It is a marvellous library admirably arranged, open day and night to poets, and looked after by little librarians with cymbals who make music all the time for you. I spent several delightful days there, and after a week's research – on my back – I finally found what I was looking for, the story of the mule and this famous kick she kept for seven years. It's a charming little tale, if a little naïve, and I will try to tell it to you just as I read it yesterday morning in a manuscript, the colour of the time of the year, which smelt sweetly of dried lavender and had long gossamer threads for bookmarks.   Whoever did not see Avignon in the days of the Popes has seen nothing. There was never such a town for life, bustle, gaiety and endless feast-days. From morning till night there were processions, pilgrimages, streets strewn with flowers and hung with high-warp tapestries, arrivals of Cardinals, banners flying in the wind, flags flying from galleys on the Rhône, the Pope's soldiers singing in

Latin in the squares, the rattles of the begging friars. And from all the high
houses crowded around the great Papal Palace, there was heard a continual
humming and buzzing: lace-makers' needles clicking and weavers' shuttles
darting, making fold-threaded vestments; little hammers tapping, shaping
communion vessels for the altars; sounding boards twanging, being turned
by the lute-makers; women at their looms singing hymns. Louder still, there
rose the noise of the bells, and always the long, narrow drums of Provence
were to be heard kicking up a din down there on the bridge. Because in our
country, when people are happy they must dance, and since at that time the
streets of the town were too narrow for the farandole, fife-players and
drummers took up positions on the bridge of Avignon in the fresh wind
sweeping down the Rhône, day and night everybody danced there, everybody
danced there ... Ah, what happy times! And what a happy, happy town!
Halberds that did not cut, state-prisons where the wine was put to keep cool.
No famines, no wars ... That was how the Popes of Avignon governed
their people; that was why the people missed them so greatly when they had
gone! ...

There was one of them in particular, a good old man called Boniface ...
Many tears indeed were shed for him in Avignon when he died! Such a
friendly, such an affable prince, he was! He would joke with you so pleasantly
from up on the back of his mule. And when you passed near him – even
though you were a poor little madder-gatherer, or the chief provost of the
town – he would give you his blessing so civilly! A true prince of the church,
but a prince of Provence, whose laugh hid a certain shrewdness, whose biretta
had a sprig of sweet marjoram in it, and for whom serving wenches had no
attraction. The only thing to which this good father was known to be devoted
was his vineyard – a little vineyard he had planted himself, three leagues
from Avignon, among the myrtles of Château Neuf.
    Every Sunday, when he came out from Vespers, the good man would go
and visit the object of his affection, and when he was up there, seated in the
warm sunshine, with his mule near him, and his cardinals reclining around
him at the foot of the vines, then he would have a bottle of his own wine
opened – that beautiful wine, the colour of rubies, which has ever since been
known as Château-Neuf des Papes – and he would savour it slowly in little
sips, whilst gazing around fondly at his vineyard. Then, the bottle empty
and evening drawing on, he would return happily to the town, followed by
all his chapter. And when he passed over the bridge of Avignon, amid the

drums and the farandoles, his mule, aroused by the music, would begin to amble skippingly, while the Pope himself would beat time to the dance with his biretta, thus greatly scandalizing his cardinals, but causing all the people to say: 'Oh, what a kind prince! What a good Pope!'

After his vineyard at Château-Neuf, what the Pope loved most was his mule. The good man made a complete fool of the beast. Every evening before going to bed, he used to go to her stall to make sure her door was shut and her manger full of food. And he'd never leave the table without seeing with his own eyes a great bowl of wine prepared with plenty of sugar and spice in the French fashion. This he would then carry to his mule himself, despite all the comments of his cardinals ... It must be admitted nevertheless that the animal was worth it. She was a beautiful mule, black with red flecks, sure-footed, with a glossy coat and a full broad back. She carried proudly her shapely little head, adorned with tassels, knots, bows and silver bells. Added to that, she was as gentle as an angel, with guileless eyes and long ears, always flapping, that gave her a good-natured look. All Avignon respected her and when she went along the streets every kind of courteous attention was paid her, for everyone knew that that was the best way of finding favour at court, that with her innocent look the Pope's mule had led more than one person to fortune, as was proved by Tistet Védène and his stupendous adventure.

From the very beginning, this Tistet Védène was an impudent young ne'er-do-well, whom his father, the sculptor in gold, Guy Védène, had had to turn out of his house because he wouldn't work and kept leading the apprentices into trouble. For six months he was seen lofing about the streets of Avignon, chiefly in the neighbourhood of the Papal Palace, since for quite a while the young rascal had had his own ideas about the papal mule, and quite cunning ideas they were too, as you shall see ...

One day when His Holiness was riding on his mule along the ramparts all by himself, who should happen to meet him but our Tistet. And what should our Tistet do but clasp his hands together in admiration and exclaim:

'Good Heavens! What a fine mule you've got, Holy Pather! ... Do let me look at her a little ... Oh, Your Holiness, what a mule, what a mule! ... Even the Emperor of Germany hasn't her equal.'

And he stroked her gently and spoke soft words to her as to a young girl.

'Come, my jewel, my treasure, my precious pearl ...'

And the good Pope, deeply moved, said to himself:

'What a nice boy! ... To be so kind to my mule! ...'

And then do you know what happened the next day? Tistet Védène exchanged his old yellow coat for a beautiful lace alb, a surplice cape in violet silk, and buckled shoes, and he entered the Pope's choir school, where before him only the sons of noblemen and the nephews of cardinals had been admitted as pupils. So you can see what cunning can achieve! ... But Tistet did not stop there.

Once he was in the Pope's service, the scalliwag continued to play the game which had proved so successful. Insolent to everybody, he paid no attention to anyone but the mule and he was always found in the palace courtyards with a handful of oats or a bundle of sainfoin whose pink clusters he would shake gently as he looked up at the Holy Father's balcony, as much as to say: 'Now, who do you think this is for?' ... So in the end it came about that the Pope, who felt himself growing old, entrusted to Tistet the care of the stables, and allowed him to carry the mule's bowl of spiced wine to her, which did not make the cardinals laugh at all.

Nor, as you shall see, was it a laughing matter for the mule ... When the time for her wine arrived, there would now always first appear five or six little choir boys who would squat down quickly on the hay in their capes and their surplices. A moment later, a nice warm smell of caramel and spice would spread through the stable and Tistet would appear, carefully carrying the bowl of wine. The martyrdom of the poor animal would then begin.

The scented wine which she loved so much, which kept her warm, which gave her wings, they were so cruel as to bring right up to her and allow her to sniff. Then, when she was overcome with the smell of it, every drop of that beautiful rose-red liquid would disappear down those little rascals' throats ... And then, as if stealing her wine were not enough, after they had drunk it those little choir boys became little devils. One of them would pull her ears, another would pull her tail. Quiquet would get up on her back, Béluguet would stick his biretta on her, and not one of those young scamps ever stopped to think that, with a single twist of her hindquarters and one flying kick, the good creature could have sent them all to the Pole-Star and even further ... But no! Not for nothing was she the Pope's mule, the mule of blessings and indulgences ... Whatever those boys did, she did not lose control of herself; though she would have liked to with one of them ... Whenever she sensed Tistet Védène was behind her, she felt an itching in her hoof, and there was every reason that she should. That good-for-nothing

Tistet played such vicious tricks on her! The wine gave him such cruel ideas ...

One day, what should come into his head but to pull her after him up the bell-turret of the choir school, high up to the very topmost point of the palace! ... And this is not a tale I'm making up for you, two hundred thousand people of Provence saw it. Imagine to yourself the terror of that unhappy mule, when, having turned blindly round and round for an hour up a spiral staircase, climbed I don't know how many steps, she found herself suddenly on a platform in a blaze of light and saw spread out a thousand feet below her a completely fantastic Avignon, the market stalls no bigger than nuts, the Pope's soldiers in front of their barracks like ants, and away down there on a silver thread a microscopically little bridge where people danced ... Oh, the poor, panic-stricken animal! The cry of terror she let forth made every window of the palace shake.

'What's the matter? What are they doing to her?' shouted the good Pope, rushing out on to his balcony.

Tistet Védène was already in the courtyard, pretending to weep and tear his hair.

'Oh, Holy Father! What a thing to happen! It's your mule ... Oh, heavens, how can such things happen? Your mule has climbed the bell-turret! ...'

'What! All by herself???'

'Yes, Holy Father, all by herself. Up there, look! Do you see the tips of her ears? You'd think they were two swallows ...'

'Oh, mercy upon us!' exclaimed the Pope, looking up. 'But she must have gone mad! She'll kill herself ... Come down at once, you foolish animal! ...'

Alas! There was nothing she wanted to do more ... but how? The staircase was out of the question: those things can be climbed, but getting down them could break one's leg a hundred times ... The poor mule was in despair and as she went to and fro on the platform, her big eyes glazed with vertigo, she kept thinking of Tistet Védène:

'Oh, the villain! If I get out of this alive, what a kick he's going to get tomorrow morning!'

The thought of this kick restored her courage a little; without the thought of it she would not have been able to hold out ... At last, they succeeded in bringing her down; but it was quite a business. It was necessary to lower her by means of a pulley, ropes and a sling. You can imagine what humiliation it was for a Pope's mule to be dangling in the air at that height, waving her legs in space like a beetle on the end of a string. And with all Avignon watching her!

The poor animal did not sleep that night. It seemed to her she was still wandering round on that accursed platform, with all the town shaking with laughter below her. Then she would think of that scoundrel Tistet Védène and of the beautiful kick she would let loose at him the next morning. Oh, what a kick that was going to be, my friends! They would see the smoke from it as far away as Pampérigouste ... But, whilst this stupendous kick was being prepared for him in the stable, do you know what Tistet Védène was doing? He was singing on board a papal galley as it sailed down the Rhône to the Court of Naples with the company of young nobles the town sent each year to Queen Jeanne to be trained in diplomacy and courtly manners. Tistet was not of noble birth, but the Pope had insisted on rewarding him for the care he had taken of his mule, and most especially for the zeal he had just shown during the work of rescue.

It was the mule who was greatly put out the next morning!

'The villain! He suspected something!' she thought, shaking her bells furiously. 'All right, you rogue! You'll find your kick still here when you get back ... I'll keep it for you!'

And she kept it for him.

After Tistet's departure, the mule went back to her quiet life, to all the pleasures she had formerly enjoyed. No more of Quiquet and Béluguet in the stable! The good old days of spiced wine came back again, and with them her good humour, her long siestas, and her little gavotte as she ambled across the bridge of Avignon. Nevertheless, ever since her adventure, a slight coldness on the part of the townspeople was noticeable. As she passed by, people whispered, old women shook their heads, and children used to laugh and point to the bell-turret. The good Pope himself no longer had the same confidence in his friend, and, whenever he allowed himself a short nap as he rode home on her from the vineyard on Sundays, there was always the thought at the back of his mind: 'Suppose I woke up and found myself up there on top of the bell-turret!' The mule saw all this and suffered it all silently; only, whenever the name of Tistet Védène was mentioned in front of her, her long ears used to quiver and with a little laugh she would sharpen the iron of her hoofs on the paving-stones.

Thus did seven years pass. Then, at the end of these seven years, Tistet Védène came back from the Court of Naples. His time there was still not finished, but he had heard that the First Bearer of the Pope's Mustard Pot had died suddenly at Avignon, and, as it seemed just the right post for him, he arrived back in great haste in order to get in first.

When this schemer entered the great hall of the Palace, the Pope had difficulty in recognizing him, so much taller and stouter had he grown. It must also be said, on his side, the Pope had grown old and did not see well without his spectacles.

Tistet did not allow himself to become nervous.

'What, Holy Father! You don't recognize me? It's me, Tistet Védène! ...'

'Védène?'

'Yes, you know ... I used to take your mule her spiced wine.'

'Ah! ... yes ... yes ... I remember ... Tistet Védène ... yes, he was a nice little lad ... Yes, now, what is it he wants from us?'

'Oh, just a small thing, Holy Father ... I was wondering ... By the way, have you still got your mule? And is she keeping well? Oh, good! I'm so glad! ... Yes, well, I was wondering if you would let me have the post of the first Mustard Cup Bearer who has just died.'

'First Mustard Cup Bearer! You! But you are too young! How old are you?'

'Twenty years and two months, Illustrious Pontiff. Exactly five years older than your mule ... Oh, that wonderful animal, how I missed her in Italy! ... Won't you allow me to see her?'

'Yes, my son, you shall see her,' the good Pope exclaimed, deeply moved. 'And since you are so fond of the dear creature, I don't wish you to be living so far away from her. From this day forth, I attach you to my person as First Bearer of the Mustard Pot. My cardinals will start shouting, but I don't care! I'm used to that. Come and see me tomorrow after Vespers and I shall bestow upon you the insignia of your office in the presence of the whole Chapter, and then ... I shall take you to see my mule and you shall accompany us both to the vineyard ... Yes, yes! It will be as you wish! Leave us now ...'

So Tistet Védène went out of the great hall a happy man and I've no need to tell you how impatiently he now awaited the morrow's ceremony. Yet there was someone in the palace even happier and even more impatient than he: and that was the mule. From the moment Védène came back, until Vespers the following day, the terrible beast did not stop stuffing herself with oats and letting fly with her hoofs at the wall behind her. She, too, was getting ready for the ceremony.

So next day, after Vespers, Tistet Védène made his entrance into the

Courtyard of the Papal Palace. All the higher clergy were there, the cardinals in their scarlet robes, the devil's advocate in his black velvet, the abbots of the monastery with their little mitres, the churchwardens from the church of St Agricol, the violet capes of the choir boys, the lower clergy too, the Pope's soldiers in full uniform, the three Brotherhoods of the penitents, the wild-looking hermits from Mont Ventoux and the little clerk who brings up the rear carrying the little bell, the Flagellant Brothers naked to the waist, the florid sacristans in their judges' robes, they were all there, all of them, even the givers of holy water, the lighters of candles, and those who extinguish candles ... not one of them was missing ... It was indeed a most wonderful ordination! Bells were ringing, fireworks cracking, the sun was shining and music playing, and always the wild beating of those drums that were leading the dance, down below, on the bridge of Avignon ...

When Védène appeared in the midst of this assembly, his noble bearing and handsome looks aroused a murmur of admiration. He was a magnificent son of Provence, of the blond type, with long hair which curled at the ends, and a little, curly beard that seemed to consist of the shavings of precious metal fallen from the graving-tool of his father, the sculptor in gold. Rumour had it that the fingers of Queen Jeanne had sometimes played with that beard, and my lord Védène had indeed the proud look and careless glance of those men whom queens have loved ... On this day, in honour of his native land of Provence, he had replaced his Neapolitan clothes with a coat bordered with pink in the Provençal style, and, on his sleeved cap, there quivered a long ibis feather from the Camargue.

As soon as he had entered, the First Bearer of the Mustard Pot bowed elegantly, and advanced towards the lofty flight of steps on which the Pope was waiting to invest him with the insignia of his office: the spoon of yellow boxwood and the saffron coat. The mule was at the foot of the steps, harnessed and ready to depart for the vineyard ... As he passed near her, Tistet Védène had a smile on his face and stopped to give her two or three friendly little pats on her back, looking out of the corner of his eye to see if the Pope was watching. The position was just right ... The mule let loose:

'There! Take that, villain! Seven years I've kept that for you!'

And the kick she let fly was so terrible, so terrible, that in far-off Pampérigouste they saw the smoke of it, vast clouds of yellow smoke in which there fluttered an ibis feather; all that was left of the unfortunate Tistet Védène!

Mule's kicks are not usually so annihilating; but this was a papal mule; besides, you must not forget she had been saving it for him for seven years ... There cannot be a more perfect example of clerical rancour.

Too Much of a Good Thing

Tom Sharpe

Zipser, a reclusive research graduate at Porterhouse College, Cambridge, is obsessed with the gargantuan charms of his bedder Mrs Briggs. But, through his clumsy attempts to get a little closer to her, he lands himself in a desperate and embarrassing predicament ...

Zipser stirred on the floor of his room. His face in contact with the carpet felt sore and his head throbbed. Above all he was cold and stiff. He turned on his side and stared at the window, where an orange glow from the sky over Cambridge shone dimly through the falling snow. Slowly he gathered himself together and got to his feet. Feeling distinctly weak and sick he went to the door and turned on the light and stood blinking at the two large cartons on the floor. Then he sat down hurriedly in a chair and tried to remember what had happened to him and why he was the possessor of two gross of guaranteed electronically tested 3-teat vending machine pack contraceptives. The details of the day's events slowly returned to him and with them the remembrance of his misunderstanding with the Dean. 'Gated for a week,' he murmured and realized the implications of his predicament. He couldn't deliver the beastly things to the Unicorn now and he had signed the slip at the wholesale office. Enquiries would be made. The barman at the Unicorn would identify him. So would the wretched clerk at the wholesale office. The police would be informed. There would be a search. He'd be arrested. Charged with being in felonious possession of two gross of ... Zipser clutched his head in his hands and tried to think what to do. He'd have to get rid of the things. He looked at his watch. Eleven o'clock. Got to hurry. Burn them? He looked at the gas fire and gave up the idea. Out of the question. Flush them down the lavatory? Better idea. He threw himself at the cartons and began to open them. First the outer carton, then the inner one, then the packet itself and finally the foil wrapper. It was a laborious job. He'd never do it. He'd got to do it.

Beside him on the carpet a pile of empty packets slowly grew and with it a pile of foil and a grotesque arrangement of latex rings looking like flattened and translucent button mushrooms. Lubricated with sensitol, his hands were sticky, which made it even more difficult to tear the foil. Finally after an hour he had emptied one carton. It was twelve o'clock. He gathered the contraceptives up and took a handful out on to the landing and into the lavatory. He dropped them into the pan and pulled the chain. A rush of water, swirls, bubbles, gone? The water subsided and he stared down at two dozen rubber rings floating defiantly in the pan. 'For God's sake,' said Zipser desperately and waited until the cistern had filled again. He waited a minute after the water had stopped running and pulled the chain again. Two dozen contraceptives smiled up at him. One or two had partially unfurled and were filled with air. Zipser stared at the things frantically. Got to get them to go down somehow. He reached behind the pan and grabbed the cleaning brush and shoved it down on them. One or two disappeared round the U bend but for the most part they resisted his efforts. Three even had the audacity to adhere to the brush itself. Zipser picked them off with fastidious disgust and dropped them back into the water. By this time the cistern had filled again, gurgling gently and ending with a final swish. Zipser tried to think what to do. If buying the damned things had been fraught with appalling difficulties, getting rid of them was a nightmare.

He sat down on the lavatory seat and considered the intractability of matter. A tin of lavatory cleanser caught his attention. He picked it up and wondered if it would dissolve rubber. Then he got off the seat and emptied the contents on to the rings floating in the water. Whatever chemical action the cleanser promised failed altogether. The contraceptives remained unaffected. Zipser grabbed the brush again and plunged it into the pan. Wafts of disinfectant powder irritated his nose. He sneezed loudly and clutched the chain. For the third time the cistern flushed and Zipser was just studying the subsidence and counting the six contraceptives which remained immune to chemistry and the rush of water when someone knocked on the door.

'What the hell's going on in there?' a voice asked. It was Foxton, who lived in the room next door.

Zipser looked hauntedly at the door. 'Got diarrhoea,' he said weakly.

'Well, must you pull the bloody chain so often?' Foxton asked. 'Making a bloody awful noise and I'm trying to sleep.' He went back to his room and Zipser turned back to the pan and began fishing for the six contraceptives with the lavatory brush.

Twenty minutes later he was still searching for some method of disposing of his incriminating evidence. He had visited six lavatories on neighbouring staircases and had found a method of getting the things to disappear by first filling them with water from a tap and tying the ends. It was slow and cumbersome and above all noisy and when he had tried six at a time on J staircase he had had to spend some time unblocking the U pipe. He went back to his room and sat shivering with cold and anxiety. It was one o'clock and so far he had managed to rid himself of thirty-eight. At this rate he would still be flushing lavatories all over the College when Mrs Biggs arrived in the morning. He stared at the pile of foil and the packets. Got to get rid of them too. Put them behind the gas fire and burn them he thought and he was just wrestling with the gas fire and trying to make space behind it when the howling draught in the chimney gave him a better idea. He went to the window and looked out into the night. In the darkness outside snowflakes whirled and scattered while the wind battered at the window pane. Zipser opened the window and poked his head out into the storm before wetting his finger and holding it up to the wind. 'Blowing from the East,' he muttered and shut the window with a smile of intense satisfaction. A moment later he was kneeling beside the gas fire and undoing the hose of his gas ring and five minutes afterwards the first of 250 inflated contraceptives bounced buoyantly against the sooty sides of the medieval chimney and disappeared into the night sky above. Zipser rushed to the window and gazed up for a glimpse of the winsome thing as it whirled away carrying its message of abstinence far away into the world, but the sky was too dark and there was nothing to see. He went back and fetched a torch and shone it up the chimney but apart from one or two errant snowflakes the chimney was clear. Zipser turned cheerfully back to the gas ring and inflated five more. Once again the experiment was entirely successful. Up the chimney they floated, up and away. Zipser inflated twenty and popped them up the chimney with equal success. He was just filling his hundredth when the gas gave out, with a hideous wheeze the thing deflated. Zipser rummaged in his pockets for a shilling and finally found one. He put it into the meter and the contraceptive assumed a new and satisfactory shape. He tied the end and stuffed it up the chimney. The night wore on and Zipser acquired a wonderful dexterity. On to the tube, gas on, gas off, a knot in the end and up the chimney. Beside him on the floor the cartons filled with discarded foil and Zipser was just wondering if there were schoolchildren who collected used contraceptive containers like milk-bottle tops when he became aware that something had gone wrong in the chimney. The bloated and strangulated rear of his last contraceptive was hanging suspended in the fireplace. Zipser gave it a shove of encouragement but the poor thing merely bulged dangerously. Zipser pulled it out and peered up the chimney. He couldn't peer very far. The chimney was crowded with eager contraceptives. He extracted another, smeared with soot and put it down on the floor. He extracted a third and thrust it behind him. Then a fourth and a fifth, both deeply encrusted with soot. After that he gave up. The rest were too high to reach. He clambered out of the fireplace and sat on the floor wondering what to do. At least he had disposed of all two gross, even if some were lodged in the chimney stack. They were well hidden there – or would be once he had put the gas fire back in place. He would think of some way of disposing of them in the morning. He was too tired to think of anything now. He turned to reach for the five he had managed to extract only to find that they had disappeared. 'I put them down on the carpet. I'm sure I did,' he muttered lightheadedly to himself and was about to look under the bookcase when his eye caught sight of a movement on the ceiling. Zipser looked up. Five sooty contraceptives had lodged themselves in a corner by the door. Little bits of soot marked the ceiling where they had touched.

Zipser got wearily to his feet and climbed on to a chair and reached up. He could just manage to get his fingers on to the belly of one of the things but the sensitol made it impossible to get a grip. Zipser squeezed and with a coy squeak the contraceptive evaded his grasp and lumbered away across the room, leaving a track of soot behind it. Zipser tried again on another with the same result. He moved the chair across the room and reached up. The contraceptive waddled gently into the corner by the window. Zipser moved the chair again but the contraceptive rolled away. Zipser climbed down and stared manically at his ceiling. It was covered in delicate black trails as if some enormous snail had called after a stint of coal-heaving. The self-control Zipser had been exercising began to slip. He picked up a book and lobbed it at a particularly offensive-looking contraceptive, but apart from driving it across the room to join the flock in the corner by the door the gesture was futile. Zipser crossed to the desk and pushed it over to the door. Then he fetched the chair and stood it on the desk and climbed precariously up and seized a contraceptive by its knotted tail. He climbed down and thrust it up the chimney. Five minutes later all five were back in place and although the last one still protruded below the lintel, when he pushed the gas fire back into position it was invisible. Zipser collapsed on to his sofa and stared at the ceiling. All that remained was to clean the soot off the plaster. He went out into the gyp room and fetched a duster and spent the next half hour pushing his desk round the room and climbing on to it to dust the ceiling. Traces of soot still remained but they were less noticeable now. He pushed the desk back into its corner and looked round the room. Apart from a noticeable smell of gas and the more intransigent stains on the ceiling there was nothing to connect him with two gross of contraceptives fraudulently obtained from the wholesalers. Zipser opened the window to clear the room of gas and went through to his bedroom and went to bed. In the eastern sky the first light of dawn was beginning to appear, but Zipser had no eyes for the beauties of nature. He fell into a restless sleep haunted by the thought that the logjam in his chimney might break during the coming day to issue with shocking ebullience above the unsuspecting College. He need not have worried. Porterhouse was already infested. The falling snow had seen to that. As each porcine sensitol-lubricated protective had emerged from the chimney stack the melting snow had ended its night flight almost abruptly. Zipser had not foreseen the dangers of icing.

The Dean arrived back at Porterhouse in Sir Cathcart's Rolls-Royce at two o'clock. He was spiritually restored though physically taxed by the day's excitements and Sir Cathcart's brandy. He knocked on the main gate and Skullion, who had been waiting up obediently for him, opened the postern and let him in.

'Need any help, sir,' Skullion asked as the Dean tottered through.

'Certainly not,' said the Dean thickly and set off across the Court. Skullion followed him at a distance like a good dog and saw him through the Screens before turning back to his Porter's Lodge and bed. He had already shut the door and gone through into his backroom when the Dean's strangled cry sounded from the New Court. Skullion heard nothing. He took off his collar and tie and climbed between the sheets. 'Drunk as a lord,' he thought fondly, and closed his eyes.

The Dean lay in the snow and cursed. He tried to imagine what he had slipped on. It certainly wasn't the snow. Snow didn't squash like that. Snow certainly didn't explode like that and even in these days of air pollution snow didn't smell of gas like that. The Dean eased himself on to a bruised hip and peered into the darkness. A strange rustling sound in which a sort of wheeze and the occasional squeak were intermingled came from all sides. The Court seemed to be alive with turgid and vaguely translucent shapes which gleamed in the starlight. The Dean reached out tentatively towards the nearest one and felt it bounce delicately away from him. He scrambled to his feet and kicked another. A ripple of rustling, squeaking, jostling shapes issued across the Court. 'That damned brandy,' muttered the Dean. He waded through the mass to the door of his staircase and stumbled upstairs. He was feeling distinctly ill. 'Must be my liver,' he thought, and slumped into a chair with the sudden resolution to leave brandy well alone in future. After a bit he got up and went to the window and looked out. Seen from above the Court looked empty, white with snow but otherwise normal. The Dean shut the window and turned back into the room. 'I could have sworn there were ...' He tried to think just what he could have sworn the Court was filled with, but couldn't think of anything appropriate. Balloons was as near as he could get, but balloons didn't have that awful translucent ectoplasmic quality about them.

He went into his bedroom and undressed and put on his pyjamas and got into bed but sleep was impossible. He had dozed too long at Sir Cathcart's, and, besides, he was haunted by his recent experience. After an hour the Dean got out of bed again and put on his dressing-gown and went downstairs. At the bottom he peered out into the Court. There was the same indelicate squeaking sound but apart from that the night was too dark to see anything clearly. The Dean stepped out into the Court and banged into one of the objects. 'They *are* there after all,' he muttered and reached down to pick whatever it was up. The thing had a soft vaguely oily feel about it and scuttled away as soon as the Dean's fingers tightened on it. He tried another and missed and it was only at the third attempt that he managed to obtain a grip. Holding the thing by its tail the Dean took it into the lighted doorway and looked at it with a growing sense of disgust and outrage. He held it head down and the thing righted itself and turned head up. Holding it thus he went out into the Court and through the Screens to Old Court and the Porter's Lodge.

To Skullion, emerging sleepily from his backroom, the sight of the Dean in his dressing-gown holding the knotted end of an inflated contraceptive had about it a nightmare quality that deprived him of his limited amount of speech. He stood staring wild-eyed at the Dean while on the periphery of his vision the contraceptive wobbled obscenely.

'I have just found this in New Court, Skullion,' said the Dean, suddenly conscious that there was a certain ambiguity about his appearance.

'Oh ah,' said Skullion in the tone of one who has his private doubts. The Dean let go of the contraceptive hurriedly.

'As I was saying ...' he began only to stop as the thing slowly began to ascend. Skullion and the Dean watched it, hypnotized. The contraceptive reached the ceiling and hovered there. Skullion lowered his eyes and stared at the Dean.

'There seem to be others of that ilk,' continued the Dean.

'Oh ah,' said Skullion.

'In the New Court,' said the Dean. 'A great many others.'

'In the New Court?' said Skullion slowly.

'Yes,' said the Dean. In the face of Skullion's evident doubts he was beginning to feel rather heated. So was the contraceptive. The draught from the door had nudged it next to the light bulb in the ceiling and as the Dean opened his mouth to say that the New Court was alive with the things, the one above their heads touched the bulb and exploded. In fact there were three explosions. First the contraceptive blew. Then the bulb, and finally and most alarmingly of all the gas ignited. Blinded momentarily by the flash and bereft of the light of the bulb, the Dean and Skullion stood in darkness while fragments of glass and rubber descended on them.

'There are more where that one came from,' said the Dean finally, and led the way out into the night air. Skullion groped for his bowler and put it on. He reached behind the counter for his torch and followed the Dean. They passed through the Screens and Skullion shone his torch into New Court.

Huddled like so many legless animals, some two hundred contraceptives gleamed in the torchlight. A light dawn breeze had risen and with it some of the more inflated contraceptives, so that it seemed as though they were attempting to mount their less active neighbours while the whole mass seethed and rippled. One or two were to be seen nudging the windows on the first floor.

'Gawd,' said Skullion irreverently.

'I want them cleared away before it gets light, Skullion,' said the Dean. 'No one must hear about this. The College reputation, you understand.'

'Yes, sir,' said Skullion. 'I'll clear them away. Leave it to me.'

'Good, Skullion,' said the Dean and with one last disgusted look at the obscene flock went up the stairs to his rooms.

Mrs Biggs had a bath. She had poured bath salts into the water and the pink suds matched the colour of her frilly shower cap. Bath night for Mrs Biggs was a special occasion. In the privacy of her bathroom she felt liberated from the constraints of commonsense. Standing on the pink bath mat surveying her reflection in the steamed-up mirror it was almost possible to imagine herself young again. Young and fancy free, and she fancied Zipser. There was no doubt about it and no doubt too that Zipser fancied her. She dried herself lovingly and put on her nightdress and went through to her bedroom. She climbed into bed and set the alarm clock for three. Mrs Biggs wanted to be up early. She had things to do.

In the early hours she left the house and cycled across Cambridge. She locked the bicycle by the Round Church and made her way on foot down Trinity Street to the side entrance of Porterhouse and let herself in with a key she had used in the old days when she had bedded for the Chaplain. She passed through the passage by the Buttery and came out by the Screens and was about to make her way across New Court when a strange sound stopped her in her tracks. She peered round the archway. In the early morning light Skullion was chasing balloons. Or something. Not chasing. Dancing seemed more like it. He ran. He leapt. He cavorted. His outstretched arms reached yearningly towards whatever it was that floated jauntily beyond his reach as if to taunt the Porter. Backwards and forwards across the ancient court the strange pursuit continued until just as it seemed the thing was about to escape over the wall into the Fellows' Garden there was a loud pop and whatever it was or had been hung limp and tatterdemalion upon the branches of a climbing rose like some late-flowering bloom. Skullion stopped, panting, and stared up at the object of his chase and then, evidently inspired by its fate, turned and hurried towards the Screens. Mrs Biggs retreated into the darkness of the Buttery passage as Skullion hurried by and then, when she could see him heading for the Porter's Lodge, emerged and tiptoed through the contraceptives to the Bull Tower. Around her feet the contraceptives squeaked and rustled. Mrs Biggs climbed the staircase to Zipser's room with a fresh sense of sexual excitement brought on by the presence of so many prophylactics. She couldn't remember when she had seen so many. Even the American airmen with whom she had been so familiar in the past had never been quite so prolific with their rubbers, and they'd been generous enough in all conscience if her memory served her aright. Mrs Biggs let herself into Zipser's room and sported the oak. She had no intention of being disturbed. She crossed to Zipser's bedroom and went inside. She switched on the bedside light.

Zipser awoke from his troubled sleep and blinked. He sat up in bed and stared at Mrs Biggs brilliant in her red coat. It was evidently morning. It didn't feel like morning but there was Mrs Biggs so it must be morning. Mrs Biggs didn't come in the middle of the night. Zipser levered himself out of bed.

'Sorry,' he mumbled groping for his dressing-gown. 'Must have overslept.' Zipser's eye caught the alarm clock. It seemed to indicate half-past three. Must have stopped.

'Shush,' said Mrs Biggs with a terrible smile. 'It's only half-past three.'

Zipser looked at the clock again. It certainly said half-past three. He tried to equate the time with Mrs Biggs' arrival and couldn't. There was something terribly wrong with the situation.

'Darling,' said Mrs Biggs, evidently sensing his dilemma. Zipser looked up at her open-mouthed. Mrs Biggs was taking off her coat. 'Don't make any noise,' she continued, with the same extraordinary smile.

'What the hell is going on?' asked Zipser. Mrs Biggs went into the other room.

'I'll be with you in a minute,' she called out in a hoarse whisper.

Zipser stood up shakily. 'What are you doing?' he asked.

There was a rustle of clothes in the other room. Even to Zipser's befuddled mind it was evident that Mrs Biggs was undressing. He went to the door and peered out into the darkness.

'For God's sake,' he said, 'you mustn't do that.'

Mrs Biggs emerged from the shadows. She had taken off her blouse. Zipser stared at her enormous brassière.

'Darling.' she said. 'Go back to bed. You mustn't stand and watch me. It's embarrassing.' She gave him a push which sent him reeling on to the bed. Then she shut the door. Zipser sat on his bed shaking. The sudden emergence of Mrs Biggs at half-past three in the morning from the shadows of his own private fantasies into a real presence terrified him. He tried to think what to do. He couldn't shout or scream for help. Nobody would believe he hadn't invited her to ... He'd be sent down. His career would be finished. He'd be disgraced. They'd find the French letters up the chimney. Oh God. Zipser began to weep.

In the front room Mrs Biggs divested herself of her bra and panties. It was terribly cold. She went to the window to shut it when a faint popping noise from below startled her. Mrs Biggs peered out. Skullion was running round the Court with a stick. He appeared to be spearing the contraceptives. 'That'll keep him busy,' Mrs Biggs thought happily, and shut the window. Then she crossed to the gas fire and lit it. 'Nice to get dressed in the warm,' she thought, and went into the bedroom. Zipser had got back into bed and had switched off the light.

'Wants to spare me,' Mrs Biggs thought tenderly and climbed into bed. Zipser shrank from her but Mrs Biggs had no sense of his reluctance. Grasping him in her arms she pressed him to her vast breasts. In the darkness Zipser whimpered. Mrs Biggs's hand slid down his pyjamas. Zipser squeaked frantically and Mrs Biggs's mouth found his. To Zipser it seemed that he was in the grip of a great white whale. He fought desperately for air, surfaced for a moment and was engulfed again.

Skullion, who had returned from the Porter's Lodge armed with a broom handle to which he had taped a pin, hurled himself into the shoal and struck about him with a fury that was only partially explained by having to work all night. It was rather the effrontery of the things that infuriated him. Skullion had little use for contraceptives at the best of times. Unnatural, he called them, and placed them in the lower social category of things along with elastic-sided boots and made-up bow ties. Not the sort of attire for a gentleman. But even more than their humble origins, he was infuriated by the insult to Porterhouse that the presence of so great and so inflated a number represented. The Dean's admonition that news of the infestation must not leak out was wasted on Skullion. He needed no telling. 'We'd be the laughing-stock of the University,' he thought, lancing a particularly large one. By the time dawn broke over Cambridge Skullion had cleared New Court. One or two had escaped into the Fellows' Garden and he went through the archway in the wall and began spiking the remainder. Behind him the Court was littered with tattered latex, almost invisible against the snow. 'I'll wait until it's a bit lighter to pick them up,' he muttered. 'Can't see them now.' He had just run a small but agile one to earth in the rose garden when a dull rumbling noise at the top of the Tower made him turn and look up. Something was going on in the old chimney. The chimney pot at the top was shaking. The brickwork silhouetted against the morning sky appeared to be bulging. The rumbling stopped, to be succeeded by an almighty roar as a ball of flame issued from the chimney and billowed out before ascending above the College. Below it the chimney toppled sideways, crashed on to the roof of the Tower and with a gradually increasing rumble of masonry the fourteenth-century building lost its entire façade. Behind it the rooms were clearly visible, their floors tilted horribly and sagging. Skullion stood mesmerized by the spectacle. A bed on the first floor slid sideways and dropped on to the masonry below. Desks and chairs followed suit. There were shouts and screams. People poured out of doorways and windows opened all round the Court. Skullion ignored the screams for help. He was busy chasing the last few remaining contraceptives when the Master, clad in his dressing-gown, emerged from the Master's Lodge and hurried to the scene of the disaster. As he rushed across the garden he found Skullion trying to spear a contraceptive floating in the fishpond.

'Go and open the main gates,' the Master shouted at him.

'Not yet,' said Skullion taciturnly.

'What do you mean, not yet?' the Master demanded. 'The ambulance men and the fire brigade will want to get in.'

'Not having any strangers in College till I've cleared these things up. Wouldn't be right,' said Skullion.

The Master stared at the floating contraceptive furiously. Skullion's obstinacy enraged him. 'There are injured people in there,' he screamed.

'So there are,' said Skullion, 'but there's the College reputation to be thought of too.' He leant across the pond and burst the floating bubble. Sir Godber turned and ran on to the scene of the accident. Skullion turned and followed him slowly. 'Got no sense of tradition,' he said sadly, and shook his head.

The Cruel C. E.

Jilly Cooper

This is an account of what is believed to be a unique educational experiment which took place in the spring of 1981.

On Monday 8 June, thousands of prep-school boys all over the country will begin probably the first really harrowing ordeal of their lives. They will be taking Common Entrance – or C.E. as it's known – an exam they must pass to get into the public school of their parents' choice. The exam is spread over four days with a maximum of fifteen hours of papers, including French, Latin, Greek, Science, and three Maths papers which would unsettle the most senior Wrangler.

The little examinees are by no means the only people biting their nails. So are their parents and the prep-school heads who stake their reputation on how many pupils make it. To make matters worse, candidates can't play the field and try several schools simultaneously. If little Charles ploughs Eton, where his family have been for generations, only then can his papers be handed on to another less academically demanding school. Even if this second school takes him, which is no means certain, it is likely that Granny who has set her heart on Eton, may not now be prepared to flog the last of the silver to help pay the fees. Pressures on candidates to pass are, therefore, from all quarters, colossal.

Being an interested party, having a son at prep school who is already grumbling darkly about taking C.E. in a year's time, and having been bored rigid at countless dinner parties by neurotic mothers describing their C.E traumas, I thought it would be illuminating to ask a team of illustrious grown-ups to take some of last years' papers under strict exam conditions and see how they fared.

The final line-up who accepted my invitation were: the newly ennobled Lord Beloff; A. J. P. Taylor; Ludovic Kennedy; Brian Inglis; our own Godfrey Smith; Frank Muir, who despite his dazzling erudition left school at fourteen and claims to have never taken an exam in his life; Joanna Lumley; Susan Stranks, who went to four different schools ending up at Mrs Hampshire's Dancing School; and myself. A pretty catholic bunch. The only common denominator was that the other candidates, at least, were all secure enough not to mind making complete idiots of themselves.

Finding a day when everyone was free was a bit like putting on a stage play. We settled for Monday the 13th. Westminster School kindly lent us a classroom. I chose one lined with ancient copies of Pliny and Sophocles, which had been built over the site of the original monastic dungeons, and which had chairs far enough apart to enable the candidates not to cheat. As we had only one day, it was decided just to take Scripture, History, Maths I, French II, Geography and English Comprehension.

The night before the exam, my son got into an understandable panic that I'd fail and offered to coach me in Maths. Instead I took his Scripture exercise book to bed. The first essay on the birth of Christ was all about the 'sky being filled with angles', which sounded more like geometry. Turning the page, I read that 'Goliarth was a philistine giant three metres high,' and gave up.

C.E. dawned absolutely arctic. Earth had a great deal to show more fair than Westminster Bridge blocked solid with traffic. Examinees were coming from all over the country would they ever make it on time?

Under disapproving grey skies, the russet Westminster courtyard had lost all its warmth. The double sherry shivering in the icy wind could not have looked more forlorn than Susan Stranks, the first candidate to clock in, her bright pink dungarees emphasizing a face as white as blackboard chalk.

No, she felt too sick for coffee, and did I think they'd have a question on the Roman conquest? Husband Robin Ray had been coaching her all night. A. J. P. Taylor arrived next, a small indomitable figure in a deerstalker. He reminds one of an irreverent mole who delights in pushing up molehills to disturb the smooth green lawns of conventional historical thought. He was followed by another distinguished historian, Max Beloff, who'd been brave enough to wear his All Souls' tie. Then came Frank Muir in a black schoolboy cap towering over them both – a very unphilistine giant two metres high.

'What a terrible idea,' he moaned, rolling his R's balefully. 'Why on earth are we all here?'

Collective disenchantment was increased by Ludovic Kennedy, glamorous in a pin-striped suit, who'd just come out of hospital, and Brian Inglis, feeling possibly even frailer, after an assault-course weekend of Dublin hospitality. Finally our own Godfrey Smith shambled in, for once not his usual jolly self.

> QUESTION: Describe the events surrounding the birth of Jesus as seen through the eyes of the inn-keeper.
> FRANK MUIR: Well, the authorities, bless 'em decided to hold a big nationwide census in our little town of Bethlehem – an absolute God-send to us of the Bethlehem Chamber of Commerce and Round Table – and the lady wife and I got stuck in cleaning up the old inn, washing a few of the dirtier sheets, watering the wine and other professional chores. ...
> Then, if you please, along comes this pair of peasants from some hick village called Nazareth. 'A room, please, landlord,' he calls, bold as brass, as though it was a wet weekend in Feb. and the inn was empty. Seems the girl was very preggers so the wife let them sit in the warm for a bit. ...
> I reckoned they were trouble-makers and I was right. Soon my stable was a-wash with greasy shepherds dropping cheese and pie and other rubbish into the straw. And some concert party, or pop group, called The Three Kings cluttered up the place with their groupies – the girl gave birth to a lad. Often wonder what became of him.

Big Ben tolled the hour. As it was essential that the examinees should be marked anonymously, they were asked to put a number rather than their name at the top of the page. Trembling with nerves, I passed out the Scripture papers. There followed a stunned, horrified silence. Then Frank Muir rose to his feet.

'I'm off, chaps,' he said. 'I've already got a place at Guildford Grammar.'

Everyone collapsed into giggles, and, very tentatively, pens started to move over the lined paper. Soon coats were removed; Frank whipped off his pink bow tie. Godfrey's gusty sighs were ruffling everyone's papers.

'Some of us are trying to work, Smith,' said Frank tartly.

A. J. P. was writing steadily, stopping every so often to shake with helpless laughter. Everyone else was tearing their hair. Few of us in fact would have escaped the scissors of the school barber. He'd have certainly hacked off

Ludo's pin-striped locks, had an inch off Smiths and Inglis, and at least a foot off Cooper.

Big Ben told us time was up.

'Please Miss,' piped up the irrepressible Muir, 'Kennedy's cheating, he's still writing.'

'Just finishing my sentence,' said Ludo airily, carrying on sub-clausing down the page, with almost Proustian felicity.

'How do you spell "myrrh"?' asked Muir of the room at large

'M-U-I-R,' came back Ludo, quick as a flash, as he handed in his paper.

On to History, which I found stymingly difficult, but which at least had some questions where you could waffle like 'Write a letter home to your mother describing a journey on the Royal Mail Coach'.

Despite initial groaning, reminiscent of a labour ward in the rush hour, everyone was happier now. Beloff, Taylor, Inglis, Muir, Kennedy and Smith had already written whole books in answer to many of the questions. The problem was what to leave out, or they'd still be finishing the paper next year. Most candidates used to typewriters were suffering from writer's cramp. 'Slaving over a hot IBM is nothing to this,' grumbled Max Beloff, waving his fingers like a typist drying her nails.

Once again Big Ben told us time had run out.

'Never send to know for whom the bell tolls,' intoned Muir lugubriously.

Everyone fell on the elevenses' champagne, which seemed more fitting than school milk.

'Who are those two distinguished-looking actors coming across the courtyard?' whispered my secretary.

They turned out to be Michael and John Farebrother, headmasters of St Peter's School, Seaford, who manage miraculously to maintain a sense of humour while running a very successful prep school. They had nobly agreed to mark our papers, and invigilate Maths and French. By a strange coincidence, Mike Farebrother and Ludo discovered they'd once played in a jazz group at Oxford with Humphrey Lyttleton, and were soon remembering a gig at the W.I. at which they strummed away for four hours, sustained only by tea and rock buns.

By an even stranger coincidence, Godfrey said, when he was taking his degree at Oxford, Max Beloff had been the invigilator. 'The candidate in front of me was scattering sweet papers as he wrote,' said Godfrey. 'Max, always a stickler for law and order, insisted he pick them up. The candidate, Michael Drummond, is now Wykeham Professor of Logic at Oxford.'

We all agreed that the exams so far had been incredibly difficult, particularly for small boys, but buoyed up by several glasses of champagne on empty stomachs, we now felt quite sanguine about taking Maths I. It turned out to be a stinker, reducing the whole room to hysterics. Suddenly an ear-splitting explosion shook the corridor outside. 'Beloff's shot himself,' said Muir.

But it was only another bottle being opened. Totally nonplussed by a geometry question, I was just praying that some angles might appear out of the sky, when there was a commotion in the courtyard outside. On investigation it turned out to be an unctuous cleric in a black cassock guiding a party of blue-rinsed Americans over the school. He was only just deflected from sweeping them into our classroom. Imagine the letters back to Iowa:

'Dearest Elmer, Today we visited a darling antique British public school in London, England. Even the boys are antiques there, Elmer, and they have liquor and girls in the classroom. No wonder Britain is going to the dogs.'

> QUESTION: What advantage is it to the UK if North Sea
> oil is sold to other countries?
> A. J. P. TAYLOR: Cash intake – you imbecile.

We were wrestling with an impossible question about crumpets costing x pence per dozen, when any serious attempts at work were totally sabotaged by the very uncommon entrance of Joanna Lumley, ravishingly dressed as a schoolboy. In the final week of rehearsing *Private Lives*, in which she played Amanda, she'd only been allowed off for an hour to take a quick Math's paper and pose for the group photograph. Later she was going to do the exams under strict supervision at home.

'I can't remember what paper I'm taking,' wailed Brian Inglis.

'Probably something about the effects of alcohol on small boys,' said Ludo.

A. J. P. gave up at this juncture, content to gaze instead at Joanna's emerald-green back.

'Not too bored?' I whispered.

'Not nearly as bored as I would be if I were doing the paper,' he replied.

Maths despatched, we all lined up for the group photo. We had reached the silly stage of paper darts and itching powder. The photographer had great difficulty stopping Brian Inglis running round the back to get in the picture twice. Next we moved on to lunch at Locketts, haunt of cabinet ministers. Conversation was very high table. 'I told the examiners they'd spelt Pearl Harbor wrong,' said A. J. P. with evident satisfaction, plunging his spoon into some seaford cocktail. I talked to Michael Farebrother (who before becoming a headmaster, had coached Prince Charles) about the pressures endured by boys taking C.E.

'They go round as if under hypnosis until they get the results,' he said. 'We had one very quiet, undemonstrative boy a few years ago. When I called him in to tell him he'd passed, he suddenly started to shout and shout, then he flung his arms round me, and when I extricated myself, he started shouting again.'

On another occasion, Michael had been walking down the passage after lights out, and, hearing noises coming from one of the dormitories, had tiptoed closer and peered in. All the little boys were kneeling down, and the somewhat overbearing dormitory captain was whispering fiercely: 'While you're all saying your prayers, you might like to remember I'm taking C.E. on Monday.'

> QUESTION: Tell in your own words what happened during Elijah's stay in the house of the widow.
> FRANK MUIR: It has been a matter of rumour and gossip ever since. The Scripture gives one version. The version based on local gossip is too vile to repeat. In my view exactly what occurred between Elijah and the widow should be left in the decent obscurity of the New English Bible.

Meanwhile down the table, John Farebrother was regaling everyone with C.E. howlers.

'Queen Elizabeth knitted Sir Walter Raleigh on the deck,' one boy had written, to which the examiner had added: 'Presumably into Lord Cardigan.'

My favourite was 'When Mary heard she was to be the mother of Jesus, she went off and sang the Magna Carta'.

Back to the classroom and French II. The day was taking on a dreamlike quality. John Farebrother read out the dictation twice in sepulchral English Milor French, and earned a round of applause from all the candidates. French was pretty easy for some. Geography on the other hand was a brute, with an incomprehensible Ordnance Survey map, and impossible questions about oil rigs and the third world. This was, on the other hand, one of the few papers which seemed to have dragged itself into the eighties.

A quick champagne break was followed by the last paper English Comprehension, which I finished in a canter because I omitted to turn the page and do all the compulsory questions on the other side. Everyone else did very well, although some examinees' writing, I noticed, was blurred by drink rings – talk about the wine-dark C.E. The last candidate put down her pen.

It had been a magnificent day, which probably worked because we all dreaded it, and because everyone rose so splendidly to the occasion. I have never been more tired in my life (and we'd only done a third of the papers) but I was very proud of my team, as they staggered exhausted out of Westminster. They all reported falling asleep like puppies the moment they got home. Except for A. J. P. who trotted off to the tube as sprightly as a lark.

'Next year,' was his parting shot, 'we'll all take finals.'

Schoolboys taking C.E. often have to wait a fortnight to get their results. The noble Farebrothers took the papers back to Seaford, and returned them in under a week. Scripture came back first and was quite hilarious, although most of the candidates would probably have ended up in the monastic dungeons for blasphemy. Here is Frank Muir on how St Peter escaped from prison, as described by one of the screws:

> I padlocked Peter to the wall; at that moment he began to cry.
> 'What ails thee, prisoner?' I cried.
> 'Nosebleed, sir,' he responded. 'Could I have a bit of cold metal to put down my back?'
> Looking back, sir, I felt I made my big mistake there, I gave him the key.

More people did well in History, perhaps because many of the candidates were alive during the events they were asked to describe. Happily A. J. P. and Max Beloff tied top with 96 per cent.

Everyone failed Maths disgracefully. Godfrey came top with 45 per cent. 'If x is ten,' wrote Frank, in answer to one question, 'does that make me an existentialist?' He got no marks. A. J. P. came second bottom, obviously penalized for being cheeky, and peppering the paper with remarks like 'incomprehensible', 'God knows', and 'What is this?'.

French was also hilarious. The last question asked examinees what they wanted for their birthday. Ludo was penalized for greed for asking for an enormous cake, as was I for demanding twelve bottles of champagne. Godfrey, on the other hand, only asked for one bottle and got two marks. Frank Muir wrote '*Je veux Raquel Welch*,' to which the examiner had added: '*Un peu trop long dans des dents pour vous, mon petit.*'

Frank came top in Geography; A. J. P. who'd got even cheekier came bottom. 'It is a scandal,' he wrote in answer to one question, 'that English landscape should be measured in kilometres.' For a source of energy, he suggested cabinet ministers harnessed to a treadmill for eight hours a day. In answer to questions 5–7, he simply wrote: 'To hell with the third world.'

Godfrey came top in English. All the papers were marked now except Joanna Lumley's. Not actually visualizing her as a top academic heavyweight. I averaged out the candidates. Godfrey came top over the six papers with 74 per cent. When I rang to congratulate him, he gave his great ear-splitting bellow of laughter: 'Oh dear, I hope the others won't de-bag me for being a swot.'

Next day, however, Joanna's papers were mailed down to St Peter's, Seaford. Suddenly the competition took on a Eurovision Song Contest excitement, as the Farebrothers marked them, ringing me up through the night, with each result more staggering than the last. She was top in Scripture with 92 per cent, third in History only two points below Beloff and A. J. P., second in Maths, second in French, and finally tied with Godfrey in English, coming out an incredible average of 82 per cent. What a triumph for the women's movement.

Merci St Peter's, Come in Westminster, where Dr John Rae, the Head Master, had been going through the marked papers, deciding which of the candidates to take. Westminster has a very high C.E. pass mark of 65 per cent.

'I'll take candidate nine at any price,' he said. 'Who is it?'

'Joanna Lumley,' I said.

'My goodness,' gasped Dr Rae. 'She can have a place at Westminster at any time.'

Brian Inglis, Max Beloff, Godfrey and Ludo had also passed and were assured of places. Frank had just failed by *un point*, probably because he'd sent up so many of the papers, but with marks like that he'd have no difficulty getting into a very good school.

> BRIAN INGLIS: Edward VIII was a disaster as a king – pro-Hitler, pro-Mussolini, worst of all pre-Wallis Simpson ... couldn't read ... more than a paragraph at a time.

Sue Stranks and I alas had both failed. But it was nice that both **Dr Rae**, and Mike Farebrother in his general summing up, commented on Sue's brilliant talent for improvisation which would no doubt lead to a successful career in politics. Perhaps she should become the much needed leader of the SDP.

The final irony was that A. J. P. failed C.E., but Dr Rae waived the rules and gave him a scholarship to Westminster on the brilliance of his history paper. I hope he doesn't reduce all the masters to pulp, I would have thought Dr Rae might have been wiser to recommend A. J. P. to a special school for gifted pupils.

Here are Dr Rae's comments:

Muir: 64 per cent. Fail. Plausible and unconvincing candidate despite an occasional touch of humour. Pin-up mentality on sex and rather a low moral tone throughout. Would do better at a country boarding school.

Kennedy: 70 per cent. Pass. Good all-rounder: safe rather than exciting. There is perhaps rather an unhealthy knowledge of the Old Testament. But well worth taking on.

Taylor: 60 per cent. Fail. But awarded scholarship on 'outstanding single subject' principle. Best History paper I have ever seen. In general rather arrogant and opinionated though one answer in the Maths paper – 'God knows' – suggests an endearing naïvety. Will certainly need watching. Place with resilient housemaster.

Beloff: 67 per cent. Pass. Another outstanding History paper. Irreverent attitude to Scripture suggests independence of mind. Dotheboys Hall is his first choice, I see, but we will take him.

Smith: 74 per cent. Pass. Very able candidate; only one to make sense of the Maths paper. Rather too well informed about psychiatry for a boy of his age.

Inglis: 66 per cent. Pass – just. Typical product of a certain type of English education: great verbal facility combined with numerical incompetence of striking dimensions.

Stranks: 45 per cent. Fail. On the face of it very weak though with some interesting talents. Makes a little knowledge go a very long way (future politician?) and shows considerable ingenuity in scoring 4 per cent in Maths. Will probably make a million and contribute to some other school's appeal.

Cooper: 58 per cent. Fail. Worthy but lacking in sparkle.

Lumley: 82 per cent. Pass. I like the look of this candidate: thorough, efficient, not spoonfed but equally not falling over backwards to be clever. Just the sort to benefit from education in a good boys' school.

Abbie at the Zoo

Dane Chandos

'This afternoon you're going to the zoo with your Aunt Abbie alone.'

'Why?'

'Because she specially asked to take you along without Nannie or me.'

'Why?'

'Because she says that parties with nannies or mothers along aren't proper parties.'

'Why?'

'Because I think she wants to spoil you.'

'Why?'

'Because she says it's good for all boys to be spoiled once a week.'

'Why?'

'Because she hasn't any of her own.'

'Why?'

'Because she can't have any children of her own.'

'Why?'

'Because now I'd like you to go over to the window and sit there quietly and watch for your Aunt Abbie to arrive.'

I went.

A car like the one I had once seen the King in stopped at the house. The footman, who had a uniform the same colour as the car, got out, opened the door for the chauffeur, and saluted. Then there was a long pause. The chauffeur hooted the horn twice, and then another horn once. Then I saw a pair of very small feet come out of the car. The chauffeur was a nurse who wore a big cape, held together at the throat with some diamonds that glittered in the sunlight. It was a smaller nurse than the one I had when I caught scarlet fever. She said something to the footman, who was the chauffeur really, and then she ran across the sidewalk and, although I nearly fell out of the window, I couldn't see where she went. I heard our front doorbell ring. And then I saw the nurse run back across the sidewalk to the car and start handing out parcels to the chauffeur. He dropped one, and I heard her say, 'Prenez garde, Perkins.'

My mother said:

'That's your Aunt Abbie.'

'Do I like her?'

'Yes, I think you'll like her very much.'

'That's like the King's car. Is Aunt Abbie as rich as the King?'

'Very nearly.'

'Oh, boy!'

Aunty Abbie ran up the stairs and the chauffeur came behind her, holding the parcels out in front of him, balanced one on top of the other. He had quarter-to-three feet like a policemen's, and he put them down with a bump on each step, turned out like the hands on our grandfather clock in the dining-room. Aunt Abbie was very beautiful. 'Prenez garde, Perkins,' she said, 'take care.' Then she saw me. 'Why, you little dear!' And her voice, which was low and husky anyway, was lower and huskier when she said that. Then she knelt down on the top step, took me in her arms, and hugged me. She hugged so hard that it hurt. She said to my mother, 'Well, my dear,' and held out one side of her face. But when my mother kissed her, Aunt Abbie only kissed into the air. It was then that I noticed the beauty spot, high up on her left cheek.

'You may put the parcels down on the table, Perkins,' she said. 'No, on the other one, the one with the chipped leg, only take care, it may be fragile.'

'I've had scarlet fever,' I said. 'But I'm better now.'

Then we opened all the parcels, and Ivy, our maid, brought in the coffee on the silver tray we only used for parties, and Aunt Abbie told my mother about a very reasonable place she knew where one could buy caps for house-parlourmaids to wear in the afternoons, though she said she found London very expensive after Paris. And every time she reached for her coffee cup, lots of little toy things jingled together on her big gold bracelet. I liked the penknife and the whistle and the little stick French people cleaned their teeth with best. Aunt Abbie said that the Kaiser had just sunk the *Lusitania* and that we'd hang him when we caught him as sure as eggs were eggs. I wasn't sure what the Kaiser was, but Aunt Abbie soaked a piece of sugar in her coffee and gave it me in her fingers. She said it was very nourishing and told my mother I looked as thin as some of the children she had seen in France.

After that we went downstairs and got into the car. The chauffeur drove, and Aunt Abbie told him through a long tube which was the best way to get to the zoo. Then she looked at me for a very long time and said I was just like my poor father, her dear brother who had died, and not at all like the American side of my family.

'What's your name?' I said.

'Abbie.'

'No. Your other name?'

'Do you mean my surname? My surname is Abbott-Acland.'

'No, I mean your other name. Haven't you got another name, like my mother's?'

'Yes, but I never use it.'

'What is your other name?'

'Amy. But nobody calls me that.'

'You have a lot of names to remember.'

'It's very easy. Just say to yourself, AA AA, Aunt Abbie Abbott-Acland. But you shall call me just Abbie.'

'Why?'

'Because that is what I should like you to call me.'

'Why?'

'Because it's nice and easy to remember.'

'Why?'

Aunt Abbie didn't answer, so I said:

'I like you much better than the nurse that came when I had scarlet fever.'

'Why?'

'Because when she asked to see my tongue I put it out at her and I really meant it.'

'Why?'

'Because she was ugly. But if you asked to see my tongue I shouldn't mean it when I put it out.'

'Why?'

'Because you're pretty.'

'Why?'

And I didn't say why to Aunt Abbie again unless it was very important. Instead, I said:

'Would you like to see my tongue?'

'Yes, darling boy, very much, but after tea.'

Then we came to Regent's Park and turned in at the gates.

'I like this car,' I said. 'Is it yours?'

'Half of it is. The other half belongs to your Uncle Arthur.'

'Who's he?'

'He's my husband.'

'Which is your half?'

'Usually the front half, darling,' said Aunt Abbie, 'because I usually drive.'

'That's where the engine is. I like engines. So now we're sitting in Uncle Arthur's half.'

'Yes, but he lent it to us for today.'

'Do you ever lend him your half?'

'Sometimes. But he doesn't like driving. You see, it doesn't really matter because your Uncle Arthur and I share everything. When we were first married, he used to come home in the evening and drop all the golden sovereigns he had earned into my lap.

'Then what'd you do?'

'Then we counted them, and after that I gave him back his half. But he always let me keep the new shiny ones. We are going to see your Uncle Arthur later on.'

'At the zoo?'

'No. But perhaps afterwards.'

'Oh, boy!'

'That is not good English dear.'

Then we arrived at the zoo, and Perkins handed Aunt Abbie a big bag. We both sat down on the pavement, which I wasn't allowed to do in those trousers, and Aunt Abbie showed me what was in her bag.

'Here are thirteen buns for the bears and the elephants,' she said, 'though you mustn't give any to the polar bears. I don't suppose you have been taught much about the value of money. Each bun cost a penny.'

There was a big bag of peanuts for the deer which cost fourpence, and for the monkeys a piece of cracked-looking glass which had once been very expensive because it was French. And there were some bananas that cost one and sixpence because of the war and the Germans, although bananas didn't come from Germany. But all these things would have cost far more inside the zoo, and that was why Aunt Abbie had brought them with her.

'It is most important to know about money,' she said, 'because nowadays one had to pay for everything through the nose. But always remember that if you look after the pence the pounds will look after themselves.'

But at the gates of the zoo she said something much funnier than that. She said:

'Janitor, I am a fellow.' And we went in without paying anything. But when I tried this myself next time I went with my nurse it didn't work at all.

We saw the monkeys first, and I caught a flea. But Aunt Abbie said I hadn't caught it from the monkeys because they were really very clean and didn't have fleas, I must have caught it from the very dirty little boy with a runny nose who was standing near us. Aunt Abbie asked him if he didn't have a handkerchief, and she took a special coarse linen one out of her big bag and blew his nose for him. This made the boy's mother cross, and she told him to give the handkerchief to the monkeys. It made me laugh to see a monkey trying to blow his nose while another held up the piece of cracked looking glass for him to see, but Aunt Abbie was quite cross too, and so, after she got the handkerchief back from a keeper, we went to see the tropical birds.

On the way we came to some green hoops round a piece of grass on which my nurse always told me we weren't allowed to walk. But Aunt Abbie said:

'Nonsense! As you will learn in your geometry at school, the shortest distance between two points is a straight line. Come along, dear.'

We stepped over the hoops, and a little farther on Aunt Abbie stopped, took the little penknife off her bracelet, and snipped off a piece of geranium because she wanted to see if that colour would grow in Essex, where she and Uncle Arthur had a house called Abberton. A man came up to us and looked as if he was going to say something. But Aunt Abbie said, 'Good day to you, keeper. Are we right for the tropical birds?' And he said we were, although he didn't seem too sure, and he stared at us very hard.

'Now I am going to show you a map,' said Aunt Abbie. 'Let's sit down.'

It was a map of the zoo drawn by Uncle Arthur, and big red arrows, like the map of the trains in the Underground, showed us the best routes. But Aunt Abbie had made lots of notes on it.

'What does that one say?' I asked.

'The last time I was here one of the zebras was ill. That is to remind me to see if the zoo doctor is looking after him properly.'

'Did the zebra have scarlet fever?'

'No, but something very similar,' said Aunt Abbie, and, although I had never seen any before, I knew I was going to like the zebras.

I don't any longer remember exactly what our route was. We passed the lion house twice without going in because the map said it wasn't their feeding time yet. We rode on the elephant, but only for half the journey. At the place where the elephant turns we got off because it made a shorter walk to the eagles. Several other children thinking the ride was over, got off too and had to get back on again. The elephant man's face got red.

'That is no concern of mine, keeper,' said Aunt Abbie. 'This point is convenient for our next objective, and I wish my nephew to enjoy himself with the minimum of fatigue.'

We walked quickly along a wide path, and Aunt Abbie greeted every keeper we met. She seemed to know them all. Mostly she just said, 'Good day,' but once she said, 'Good afternoon, Dawkins, did the baby emu pull through?' And another time she said, 'Have you replaced Hobson of the Alpine goats, keeper?' And the man said he had, which made me think Aunt Abbie knew everything as well as everybody.

I wanted to ride in the llama cart.

'No,' said Aunt Abbie. 'Though everything here is kept as clean as possible, you can never be sure with wickerwork and you might get a tick. But we'll go and look at the other llamas in their cage.'

She read me the notice warning people that the llamas spat.

'Nannie won't let me spit. She says it's common to spit. She didn't say about llamas.'

'She is quite wrong to tell you never to spit. You must never swallow phlegm. If you've forgotten your handkerchief, always spit it out. Wouldn't you like to spit at the llamas?'

'Nurse said to be sure I had my English party manners,' I said doubtfully.

'Rubbish! The manners that are good enough at home are good enough for everybody. And if your manners aren't good enough for everybody they're not good enough at home.'

I would have loved to spit, but suddenly, though I tried and tried, my mouth was quite dry.

'Look, like this,' said Aunt Abbie, and spat vigorously through the bars at a llama, which took no notice at all. And after that I always called her Abbie without any Aunt. And suddenly I had lots of spit in my mouth, and I went round the cage spitting at every llama in turn.

'That will do,' said Abbie. 'You must learn to aim. I shall give you a dart board for Christmas. Now we must go to see the sea lions. As it is rather a long way I am going to carry you.'

She picked me up and set off, and all the way one of the studs in the belt of her uniform stuck into my hip. I didn't say anything about it because we still had a lot of things to see and I was liking Abbie.

When we arrived, Abbie looked at her map and at the watch on her big gold bracelet. Then she called a keeper.

'It is exactly on feeding time,' she said. 'We have arrived on purpose.'

But the feeding time had been altered. Abbie frowned, and a funny little crease ran down from the beauty spot to the corner of her mouth.

'Kindly send the head sea-lion keeper here to speak to me,' she said. 'If I am farther away than this bench, it will only be to look at the African birds in the next cage.'

We sat on the bench and then watched the birds for a while, but the sea-lion keeper didn't come; in fact, there wasn't a keeper in sight. Abbie was getting crosser and crosser, and she kept on looking at her watch.

'I have had enough of this,' she said, and, taking the small gold whistle off her bracelet, she blew on it several times with her cheeks puffed out like the bugler I had seen at the Tower of London.

Several people stopped and stared, and Abbie told one small boy that the wind was going to change and if he wasn't careful his mouth would stay open like that for the rest of his life. I shut my mouth too.

At last the head sea-lion keeper came running, and I remember Abbie saying something about 'a disgrace' and 'the public' and 'let alone a fellow of the society'. And once she said, 'Sea-lion keeper, do you value your job?'

Then another man came, not in a keeper's uniform, and whom Abbie called 'superintendent'.

And then the sea-lion keeper who had gone away came back with a bucketful of fish. Abbie looked at the fish, and then she sniffed and said, 'Job lot.' She threw a fish to the sea-lions, and told me to throw one too.'

'Now we mustn't give Old Jim any more,' she said. 'He always gets more than his share, and he's too fat already. Let's try and give Maud some. She's young and not quite so quick as the others. Look, like this.'

She guided my hand, and Maud, who was half the size of Old Jim, caught the fish with a leap and a slither.

There was one fish left in the bucket. Abbie picked it up.

'Since I have been forced to pay for the sea-lion's lunch out of my own pocket,' she said, 'I take it, keeper, that there can be no objection to my taking this fish home for my cat.' And in a trice she had slipped it into one of the pockets of her big bag.

'Good day, superintendent. Good day, sea-lion keeper,' she said, and we moved off to the lions. This time there was no mistake about the feeding hour, and just as we arrived a keeper was throwing a big red joint of meat into the first cage. But we only stayed a little while, because Abbie said:

'You look a little tired, dear. I think it's time we had tea.'

'Did you see the keeper's feet?' I said. 'They were ten-to-two's.'

I explained to Abbie about Perkins, her chauffeur, having quarter-to-three feet. It made her laugh.

'What are my feet?' she asked.

'Oh, yours are just five-to-one's, like mine, but sometimes I turn mine in like this, and then they're "won't" feet.'

'Can you do this?' asked Abbie, and she turned both her feet outward, much later than quarter to three, and ran out of the lion house like that in front of me. It made me roar with laughter.

'They're twenty-to-fours, Abbie,' I said.

'Or twenty-past-eight's, dear. Now. I'm going to carry you part of the way.'

She picked me up in her arms and the stud of her belt dug into my hip. The camel went in the direction of the tea-rooms, but we didn't ride on him.

'Fleas,' said Abbie.

But at last we reached the tea-rooms. Every table was occupied, and lots of people were waiting. Abbie marched in and spoke to a waitress who was carrying a tray of used teacups.

'I am a fellow of this society, waitress,' she said. 'Kindly take me to the manageress.' And she followed the girl down the room, leaving me in charge of the cashier.

Beyond the crowded tables I saw Abbie talking to one person after another, pointing to this and that corner, and bumping into people. I couldn't hear what she said, but in a few minutes a table was brought from somewhere at the back, three groups of people had to move their tables slightly, and Abbie stayed there watching while our table was set. A man in a bowler hat, one of those waiting for a table, said:

'Who does that woman think she is, shoving in like that?'

I reached up and socked him as hard as I could, and my fist landed on something hard in his pocket. Then I burst into tears. I don't remember what happened then, but the next thing I knew Abbie had me by the hand and the man, very red in the face, was trying to say something. But Abbie had put an eyeglass on one eye, and she was saying something too.

'And,' she added, 'I would like to point out that you are indoors and that your hat is nevertheless on your head. Take it off.'

She led me quickly away between the rows of tables.

'I expect he's a bolshie,' she said. 'Next time we'll come on a Sunday, when only fellows and their guests are admitted. I am always telling your mother that to play with socialism is to play with fire. You see what it leads to. Have you hurt your knuckles? Never mind, éclairs are especially good for knuckles. Sit down and you shall have one at once. No, waitress, no bread and butter. Éclairs and macaroons and –'

'Do they have those little pots of jam you have all to yourself like at Kew?' I asked.

They did.

After three or four cakes and a little rest ('In that case, waitress, I fear they will have to wait for the table a little longer. We still have many things to see, and I do not wish my nephew to get over-tired') we set out again.

We saw the kangaroos and the zebras (the sick one was better), and we gave the peanuts to all the different kinds of deer.

'Everybody always gives them to the monkeys,' said Abbie. 'But see how the deer appreciate them, and what a lot of pleasure one can give them for fourpence.'

The deer loved them, and I shouted when their muzzles tickled the inside of my hand.

Whenever I asked something Abbie couldn't answer she called a keeper to explain, and she always told me whether an animal had been born in captivity or not, because if it had, she said, it was quite happy. She saw to it that I didn't walk too much, and I never breathed a word about the place on my hip that was getting sorer and sorer. But at last we had finished. Abbie's map brought us out close to the gate where the car was. And before leaving she told the gatekeeper to put up a notice warning the public about the different feeding time for the sea lions.

'Now we'll go and have tea,' she said. 'Oh, I often have two teas on Mondays.'

We drove down to a teashop in Bond Street, and here everybody knew Abbie and we got a big table in a corner at once. Abbie took off her hat, and I saw that her hair was a sort of blue-white, although my mother had said she wasn't old at all.

'Now for my second tea,' she said, 'I always like an ice cream and a pure still lemonade. And I am going to read you a story.'

She took a book out of her big bag and began to read in a clear voice all about an Ethiopian and a rhinoceros. She was interrupted once because the people near us all moved away to other tables and the waitress came and put a large wooden screen round us.

'Isn't this fun?' said Abbie. 'It's just like having a room to ourselves. Now I think you should have that big chocolate cream to finish up with. But first you must swallow this, so that you won't be sick when you get home.' And she took a large pink pill out of one of the little gold boxes on her bracelet and gave it me to have with my lemonade.

It was getting late, and the only thing my mother was ever strict with me about was my bedtime. I told Abbie.

'I'll tell your mother it was my fault, dear,' she said. 'But don't worry. It's quite all right because I always keep this watch on my bracelet half an hour ahead of Greenwich in order to give myself time to be late.'

And when we got home there was Uncle Arthur. He got up and walked across the room to greet us, and I noticed that he had the most twelve o'clock feet I'd ever seen. He patted my head and gave me a shiny new sovereign. But I think I liked Uncle Arthur best because we found out that his birthday was exactly the same day as mine, and I simply couldn't understand why he wasn't exactly the same age too.

'Your mother will put that sovereign in the savings bank for you, dear,' said Abbie, 'so Arthur is going to give you something you can spend. Haven't you a florin, Arthur?'

'You'll upset his ideas of the value of money for life,' he said. But the coin he gave me was much bigger than the sovereign and just as shiny.

'Not at all,' said Abbie. 'You remember what I told you, Dane, about the pence and the pounds? Well, a florin is twenty-four whole pence, and if you look after them they might grow into twenty-four golden pounds, like the one your mother is going to keep for you.'

When I kissed Abbie good night, I kissed her on her beauty spot to see what it felt like. And as I was going upstairs to bed, I heard her say:

'Arthur, I was charged ninepence for those little sample pots of jam at the zoo today, and at Kew they are only sixpence. I didn't want any unpleasantness in front of the child – he was a little tired – but I think, as a fellow of the society, you should write at once and complain.'

A Flying Visit

Richard Ingrams and John Wells

In one of the regular and revealing letters which the fictional
Denis Thatcher writes to his golfing partner, Bill, he describes
an unexpected trip to the Falkland Islands.

Dear Bill,

First things first. I wouldn't bother if I were you to go up to town for the
Lillywhites sale. I had a quick whizz round en route for the Ritz Bar, and
quite frankly, apart from the evil-smelling horde of Arabs hurling athletic
supports from hand to hand in the jogging department there didn't seem
much of interest to you. I made do with a set of thermal Japanese golf hats
in pastel shades, knocked down to practically nothing. Maurice's friend with
the funny leg swears by them, and I thought they might enliven the scene
at Worplesdon.

You'll forgive me for not giving you prior notice of this present little
excursion, but we were all sworn to keep absolutely mum, lest the Argies
bomb the airstrip prior to our arrival. When it was first mooted, in company
with assorted brasshats and other Whitehall buffers all drawing her attention
to the various hazards attached, I wrang my hands imploring M. to think
again. Pym however seemed singularly sanguine urging her to press on and
fulfil her destiny. (I wonder why?).

Needless to say the Boss had her way, but agreed to throw sand in the
eyes of the reptiles with talk of a cancellation, and limit the operation to an
Ulster-style 'inner and outer'. I thought it only right and proper to motor
the old girl out to Brize Norton and flutter my hanky from the waving base,
telling her as she studied her red boxes in the passenger seat of my deep
regrets that I couldn't come along and enjoy all the fun. After she said 'But
you *are* coming, Denis' for the third time the penny finally dropped and I

began to feel very queasy indeed. Not only was I unsuitably accoutred for the Antarctic, but I had several dates lined up on the old While the Cat's away the Mice will play syndrome, and therefore had to ring round from the only available telephone in the Nissen Hut at the drome. All slightly embarrassing.

Next thing I know it's up a little ladder into the boneshaker, chocks away, and eyes down for seven hours hardarse nonstop to Ascension. The worse thing about it, Bill, was that not being forewarned I was deprived even of the solace of my little flask which I always pack for these occasions. I tried to light a gasper, but it was immediately knocked out of my hand by some Air Commodore, roaring above the din of the engines that I must be mad, didn't I realize I was sitting on forty thousand gallons of high octane fuel? You can imagine my mental state when we tottered out at Ascension, a godforsaken spot if I ever saw one, or so I thought until we reached the Falklands. My hopes of a quick dash to the Duty Free were immediately put paid to as we were frog-marched up another ladder into an even older biplane, and off for another thirteen hours of unmitigated hell, teeth chattering with the vibration, as we nose-dived towards the sea to take on fuel from a stalling nuclear bomber, Margaret unruffled by it all still deep in her boxes and writing her Christmas thank-you letters.

Finally I was awakened from a nightmarish doze and hustled out into the blizzard to be met by that awful little slug Hunt, who used to be the Governor, and a small crowd of blue-nosed Sheepshaggers, the surrounding view bringing back unhappy memories of our grisly holidays with Lord Pucefeatures on the Isle of Muck. M. strikes in, a dreadful gleam in her eye, and begins to press the flesh, a half-witted photographer from the local roneoed news-sheet The Shaggers' Weekly falling about in the background popping off his flashbulbs.

I think we had shaken hands with the entire population of the benighted settlement before the wretched Hunt's better half brightly announced that she had put the kettle on. We were then, if you are still with me, invited to climb into a ridiculous London taxi, and driven off through the minefield to Mon Repos, locally known as Dunshaggin. On arrival we are greeted by a smouldering peat fire, tea and rock buns arranged on tasteful doylies, whereupon Hunt, catching the light of insanity in my eye, mutters that if I like to accompany him upstairs he has something that might interest me. This proved to be a captured pair of underpants once belonging to General Menendez, now mounted by his good lady in a pokerwork frame.

Controlling my emotions, I suggested a stroll to stretch the legs after our long ordeal. Resisting the fool Hunt's suggestion of a trek up Mount Tumbledown, I reached the Goose six minutes later, only to find the bar crammed with inebriate reptiles, brasshats, airline stewards and one or two cross-eyed Sheepshaggers of idiotic mien sitting in a corner reminiscing gloomily about the good old days under the Argies when at least they could get a drink.

As I write our time of departure is still very much under wraps, Margaret having toddled off to a small thanksgiving service at the local tin tabernacle and showing every desire to stay on indefinitely. At least, thanks to Mine Host, Bill Voletrouser, I am now well prepared for the return trip, a miniature in every pocket and a fire extinguisher full of the amber fluid for discreet in-flight refuelling.

Yours in transit

DENIS

Rodney Fails to Qualify

P. G. Wodehouse

There was a sound of revelry by night, for the first Saturday in June had arrived and the Golf Club was holding its monthly dance. Fairy lanterns festooned the branches of the chestnut trees on the terrace above the ninth green, and from the big dining-room, cleared now of its tables and chairs, came a muffled slithering of feet and the plaintive sound of saxophones moaning softly like a man who has just missed a short putt. In a basket-chair in the shadows, the Oldest Member puffed a cigar and listened, well content. His was the peace of the man who has reached the age when he is no longer expected to dance.

A door opened, and a young man came out of the club-house. He stood on the steps with folded arms, gazing to left and right. The Oldest Member, watching him from the darkness, noted that he wore an air of gloom. His brow was furrowed and he had the indefinable look of one who has been smitten in the spiritual solar plexus.

Yes, where all around him was joy, jollity, and song, this young man brooded.

The sound of a high tenor voice, talking rapidly and entertainingly on the subject of modern Russian thought, now intruded itself on the peace of the night. From the farther end of the terrace a girl came into the light of the lantern, her arm in that of a second young man. She was small and pretty, he tall and intellectual. The light shone on his high forehead and glittered on his tortoiseshell-rimmed spectacles. The girl was gazing up at him with reverence and adoration, and at the sight of these twain the youth on the steps appeared to undergo some sort of spasm. His face became contorted and he wobbled. Then, with a gesture of sublime despair, he tripped over the mat and stumbled back into the club-house. The couple passed on and disappeared, and the Oldest Member had the night to himself, until the door opened once more and the club's courteous and efficient secretary trotted down the steps. The scent of the cigar drew him to where the Oldest Member sat, and he dropped into the chair beside him.

'Seen young Ramage tonight?' asked the secretary.

'He was standing on those steps only a moment ago,' replied the Oldest Member. 'Why do you ask?'

'I thought perhaps you might have had a talk with him and found out what's the matter. Can't think what's come to him tonight. Nice, civil boy as a rule, but just now, when I was trying to tell him about my short approach on the fifth this afternoon, he was positively abrupt. Gave a sort of hollow gasp and dashed away in the middle of a sentence.'

The Oldest Member sighed.

'You must overlook his brusqueness,' he said. 'The poor lad is passing through a trying time. A short while back I was the spectator of a little drama that explains everything. Mabel Patmore is flirting disgracefully with that young fellow Purvis.'

'Purvis? Oh, you mean the man who won the club Bowls Championship last week?'

'I can quite believe that he may have disgraced himself in the manner you describe,' said the Sage, coldly. 'I know he plays that noxious game. And it is for that reason that I hate to see a nice girl like Mabel Patmore, who only needs a little more steadiness off the tee to become a very fair golfer, wasting her time on him. I suppose his attraction lies in the fact that he has a great flow of conversation, while poor Ramage is, one must admit, more or less of a dumb Isaac. Girls are too often snared by a glib tongue. Still, it is a pity, a great pity. The whole affair recalls irresistibly to my mind the story –'

The secretary rose with a whirr like a rocketing pheasant.

'– the story,' continued the Sage, 'of Jane Packard, William Bates, and Rodney Spelvin – which, as you have never heard it, I will now proceed to relate.'

'Can't stop now, much as I should like –'

'It is a theory of mine,' proceeded the Oldest Member, attaching himself to the other's coat-tails, and pulling him gently back into his seat, 'that nothing but misery can come of the union between a golfer and an outcast whose soul has not been purified by the noblest of games. This is well exemplified by the story of Jane Packard, William Bates, and Rodney Spelvin.'

'All sorts of things to look after –'

'That is why I am hoping so sincerely that there is nothing more serious than a temporary flirtation in this business of Mabel Patmore and bowls-playing Purvis. A girl in whose life golf has become a factor, would be mad to trust her happiness to a blister whose idea of enjoyment is trundling wooden balls across a lawn. Sooner or later he is certain to fail her in some crisis. Lucky for her if this failure occurs before the marriage knot has been inextricably tied and so opens her eyes to his inadequacy – as was the case in the matter of Jane Packard, William Bates, and Rodney Spelvin. I will now,' said the Oldest Member, 'tell you all about Jane Packard, William Bates, and Rodney Spelvin.'

The secretary uttered a choking groan.

'I shall miss the next dance,' he pleaded.

'A bit of luck for some nice girl,' said the Sage, equably.

He tightened his grip on the other's arm.

Jane Packard and William Bates (said the Oldest Member) were not, you must understand, officially engaged. They had grown up together from childhood, and there existed between them a sort of understanding – the understanding being that, if ever William could speed himself up enough to propose, Jane would accept him, and they would settle down and live stodgily and happily every after. For William was not one of your rapid wooers. In this affair of the heart he moved somewhat slowly and ponderously, like a motor-lorry, an object which both in physique and temperament he greatly resembled. He was an extraordinarily large, powerful, ox-like young man, who required plenty of time to make up his mind about any given problem. I have seen him in the club dining-room musing with a thoughtful frown for fifteen minutes on end while endeavouring to weigh the rival merits of a chump chop and a sirloin steak as a luncheon dish. A placid, leisurely man, I might almost call him lymphatic. I *will* call him lymphatic. He was lymphatic.

The first glimmering of an idea that Jane might possibly be a suitable wife for him had come to William some three years before this story opens. Having brooded on the matter tensely for six months, he then sent her a bunch of roses. In the October of the following year, nothing having occurred to alter his growing conviction that she was an attractive girl, he presented her with a two-pound box of assorted chocolates. And from then on his progress, though not rapid, was continuous, and there seemed little reason to doubt that, should nothing come about to weaken Jane's regard for him, another five years or so would see the matter settled.

And it did not appear likely that anything would weaken Jane's regard. They had much in common, for she was a calm, slow-moving persons, too. They had a mutual devotion to golf, and played together every day; and the fact that their handicaps were practically level formed a strong bond. Most divorces, as you know, spring from the fact that the husband is too markedly superior to his wife at golf; this leading him, when she starts criticizing his relations, to say bitter and unforgivable things about her mashie-shots. Nothing of this kind could happen with William and Jane. They would build their life on a solid foundation of sympathy and understanding. The years would find them consoling and encouraging each other, happy married lovers. If, that is to say, William ever got round to proposing.

It was not until the fourth year of this romance that I detected the first sign of any alteration in the schedule. I had happened to call on the Packards one afternoon and found them all out except Jane. She gave me tea and conversed for a while, but she seemed distrait. I had known her since she wore rompers, so felt entitled to ask if there was anything wrong.

'Not exactly wrong,' said Jane, and she heaved a sigh.

'Tell me,' I said.

She heaved another sigh.

'Have you ever read *The Love that Scorches*, by Luella Periton Phipps?' she asked.

I said I had not.

'I got it out of the libarary yesterday,' said Jane, dreamily, 'and finished it at three this morning in bed. It is a very, very beautiful book. It is all about the desert and people riding on camels and a wonderful Arab chief with stern, yet tender, eyes, and a girl called Angela, and oases and dates and mirages, and all like that. There is a chapter where the Arab chief seizes the girl and clasps her in his arms and she feels his hot breath searing her face and he flings her on his horse and they ride off and all around was sand and night, and the mysterious stars. And somehow – oh, I don't know –'

She gazed yearningly at the chandelier.

'I wish mother would take me to Algiers next winter,' she murmured, absently. 'It would do her rheumatism so much good.'

I went away frankly uneasy. These novelists, I felt, ought to be more careful. They put ideas into girls' heads and made them dissatisfied. I determined to look William up and give him a kindly word of advice. It was no business of mine, you may say, but they were so ideally suited to one another that it seemed a tragedy that anything should come between them.

And Jane was in a strange mood. At any moment, I felt, she might take a good, square look at William and wonder what she could ever have seen in him. I hurried to the boy's cottage.

'William,' I said, 'as one who dandled you on his knee when you were a baby, I wish to ask you a personal question. Answer me this, and make it snappy. Do you love Jane Packard?'

A look of surprise came into his face, followed by one of intense thought. He was silent for a space.

'Who, me?' he said at length.

'Yes, you.'

'Jane Packard?'

'Yes, Jane Packard.'

'Do I love Jane Packard?' said William, assembling the material and arranging it neatly in his mind.

He pondered for perhaps five minutes.

'Why, of course I do,' he said.

'Splendid!'

'Devotedly, dash it!'

'Capital!'

'You might say madly.'

I tapped him on his barrel-like chest.

'Then my advice to you, William Bates, is to tell her so.'

'Now that's rather a brainy scheme,' said William, looking at me admiringly. 'I see exactly what you're driving at. You mean it would kind of settle things, and all that?'

'Precisely.'

'Well, I've got to go away for a couple of days tomorrow – it's the Invitation Tournament at Squashy Hollow – but I'll be back on Wednesday. Suppose I take her out on the links on Wednesday and propose?'

'A very good idea.'

'At the sixth hole, say?'

'At the sixth hole would do excellently.'

'Or the seventh?'

'The sixth would be better. The ground slopes from the tee, and you would be hidden from view by the dog-leg turn.'

'Something in that.'

'My own suggestion would be that you somehow contrive to lead her into that large bunker to the left of the sixth fairway.'

'Why?'

'I have reason to believe that Jane would respond more readily to your wooing were it conducted in some vast sandy waste. And there is another thing,' I proceeded, earnestly, 'which I must impress upon you. See that there is nothing tame or tepid about your behaviour when you propose. You must show zip and romance. In fact, I strongly recommend you, before you even say a word to her, to seize her and clasp her in your arms and let your hot breath sear her face.'

'Who, me?' said William.

'Believe me, it is what will appeal to her most.'

'But, I say! Hot breath, I mean! Dash it all, you know, what?'

'I assure you it is indispensable.'

'Seize her?' said William blankly.

'Precisely.'

'Clasp her in my arms?'

'Just so.'

William plunged into silent thought once more.

'Well, you *know*, I suppose,' he said at length. 'You've had experience, I take it. Still – Oh, all right, I'll have a stab at it.'

'There spoke the true William Bates!' I said. 'Go to it, lad, and Heaven speed your wooing!'

In all human schemes – and it is this that so often brings failure to the subtlest strategists – there is always the chance of the Unknown Factor popping up, that unforeseen X for which we have made no allowance and which throws our whole plan of campaign out of gear. I had not anticipated anything of the kind coming along to mar the arrangements on the present occasion; but when I reached the first tee on the Wednesday afternoon to give William Bates that last word of encouragement, which means so much, I saw that I had been too sanguine. William had not yet arrived, but Jane was there, and with her a tall, slim, dark-haired, sickeningly romantic-looking youth in faultlessly fitting serge. A stranger to me. He was talking to her in a musical undertone, and she seemed to be hanging on his words. Her beautiful eyes were fixed on his face, and her lips slightly parted. So absorbed was she that it was not until I spoke that she become aware of my presence.

'William not arrived yet?'

She turned with a start.

'William? Hasn't he? Oh! No, not yet. I don't suppose he will be long. I want to introduce you to Mr Spelvin. He has come to stay with the Wyndhams for a few weeks. He is going to walk round with us.'

Naturally this information came as a shock to me, but I masked my feelings and greeted the young man with a well-assumed cordiality.

'Mr George Spelvin, the actor?' I asked, shaking hands.

'My cousin,' he said. 'My name is Rodney Spelvin. I do not share George's histrionic ambitions. If I have any claim to – may I say renown? – it is as a maker of harmonies.'

'A composer, eh?'

'Verbal harmonies,' explained Mr Spelvin. 'I am, in my humble fashion, a poet.'

'He writes the most beautiful poetry,' said Jane, warmly. 'He has just been reciting some of it to me.'

'Oh, that little thing?' said Mr Spelvin, deprecatingly. 'A mere *morceau*. One of my juvenilia.'

'It was too beautiful for words,' persisted Jane.

'Ah, you,' said Mr Spelvin, 'have the soul to appreciate it. I could wish that there were more like you, Miss Packard. We singers have much to put up with in a crass and materialistic world. Only last week a man, a coarse editor, asked me what my sonnet, 'Wine of Desire', *meant*.' He laughed indulgently. 'I gave him answer, 'twas a sonnet, not a mining prospectus.'

'It would have served him right,' said Jane, heatedly, 'if you had pasted him one on the nose!'

At this point a low whistle behind me attracted my attention, and I turned to perceive William Bates towering against the skyline.

'Hoy!' said William.

I walked to where he stood, leaving Jane and Mr Spelvin in earnest conversation with their heads close together.

'I say,' said William, in a rumbling undertone, 'who's the bird with Jane?'

'A man named Spelvin. He is visiting the Wyndhams. I suppose Mrs Wyndham made them acquainted.'

'Looks a bit of a Gawd-help-us,' said William critically.

'He is going to walk round with you.'

It was impossible for a man of William Bates's temperament to start, but his face took on a look of faint concern.

'Walk round with us?'

'So Jane said.'

'But look here,' said William. 'I can't possibly seize her and clasp her in my arms and do all that hot-breath stuff with this pie-faced exhibit hanging round on the outskirts.'

'No, I fear not.'

'Postpone it, then, what?' said William, with unmistakable relief. 'Well, as a matter of fact, it's probably a good thing. There was a most extraordinarily fine steak-and-kidney pudding at lunch, and, between ourselves, I'm not feeling what you might call keyed up to anything in the nature of a romantic scene. Some other time, eh?'

I looked at Jane and the Spelvin youth, and a nameless apprehension swept over me. There was something in their attitude which I found alarming. I was just about to whisper a warning to William not to treat this new arrival too lightly, when Jane caught sight of him and called him over and a moment later they set out on their round.

I walked away pensively. This Spelvin's advent, coming immediately on top of that book of desert love, was undeniably sinister. My heart sank for William, and I waited at the club-house to have a word with him, after his match. He came in two hours later, flushed and jubilant.

'Played the game of my life!' he said. 'We didn't hole out all the putts, but, making allowance for everything, you can chalk me up at eighty-three. Not so bad, eh? You know the eighth hole? Well, I was a bit short with my drive, and found my ball lying badly for the brassie, so I took my driving-iron and with a nice easy swing let the pill have it so squarely on the seat of the pants that it flew –'

'Where is Jane?' I interrupted.

'Jane? Oh, the bloke Spelvin has taken her home.'

'Beware of him, William!' I whispered, tensely. 'Have a care, young Bates! If you don't look out, you'll have him stealing Jane from you. Don't laugh. Remember that I saw them together before you arrived. She was gazing into his eyes as a desert maiden might gaze into the eyes of a sheik. You don't seem to realize, wretched William Bates, that Jane is an extremely romantic girl. A fascinating stranger like this, coming suddenly into her life, may well snatch her away from you before you know where you are.'

'That's all right,' said William, lightly. 'I don't mind admitting that the same idea occurred to me. But I made judicious inquiries on the way round, and found out that the fellow's a poet. You don't seriously expect me to believe that there's any chance of Jane falling in love with a poet?'

He spoke incredulously, for there were three things in the world that he held in the smallest esteem – slugs, poets, and caddies with hiccups.

'I think it extremely possible, if not probable,' I replied.

'Nonsense!' said William. 'And, besides, the man doesn't play golf. Never had a club in his hand, and says he never wants to. That's the sort of fellow he is.'

At this, I confess, I did experience a distinct feeling of relief. I could imagine Jane Packard, stimulated by exotic literature, committing many follies, but I was compelled to own that I could not conceive of her giving her heart to one who not only did not play golf but had no desire to play it. Such a man, to a girl of her fine nature and correct upbringing, would be beyond the pale. I walked home with William in a calm and happy frame of mind.

I was to learn but one short week later that Woman is the unfathomable, incalculable mystery, the problem we men can never hope to solve.

The week that followed was one of much festivity in our village. There were dances, picnics, bathing-parties, and all the other adjuncts of high summer. In these William Bates played but a minor part. Dancing was not one of his gifts. He swung, if called upon, an amiable shoe, but the disposition in the neighbourhood was to refrain from calling upon him; for he had an incurable habit of coming down with his full weight upon his partner's toes, and many a fair girl had had to lie up for a couple of days after collaborating with him in a fox-trot.

Picnics, again, bored him, and he always preferred a round on the links to the merriest bathing-party. The consequence was that he kept practically aloof from the revels, and all through the week Jane Packard was squired by Rodney Spelvin. With Spelvin she swayed over the waxed floor; with Spelvin she dived and swam; and it was Spelvin who, with zealous hand, brushed ants off her mayonnaise and squashed wasps with a chivalrous teaspoon. The end was inevitable. Apart from anything else, the moon was at its full and many of these picnics were held at night. And you know what that means. It was about ten days later that William Bates came to me in my little garden with an expression on his face like a man who didn't know it was loaded.

'I say,' said William, 'you busy?'

I emptied the remainder of the water-can on the lobelias, and was at his disposal.

'I say,' said William, 'rather a rotten thing has happened. You know Jane?'

I said I knew Jane.

'You know Spelvin?'

I said I knew Spelvin.

'Well, Jane's gone and got engaged to him,' said William, aggrieved.

'What?'

'It's fact.'

'Already?'

'Absolutely. She told me this morning, And what I want to know,' said the stricken boy, sitting down thoroughly unnerved on a basket of strawberries, 'is, where do I get off?'

My heart bled for him, but I could not help reminding him that I had anticipated this.

'You should not have left them so much alone together,' I said. 'You must have known that there is nothing more conducive to love than the moon in June. Why, songs have been written about it. In fact, I cannot at the moment recall a song that has not been written about it.'

'Yes, but how was I to guess that anything like this would happen?' cried William, rising and scraping strawberries off his person. 'Who would ever have supposed Jane Packard would leap off the dock with a fellow who doesn't play golf?'

'Certainly, as you say, it seems almost incredible. You are sure you heard her correctly? When she told you about the engagement, I mean. There was no chance that you could have misunderstood?'

'Not a bit of it. As a matter of fact, what led up to the thing, if you know what I mean, was me proposing to her myself. I'd been thinking a lot during the last ten days over what you said to me about that, and the more I thought of it the more of a sound egg the notion seemed. So I got her alone up at the club-house and said, 'I say, old girl, what about it?' and she said, 'What about what?' and I said, 'What about marrying me? Don't if you don't want to, of course,' I said, 'but I'm bound to say it looks pretty good to me.' And then she said she loved another – this bloke Spelvin, to wit. A nasty jar, I can tell you, it was. I was just starting off on a round, and it made me hook my putts on every green.'

'But did she say specifically that she was engaged to Spelvin?'

'She said she loved him.'

'There may be hope. If she is not irrevocably engaged the fancy may pass. I think I will go and see Jane and make tactful inquiries.'

'I wish you would,' said William. 'And, I say, you haven't any stuff that'll take strawberry-juice off a fellow's trousers, have you?'

My interview with Jane that evening served only to confirm the bad news. Yes, she was definitely engaged to the man Spelvin. In a burst of girlish confidence she told me some of the details of the affair.

'The moon was shining and a soft breeze played in the trees,' she said. 'And suddenly he took me in his arms, gazed deep into my eyes, and cried, "I love you! I worship you! I adore you! You are the tree on which the fruit of my life hangs; my mate; my woman; predestined to me since the first star shone up in yonder sky!"'

'Nothing,' I agreed, 'could be fairer than that. And then?' I said, thinking how different it all must have been from William Bates's miserable, limping proposal.

'Then we fixed it up that we would get married in September.'

'You are sure you are doing wisely?' I ventured.

Her eyes opened.

'Why do you say that?'

'Well, you know, whatever his other merits – and no doubt they are numerous – Rodney Spelvin does *not* play golf.'

'No, but he's very broad-minded about it.'

I shuddered. Women say these things so lightly.

'Broad-minded?'

'Yes. He has no objection to my going on playing. He says he likes my pretty enthusiasms.'

There seemed nothing more to say on that subject.

'Well,' I said, 'I am sure I wish you every happiness. I had hoped, of course – but never mind that.'

'What?'

'I had hoped, as you insist on my saying it, that you and William Bates –'

A shadow passed over her face. Her eyes grew sad.

'Poor William! I'm awfully sorry about that. He's a dear.'

'A splendid fellow,' I agreed.

'He has been so wonderful about the whole thing. So many men would have gone off and shot grizzly bears or something. But William just said 'Right-o!' in a quiet voice, and he's going to caddy for me at Mossy Heath next week.'

'There is good stuff in the boy.'

'Yes.' She sighed. 'If it wasn't for Rodney – Oh, well!'

I thought it would be tactful to change the subject.

'So you have decided to go to Mossy Heath again?'
'Yes. And I'm really going to qualify this year.'

The annual Invitation Tournament at Mossy Heath was one of the most important fixtures of our local female golfing year. As is usual with these affairs, it began with a medal-play qualifying round, the thirty-two players with the lowest net scores then proceeding to fight it out during the remainder of the week by match-play. It gratified me to hear Jane speak so confidently of her chances, for this was the fourth year she had entered, and each time, though she had started out with the brightest prospects, she had failed to survive the qualifying round. Like so many golfers, she was fifty per cent better at match-play than at medal-play. Mossy Heath, being a championship course, is full of nasty pitfalls, and on each of the three occasions on which she had tackled it one very bad hole had undone all her steady work on the other seventeen and ruined her card. I was delighted to find her so undismayed by failure.

'I am sure you will,' I said. 'Just play your usual careful game.'

'It doesn't matter what sort of a game I play this time,' said Jane, jubilantly. 'I've just heard that there are only thirty-two entries this year, so that everybody who finishes is bound to qualify. I have simply got to get round somehow, and there I am.'

'It would seem somewhat superfluous in these circumstances to play a qualifying round at all.'

'Oh, but they must. You see, there are prizes for the best three scores, so they have to play it. But isn't it a relief to know that, even if I come to grief on that beastly seventh, as I did last year, I shall still be all right?'

'It is, indeed. I have a feeling that once it becomes a matter of match-play you will be irresistible.'

'I do hope so. It would be lovely to win with Rodney looking on.'

'Will he be looking on?'

'Yes. He's going to walk round with me. Isn't it sweet of him?'

Her *fiancé's* name having slid into the conversation again, she seemed inclined to become eloquent about him. I left her, however, before she could begin. To one so strongly pro-William as myself, eulogistic prattle about Rodney Spelvin was repugnant. I disapproved entirely of this infatuation of hers. I am not a narrow-minded man; I quite appreciate the fact that non-golfers are entitled to marry; but I could not countenance their marrying potential winners of the Ladies' Invitation Tournament at Mossy Heath.

The Greens Committee, as greens committees are so apt to do in order to justify their existence, have altered the Mossy Heath course considerably since the time of which I am speaking, but they have left the three most poisonous holes untouched. I refer to the fourth, the seventh, and the fifteenth. Even a soulless Greens Committee seems to have realized that golfers, long-suffering though they are, can be pushed too far, and that the addition of even a single extra bunker to any of these dreadful places would probably lead to armed riots in the club-house.

Jane Packard had done well on the first three holes, but as she stood on the fourth tee she was conscious, despite the fact that this seemed to be one of her good days, of a certain nervousness; and oddly enough, great as was her love for Rodney Spelvin, it was not his presence that gave her courage, but the sight of William Bates's large, friendly face and the sound of his pleasant voice urging her to keep her bean down and refrain from pressing.

As a matter of fact, to be perfectly truthful, there was beginning already to germinate within her by this time a faint but definite regret that Rodney Spelvin had decided to accompany her on this qualifying round. It was sweet of him to bother to come, no doubt, but still there was something about Rodney that did not seem to blend with the holy atmosphere of a championship course. He was the one romance of her life and their souls were bound together for all eternity, but the fact remained that he did not appear to be able to keep still while she was making her shots, and his light humming, musical though it was, militated against accuracy on the green. He was humming now as she addressed her ball, and for an instant a spasm of irritation shot through her. She fought it down bravely and concentrated on her drive, and when the ball soared over the cross-bunker she forgot her annoyance. There is nothing so mellowing, so conducive to sweet and genial thoughts, as a real juicy one straight down the middle, and this was a pipterino.

'Nice work,' said William Bates, approvingly.

Jane gave him a grateful smile and turned to Rodney. It was his appreciation that she wanted. He was not a golfer, but even he must be able to see that her drive had been something out of the common.

Rodney Spelvin was standing with his back turned, gazing out over the rolling prospect, one hand shading his eyes.

'That vista there,' said Rodney. 'That calm, wooded hollow, bathed in the golden sunshine. It reminds me of the island valley of Avilion –'

'Did you see my drive, Rodney?'

'– where falls not rain nor hail nor any snow, nor ever wind blows loudly. Eh? Your drive? No, I didn't.'

Again Jane Packard was aware of that faint, wistful regret. But this was swept away a few moments later in the ecstasy of a perfect iron-shot which plunked her ball nicely on to the green. The last time she had played this hole she had taken seven, for all round the plateau green are sinister sand-bunkers, each beckoning the ball into its hideous depths; and now she was on in two and life was very sweet. Putting was her strong point, so that there was no reason why she should not get a snappy four on one of the nastiest holes on the course. She glowed with a strange emotion as she took her putter, and as she bent over her ball the air seemed filled with soft music.

It was only when she started to concentrate on the line of her putt that this soft music began to bother her. Then, listening, she became aware that it proceeded from Rodney Spelvin. He was standing immediately behind her, humming an old French love-song. It was the sort of old French love-song to which she could have listened for hours in some scented garden under the young May moon, but on the green of the fourth at Mossy Heath it got right in amongst her nerve-centres.

'Rodney, *please!*'

'Eh?'

Jane found herself wishing that Rodney Spelvin would not say 'Eh?' whenever she spoke to him.

'Do you mind not humming?' said Jane. 'I want to putt.'

'Putt on, child, putt on,' said Rodney Spelvin, indulgently. 'I don't know what you mean, but, if it makes you happy to putt, putt to your heart's content.'

Jane bent over her ball again. She had got the line now. She brought back her putter with infinite care.

'My God!' exclaimed Rodney Spelvin, going off like a bomb.

Jane's ball, sharply jabbed, shot past the hole and rolled on about three yards. She spun round in anguish. Rodney Spelvin was pointing at the horizon.

'*What* a bit of colour!' he cried. 'Did you ever see such a bit of colour?'

'Oh, Rodney!' moaned Jane.

'Eh?'

Jane gulped and walked to her ball. Her fourth putt trickled into the hole.

'Did you win?' said Rodney Spelvin, amiably.

Jane walked to the fifth tee in silence.

The fifth and sixth holes at Mossy Heath are long, but they offer little trouble to those who are able to keep straight. It is as if the architect of the course had relaxed over these two in order to ensure that his malignant mind should be at its freshest and keenest when he came to design the pestilential seventh. This seventh, as you may remember, is the hole at which Sandy McHoots, then Open Champion, took an eleven on an important occasion. It is a short hole, and a full mashie will take you nicely on to the green, provided you can carry the river that frolics just beyond the tee and seems to plead with you to throw it a ball to play with. Once on the green, however, the problem is to stay there. The green itself is about the size of a drawing-room carpet, and in the summer, when the ground is hard, a ball that has not the maximum of back-spin is apt to touch lightly and bound off into the river beyond; for this is an island green, where the stream bends like a serpent. I refresh your memory with these facts in order that you may appreciate to the full what Jane Packard was up against.

The woman with whom Jane was partnered had the honour, and drove a nice high ball which fell into one of the bunkers to the left. She was a silent, patient-looking woman, and she seemed to regard this as perfectly satisfactory. She withdrew from the tee and made way for Jane.

'Nice work!' said William Bates, a moment later. For Jane's ball, soaring in a perfect arc, was dropping, it seemed on the very pin.

'Oh, Rodney, look!' cried Jane.

'Eh?' said Rodney Spelvin.

His remark was drowned in a passionate squeal of agony from his betrothed. The most poignant of all tragedies had occurred. The ball, touching the green, leaped like a young lamb, scuttled past the pin, and took a running dive over the cliff.

There was a silence. Jane's partner, who was seated on the bench by the sand-box reading a pocket edition in limp leather of Vardon's *What Every Young Golfer Should Know*, with which she had been refreshing herself at odd moments all through the round, had not observed the incident. William Bates, with the tact of a true golfer, refrained from comment. Jane was herself swallowing painfully. It was left to Rodney Spelvin to break the silence.

'Good!' he said.

Jane Packard turned like a stepped-on worm.

'What do you mean, good?'

'You hit your ball farther than she did.'

'I sent it into the river,' said Jane, in a low, toneless voice.

'Capital!' said Rodney Spelvin, delicately masking a yawn with two fingers of his shapely right hand. 'Capital! Capital!'

Her face contorted with pain, Jane put down another ball.

'Playing three,' she said.

The student of Vardon marked the place in her book with her thumb, looked up, nodded, and resumed her reading.

'Nice w–' began William Bates, as the ball soared off the tee, and checked himself abruptly. Already he could see that the unfortunate girl had put too little beef into it. The ball was falling, falling. It fell. A crystal fountain flashed up towards the sun. The ball lay floating on the bosom of the stream, only some few feet short of the island. But, as has been well pointed out, that little less and how far away!

'Playing five!' said Jane, between her teeth.

'What,' inquired Rodney Spelvin, chattily, lighting a cigarette, 'is the record break?'

'Playing *five*,' said Jane, with a dreadful calm, and gripped her mashie.

'Half a second,' said William Bates, suddenly. 'I say, I believe you could play that last one from where it floats. A good crisp slosh with a niblick would put you on, and you'd be there in four, with a chance for a five. Worth trying, what? I mean, no sense in dropping strokes unless you have to.'

Jane's eyes were gleaming. She threw William a look of infinite gratitude.

'Why, I believe I could!'

'Worth having a dash.'

'There's a boat down there!'

'I could row,' said William.

'I could stand in the middle and slosh,' cried Jane.

'And what's-his-name – *that*,' said William, jerking his head in the direction of Rodney Spelvin, who was strolling up and down behind the tee, humming a gay Venetian barcarolle, 'could steer.'

'William,' said Jane, fervently, 'you're a darling.'

'Oh, I don't know,' said William, modestly.

'There's no one like you in the world. Rodney!'

'Eh?' said Rodney Spelvin.

'We're going out in that boat. I want you to steer.'

Rodney Spelvin's face showed appreciation of the change of programme. Golf bored him, but what could be nicer than a gentle row in a boat.

'Capital!' he said. 'Capital! Capital!'

There was a dreamy look in Rodney Spelvin's eyes as he leaned back with the tiller-ropes in his hands. This was just his idea of the proper way of passing a summer afternoon. Drifting lazily over the silver surface of the stream. His eyes closed. He began to murmur softly:

'All today the slow sleek ripples hardly bear up shoreward, Charged with sighs more light than laughter, faint and fair, Like a woodland lake's weak wavelets lightly lingering forward, Soft and listless as the – Here! Hi!'

For at this moment the silver surface of the stream was violently split by a vigorously-wielded niblick, the boat lurched drunkenly, and over his Panama-hatted head and down his grey-flannelled torso there descended a cascade of water.

'Here! Hi!' cried Rodney Spelvin.

He cleared his eyes and gazed reproachfully. Jane and William Bates were peering into the depths.

'I missed it,' said Jane.

'There she spouts!' said William, pointing. 'Ready?'

Jane raised her niblick.

'Here! Hi!' bleated Rodney Spelvin, as a second cascade poured damply over him.

He shook the drops off his face, and perceived that Jane was regarding him with hostility.

'I do wish you wouldn't talk just as I am swinging,' she said, pettishly. 'Now you've made me miss it again! If you can't keep quiet, I wish you wouldn't insist on coming round with one. Can you see it, William?'

'There she blows,' said William Bates.

'Here! You aren't going to do it *again*, are you?' cried Rodney Spelvin.

Jane bared her teeth.

'I'm going to get that ball on to the green if I have to stay here all night,' she said.

Rodney Spelvin looked at her and shuddered. Was this the quiet, dreamy girl he had loved? This Mœnad? Her hair was lying in damp wisps about her face, her eyes were shining with an unearthly light.

'No, but really –' he faltered.

Jane stamped her foot.

'What *are* you making all this fuss about, Rodney?' she snapped. 'Where is it, William?'

'There she dips,' said William. 'Playing six.'

'Playing six.'

'Let her go,' said William.

'Let her go it is!' said Jane.

A perfect understanding seemed to prevail between these two.

Splash!

The woman on the bank looked up from her Vardon as Rodney Spelvin's agonized scream rent the air. She saw a boat upon the water, a man rowing the boat, another man, hatless, gesticulating in the stern, a girl beating the water with a niblick. She nodded placidly and understandingly. A niblick was the club she would have used herself in such circumstances. Everything appeared to her entirely regular and orthodox. She resumed her book.

Splash!

'Playing fifteen,' said Jane.

'Fifteen is right,' said William Bates.

Splash! Splash! Splash!

'Playing forty-four.'

'Forty-four is correct.'

Splash! Splash! Splash! Splash!

'Eighty-three?' said Jane, brushing the hair out of her eyes.

'No. Only eighty-two,' said William Bates.

'Where is it?'

'There she drifts.'

A dripping figure rose violently in the stern of the boat, spouting water like a public fountain. For what seemed to him like an eternity Rodney Spelvin had ducked and spluttered and writhed, and now it came to him abruptly that he was through. He bounded from his seat, and at the same time Jane swung with all the force of her supple body. There was a splash beside which all the other splashes had been as nothing. The boat overturned and went drifting away. Three bodies plunged into the stream. Three heads emerged from the water.

The woman on the bank looked absently in their direction. Then she resumed her book.

'It's all right,' said William Bates, contentedly. 'We're in our depth.'

'My bag!' cried Jane. 'My bag of clubs!'

'Must have sunk,' said William.

'Rodney,' said Jane, 'my bag of clubs is at the bottom somewhere. Dive under and swim about and try to find it.'

'It's bound to be around somewhere,' said William Bates encouragingly. Rodney Spelvin drew himself up to his full height. It was not an easy thing to do, for it was muddy where he stood, but he did it.

'Damn your bag of clubs!' he bellowed, lost to all shame. 'I'm going home!'

With painful steps, tripping from time to time and vanishing beneath the surface, he sloshed to the shore. For a moment he paused on the bank, silhouetted against the summer sky, then he was gone.

Jane Packard and William Bates watched him go with amazed eyes.

'I never would have dreamed,' said Jane, dazedly, 'that he was that sort of man.'

'A bad lot,' said William Bates.

'The sort of man to be upset by the merest trifle!'

'Must have a naturally bad disposition,' said William Bates.

'Why, if a little thing like this could make him so rude and brutal and horrid, it wouldn't be *safe* to marry him!'

'Taking a big chance,' agreed William Bates. 'Sort of fellow who would water the cat's milk and kick the baby in the face.' He took a deep breath and disappeared. 'Here are your clubs, old girl,' he said, coming to the surface again. 'Only wanted a bit of looking for.'

'Oh, William,' said Jane, 'you are the most wonderful man on earth!'

'Would you go as far as that?' said William.

'I was mad, mad, ever to get engaged to that brute!'

'Now there,' said William Bates, removing an eel from his left breast-pocket, 'I'm absolutely with you. Thought so all along, but didn't like to say so. What I mean is, a girl like you – keen on golf and all that sort of thing – ought to marry a chap like me – keen on golf and everything of that description.'

'William,' cried Jane, passionately, detaching a newt from her right ear, 'I will!'

'Silly nonsense, when you come right down to it, your marrying a fellow who doesn't play golf. Nothing in it.'

'I'll break off the engagement the moment I get home.'

'You couldn't make a sounder move, old girl.'

'William!'

'Jane!'

The woman on the bank, glancing up as she turned a page, saw a man and girl embracing, up to their waists in water. It seemed to have nothing to do with her. She resumed her book.

Jane looked lovingly into William's eyes.

'William,' she said. 'I think I have loved you all my life.'

'Jane,' said William, 'I'm dashed sure I've loved *you* all *my* life. Meant to tell you so a dozen times, but something always seemed to come up.'

'William,' said Jane, 'you're an angel and a darling. Where's the ball?'

'There she pops.'

'Playing eighty-four?'

'Eighty-four it is,' said William. 'Slow back, keep your eye on the ball, and don't press.'

The woman on the bank began Chapter Twenty-five.

Barnsfather's Syndrome

Richard Gordon

Paris was a disappointment. Young Mr Edgar Barnsfather FRCS had expected to find himself in the Champs-Elysées, jammed between the Arc de Triomphe and the Eiffel Tower, with the Folies Bergère opposite. The medical conference was in an angular, concrete hotel like a hospital. A five-minute bus-ride from the airport terminal. He had never been to France before. He arrived in late afternoon, and queued for his conference documents in the hotel foyer behind a fat, ruddy, gingery, rustic-looking practitioner in tweeds.

'Awful bore, these conferences,' said the fat doctor genially.

'I wouldn't know,' Edgar replied meekly. 'I've never attended one.'

'I'm only here for the beer. Exactly like everyone else. Dreadful rackets, all scientific meetings. A most damning reflection on the way we have to live. The doctors go along for a jolly, which they can set against their income-tax. Some sinister drug company subsidises it all for the publicity. As for the hotel, at this time of the year they'd entertain a convention of cannibals to let their empty bedrooms.'

Edgar could not help feeling shocked. 'I think myself privileged to be delivering a paper.'

'Really? What about?'

'Barnsfather's syndrome. Psuedoperforation in young adults.'

'Ah! You're a surgeon?'

Edgar nodded. 'I'm a registrar at the Percival Pott.'

'An excellent London hospital.' The tweedy doctor smiled over half-moon glasses. 'And what *is* Barnsfather's syndrome?'

'I've a paper about it in the latest *BMJ*.' Edgar's voice was twisted painfully between pride and modesty. 'The first I've published, actually. I collected a series of young persons admitted with the signs and symptoms of acute perforated peptic ulcer. Abdominal pain, rigidity, vomiting, that sort of thing. But nothing physically wrong. All psychological. Stress, you know.'

Very interesting. Some were even operated upon. But perhaps this is not in your line?' he apologized.

'Not really.'

'And what do you do in the profession?'

'Oh, I just go on being President of the Royal College of Therapeutics.'

A pretty French girl in a thin white blouse stood behind a long table with piles of plastic-covered folders, each emblazoned in gold with the name of the drug company and the products it hoped the assembly would go home to prescribe. When Edgar introduced himself, she smiled delightedly and pinned to his lapel a card saying E. BARNSFARTER.

'Have a nice time,' she said.

He stared at the lace edging her bra. He was full of unsurgical thoughts. It was his first night in two years of marriage away from his wife. The girl had given him such a lovely smile. 'Is there anything to do in the evenings?'

'There are excursions by autobus to the Opéra and Comédie Française.'

'I mean of a more ... er, intimate nature.'

'You like the *boxe*? There is a tournament just near the hotel.' She smiled delightedly at the next doctor. 'Have a nice time.'

Edgar bought a postcard of Napoleon's tomb, addressed it to his wife in Putney, but could find nowhere to post it. He slipped it in the pocket of his John Collier suit. He would take it home to put on the mantelpiece. It would save postage. He went up to his cuboid bedroom. It was getting dark. He gazed through the double-glazing at the wintry fields, the brightly-lit motorway, the ugly anonymous buildings which fringe all airports. Apart from seeing people drive on the right, he could have stayed at home.

He sat down with *Le Canard Enchaîné*, which he had extravagantly bought at Heathrow to get in the mood. He had been irritated at hardly understanding a word, having imagined that anyone with his intelligence and O-levels could read French. In the plane, he had thrown back his head and laughed loudly over the pages, just to show that he could, until the other passengers started staring at him oddly. So he had read through all the leaders in the *British Medical Journal*, his pale, domed forehead stamped with critical furrows.

He went carefully through the printed conference programme, received from the girl downstairs. He would be speaking the following afternoon to the psychosomatic section, between a surgeon from Chicago on the digestive processes of confused rats and a professor from Milan on phantom tapeworms in nuns.

He drew the *BMJ* from his briefcase, its handle secured at one end with a surgical suture. The learned pages fell open at the paper on Barnsfather's syndrome. He read it again all the way through, as though returning to the oft-folded sheets of a love-letter.

He sighed, staring through the window at the cars flicking along the motorway. This would be the first conference in a lifetime full of them. He might be a mere surgical registrar, but one day he would ease himself into a professorial chair. Everyone in the hospital told him that he was far more use in a lab than an operating theatre. He looked at his watch. It was dinner-time. He could savour the famed French cuisine.

Edgar crossed the foyer towards a notice saying:

INTERNATIONAL GASTROENTEROLOGISTS AND
CHOLECYSTOLOGISTS OFFICIAL DINNER

'Monsieur?' icily demanded a man in striped trousers at the door.

'Dinner,' Edgar explained. '*Dîner. Comprenez?*'

'Monsieur has an invitation? This is the dinner for the officials of the Congress. I assure monsieur that he will find an excellent dinner in the hotel restaurant.'

The restaurant was a long room hung with brown plastic curtains, so dim nobody could see the food or read the menu. He ordered *cervelle au beurre noir*, because he was fond of kidneys. He chose half a bottle of Beaujolais, because it was the only name he recognized. When the dish appeared, he realized that he had made an error in anatomy. The wine tasted peculiar, but he was too timid to complain. He ventured afterwards into the bar, but it was jammed with doctors drinking free brandy and noisier than students. He went to his room, undressed and read *Recent Advances in Surgery* until he fell asleep.

He woke. The curtains were drawn, the room pitch dark. He felt terrible.

He groaned, clasping his stomach. It was the brains, the wine. Some vile, explosive chemical reaction had occurred between the two. Brains always solidified in alcohol. That was how pathologists kept them, in pots.

He gasped. Colic tore at him with tiger's claws. He lay back on his pillow, breathing quickly. He was ill. He was also a doctor. He must decide what was wrong with him.

Intestinal obstruction? Appendicitis? Meckel's diverticulitis? Acute pancreatitis? Alarming diagnoses leapt through his mind, like questions fired at students over the bedside. The referred pain of coronary thrombosis, perhaps? Or of acute meningitis? Bellyache could be anything.

The tiger leapt again. He sensed sweat on his brow. He groped in the darkness. His watch said it was barely midnight. He fumbled for the telephone.

'*Allo?*' said a woman's voice.

'*Je suis malade.*'

'*Vous êtes Monsieur qui?*'

'*Malade*. Ill. Kaput. OK?'

'Monsieur wants room service?'

'No, I want a doctor.'

'*Oui*, monsieur. Which doctor?'

'Any doctor.'

'But monsieur! The hotel tonight is full of doctors.'

Edgar bit his thumb-nail. It was like having a riot at the police ball and dialling 999 for the squad cars. 'Has the hotel a doctor? One who comes when the guests are taken *malade?*'

'*Mais bien sûr*, monsieur. But he is in Paris.'

'Get him,' commanded Edgar, as another pang exploded in his stomach. An hour passed. The pains were worse. He was dying.

He picked up the telephone again.

'*Allo?*' said a man.

'*Je suis presque mort.*'

'*Ah! Monsieur désire quelque chose à boire?*'

Edgar put down the telephone. He rose, reaching for the red-spotted dressing-gown his wife had given him for Christmas. He staggered to the lift, descending with his forehead resting on the cool metal side. The foyer was empty. Edgar knew his materialisation was alarming, but desperate diseases needed desperate remedies.

'Why, there's the surgeon,' exclaimed the ruddy-faced President of the Royal College of Therapeutics. 'Sleepwalking, eh? Or astray on your way to some nice lady's bedroom? You surgical registrars, all guts and gonads. Or is there a fire?'

The official dinner was breaking up. From the door earlier barred to him drifted twenty or so doctors in dinner-jackets, all chattering noisily and slapping each other on the back.

'I'm ill,' said Edgar shortly.

'*Ill?*' The President was amazed. 'But you can't be ill here. We're all off duty. Enjoying ourselves at some crooked drug company's expense. Excellent dinner, Harry, don't you think?' he inquired of a tall man swaying beside him. 'I'm so fond of *cailles à la gourmande*. But of course, I should never dream of paying for them.'

'The wine was fine, Sir Marmaduke,' said the tall doctor, an American.

'I'm *so* glad you liked it. I chose it myself,' disclosed the President smugly. 'I must confess a favouritism towards claret rather than burgundy, and the Château Figeac '72 *is* very good. On the other hand, the champagne they gave us – I say,' he added irritably, as Edgar groaned loudly. 'Can't you do all that sort of thing in your room?'

'I'm in agony.' Edgar doubled up. 'I've got an acute abdomen.'

'Really? Well, I suppose you should know. I'm only a physician. I never feel at home below the umbilicus.'

'Sir, Sir Marmaduke –' Edgar staggered towards him imploringly. 'Can't you help me? I'm dying.'

'My dear fellow, of course, if *that's* the case,' said Sir Marmaduke more amiably, blowing into Edgar's strained face billows of brandy. 'One has one's Hippocratic tradition, and all that, eh? Human life must be preserved, however unworthy. Better have a dekko at your belly. Just jump up there.' He indicated the table previously supervised by the girl with the see-through blouse. He pulled up Edgar's mauve pyjama-top and pulled down his pyjama trousers. The other doctors crowded round. It was an unexpected after-dinner entertainment.

'Where does it hurt?' asked Sir Marmaduke, staggering steeply forward and pressing hard.

'Ouch!' screamed Edgar.

'Jolly interesting. You've got a retroperitoneal abscess.'

'Can anyone have a feel?' murmured Harry.

'My dear fellow, help yourself.'

'You're wrong, Sir Marmaduke,' Harry disagreed. 'It's a case of haemoperitoneum.'

'Don't really think so, my dear old boy.' Sir Marmaduke had his eyes closed. 'Patient would be more collapsed.'

'Ah! But they collapse and die suddenly. Like that.' Harry tried to snap his fingers, but missed.

'Excuse, please.' A Japanese doctor wriggled to the front, grinning. 'Please?' he asked, hand poised over Edgar's goosepimples.

'Dear Saki-san, do plunge in. I'm sure we can all benefit from your oriental wisdom.'

'Please.' decided the Japanese. 'Clear case, hernia foramen of Winslow.'

'Now *that's* a jolly good diagnosis,' agreed Sir Marmaduke warmly. 'Any improvement on a herniated foramen of Winslow, gentlemen?' he invited, looking round.

'*Ja so*, we haf the jaundice?' asked another doctor, pulling down Edgar's eyelid.

'*Mon cher confrère*,' suggested another. 'This case reminds me of one I saw some years ago in Algeria. Ruptured amoebic cyst of the liver. Has your patient lived abroad?'

Edgar shook his head violently.

'Well, that is not necessary to get amoeba,' the French doctor consoled himself. 'My case was fatal, by the way. They nearly always are.'

'How about Legionnaires' pneumonia?' remarked another brightly. 'It's very popular just now.'

'Lassa fever can present like this,' came a voice from the back. 'Though of course I've never seen a case, nor even done a post-mortem on one. They whisk the bodies away so quickly in metal coffins.'

'Well, I must be toddling off to bed,' said Sir Marmaduke. 'Delightful evening. Delightful chaps. Don't forget the golf tomorrow, Harry. Anything to avoid the bloody papers.'

'What about me?' cried Edgar, sitting up.

Sir Marmaduke seemed to have forgotten him. 'I should get a glass of hot water from room service. Do you the world of good. Old remedies are best. If you're not better in the morning, toddle along to my suite and we'll have another prod.'

The doctors disappeared, yawning. Edgar crawled to the lift. He fell into his bedroom. He dialled Putney.

There was a long wait. 'Who's that?' began his wife suspiciously.

'Edgar.'

She gasped. 'Did you miss your plane? God knows, you insisted on getting there early enough.'

'I'm in Paris –'

'What do you mean, phoning?' she demanded crossly. 'It's dreadfully expensive. And at this hour, too. You scared me to death. Or perhaps you imagined I was out for the night,' she added cuttingly, 'and were just checking up on me?'

'I'm ill.'

'There's plenty of doctors to look after you.'

'They're all drunk.'

'What's the matter?' she asked with more concern.

'I've some sort of abdominal catastrophe. I'm coming home. There's a plane at five a.m. I'll try and get on it.'

'But what about your paper?'

'It'll be printed in the Congress proceedings. I should have liked to read it, but ... what's the point, if I'm dead by tonight?'

'Oh, Edgar!' she cried. 'I'd no idea you were as bad as that.'

'I am. I must see a sober English doctor as soon as possible.'

'Oh, Edgar!' she said again, bursting into tears.

Groaning, gurgling, gagging, Edgar collected his luggage, ordered a taxi, staggered into the airport, changed his ticket, relaxed in his seat on the half-empty plane. He slept, exhausted.

He woke with the stewardess gently shaking him. 'Where am I?' he cried in panic.

'We've just landed at Heathrow. Don't worry, sir,' she said caringly. 'The captain had a radio message about you. You're in good hands.'

She tenderly helped him to the aircraft door. He found himself sitting on a fork-lift truck. Two uniformed men were waiting below with a stretcher. They slid him into an ambulance, which instantly raced across the tarmac with light flashing and horn blaring. A young man with glasses was leaning over him.

'I'm a doctor,' said Edgar.

'Are you? Well, so am I. Your wife alerted the airport. An acute abdomen, isn't it? I'd better take a look at it.'

He felt Edgar's tummy in silence. 'H'm.'

'What's the diagnosis?' Edgar asked anxiously.

'Without doubt, I'd say a clear case of Barnsfather's syndrome. There was a lot of guffle about it in this week's *BMJ*.'

Mipsie

Mary Dunn

The Lady Addle of Eigg hesitated at first to publish her
memoirs, but it is our good fortune that she was finally
persuaded to do so. They give us a unique view of the
dazzling life of high society at the turn of the century – as
in this extract which describes her unusual sister, Mipsie.

A good woman is a wondrous creature, cleaving to the
right and to the good under all change.

Life of Tennyson.

It seems hopelessly inadequate to devote only two short chapters to Mipsie
when several volumes could be written about her enchanting loveliness, her
talents, and her strange vivid life. It was, above all, Life which she loved –
loved so passionately that it led her into paths which would, possibly, have
been better left untrodden. But '*tout comprendre est tout pardoner*', and I hope
in this short space to throw a new and more intimate light on some of the
events in her life which made the world talk so much, and sometimes so
unkindly.

It was in spring of 1902 that I first began to realize that things were not
going right between her and Oxo, chiefly through his fault, I must say. While
he was fighting in South Africa, Mipsie had done the obviously sensible thing
which was to save the vast expense of Brisket Castle by shutting it up and
taking a house in Paris instead. He raised no objection at the time, yet on
his return, although Mipsie came home within six months, which was as soon
as she could manage to wind up her affairs in France, he was furious and
practically refused to pay her Paris debts. He actually seemed to expect her

to have existed there on the same money as she would have lived on at
Brisket, which was frankly ridiculous. That was the beginning of the rift. The
next quarrel was over the children. There were two, a girl and a boy, whom
Mipsie worshipped and made a point of seeing at least twice a week. But she
was always adorably vague and one day when Soppy and her family of eight
were staying there Mipsie lifted up little Archie Hogshead and said to a
caller: 'This is my baby.' It was a very natural mistake to make – they were,
after all, first cousins – but Oxo chose to take umbrage and accused her
of not knowing which were her own children. Mipsie, with her flashing
wit, tried to ease matters by a playful rejoinder: 'Well, how do you know
which are yours?' but he was too angry to be soothed. The breach
widened.

The end came over a stupid misunderstanding. Mipsie was expected back
from Brussels, where she had been on a visit, to act as hostess to a large
shooting party at Brisket, but was taken suddenly ill and telegraphed: 'Cannot
return. In bed with *migraine*.' Oxo, who was always a very poor French
scholar, had never heard of the word, so completely misconstruing the
contents of the message rushed frantically to Brussels, where, as bad luck
would have it, Mipsie's attack had suddenly subsided and she was trying to
revive her strength for the journey by a quiet little dinner with an old friend
in the private room of an hotel. Explanations were all in vain. After a
distressing scene of violent recriminations on both sides Oxo left for England,
and we learnt that they had separated.

Poor darling brave Mipsie! What she must have suffered during the divorce
proceedings, losing not only her good name but her children and the famous
Brisket pearls as well as having her allowance cut down to a beggarly £3,000
a year, I dread to think. She was always so sensitive and so proud – the
pride of a thoroughbred – and hated to fall short of any standard or ideal
she had set for herself. That was the reason why she accepted the offer of Fr.
50,000 a year as an allowance from another old friend, the Marquis de
Pelouse. It was to enable her to live as Oxo, in the days when he had loved
her, would have liked her to. It was amazing loyalty for a woman who had
been treated as Mipsie had; yet the world said malicious and bitter things
even about that.

She soon married again. She never could bear loneliness and plenty of
men were only too willing. Her second husband was Sir Constant Standing,
a baronet of good family and a nice fellow, but somewhat weak and easily

persuaded and far from clever. He had a comfortable income but quite inadequate to keep up the beautiful villa which they – especially Mipsie – had set their hearts on at Monte Carlo. It would really have been wiser if he had said so straight away instead of struggling on and attempting to recover by gambling, for which he had no aptitude whatever, or even liking. In fact he had never played at all until Mipsie taught him to, as she taught him many other things.

However, they were happy enough for a time and people seeing them together have often said what a wonderful wife she was and how she would never put on even the smallest stake at the tables without asking him for the money first. She tried to do him good in many other ways too, encouraging him to take life more seriously and put his back into some regular occupation and as a result he worked so hard on a system at baccarat that he spent a great deal more money than he should in testing it, and the worry of it produced a bad nervous breakdown, which made life even harder for my poor sister.

But it was not until after his bankruptcy that Mipsie began to realize that Constant was not, somehow, the same man as she thought she had married. I think it all came as rather a shock to her. And then she found out that the vastly rich uncle who had been intending to leave all his money to him had changed his will when Constant had declared his intention of marrying Mipsie and that quite broke her up. The cruelty of the uncle in taking that line just because she had the misfortune to be badly treated by her first husband, and above all the deceit, the base dishonesty of Constant in marrying her without telling her of the changed will – he gave the paltry excuse that he 'Didn't want to worry her and thought the old boy would come round' – were too much for my sister, who was always the soul of honour. She felt she could no longer live with one who had wounded and disappointed her so greatly and in the summer of 1906 she left him. I am told he has gone sadly downhill since that date. He now lives at Cannes and is to be found every day in a not very reputable bar where he will say to the merest stranger: 'Have I ever told you about my wife?' He will then proceed to use such indecent language that even the visitors from Palm Beach cannot stand it.

But to return to my sister. After she had procured her divorce she passed through a time of great loneliness and hardship, struggling to live on the pittance allowed her by Brisket, augmented only by gifts from one or two friends, and without any real background to her life. There were happy times, of course, for she was always incurably gay, but sometimes she longed for security again – some one of solid worth to fall back upon in every necessity. It was, I think, this instinctive craving for safety that prompted her to decide to go to America. She was greatly attracted by what she heard of the satisfactory and solid nature of American home life at that date, and her always vivid imagination was caught by an exquisite diamond-studded vanity-box which she had been shown by a friend and told it was a favour given in a cotillion at Newport, which was picturesquely known as 'the Millionaires' playground'. The idea of such fairy godmother presents being given at a mere ball appealed to the childish, almost elfin element in her nature and she, of course, always adored beauty in any form. I remember how once during a house party at Coots Balder, when we were girls and shared a room, I woke three nights running to discover Mipsie's bed empty, and each time when she returned she told me she had been in the garden listening to the nightingales. I longed to share her joy and begged to go with her one night, but she said the nightingales sang a different song for her, which I thought a charming whimsy. She was, indeed, a child of nature.

Had she gone to America that autumn her life might have been very different, for with her birth and beauty and brilliance she would soon, I am convinced, have been queen of the Four Hundred and perhaps married happily, though, of course, an American husband would have been rather a shock to the family! But once again it was her very womanhood – those qualities of sweet unselfishness and generosity that made her what she was – which directed her destiny otherwise.

She was actually on the eve of departure. I had lent her the money for her ticket as some of her investments had been giving her trouble – when at a soirée given by the Russian Ambassador in London a very old man was introduced to her as Prince Fédor Ubetzkoi, and with her invariable charming courtesy to the aged, who as she rightly says are often worth so much more than the younger generation – she sat and conversed with him in an alcove for a while. As they talked she became more and more impressed by his courtly manner and distinguished bearing and found her eyes riveted by the beauty of his finely-modelled hands, their delicate tapering fingers set off to perfection by the simple severity of two uncut emeralds the size of pigeons' eggs. Gently she drew him out about himself in the winning way she knew so much better than any one, and when she learnt that he owned the whole of Goulashia with its vast platinum mines, that he was seventy-nine and a widower with one of the most beautiful palaces in Europe full of world-famous treasures, her whole woman's heart went out to the poor old man; his loneliness amidst such great possessions, his helplessness, his very age appealed to something deep within her. She could not bear to think of him growing nearer the grave each day, perhaps without even the consolation of knowing that after his death his treasures would give joy to some one dear to him. With characteristic impulsiveness she threw all her previous plans to the winds. She saw her duty, her destiny, clearly before her. Within a week they were married and the Prince and Princess Fédor Ubetzkoi had left for the palace at Ekaterinbog.

Mipsie told me that the treasures of Ekaterinbog Palace came up to her fullest expectations. The walls were lined with Old Masters, some of which she was able to recognize from their famous originals in the Louvre and elsewhere. Experts came from all over the world to see the equestrian portrait of Charles I by Van Eyck, and the famous collection, formed by Prince Fédor's father, of oleographs from Landseer. The ballroom, designed as a grotto, was made entirely of Dresden china; while each step of the grand staircase was of a different coloured marble, quarried from the Ubetzkoi domains – a lovely rainbow effect, making a gay contrast to the carved platinum banisters and handrail.

Every room contained *objets d'art* which would have dignified any museum. Perhaps the most interesting to a foreigner was the array of assassination daggers, as the right to wear them had been conferred on the family by the Czarina Elizabeth for their share in the removal of one of her lovers. The Ubetzkois, always a powerful landowning family, had indeed played their part in Russian history, and the palace was full of reminiscences of it. One local custom was recalled by a case of beautiful knouts, the exquisite chasing of their silver handles worn smooth with use. By the great stove in each room stood a rack, also of solid silver, on which a knout was always suspended, so that the prince should never have to go from one room to another if he wanted to flog a serf.

In many ways the finest thing in the house was also an imperial gift. Prince Fédor's grandfather had been a grand chamberlain in the times of the Nihilists, and lost his life in a bomb outrage, when his resplendent carriage

was mistaken for that of the Czar. In sympathetic recognition of his services
the Czar presented the family with a large model of the bomb in gold, which
stood on a malachite base in the entrance hall. It was over seven feet high,
and very picturesque, Mipsie said.

THE FOLKSONG WHICH WAS COMPOSED
IN MIPSIE'S HONOUR

Yumpa! yumpa! oglo pzrhwlt!
Brisketinski Fédor bgmkwlt.
Lappup vodka, būzov grog.
Yumpa hak Ekaterinbog!

I always think one of the greatest tragedies of life is a really noble action
that goes unrewarded and even misunderstood. It is, of course, impossible to
blame Prince Fédor for part of that very senility that had so appealed to
Mipsie's sympathy, but it was unfortunate, to say the least of it, that his
memory was so bad and that he entirely forgot to mention that he had two
children by his previous marriage, a daughter of forty-one, Irina, who ruled
almost as Queen at the Palace of Ekaterinbog, and a son of twenty-five,
Michel, who would inherit Goulashia and everything in it, on his father's
death. So that for a time it seemed almost as if my sister's sacrifice were in
vain and she felt it very deeply, I think. But out of sorrow and disappointment
sometimes joy emerges and this was now the case for Mipsie, who certainly
needed a little happiness after all she had gone through. With wonderful
philosophy she accepted the situation as she found it and calmly and
dispassionately set to work to think out where her duty lay. At once she saw
that the future of Goulashia was the vital thing. Fédor was old, and still, in
spite of marriage, under his daughter's thumb. But Michel was young and
impressionable and the future heir. Mipsie knew instinctively that she could
best influence her adopted country through him and she now concentrated,
with all the charm and ability of her command, on winning his allegiance
and affection.

    She was abundantly successful; for two years – from 1909–1911 – there
followed for my sister what she still refers to, with tears in her eyes, as the
happiest time in her life, and one of the most perfect relationships I have

ever encountered. She has allowed me to reprint excerpts from her diary of the time which show something of the beauty of that friendship.

'Ekaterinbog.   Sept. 12th, 1909.

'Woke early, before 11, with my heart singing "Mich is coming today". He drove out to lunch, bringing me an immense bouquet of roses, and we went for a long ride afterwards, seen off by Irina, with a face like a thunder-cloud, but who cares! Mich was as sweet as ever. He says I am his good angel and when he reigns over Goulashia he will never do anything without my approval. I am so happy to feel I can help.

'Nov. 3rd.   The Palace Ball tonight. Mich sent me a lovely ruby star which was perfect on my new Paquin. How happy I am. Irina looked revolting in purple poplin.'

It is a pity that Princess Irina never managed to win her affection. I am certain it cannot have been Mipsie's fault. The next entry I had selected at random shows something of the difficulties of her life, of which her friendship with Michel (often spoken of very harshly by unkind people) was the only happy side.

'July 18th, 1910.   How tired I am of it all. This dull old Palace, Fédor's everlasting recollections of the past, Irina's sulks, the sameness of it. Thank Heaven, Mich is coming for the week-end. I really am overdone and need a holiday badly.

'July 19th.   Spoke to Fédor about a holiday and he was quite reasonable though he tried for a bit to suggest coming too, but I told him travelling is much too tiring for him. I suggested a month at Baden-Baden. He agrees. What a prospect!

'July 21st.   Mich came today. He looks tired and overdone though as sweet as ever. I told him he should have a change of air.

'July 22nd.   Such a lovely day. Rode with Mich and broke it to him that I was going away. He was too touching and said he couldn't bear it and why shouldn't he come too? I think it *might* be rather a good play as he really does not look well. I said we would speak to his father about it after Irina had retired.

'July 23rd.   It is all fixed and Mich and I with a small staff go to Baden-Baden next week. Hooray! Fédor quite agreed about the importance of Mich's health – at least I think he did, but he was so sleepy. Anyway, he consented, and couldn't be bothered to alter his decision even when Irina tried to make him, on hearing the news this morning. I wonder why she detests me so.

'Baden-Baden. Aug. 12th.   Spent a perfect day with Mich at my side every minute and more devoted than ever. I tell him he shouldn't waste his time with an old woman of thirty-four,[1] but he only laughs and says no girl of eighteen can hold a candle to me. Foolish boy.

'Aug. 19th.   Mich gave me the most exquisite diamond-and-sapphire bracelet today. How very beautiful life is.

'Aug. 28th.   Nothing could be more perfect than this life. Mich is talking of making a settlement on me. It makes me proud to think how he trusts and looks up to me. Only three days more. I must make the most of them.'

Alas, that was the nearest Prince Michel ever got to making the settlement on Mipsie which she so richly deserved. They were recalled next day because Prince Fédor developed a chill, which proved to be very slight. But soon after that other troubles began to appear. The very strength of Mipsie's devotion to her step-son brought about worries which acted as a canker to her happiness, eventually destroying it. In November 1910, she writes:

'Had a most worrying day. Telephoned to Mich as usual and remarked on his seeming *distrait*. He denied it, but after a bit confessed that he had just been over to lunch with the Nastikoffs, who have never been at all friendly to me, so it was rather disloyal of him. He further said that Xenia,

---

[1] *Mipsie must have made a mistake here. She was thirty-seven in 1910.*

the ugly little round daughter, had grown into a lovely and charming girl. Don't believe a word of it and told him I didn't trust Prince Nastikoff or any of them a yard. Mich seemed very upset.

'Nov. 25th.   A cold raw day. How I loathe Ekaterinbog in winter. Mich came over to lunch, but couldn't or wouldn't ride as he said he must get back quickly. I was very disappointed and burst into tears. He was sweet but left early all the same.

'Dec. 12th.   Is life worth while? I wrote a long letter to Mich saying that I hadn't seen him for a fortnight and had I lost a friend. Worry for the future, and fear that he will make an unfortunate marriage are making me ill. Why must all lovely things end?

'Dec. 15th. Mich writes and just says: "Don't be silly." Silly, *me*! I am furious.

'Dec. 19th.   The blow has fallen. Mich is going to marry Xenia Nastikoff. I have told him he will be miserable and I know she is not the wife for him, but he won't listen to me. To make it worse, Fédor and Irina seem delighted. I am utterly wretched.'

In March the following year she wrote: 'Mich married. Our wonderful friendship is over and my happiness gone.' It almost breaks my heart to read of such suffering. It was amazing devotion for a step-mother to have given.

Mich's marriage seemed to have the effect of making her turn again very much to her husband who was becoming increasingly frail and for two long weary years she scarcely left his side. He died in 1914, leaving her quite comfortably off, though the bulk of his vast fortune went, of course, to Michel. She left Goulashia, which was hateful to her with past memories, and went to live in Paris until the war, when she plunged herself in war work like all of us. One day news came to her of the Russian Revolution. The palace at Ekaterinbog had been seized. Mich and his family had fled. 'Then what will happen about my money?' asked poor Mipsie desperately. She was told it was not worth the paper it was printed on. She was ruined, except for £3,000 a year.

After the war she revived her old plan of going to the USA. Although it was not the same as the America of the golden days, she felt she craved 'fresh woods and pastures new' after all she had suffered in Europe. Besides, her allowance from Brisket was worth even less now and she was hard put to it to keep body and soul together. So with superb pluck she set to work to earn her living by giving her name to trade advertisements, and the face that had launched a thousand cheques was now seen in every paper, recommending soap and patent foods and toilet preparations. What it must have cost her – a Coot, a Duchess and a Princess – I hate to think, but *noblesse oblige* was part of her very being.

However, romance was not quite over for my dear sister. Even in that land of hard cash love can bloom. She met one day, on business, Mr Julius K. Block of Block's Skin Bleaching Cream. He had been very struck by Mipsie's photograph in a dentifrice campaign and came to ask her to pose for his cream. Something about his childlike simplicity combined with his undoubted stability and business integrity struck a chord in her weary heart. She saw him again – and again. And then one day he took her to his magnificent home in Fifth Avenue and she sat on a Gobelin settee while he told her of his country home in Long Island. As he spoke of the solid lapis swimming pool his face lit up with boyish enthusiasm. In that instant she knew that she loved again.

For a few years they were very happy. Then again cruel fate intervened. The rage for sun-bathing and outdoor sports came in and with it the decline in the fashion for white skin. Block's bleaching cream went smash and Mipsie's husband was a ruined man. He felt he couldn't face going back and telling her the news. They found him in his office, shot through the head ... once again Mipsie was a widow and practically penniless.

It is small wonder that after this last tragedy my poor sister felt despair knocking at her heart. But her life had taught her nothing if not resignation. In 1930 she decided to give up the world, which had let her down so badly, and become a decorator. With the remnants of the Block money she opened the establishment in Mayfair which she still carries on, under the name of *MIPSIE BRISKET*. She felt that as she had had no previous experience of decorating and her mind was not confused with any historical or artistic knowledge she would come fresh to it and the public would benefit by entirely new ideas. The first room she decorated proved the truth of her theory – it was like nothing else on earth, as one critic said – and her *clientèle* grew rapidly each season, so that, with the occasional help of old friends, she now manages to live quite comfortably, I am thankful to say, and has had particular success with her unseasoned wood furniture. She is still the same gay, delightful, sympathetic Mipsie, though, to one who has known her all her life, it is clear that her troubles have set their mark upon her, her hair, on one occasion, having turned chestnut in a single night.

Letters to Warner Brothers

Groucho Marx

When the Marx Brothers were about to make a movie called 'A Night in Casablanca', there were threats of legal action from the Warner Brothers, who, five years before, had made a picture called, simply 'Casablanca' (with Humphrey Bogart and Ingrid Bergman as stars). Whereupon Groucho, speaking for his brothers and himself, immediately dispatched the following letters:

Dear Warner Brothers:

Apparently there is more than one way of conquering a city and holding it as your own. For example, up to the time that we contemplated making this picture, I had no idea that the city of Casablanca belonged exclusively to Warner Brothers. However, it was only a few days after our announcement appeared that we received your long, ominous legal document warning us not to use the name Casablanca.

It seems that in 1471, Ferdinand Balboa Warner, your great-great-grandfather, while looking for a shortcut to the city of Burbank, had stumbled on the shores of Africa and, raising his alpenstock (which he later turned in for a hundred shares of the common), named it Casablanca.

I just don't understand your attitude. Even if you plan on re-releasing your picture, I am sure that the average movie fan could learn in time to distinguish between Ingrid Bergman and Harpo. I don't know whether I could, but I certainly would like to try.

You claim you own Casablanca and that no one else can use that name without your permission. What about 'Warner Brothers'? Do you own that, too? You probably have the right to use the name Warner, but what about Brothers? Professionally, we were brothers long before you were. We were touring the sticks as The Marx Brothers when Vitaphone was still a gleam in the inventor's eye, and even before us there had been other brothers – the Smith Brothers; the Brothers Karamazov; Dan Brothers, an outfielder with Detroit; and 'Brother, Can You Spare a Dime?' (This was originally 'Brothers, Can You Spare a Dime?' but this was spreading a dime pretty thin, so they threw out one brother, gave all the money to the other one and whittled it down to, 'Brother, Can You Spare a Dime?')

Now Jack, how about you? Do you maintain that yours is an original name? Well, it's not. It was used long before you were born. Offhand, I can think of two Jacks – there was Jack of 'Jack and the Beanstalk,' and Jack the Ripper, who cut quite a figure in his day.

As for you, Harry, you probably sign your checks, sure in the belief that you are the first Harry of all time and that all other Harrys are imposters. I can think of two Harrys that preceded you. There was Light-house Harry of Revolutionary fame and a Harry Appelbaum who lived on the corner of 93rd Street and Lexington Avenue. Unfortunately, Appelbaum wasn't too well known. The last I heard of him, he was selling neckties at Weber and Heilbroner.

Now about the Burbank studio. I believe this is what you brothers call your place. Old man Burbank is gone. Perhaps you remember him. He was a great man in a garden. His wife often said Luther had ten green thumbs. What a witty woman she must have been! Burbank was the wizard who crossed all those fruits and vegetables until he had the poor plants in such a confused and jittery condition that they could never decide whether to enter the dining room on the meat platter or the dessert dish.

This is pure conjecture, of course, but who knows – perhaps Burbank's survivors aren't too happy with the fact that a plant that grinds out pictures on a quota settled in their town, appropriated Burbank's name and uses it as a front for their films. It is even possible that the Burbank family is prouder of the potato produced by the old man than they are of the fact that from your studio emerged 'Casablanca' or even 'Gold Diggers of 1931'.

This all seems to add up to a pretty bitter tirade, but I assure you it's not meant to. I love Warners. Some of my best friends are Warner Brothers. It is even possible that I am doing you an injustice and that you, yourselves, know nothing at all about this dog-in-the-Wanger attitude. It wouldn't surprise me at all to discover that the heads of your legal department are unaware of this absurd dispute, for I am acquainted with many of them and they are fine fellows with curly black hair, double-breasted suits and a love of their fellow man that out-Saroyans Saroyan.

I have a hunch that this attempt to prevent us from using the title is the brainchild of some ferret-faced shyster, serving a brief apprenticeship in your legal department. I know the type well – hot out of law school, hungry for success and too ambitious to follow the natural laws of promotion. This bar sinister probably needled your attorneys, most of whom are fine fellows with curly black hair, double-breasted suits, etc., into attempting to enjoin us. Well, he won't get away with it! We'll fight him to the highest court! No pasty-faced legal adventurer is going to cause bad blood between the Warners and the Marxes. We are all brothers under the skin and we'll remain friends till the last reel of 'A Night in Casablanca' goes tumbling over the spool.

Sincerely,
Groucho Marx

> For some curious reason, this letter seemed to puzzle the Warner Brothers legal department. They wrote – in all seriousness – and asked if the Marxes could give them some idea of what their story was about. They felt that something might be worked out. So Groucho replied:

Dear Warners:

There isn't much I can tell you about the story. In it I play a Doctor of Divinity who ministers to the natives and, as a sideline, hawks can openers and pea jackets to the savages along the Gold Coast of Africa.

When I first meet Chico, he is working in a saloon, selling sponges to barflies who are unable to carry their liquor. Harpo is an Arabian caddie who lives in a small Grecian urn on the outskirts of the city.

As the picture opens, Porridge, a mealy-mouthed native girl, is sharpening some arrows for the hunt. Paul Hangover, our hero, is constantly lighting two cigarettes simultaneously. He apparently is unaware of the cigarette shortage.

There are many scenes of splendor and fierce antagonisms, and Color, an Abyssinian messenger boy, runs Riot. Riot, in case you have never been there, is a small night club on the edge of town.

There's a lot more I could tell you, but I don't want to spoil it for you. All this has been okayed by the Hays Office, Good Housekeeping and the survivors of the Haymarket Riots; and if the times are ripe, this picture can be the opening gun in a new worldwide disaster.

Cordially,
Groucho Marx

> Instead of mollifying them, this note seemed to puzzle the attorneys even more; they wrote back and said they still didn't understand the story line and they would appreciate it if Mr Marx would explain the plot in more detail. So Groucho obliged with the following:

Dear Brothers:

Since I last wrote you, I regret to say there have been some changes in the plot of our new picture, 'A Night in Casablanca'. In the new version I play Bordello, the sweetheart of Humphrey Bogart. Harpo and Chico are itinerant rug peddlers who are weary of laying rugs and enter a monastery just for a lark. This is a good joke on them, as there hasn't been a lark in the place for fifteen years.

Across from this monastery, hard by a jetty, is a waterfront hotel, chockfull of apple-cheeked damsels, most of whom have been barred by the Hays Office for soliciting. In the fifth reel, Gladstone makes a speech that sets the House of Commons in a uproar and the King promptly asks for his resignation. Harpo marries a hotel detective; Chico operates an ostrich farm. Humphrey Bogart's girl, Bordello, spends her last year in a Bacall house.

This, as you can see, is a very skimpy outline. The only thing that can save us from extinction is a continuation of the film shortage.

Fondly,
Groucho Marx

> After that, the Marxes heard no more from the Warner Brothers' legal department.

The Luck of the Irish

Bernard Levin

Friday, October 31st

This must be the fourteenth time I have been to Wexford. The thirteenth? The fifteenth? Just as, at Wexford itself, the days and nights blur into each other with less distinction made between them than at any other place on earth with the exception of Las Vegas, so memories of my annual visits have become one extended memory. It is not just a matter of assigning particular moments to particular years, like Americans, back home after doing Europe in three weeks, unable to agree whether the place with the Eiffel Tower was Brussels or London; I have long since stopped trying to remember which was The Year of the Grape-Lady, The Year of the Police Raid, The Year of the Disastrous *Oberon*, The Year There Was No Boat.

But I can remember at once that 1979 was The Year of the Missing Lemon Juice. The Theatre Royal in Wexford holds 440; it was completely full that night, so there are, allowing for a few who have already died (it is not true, though it might well have been, that some died of laughter at the time), hardly more than four hundred people who now share, to the end of their lives, an experience from which the rest of the world, now and for ever, is excluded. When the last of us dies, the experience will die with us, for although it is already enshrined in legend, no one who was not an eye witness will ever really understand what we felt. Certainly I am aware that these words cannot convey more than the facts, and the facts, as so often and most particularly in this case, are only part, and a small part, too, of the whole truth. But I must try.

The opera that night was *La Vestale*, by Spontini. It has been described as 'a poor man's *Norma*', since it tells, in music and drama much inferior to Bellini's, of a vestal virgin who betrays her charge for love. It was revived for Maria Callas, but otherwise figures rarely in the repertoire of the world's leading opera houses. But it is part of Wexford's business to revive operas which other opera houses and festivals unjustly neglect, and I have been repeatedly surprised in a most pleasant manner to discover much of interest and pleasure in some of them; Lalo's *Le Roi d'Ys*, for instance, or Prokoviev's *The Gambler*, or Bizet's *Les Pêcheurs des Perles*. (The Year of the Disastrous *Oberon* was a notable exception, though even then mainly because of the terrible production rather than the opera itself. The Year of the Grape-Lady was the year I found myself lolling in an armchair after a gigantic lunch, while the most beautiful woman in Ireland dropped luscious black grapes, one by one, into my mouth. The Year There Was No Boat was the year in which Mr Fletcher, who runs the lunch-cruising excursion from nearby New Ross was refitting his vessel and therefore not operating the cruise. Of The Year of the Police Raid I shall speak in due course.)

Well, in 1979 it was *La Vestale*. The set of Act I of the opera consisted of a platform laid over the stage, raised about a foot at the back and sloping evenly to the footlights. This was meant to represent the interior of the Temple where burned the sacred flame, and had therefore to look like marble; the designer had achieved a convincing alternative by covering the raised stage in Formica. But the Formica was slippery; to avoid the risk of a performer taking a tumble, designer and stage manager had between them discovered that an ample sprinkling of lemon juice would make the surface sufficiently sticky to provide a secure foothold. The story now forks; down one road there lies the belief that the member of the stage staff whose duty it was to sprinkle the lifesaving liquid, and who had done so without fail at rehearsal and at the earlier performances (this was the last one of the Festival), had simply forgotten. Down the other branch in the road is a much more attractive rumour: that the theatre charlady, inspecting the premises in the afternoon, had seen to her horror and indignation that the stage was covered in the remains of some spilt liquid, and, inspired by professional pride, had thereupon set to and given it a good scrub and polish all over.

The roads now join again, for apart from the superior charm of the second version, it makes no difference what the explanation was. What matters is what happened.

What happened began to happen very early. The hero of the opera strides on to the stage immediately after the curtain has gone up. The hero strode; and instantly fell flat on his back. There was a murmur of sympathy and concern from the audience for his embarrassment and for the possibility that he might have been hurt; it was the last such sound that was to be heard that night and it was very soon to be replaced by sounds of a very different nature.

The hero got to his feet, with considerable difficulty, and, having slid some way down the stage in falling, proceeded to stride up-stage to where he should have been in the first place; he had, of course, gone on singing throughout, for the music had not stopped. Striding upstage, however, was plainly more difficult than he had reckoned on, for every time he took a step and tried to follow it with another, the foot with which he had taken the first proceeded to slide down-stage again, swiftly followed by its companion: he may not have known it but he was giving a perfect demonstration of what is called *marcher sur place*, a graceful manoeuvre normally used in mime, and seen at its best in the work of Marcel Marceau.

Finding progress uphill difficult, indeed impossible, the hero wisely decided to abandon the attempt and stay where he was, singing bravely on, no doubt calculating that, since the stage was brightly lit, the next character to enter would notice him and adjust his own movements accordingly. So it proved, in a sense at least, for the next character to enter was the hero's trusted friend and confidant, who, seeing his hero further down-stage than he was supposed to be, loyally decided to join him there. Truth to tell, he had little choice, for from the moment he had stepped on to the stage he had begun to slide downhill, arms semaphoring, like Scrooge's clerk on the way home to his Christmas dinner. His downhill progress was arrested by his fetching up against his friend with a thud; this, as it happened, was not altogether inappropriate, as the opera called for them to embrace in friendly greeting at that point. It did not, however, call for them, locked in each other's arms and propelled by the impetus of the friend's descent, to career helplessly further down-stage with the evident intention of going straight into the orchestra pit with vocal accompaniment – for the hero's aria had, on the arrival of his companion, been transformed into a duet.

On the brink of ultimate disaster they managed to arrest their joint progress to destruction and, working their way along the edge of the stage like mountaineers seeking a route round an unbridgeable crevasse, most gallantly began, with infinite pain and by a form of progress most aptly described in the title of Lenin's famous pamphlet, *Four Steps Forward, Three Steps Back*, to climb up the terrible hill. It speedily became clear that the hazardous ascent was not being made simply from a desire to retain dramatic credibility; it had a much more practical object. The only structure breaking the otherwise all too smooth surface of the stage was a marble pillar, a yard or so high, on which there burned the sacred flame of the rite. This pillar was embedded firmly in the stage, and it had obviously occurred to both mountaineers at once that if they could only reach it it would provide a secure base for their subsequent operations, since if they held on to it for dear life they would at any rate be safe from any further danger of sliding downhill and/or breaking their necks.

It was soon borne in upon them that they had undertaken a labour of truly Sisyphean proportions, and would have been most heartily pardoned by the audience if they had abandoned the librettist's words at this point, and fitted to the music instead the old moral verse:

> *The heights by great men reached and kept,*
> *Were not attained by sudden flight;*
> *But they, while their companions slept,*
> *Were toiling upwards in the night.*

By this time the audience – all 440 of us – were in a state of such abandon with laughter that several of us felt that if this were to continue a moment longer we would be in danger of doing ourselves a serious internal mischief; little did we know that the fun was just beginning, for shortly after Mallory and Irvine reached their longed-for goal, the chorus entered, and instantly flung themselves *en masse* into a very freely choreographed version of *Les Patineurs*, albeit to the wrong music. The heroine herself, the priestess Giulia, with a survival instinct strong enough to suggest that she would be the one to get close to should any reader of these lines happen to be shipwrecked along with the Wexford opera company, skated into the wings and kicked her shoes off and then, finding on her return that this had hardly improved matters, skated back to the wings and removed her tights as well.

Now, however, the singing never having stopped for a moment, the chorus had come to the same conclusion as had the hero and his friend, namely that holding on to the holy pillar was the only way to remain upright and more or less immobile. The trouble with this conclusion was that there was only one such pillar on the stage, and it was a small one; as the cast crowded round it, it seemed that there would be some very unseemly brawling among those seeking a hand-hold, a foothold, even a bare finger-hold, on this tiny island of security in the terrible sea of impermanence. By an instinctive understanding of the principles of co-operation, however, they decided the matter without bloodshed; those nearest the pillar clutched it, those next nearest clutched the clutchers, those farther away still clutched those, and so on until, in a kind of daisy-chain that snaked across the stage, everybody was accommodated.

The condition of the audience was now one of fully extended hysteria, which was having the most extraordinary effect – itself intensifying the audience's condition – on the orchestra. At Wexford, the orchestra pit runs under the stage; only a single row of players – those at the edge of the pit nearest the audience, together, of course, with the conductor – could see what was happening on the stage. The rest realized that *something* out of the ordinary was going on up there, and would have been singularly dull of wit if they had not, for many members of the audience were now slumped on the floor weeping helplessly, in the agony of their mirth, and although the orchestra at Wexford cannot see the stage, it can certainly see the auditorium.

Theologians tell us that the delights of the next world are eternal. Perhaps; but what is certain is that all earthly ones, alas, are temporary, and duly, after giving us a glimpse of the more enduring joy of Heaven that must have strengthened the devout in their faith and caused instant conversion among many of the unbelievers, the entertainment came to an end when the first act of the opera did so, amid such cheering as I had never before heard in an opera house, and can never hope to hear again. In the interval before Act II, a member of the production staff walked back and forth across the stage, sprinkling it with the precious nectar, and we knew that our happiness was at an end. But he who, after such happiness, would have demanded more, would be greedy indeed, and most of us were content to know that, for one crowded half-hour, we on honeydew had fed, and drunk the milk of Paradise.

Henry VIII and Elizabeth I

Will Cuppy

Henry VIII was married six times and was called the Defender of the Faith or Old Pudding-Face.[1] He was passionately fond of sweets. He would also eat roast bustard, barbecued porpoises, quince preserves, and boiled carp.

Either you like Henry VIII or you don't. He has been much criticized for beheading two of his wives.[2] In a way, he has only himself to blame. Any man who beheads two of his wives must expect a little talk. He shouldn't have done it, but you know how those things are. As a matter of fact, Henry merely let the law take its course, but some people feel that a really thoughtful husband would have done something about it.

Besides, he let some of them live, for those were the days of chivalry, when knighthood was in flower.

Henry VIII had so many wives because his dynastic sense was very strong whenever he saw a maid of honor.[3] The maids of honor were supposed to employ their time at needlework, but few of them took it seriously.

Henry's first wife was Catherine of Aragon, who was not much fun. She was rather glum and aloof, and she was always mending. Her only child was Bloody Mary, who was nothing to brag of – she wore mittens and had neuralgic headaches.

Catherine of Aragon was one of the most virtuous women who ever lived and she didn't mind saying so. Henry often told her to get the hell out, but she couldn't understand English. She seldom smiled.[4] Later on, she became

---

[1] As time went on, he came to resemble a pudding.

[2] He beheaded only two out of six, or thirty-three and a third per cent. That's not a bad average, considering.

[3] The regulations of the house read that 'officers of the chamber will not caress the maids on the stairs, as many household utensils are apt to be broken as a result.' This did not apply to Henry.

[4] Why should she? The joke was on her.

contumacious and was declared null and void *ab initio*. She had been sort of wished on him, anyway.[5]

Anne Boleyn was younger and prettier and she was not aloof.[6] She was very witty and quick at repartée. That sort of thing is all right for a while, but it seldom pays in the long run. Strangely enough, she wore black satin nightgowns lined with black taffeta and stiffened with buckram.[7] She gave birth to Queen Elizabeth in 1533 and was beheaded by an elegant, two-handed broadsword.

Professor Pollard says of Anne: 'Her place in English history is due solely to the circumstance that she appealed to the less refined part of Henry's nature.' There you have it.[8]

The rest of Henry's wives were run-of-the-mill. Jane Seymour had Edward VI and died of excitement. Anne of Cleves had been much admired in the Low Countries, but in England she just wouldn't do. The way she got herself up, they thought she was playing charades.[9] Anne of Cleves couldn't play or sing like Anne Boleyn. She could only spin, and nobody asked her to spin. Henry had seen her portrait by Holbein. She was a picture bride.[10] Cromwell, who had helped arrange the wedding, was beheaded nineteen days after the divorce.[11] After the divorce, she became twice as beautiful as before, but she was still very plain. She never married again. She'd had enough.

Catherine Howard was beheaded for committing high treason with Francis Dereham and Thomas Culpepper.[12] When Henry heard of her treason, he burst into tears. I guess he was pretty discouraged.

Henry didn't give them much warning. It was all over before they knew it.

Catherine Parr didn't matter. She never committed even low treason.[13]

In his youth Henry VIII was exceptionally handsome. At the age of

---

[5] *Catherine of Aragon was largely responsible for the revival of horticulture in England.*

[6] *He married her because she was different. But she was too different.*

[7] *Chamberlin states that at night nearly all retired nude, except the very highest, who had only then begun to wear any night clothing at all. Henry's habits in this respect can easily be imagined.*

[8] *In London, not so long ago, the County Council rejected the suggestion that a new street be named after Anne Boleyn. Dr Emil Davies said that young ladies of today might be stimulated to ask who she was, and 'who knows what consequences might ensue?'*

[9] *She may have been.*

[10] *It didn't look much like her, actually.*

[11] *Henry should have beheaded Holbein instead.*

[12] *Henry gave her twenty-three quilts before they were married. Subtle, wasn't he?*

[13] *She must have been pretty smart. She outlived him.*

twenty-three he was six feet two in height and his waist measured thirty-five inches. At the age of fifty his waist measured fifty-four inches, if you can call that a waist. His armchair was simply enormous.[14]

He was fond of tennis and pole vaulting and wrestling and jousting, and he always won because he made his rules as he went along.[15] He finally developed athlete's head.

Being a Tudor, Henry dressed somewhat flashily, running to white satin, purple velvet, and a funny hat with an ostrich feather drooping over one side.[16] On special occasions he wore gold brocade lined with ermine and embroidered with jeweled rosebuds.[17] Henry even draped his horses in cloth of gold. Cardinal Wolsey draped his mule in plain crimson velvet – and quite good enough, too.

Henry legally murdered more than 72,000 people – mostly thieves. He dropped them into boiling water.[18]

Some historians attempt to make Henry out a great statesman. So far as I am concerned, these gentlemen are simply wasting their time. For my money, Henry was a clothhead. You ought to hear what Martin Luther called him.[19]

Henry loved both music and noise. He once bought himself a whistle – an enormous gold whistle, with jewels as big as warts – and hung it on a thick gold chain. On this 'he blew near as loud as a trumpet or clarinet.' He also delighted the Marines by going down to the docks and having the guns fired for him.[20]

As a husband, Henry left something to be desired. But why pick on the poor man now?[21]

It must be remembered that Henry could do entirely as he pleased. He liked gin 'marvelously well.'

---

[14] *Some of Henry's peculiarities may be traced to the amount of boiled cabbage he ate.*

[15] *He was especially fond of dressing up in armor and beating the Duke of Suffolk over the head with a heavy spear.*

[16] *He wore a baldric across his shoulder, composed of precious stones and pearls.*

[17] *He had a train four yards long. Knights of the Bath were permitted to wear violet gowns and hoods purfled with miniver.*

[18] *It was so much cheaper than boiling oil.*

[19] *Henry wrote a book on Luther. In his reply, Luther went so far as to call Henry a fool and an ass, among other things.*

[20] *Henry established the British Navy and promptly had a sailor's suit made for himself, of cloth of gold.*

[21] *One of Henry's love letters reads: 'I wolde we wer to gyder an evennyng.' The man had a soul – you have to say that for him.*

At first thought, it seems most unlikely that Henry would have a granduncle named Jasper. But he did.[22]

At his death, Henry left at Westminster Palace alone 'fifteen regalles, two clavicordes, thirty-one vyrginalles, twelve violins, five guitars, two cornettes, twenty-six lutes, sixty-two flutes, eleven phiphes, thirteen crumhornes, thirteen dulceriths, seventy-eight recorders, seventeen halmes, and five bagpipes.' I wonder whatever happened to the whistle?

Queen Elizabeth was the daughter of Henry VIII and Anne Boleyn. She resembled her father in some respects, although she beheaded no husbands. As she had no husbands, she was compelled to behead outsiders.

She never intended to behead Mary Queen of Scots and the Earl of Essex, but somehow she did.[23] Mary Queen of Scots was very beautiful, but Queen Elizabeth was not so bad herself at one time. Many people believe that Elizabeth was always a hatchet-faced old lady in a red wig. She was no such thing. She was once sweet sixteen and rather good-looking.[24]

During part of her childhood, Elizabeth was illegitimate. In 1534, Parliament ruled that it was treason to believe her illegitimate. In 1536, it was treason to believe her legitimate. Signals were changed again in 1543, and again in 1553. After that you could believe anything.

Queen Elizabeth was called the Virgin Queen or Good Queen Bess because that is what she was. She was the most intelligent woman of her day and she refused to get married in nine languages. She loved being proposed to, but something was wrong with all of her men.

Besides, she wanted to be loved for herself alone. There *was* no such thing in those days.

Queen Elizabeth had a quick temper because her endocrine balance was all upset. She hated dentists, long sermons, Lettice Knollys, and the Countess of Shrewsbury. She liked presents, flattery, dancing, swearing, prevaricating, bear-baiting, succory pottage, ale, beer, and Masters of the Horse.

Leicester and Essex were Masters of the Horse.[25] Essex had very long legs and a slender waist and a smallish head. He wore a number-six hat. He was a Cambridge man. Essex thought he could do something about Ireland, but nothing can be done about Ireland.

---

[22] *He had an Aunt Cicely, too.*
[23] *She was funny that way.*
[24] *It shows what can happen.*
[25] *It was the duty of Masters of the Horse to remain within calling distance at all times.*

Sir Walter Raleigh wore a plush cape and was very polite.[26] He sent a colony to North Carolina, but the people there were so awful that it moved away.[27]

Prince Eric of Sweden courted Queen Elizabeth for years, but she did not believe in Swedish entanglements. She could not speak Swedish and refused to learn.[28] Eric sent her eighteen large pie-bald horses, but it was no use. Later on, Eric proposed to Mary Queen of Scots and married Kate the Nut Girl and came to no good. Ivan the Terrible also proposed to Queen Elizabeth.[29]

Queen Elizabeth was rather a flirt all her life. She finally developed a bad habit of boxing her partners' ears and shouting, 'God's death, I'll have thy head!' This discouraged some of her more sensitive partners.[30]

Queen Elizabeth's subjects were called Elizabethans. They could not spell.[31] Most of the Elizabethans were armorers, pewterers, cofferers, girdlers, fellmongers, and stringers. The others were whifflers and underskinkers. There were about four million of these.

The Elizabethans exported large quantities of wool to Flanders, and nobody knows what became of it. They also robbed the Spaniards and converted the heathen and defeated the Spanish Armada to prove they were right in the first place. The Poor Law was passed in 1601, making it a crime for poor people to have no visible means of support.[32]

Elizabeth's main interests were clothes and gifts from friends and acquaintances.[33] To Good Queen Bess of England, New Year's Day was the big event of the calendar, for word had gone around that she expected plenty of presents – and guess who started the rumor. She never failed to cash in heavily. Elizabeth loved to get jewels by the quart, just to start the year

[26] *If he did throw his plush cape on a mud puddle at Elizabeth's feet, it wasn't much of a sacrifice. He had plenty of plush capes.*

[27] *Sir Walter Raleigh did not introduce tobacco to Europe. But he did bring back with him from America the Irish potato, which came from Bermuda. He also cornered the sassafras market.*

[28] *At sixteen she spoke French and Italian, as well as English, Latin with fluency, and Greek moderately well.*

[29] *He never knew what he missed.*

[30] *She was punished in her last few years by having to flirt with Robert Cecil.*

[31] *On gala occasions they liked to dress as wild men clad in ivy with decorations of clusters of ripe hazelnuts.*

[32] *Under the Poor Law, rogues and vagabonds were whipped. In those days it was very easy to tell rogues and vagabonds from other people.*

[33] *She even accepted presents from people she beheaded later on.*

right, but she would accept anything, any time, whether it was eighteen horses from Eric XIV of Sweden, several camels from Catherine de' Medici, three nightcaps from her imprisoned cousin, Mary Queen of Scots, six embroidered handkerchiefs from a Mrs Huggins, or small donations of money from Tom, Dick, and Harry.[34] What's more, on a visit to the Lord Keeper, in 1595, after she had been loaded with costly gifts, she made off as well with 'a salt, a spoon, and a fork, of fair agate.' One of her little jokes, no doubt.[35]

She wrote to Mary Queen of Scots: 'When people arrive at my age, they take all they can get, with both hands, and only give with their little finger.'[36]

Elizabeth had a constant urge for new, more extravagant clothes. As a child she never had many changes. When she was nearly seventy, she had three thousand gowns and eighty wigs of different-colored hair.[37]

When she really got in stride, she got herself up in everything she could lay her hands on. She wore a bushel of pearls and, according to Horace Walpole, 'a vast ruff and a vaster farthingale.'[38]

It was only natural, I suppose, that with all the ornaments she wore some would fall off en route. On January 17, 1568, she lost her first gold aglet, at Westminster. In June, she dropped four jeweled buttons. On November 17, she lost a golden eft. And on September 3, 1574, she missed a small, diamond-encrusted golden fish, off her hat.[39] She dropped a quart or so of pearls through the years. You'd think she'd have sewed them on better.

Her clothes were Elizabeth's most prized possessions, and when she felt like it she would show some of them off. She once showed Monsieur de Maise, the French Ambassador, how her gown opened down the front.[40] She couldn't open the collar.

On another occasion, she showed her silk stockings to Monsieur Beaumont, another French Ambassador.[41] French ambassadors seemed to bring Queen

---

[34] *Elizabeth was always hinting about presents. She usually got results. If not, she'd hint some more, a little more broadly.*

[35] *The Lord Keeper's gifts were a fan, some diamond pendants, a gown, a jupon, and a pair of virginals. This was what we know as the virginal, or spinet. She played pretty well, for a queen.*

[36] *You could usually get round her by giving her a casket of jewels. If that didn't work, two caskets generally would.*

[37] *She was bald as a coot.*

[38] *She inspired the saying: She had everything on but the Tower of London.*

[39] *After that, she stopped keeping track. So have I.*

[40] *He saw* tout l'estomac.

[41] *What did he think of them? He didn't say.*

Elizabeth out of herself.

Elizabeth wasn't the first ruler of England to own a pair of silk stockings. Henry VIII and Edward VI each had some. She *was* the first Queen of England to have them.

Queen Bess liked to have men around the court; she thought they sort of cheered things up. When she first met Essex, in 1587, she was fifty-three and he was nineteen.[42]

Others, besides Leicester, Eric, and Ivan, were Philip II of Spain, a fussbudget; Archduke Charles, whose head was too large;[43] Sir Christopher Hatton, a barrister, to whom Elizabeth once administered a posset;[44] and the Duke of Alençon and Anjou, who wore earrings and lace and was very fond of his mother, Catherine de' Medici.[45] Then there was Don John of Austria, who wrote to Philip II of Spain, his half brother: 'I blush whilst I write this, to think of accepting advances from a woman whose life and example furnished so much food for gossip.'[46] Don John was a love child himself.

Elizabeth gave Leicester a bedchamber next to hers.[47] The royal bedchamber contained a unicorn's horn, a stuffed bird of paradise, and sometimes the Master of the Horse.[48]

Elizabeth wasn't much of a gourmet, but she knew what she liked. On a visit to Colchester, she relished the oysters so greatly that they were afterwards sent for by horseloads by the Purveyors of the Royal Table. On New Year's, in addition to the usual loot, she sometimes received edible gifts – green preserved ginger, marchpane, quince pies, and perhaps some comfit cakes, of which she was especially fond.[49]

To wash it down, she preferred beer. She took wine only rarely with her meals, and then mixed with water, half and half. She was afraid she might impair her faculties and give her opponents an advantage. Her favorite tipple was mead, a mixture of honey and water, and seasoned with plenty of spices, herbs, and lemons.[50]

---

[42] *He felt he wasn't getting any younger.*

[43] *Besides, he was always broke.*

[44] *He looked like a sheep.*

[45] *He used perfume and had a thousand shirts. He wept a good deal, too.*

[46] *She really couldn't help it. She was born on September 7, 1533, making her a Virgo character.*

[47] *Some said Leicester acted as a lady-in-waiting. Could be.*

[48] *That was a cute thing to call them, anyway.*

[49] *In her last two years, she ate little but manchet and succory pottage.*

[50] *The royal mead was left to stand for three months before bottling. It was ready to slake the Queen's thirst six weeks later.*

For sheer magnificence, you can't beat the Princely Pleasures of Kenilworth, the entertainment given to Queen Elizabeth in 1575 by Robert Dudley, Earl of Leicester.[51] It cost a fortune, but the earl could well afford it, since his guest of honor, in addition to earlier presents too numerous to mention, had recently granted him emoluments worth fifty thousand pounds. Indeed, that's why he got up the party. (Can you think of a better reason?) One thing that sticks in my mind among the banquets, masques, bear-baitings, and other high jinks is the fact that during the royal splurge the folks at Kenilworth imbibed no less than three hundred and twenty hogsheads of Elizabethan beer. Good Queen Bess was rather sparing with food and drink for her time, but she could bend a royal elbow with the best. Once, after delivering an oration in faultless Latin at the University of Cambridge, she informed the chancellor in plain English that if there had been a greater provision of ale and beer she would have stayed till Friday.

Elizabeth died on March 24, 1603, in the seventieth year of her age and in the forty-fourth year of her reign.[52] She was succeeded by James I. Everything was then ready for the Gunpowder Plot, Guy Fawkes Day, the Thirty Years' War, the Authorized Version, the settlement of Virginia, cigarettes, radio, the blindfold test, and silent butlers.

[51] *Historians guess that the festivities at Kenilworth lasted anything from twelve days to three weeks.*

[52] *Lytton Strachey claims that Elizabeth succeeded as a queen, by 'dissimulation, pliability, indecision, procrastination, and parsimony.' It sounds reasonable to me.*

The Direct Orient Express

Paul Theroux

Fired by a fascination with trains that started from childhood, Paul Theroux set out one day with the intention of boarding every train that chugged into view from Victoria Station in London to Tokyo Central. And on every train there was a new, unexpected, adventure ...

Duffill had put on a pair of glasses, wire-framed and with enough Scotch tape on the lenses to prevent his seeing the Blue Mosque. He assembled his parcels and, grunting, produced a suitcase, bound with a selection of leather and canvas belts as an added guarantee against it bursting open. A few cars down we met again to read the sign on the side of the wagon-lit: DIRECT–ORIENT and its itinerary, PARIS–LAUSANNE–MILANO–TRIESTE–ZAGREB–BEOGRAD–SOFIYA–ISTANBUL. We stood there, staring at this sign; Duffill worked his glasses like binoculars. Finally he said, 'I took this train in nineteen twenty-nine.'

It seemed to call for a reply, but by the time a reply occurred to me ('Judging from its condition, it was probably this very train!') Duffill had gathered up his parcels and his strapped suitcase and moved down the platform. It was a great train in 1929, and it goes without saying that the Orient Express is the most famous train in the world. Like the Trans-Siberian, it links Europe with Asia, which accounts for some of its romance. But it has also been hallowed by fiction: restless Lady Chatterley took it; so did Hercule Poirot and James Bond; Graham Greene sent some of his prowling unbelievers on it, even before he took it himself ('As I couldn't take a train to Istanbul the best I could do was buy a record of Honegger's Pacific 231,' Greene writes in the Introduction to *Stamboul Train*). The fictional source of the romance is *La Madone des Sleepings* (1925) by Maurice Dekobra. Dekobra's heroine, Lady Diana ('the type of woman who would have brought tears to the eyes of John Ruskin'), is completely sold on the Orient Express: 'I have a ticket for Constantinople. But I may step off at Vienna or Budapest. That depends absolutely on chance or on the colour of the eyes of my neighbour in the compartment.' In the end I stopped wondering why so many writers had used this train as a setting for criminal intrigues, since in most respects the Orient Express really is murder.

My compartment was a cramped two-berth closet with an intruding ladder. I swung my suitcase in and, when I had done this, there was no room for me. The conductor showed me how to kick my suitcase under the lower berth. He hesitated, hoping to be tipped.

'Anybody else in here?' It had not occurred to me that I would have company; the conceit of the long-distance traveller is the belief that he is going so far, he will be alone – inconceivable that another person has the same good idea.

The conductor shrugged, perhaps yes, perhaps no. His vagueness made me withhold my tip. I took a stroll down the car: a Japanese couple in a double couchette – and it was the first and last time I saw them; an elderly American couple next to them; a fat French mother breathing suspicion on her lovely daughter; a Belgian girl of extraordinary size – well over six feet tall, wearing enormous shoes – travelling with a chic French woman; and (the door was shutting) either a nun or a plump diabolist. At the far end of the car a man wearing a turtleneck, a seaman's cap, and a monocle was setting up bottles on the windowsill; three wine bottles, Perrier water, a broad-shouldered bottle of gin – he was obviously going some distance.

Duffill was standing outside my compartment. He was out of breath; he had had trouble finding the right car, he said, because his French was rusty. He took a deep breath and slid off his gabardine coat and hung that and his cap on the hook next to mine.

'I'm up here,' he said, patting the upper berth. He was a small man, but I noticed that as soon as he stepped into the compartment he filled it.

'How far are you going?' I asked gamely, and even though I knew his reply, when I heard it I cringed. I had planned on studying him from a little distance; I was counting on having the compartment to myself. This was unwelcome news. He saw I was taking it badly.

He said, 'I won't get in your way.' His parcels were on the floor. 'I just have to find a home for these.'

'I'll leave you to it,' I said. The others were in the corridor waiting for the train to start. The Americans rubbed the window until they realized the dirt was on the outside; the man with the monocle peered and drank; the French woman was saying '– Switzerland.'

'Istanbul,' said the Belgian girl. She had a broad face, which a large pair of glasses only complicated, and she was a head taller than I. 'My first time.'

'I am in Istanbul two years before, said the French woman, wincing the way the French do before lapsing into their own language.

'What is it like?' asked the Belgian girl. She waited. I waited. She helped the woman. 'Very nice?'

The French woman smiled at each of us. She shook her head, and said, '*Très sale.*'

'But pretty? Old? Churches?' The Belgian girl was trying hard.

'*Sale.*' Why was she smiling?

'I am going to Izmir, Cappadocia, and –'

The French woman clucked and said, '*Sale, sale, sale.*' She went into her compartment. The Belgian girl made a face and winked at me.

The train had started to move, and at the end of the car the man in the seaman's cap was braced at his door, drinking and watching our progress. After several minutes the rest of the passengers went into their compartments – from my own I heard the smashing of paper parcels being stuffed into corners. This left the drinker, whom I had started to think of as the Captain, and me alone in the passage. He looked my way and said, 'Istanbul?'

'Yes.'

'Have a drink.'

'I've been drinking all day,' I said. 'Do you have any mineral water?'

'I do,' he said. 'But I keep it for my teeth. I never touch water on trains. Have a real drink. Go on. What will it be?'

'A beer would be nice.'

'I never drink beer,' he said. 'Have some of this.' He showed me his glass and then went to his shelf and poured me some, saying, 'It's a very drinkable Chablis, not at all chalky – the ones they export often are, you know.'

We clinked glasses. The train was now moving fast.

'Istanbul.'

'Istanbul! Right you are.'

His name was Molesworth, but he said it so distinctly that the first time I heard it I thought it was a double-barrelled name. There was something military in his posture and the promptness of his speech, and at the same time this flair could have been an actor's. He was in his indignant late fifties, and I could see him cutting a junior officer at the club – either at Aldershot or in the third act of a Rattigan play. The small glass disc he wore around his neck on a chain was not, I saw, a monocle, but rather a magnifying glass. He had used it to find the bottle of Chablis.

'I'm an actors' agent,' he said. 'I've got my own firm in London. It's a smallish firm, but we do all right. We always have more than we can handle.'

'Any actors I might know?'

He named several famous actors.

'I said, 'I thought you might be army.'

'*Did* you?' He said that he had been in the Indian army – Poona, Simla, Madras – and his duties there were of a theatrical nature, organizing shows for the troops. He had arranged Noël Coward's tour of India in 1946. He had loved the army and he said that there were many Indians who were so well bred you could treat them as absolute equals – indeed, talking to them you would hardly know you were talking to Indians.

'I knew a British officer who was in Simla in the forties,' I said. 'I met him in Kenya. His nickname was "Bunny".'

Molesworth thought a moment, then said, 'Well, I knew several Bunnys.'

We talked about Indian trains. Molesworth said they were magnificent. 'They have showers, and there's always a little man who brings you what you need. At mealtime they telegraph ahead to the next station for hampers. Oh, you'll like it.'

Duffill put his head out the door and said, 'I think I'll go to bed now.'

'He's your chap, is he?' said Molesworth. He surveyed the car. 'This train isn't what it was. Pity. It used to be one of the best, a *train de luxe* – royalty took it. Now, I'm not sure about this, but I don't think we have a dining car, which is going to be a terrible bore if it's true. Have you got a hamper?'

I said I hadn't, though I had been advised to bring one.

'That was good advice,' Molesworth said. 'I don't have a hamper myself, but then I don't eat much. I like the *thought* of food, but I much prefer drinking. How do you like your Chablis? Will you have more?' he inserted his eyeglass and found the bottle and, pouring, said, 'These French wines take an awful lot of beating.'

A half hour later I went into the compartment. The lights were blazing, and in his upper berth Duffill was sleeping; his face turned up to the overhead light gave him a grey corpselike look, and his pyjamas were buttoned to his neck. The expression on his face was one of agony; his features were fixed and his head moved as the train did. I turned out the lights and crawled into my berth. But I couldn't sleep, at first; my cold and all that I'd drunk – the fatigue itself – kept me awake. And then something else alarmed me: it was a glowing circle, the luminous dial of Duffill's watch, for his arm had slipped down and was swinging back and forth as the train rocked, moving this glowing green dial past my face like a pendulum.

Then the dial disappeared. I heard Duffill climbing down the ladder, groaning on each rung. The dial moved sideways to the sink, and then the light came on. I rolled over against the wall and heard the clunk of Duffill dislodging the chamber pot from the cupboard under the sink; I waited, and after a long moment a warbling burble began, changing in pitch as the pot filled. There was a splash, like a sigh, and the light went out and the ladder creaked. Duffill groaned one last time and I slept.

In the morning Duffill was gone. I lay in bed and worked the window curtain up with my foot; after a few inches it shot up on its roller, revealing a sunny mountainside, the Alps dappled with light and moving past the window. It was the first time I had seen the sun for days, this first morning on the train, and I think this is the place to say that it continued to shine for the next two months. I travelled under clear skies all the way to southern India, and only then, two months late, did I see rain again, the late monsoon of Madras.

At Vevey, I thought of Daisy and restored myself with a glass of fruit salts, and at Montreux felt well enough to shave. Duffill came back in time to admire my rechargeable electric razor. He said he used a blade and on trains always cut himself to pieces. He showed me a nick on his throat, then told me his name. He'd be spending two months in Turkey, but he didn't say what he'd be doing. In the bright sunlight he looked much older than he had in the greyness of Victoria. I guessed he was about seventy. But he was not in the least spry, and I could not imagine why anyone except a fleeing embezzler would spend two months in Turkey.

He looked out at the Alps. He said. 'They say if the Swiss had designed these mountains, um, they'd be rather flatter.'

I decided to have breakfast, but I walked to both ends of the Direct–Orient and saw no dining car – nothing except more sleeping cars and people dozing in their second-class seats. On my way back to Car 99 I was followed by three Swiss boys who, at each compartment door, tried the handle; if it responded they slid the door open and looked in, presumably at people dressing or lounging in bed. Then the boys called out, '*Pardon, Madame!*' '*Pardon, Monsieur!*' as the occupants hastily covered themselves. As these ingenious voyeurs reached my sleeping car they were in high spirits, hooting and shrieking, but it was always with the greatest politeness that they said, *'Pardon, Madame!'* once they got a door open. They gave a final yell and disappeared.

The door to the Americans' compartment opened. The man was out first, swinging the knot of his tie, and then the woman, feebly balancing on a cane, tottered out and followed after, bumping the windows as she went. The Alps were rising, and in the sheerest places wide-roofed chalets were planted, as close to the ground as mushrooms and clustered in the same way at various distances from gravity-defying churches. Many of the valleys were dark, the sun showing only farther up on cliff faces and at the summits. At ground level the train passed fruit farms and clean villages and Swiss cycling in kerchiefs, calendar scenes that you admire for a moment before feeling an urge to move on to a new month.

The American couple returned. The man looked in my direction and said, 'I can't find it.'

The woman said, 'I don't think we went far enough.'

'Don't be silly. That was the engine.' He looked at me. 'Did you find it?'

'What?'

'The dining car.'

'There isn't one,' I said. 'I looked.'

'Then why the hell,' the man said, only now releasing his anger, 'why the hell did they call us for breakfast?'

'Did they call you?'

'Yes. "Last call." Didn't you hear them? "Last call for breakfast," they said. That's why we hurried.'

The Swiss boys, yelling and sliding the compartment doors open, had preceded the Americans' appearance. This commotion had been interpreted as a summons to breakfast; hunger's ear is not finely tuned.

The man said, 'I hate France.'

His wife looked out the window. 'I think we're out of it. That's not France.'

'Whatever it is,' said the man. He said he wasn't too happy, and he didn't want to sound like a complainer, but he had paid twenty dollars for a taxi from the 'Lazarus to the Lions'. Then a porter had carried their two suitcases from the taxi to the platform and demanded ten dollars. He didn't want French money; he wanted ten dollars.

I said that seemed excessive and added, 'Did you pay?'

'Of course I paid,' said the man.

'I wanted him to make a fuss,' said the woman.

The man said, 'I never get into arguments with people in foreign countries.'

'We thought we were going to miss the train,' said the woman. She crackled loudly. 'I almost had a haemorrhage!'

On an empty stomach, I found this disconcerting. I was glad when the man said, 'Well, come along, mother; if we're not going to get any breakfast we might just as well head back,' and led her away.

Duffill was eating the last of his salami. He offered me some, but I said I was planning to buy my breakfast at an Italian station. Duffill lifted the piece of salami and brought it to his mouth, but just as he bit into it we entered a tunnel and everything went black.

'Try the lights,' he said. 'I can't eat in the dark. I can't taste it.'

I groped for the light switch and flicked it, but we stayed in darkness.

Duffill said, 'Maybe they're trying to save electricity.'

His voice in the darkness sounded very near to my face. I moved to the window and tried to see the tunnel walls, but I saw only blackness. The sound of the wheels' drumming seemed louder in the dark and the train itself was gathering speed, the motion and the dark producing in me a suffocating feeling of claustrophobia and an acute awareness of the smell of the room, the salami, Duffill's woollens, and bread crusts. Minutes had passed and we were still in the tunnel; we might be dropping down a well, a great sink-hole in the Alps that would land us in the clockwork interior of Switzerland, glacial cogs and ratchets and frostbitten cuckoos.

Duffill said, 'This must be the Simplon.'

I said, 'I wish they'd turn the lights on.'

I heard Duffill wrapping his uneaten salami and punching the parcel into a corner.

I said, 'What do you aim to do in Turkey?'

'Me?' Duffill said, as if the compartment was crammed with old men bound for Turkey, each waiting to state a reason. He paused, then said, 'I'll be in Istanbul for a while. After that I'll be travelling around the country.'

'Business or pleasure?' I was dying to know and in the confessional darkness did not feel so bad about badgering him; he could not see the eagerness on my face. On the other hand, I could hear the tremulous hesitation in his replies.

'A little of both,' he said.

This was not helpful. I waited for him to say more, but when he added nothing further, I said, 'What exactly do you do, Mr Duffill?'

'Me?' he said again, but before I could reply with the sarcasm he was pleading for, the train left the tunnel and the compartment filled with sunlight and Duffill said, 'This must be Italy.'

Duffill put on his tweed cap. He saw me staring at it and said, 'I've had this cap for years – eleven years. You dry clean it. Bought it in Barrow-on-Humber.' And he dug out his parcel of salami and resumed the meal the Simplon tunnel had interrupted.

At 9.35 we stopped at the Italian station of Domodossola, where a man poured cups of coffee from a jug and sold food from a heavily laden pushcart. He had fruit, loaves of bread and rolls, various kinds of salami, and lunch bags that, he said, contained '*tante belle cose*'. He also had a stock of wine. Molesworth bought a Bardolino and ('just in case') three bottles of Chianti; I bought an Orvieto and a Chianti; and Duffill had his hand on a bottle of claret.

Molesworth said, 'I'll take these back to the compartment. Get me a lunch bag, will you?'

I bought two lunch bags and some apples.

Duffill said, 'English money, I only have English money.'

The Italian snatched a pound from the old man and gave him change in lire.

Molesworth came back and said, 'Those apples want washing. There's cholera here.' He looked again at the pushcart and said, 'I think *two* lunch bags, just to be safe.'

While Molesworth bought more food and another bottle of Bardolino, Duffill said, 'I took this train in nineteen twenty-nine.'

'It was worth taking then,' said Molesworth. 'Yes, she used to be quite a train.'

'How long are we staying here?' I asked.

No one knew. Molesworth called out to the train guard, 'I say, George, how long are we stopping for?'

The guard shrugged, and as he did so the train began to back up.

'Do you think we should board?' I asked.

'It's going backwards,' said Molesworth. 'I expect they're shunting.'

The train guard said, '*Andiamo.*'

'The Italians love wearing uniforms,' said Molesworth. 'Look at him, will you? And the uniforms are always so wretched. They really are like overgrown schoolboys. Are you talking to us, George?'

'I think he wants us to board,' I said. The train stopped going backwards.

I hopped aboard and looked down. Molesworth and Duffill were at the bottom of the stairs.

'You've got parcels,' said Duffill. 'You go first.'

'I'm quite all right,' said Molesworth. 'Up you go.'

'But you've got parcels,' said Duffill. He produced a pipe from his coat and began sucking on the stem. 'Carry on.' He moved back and gave Molesworth room.

Molesworth said, 'Are you sure?'

Duffill said, 'I didn't go all the way, then, in nineteen twenty-nine. I didn't do that until after the second war.' He put his pipe in his mouth and smiled.

Molesworth stepped aboard and climbed up – slowly, because he was carrying a bottle of wine and his second lunch bag. Duffill grasped the rails beside the door and as he did so the train began to move and he let go. He dropped his arms. Two train guards rushed behind him and held his arms and hustled him along the platform to the moving stairs of Car 99. Duffill, feeling the Italians' hands, resisted the embrace, went feeble, and stepped back; he made a half-turn to smile wanly at the fugitive door. He looked a hundred years old. The train was moving swiftly past his face.

'George!' cried Molesworth. 'Stop the train!'

I was leaning out the door. I said, 'He's still on the platform.'

There were two Italians beside us, the conductor and a bed-maker. Their shoulders were poised, preparing to shrug.

'Pull the emergency cord!' said Molesworth.

'No, no, no, no,' said the conductor. 'If I pull that I must pay five thousand lire. Don't touch!'

'Is there another train?' I asked.

'*Si*,' said the bed-maker in a tone of irritation. 'He can catch us in Milano.'

'What time does the next train get to Milano?' I asked.

'Two o'clock.'

'When do we get to Milano?'

'One o'clock,' said the conductor. 'We leave at two.'

'Well, how the hell–'

'The old man can take a car,' explained the bed-maker. 'Don't worry, He hires a taxi at Domodossola; the taxi goes *varooom*! He's in Milano before us!'

Molesworth said, 'These chaps could use a few lessons in how to run a railroad.'

The meal that followed the abandoning of Duffill only made that point plainer. It was a picnic in Molesworth's compartment; we were joined by the Belgian girl, Monique, who brought her own cheese. She asked for mineral water and got Molesworth's reprimand: 'Sorry, I keep that for my teeth.' We sat shoulder to shoulder on Molesworth's bed, gloomily picking through our lunch bags.

'I wasn't quite prepared for this,' said Molesworth. 'I think each country should have its own dining car. Shunt it on at the frontier and serve slap-up meals.' He nibbled a hard-boiled egg and said, 'Perhaps we should get together and write a letter to Cook's.'

The Orient Express, once unique for its service, is now unique among trains for its lack of it. The Indian Rajdhani Express serves curries in its dining car, and so does the Pakistani Khyber Mail; the Meshed Express serves Iranian chicken kebab, and the train to Sapporo in Northern Japan smoked fish and glutinous rice. Box lunches are sold at the station in Rangoon, and Malaysian Railways always include a dining car that resembles a noodle stall, where you can buy *mee-hoon* soup; and Amtrak, which I had always thought to be the worst railway in the world, serves hamburgers on the James Whitcomb Riley (Washington–Chicago). Starvation takes the fun out of travel, and from this point of view the Orient Express is more inadequate than the poorest Madrasi train, where you exchange stained lunch coupons for a tin tray of vegetables and a quart of rice.

Monique said, 'I hope he takes a taxi.'

'Poor old chap,' said Molesworth. 'He panicked, you see. Started going backwards. "You've got parcels," he said, "you go first." He might have got on if he hadn't panicked. Well, we'll see if he gets to Milan. He should do. What worries me is that he might have had a heart attack. He didn't look well, did he? Did you get his name?'

'Duffill,' I said.

'Duffill,' said Molesworth. 'If he's got any sense at all, he'll sit down and have a drink. Then he'll get a taxi to Milan. It's not far, but if he panics again he's lost.'

We went on eating and drinking. If there had been a dining car we would have had a simple meal and left it at that. Because there was no dining car we ate all the way to Milan, the fear of hunger producing a hunger of its own. Monique said we were like Belgians, who ate constantly.

It was after one o'clock when we arrived at Milan. There was no sign of Duffill either on the platform or in the crowded waiting room. The station, modelled on a cathedral, had high vaulted ceilings, and simple signs like USCITA gained the metaphorical quality of religious mottoes from their size and dramatic purpose than to provide roosts for brooding stone eagles that looked too fat to fly. We bought more lunch bags, another bottle of wine, and the *Herald Tribune.*

'Poor old chap,' said Molesworth, looking around for Duffill.

'Doesn't look as if he's going to make it.'

'They warn you about that, don't they? Missing the train. You think it's shunting, but really it's on its way. The Orient Express especially. There was something in the *Observer* about it. Everyone misses it. It's famous for that.'

At Car 99, Molesworth said, 'I think we'd better get aboard. I know *I* don't want to be duffilled.'

Now, as we travelled to Venice, there was no hope for Duffill. There wasn't the slightest chance of his catching up with us. We finished another bottle of wine and I went to my compartment. Duffill's suitcase, shopping bag, and paper parcels were piled in a corner. I sat down and looked out the window, resisting the urge to rummage through Duffill's effects for a clue to his going to Turkey. It had grown hotter; the corn fields were baked yellow and strewn with shocks and stubble. Beyond Brescia, the shattered windows in a row of houses gave me a headache. Moments later, drugged by the Italian heat, I was asleep.

Venice, like a drawing room in a gas station, is approached through a vast apron of infertile industrial flatlands, criss-crossed with black sewer troughs and stinking of oil, the gigantic sinks and stoves of refineries and factories, all intimidating the delicate dwarfed city beyond. The graffiti along the way are professionally executed as the names of the firms: MOTTA GELATI, LOTTA COMMUNISTA, AGIP, NOI SIAMO TUTTI ASSASSINI, RENAULT, UNITA. The lagoon with its luminous patches of oil slick, as if hopelessly retouched by Canaletto, has a yard-wide tidewrack of rubble, plastic bottles, broken toilet seats, raw sewage, and that bone white factory froth the wind beats into drifts of foam. The edges of the city have succumbed to industry's erosion, and what shows are the cracked back windows and derelict posterns of water-logged villas, a few brittle Venetian steeples, and farther in, but low and almost visibly sinking, walls of spaghetti-coloured stucco and red roofs over which flocks of soaring swallows are teaching pigeons to fly.

'Here we are, mother.' The elderly American man was helping his wife down the stairs, and a porter half-carried her the rest of the way to the platform. Oddly appropriate, this couple who had seen Venice in better days: now the city and its visitors were enfeebled, suffering the fatal poisoning of the age. But Mrs Ketchum (for that was her name: it was the very last thing she told me) looked wounded; she walked with pain, using joints that had turned to stone, leaning on her stick. The Ketchums would be going to Istanbul in a few days, though it struck me as foolhardy, to say the least, for them to carry their feebleness from one remote country to another.

I handed over Duffill's violated belongings to the Venetian *Controllare* and asked him to contact Milan and reassure Duffill. he said he would, but spoke with the kind of Italianate carelessness that mocks trust. I demanded a receipt. This he provided, showing me his sour resignation as he slowly and distastefully itemized Duffill's parcels on the chit. As soon as we left Venice I clawed it to pieces and threw it out the window. I had asked for it only to chasten him.

At Trieste, Molesworth discovered that the Italian conductor had mistakenly torn all the tickets from his Cook's wallet. The Italian conductor was in Venice, leaving Molesworth no ticket for Istanbul, or, for that matter, Yugoslavia. But Molesworth stayed calm. He said his strategy in such a situation was to say he had no money and knew only English: 'That puts the ball in their court.'

But the new conductor was persistent. He hung by the door of Molesworth's compartment. He said, 'You no ticket.' Molesworth didn't reply. He poured himself a glass of wine and sipped it. 'You no ticket.'

'Your mistake, George.'

'You,' said the conductor. He waved a ticket at Molesworth. 'You *no* ticket.'

'Sorry, George,' said Molesworth, still drinking. 'You'll have to phone Cook's.'

'You no ticket. You pay.'

'I no pay. No money.' Molesworth frowned and said to me, 'I do wish he'd go away.'

'You cannot go.'

'I go.'

'No ticket! No go!'

'Good God,' said Molesworth. This argument went on for some time. Molesworth was persuaded to go into Trieste Station. The conductor began to perspire. He explained the situation to the stationmaster, who stood up and left his office; he did not return. Another official was found. 'Look at the uniform,' said Molesworth. 'Absolutely wretched.' That official tried to phone Venice. He rattled the pins with a stumpy finger and said, '*Pronto! Pronto!*' But the phone was out of order.

Finally Molesworth said, 'I give up. Here – here's some money.' He flourished a handful of 10,000 lire notes. 'I buy a new ticket.'

The conductor reached for the money. Molesworth withdrew it as the conductor snatched.

'Now look, George,' said Molesworth. 'You get me a ticket, but before you do that, you sit down and write me an endorsement so I can get money back. Is that clear?'

But all Molesworth said when we were again underway was, 'I think they're all very naughty.'

At Seẑana, on the Yugoslav border, they were very naughty, too. Yugoslav policemen with puffy faces and black belts crossed on their chests crowded the train corridor and examined passports. I showed mine. The policeman pawed it, licked his thumb, and wiped at pages, leaving damp smudges, until he found my visa. He passed it back to me. I tried to step by him to retrieve my wine glass from Molesworth's compartment. The policeman spread his fingers on my chest and gave me a shove; seeing me stumble backwards he smiled, lifting his lips over his terrible teeth.

'You can imagine how these Jug policemen behave in third class.' said Molesworth, in a rare display of social conscience.

'"And still she cried and still the world pursues,"' I said, '"'Jug Jug' to dirty ears." Who says *The Waste Land's* irrelevant?'

'Jug' seemed uncannily exact, for outside the train little Jugs frolicked on the tracks, big parental Jugs crouched in rows, balanced on suitcases, and uniformed Jugs with leather pouches and truncheons strolled, smoking evil-smelling cigarettes with the apt brand name, 'Stop!'

More passengers had installed themselves in Car 99 at Venice: an American lady from Turkey (with a sister in Watertown, Massachusetts), who was travelling with her son – each time I talked to this pretty woman the boy burst into tears, until I got the message and went away; an Italian nun with the face of a Roman emperor and traces of a moustache; Enrico, the nun's brother, who was now in Duffill's berth; three Turkish men, who somehow managed to sleep in two berths; and a doctor from Verona.

The doctor, a cancer specialist on his way to a cancer conference in Belgrade, made a play for Monique, who, in an effort to divert the man, brought him to Molesworth's compartment for a drink. The man sulked until the conversation turned to cancer; then like William Burroughs' Doctor

Benway ('Cancer! My first love!'), he became quite companionable as he summarized the paper he was going to read at the conference. All of us tried as well as we could to be intelligent about cancer, but I noticed the doctor pinching Monique's arm and, feeling that he might have located a symptom and was planning a more thorough examination, I said good night and went to bed to read *Little Dorrit*. I found some inspiration in Mr Meagles' saying, 'One always begins to forgive a place as soon as it's left behind,' and, with that thought repeating in my brain, fell into that deep slumber familiar to infants in old fashioned rocker cradles and railway travellers in sleeping cars.

I was shaving the next morning, amazing Enrico with my portable electric razor as I had Duffill, when we pulled level with a train that bore an enamelled plate on its side inscribed MOSKVA–BEOGRAD. The Direct-Orient halted, making its couplings grunt, and Enrico dashed out of the door. This was Belgrade, calling attention to the fact with acronyms, CENTROCOOP, ATEKS, RAD, and one I loved, TRANSJUG. It was here, at Belgrade Station, that I thought I would try out my camera. I found a group of Yugoslav peasants, Mama Jug, Papa Jug, Granny Jug, and a lot of little Jugs; the men had Halloween moustaches, and one of the women wore a green satin dress over a pair of men's trousers; the granny, wearing a shawl that hid everything but her enormous nose, carried a battered Gladstone bag. The rest of their luggage, an unmanageable assortment of cardboard boxes and neatly sewn bales, was in the process of being transferred across the track, from one platform to the other. Any one of the bundles would have caused a derailment. *Migrants in Belgrade*: a poignant portrait of futility. I focused and prepared to snap, but in my view finder I saw the granny muttering to the man, who whipped around and made a threatening gesture at me.

Farther down the platform I had another excellent chance. A man in the uniform of a railway inspector, with a correct peaked cap, epaulettes, and neatly pressed trousers was walking towards me. But the interesting and photogenic feature was that he carried a shoe in each hand and was in his bare feet. They were big splayed feet, as blunt and white as turnips. I waited until he passed, and then clicked. But he heard the click and turned to yell a meaningful insult. After that I took my pictures with more stealth.

Molesworth saw me idling on the platform and said, 'I think I shall board. I don't trust this train any more.'

But everyone was on the platform; indeed, all the platforms at Belgrade Station were filled with travellers, leaving with me the unforgettable image of Belgrade as a terminal where people wait for trains that will never arrive, watching locomotives endlessly shunting. I pointed this out to Molesworth.

He said, 'I think of it now as getting duffilled. I don't want to get duffilled.' He hoisted himself into Car 99 and called out, 'Don't you get duffilled!'

We had left the Italian conductor at Venice; at Belgrade our Yugoslav conductor was replaced by a Bulgarian conductor.

'American?' said the Bulgarian as he collected my passport.

I told him I was.

'Agnew,' he said; he nodded.

'You know Agnew?'

He grinned. 'He is in bad situation.'

Molesworth, all business, said, 'You're the conductor, are you?'

The Bulgarian clicked his heels and made a little bow.

'Wonderful,' said Molesworth. 'Now what I want you to do is clean out those bottles.' He motioned to the floor of his compartment, where there was an impressive heap of wine bottles.

'The empty ones?' The Bulgarian smirked.

'Quite right. Good point. Carry on,' said Molesworth, and joined me at the window.

The Belgrade outskirts were leafy and pleasant, and as it was noon by the time we had left the station, the labourers we passed had downed their tools and were sitting cross-legged in shady spots by the railway line having lunch. The train was going so slowly, one could see the plates of sodden cabbage and could count the black olives in the chipped bowls. These groups of eaters passed loaves of bread the size of footballs, reducing them by hunks and scrubbing their plates with the pieces.

Much later on my trip, in the bar of a Russian ship in the Sea of Japan, on my way from the Japanese railway bazaar to the Soviet one beginning in Nakhodka, I met a jolly Yugoslav named Nikola who told me, 'In Yugoslavia we have three things – freedom, women, and drinking.'

'But not all three at the same time, surely?' I said, hoping he wouldn't take offence. I was seasick at the time, and I had forgotten Yugoslavia, the long September afternoon I had spent on the train from Belgrade to Dimitrovgrad, sitting in my corner seat with a full bottle of wine and my pipe drawing nicely.

There were women, but they were old, shawled against the sun and yoked to green watering cans in trampled corn fields. The landscape was low and uneven, barely supporting in its dust a few farm animals, maybe five motionless cows, and a herdsman leaning on a stick watching them starve in the same way the scarecrows – two plastic bags on a bony cross-piece – watched the devastated fields of cabbages and peppers. And beyond the rows of blue cabbage, a pink pig butted the splintery fence of his small pen and a cow lay under a goal of saplings in an unused football field. Red peppers, as crimson and pointed as clusters of poinsettias, dried in the sun outside farm cottages in districts where farming consisted of men stumbling after oxen dragging wooden ploughs and harrows, or occasionally wobbling on bicycles loaded with hay bales. Herdsmen were not simply herdsmen; they were sentries, guarding little flocks from marauders: four cows watched by a woman, three grey pigs driven by a man with a truncheon, scrawny chickens watched by scrawny children. Freedom, women, and drinking was Nikola's definition; and there was a woman in a field pausing to tip a water bottle to her mouth; she swallowed and bent from the waist to continue tying up cornstalks. Large ochre squashes sat plumply in fields of withering vines; people priming pumps and swinging buckets out of wells on long poles; tall narrow haystacks, and pepper fields in so many stages of ripeness I first took them for flower gardens. It is a feeling of utter quietness, deep rural isolation the train briefly penetrates. It goes on without a change for hours, this afternoon in Yugoslavia, and then all people disappear and the effect is eerie: roads without cars or bicycles, cottages with empty windows at the fringes of empty fields, trees heavy with apples and no one picking them. Perhaps it's the wrong time – 3.30; perhaps it's too hot. But where are the people who stacked that hay and set those peppers so carefully to dry? The train passes on – that's the beauty of a train, this heedless movement – but it passes on to more of the same. Six neat beehives, a derelict steam engine with wild flowers garlanding its smokestack, a stalled ox at a level crossing. In the heat haze of the afternoon my compartment grows dusty, and down at the front of the train Turks lie all over their seats, sleeping with their mouths open and children wakeful on their stomachs. At each river and bridge there were square brick emplacements, like Croatian copies of Martello towers, pocked by bombs. Then I saw a man, headless, bent over in a field, camouflaged by cornstalks that were taller than he; I wondered if I had missed all the others because they were made so tiny by their crops.

There was a drama outside Niš. At a road near the track a crowd of people fought to look at a horse, still in its traces and hitched to an overloaded wagon, lying dead on its side in a mud puddle in which the wagon was obviously stuck. I imagined its heart had burst when it tried to free the wagon. And it had just happened: children were calling to their friends, a man was dropping his bike and running back for a look, and farther along a man pissing against a fence was straining to see the horse. The scene was composed like a Flemish painting in which the pissing man was a vivid detail. The train, the window frame holding the scene for moments, made it a picture. The man at the fence flicks the last droplets from his penis and, tucking it in his baggy pants, begins to sprint; the picture is complete.

'I hate sightseeing,' said Molesworth. We were at the corridor window and I had just been reprimanded by a Yugoslav policeman for snapping a picture of a steam locmotive that, in the late afternoon sun, and the whirling dust the thousands of homeward-bound commuters had raised crossing the railway lines, stood amidst a magnificent exhalation of blue vapours mingling with clouds of gold gnats. Now we were in a rocky gorge outside Niš, on the way to Dimitrovgrad, the cliffs rising as we moved and holding occasional symmetries, like remainders of intelligent brickwork in the battlements of a ruined castle. The sight of this seemed to tire Molesworth, and I think he felt called upon to explain his fatigue. 'All that tramping around with guidebooks,' he said after a moment. 'In those horrible crocodiles of tourists, in and out of churches, museums, and mosques. No, no, no. I just like to be still, find a comfortable chair. Do you see what I mean? I like to *absorb* a country.'

He was drinking. We were both drinking, but drink made him reflective and it made me hungry. All I had had to eat during the day was a cheese bun in Belgrade, an envelope of pretzels, and a sour apple. The sight of Bulgaria, with its decrepit houses and skinny goats, did not make me hopeful of a good meal at Sofia Station, and at the fearfully named town of Dragoman a number of people, including several from Car 99, were taken off the train because they hadn't had cholera shots. Italy, the Bulgarians said, was stricken.

I found the Bulgarian conductor and asked him to describe for me a typical Bulgarian meal. Then I wrote down the Bulgarian words for the delicacies he had mentioned: cheese, potatoes, bread, sausages, salad with beans, and so forth. He assured me that there would be food in Sofia.

'This is an awfully slow train,' said Molesworth as the Direct-Orient creaked through the darkness. Here and there was a yellow lantern, a fire far off, a light in a hut at a remote halt where, barely visible, the stationmaster could be seen five paces from his hut, presenting his flag to the dawdling express.

I showed Molesworth my list of Bulgarian foods, and said I planned to buy what was obtainable at Sofia; it would be our last night on the Direct-Orient – we deserved a good meal.

'That should be very useful,' said Molesworth. 'Now, what are you going to use for money?'

'I haven't the slightest idea,' I said.

'They use the lev here, you know. But the snag is, I couldn't find a quotation for it. My bank manager said it was one of those hopeless currencies – I suppose it's not really money at all, just pieces of paper.' From the way he talked I could tell he wasn't hungry. He went on, 'I always use plastic. Plastic's incredibly useful.'

'Plastic?'

'Well, these things.' He set his drink down and took out a wad of credit cards, shuffled them, and read their names.

'Do you think the Barclaycard has hit Bulgaria yet?'

'Let's hope so,' he said. 'But if not, I still have some lire left.'

It was after eleven at night when we pulled into Sofia, and, as Molesworth and I leaped off the train, the conductor told us to hurry: 'Fifteen minutes, maybe ten.'

'You said we'd have a half-hour!'

'But we are running late now. Don't talk – hurry!'

We quick-marched down the platform, searching for food. There was a cafeteria with a mob at the counter and then nothing more except, at the far end of the platform, a man with a steaming metal pushcart. He was bald. He held a small paper bag in one hand and with the other he flipped open the several tabernacles of his pushcart and stabbed at white buns and red, dripping sausages, the size of bananas, with pink meat showing in slightly burst seams. There were three customers ahead of us. He served them, taking his time, urging buns and sausages into the bags with his busy fork. When my turn came I showed him two fingers, changed my mind, three fingers. He bagged three of each.

'The same again,' said Molesworth and handed him a 1000-lire note.

'No, no,' said the man; he pushed my dollar away and at the same time took my bag from me and put it on the pushcart.

'He won't take our money,' said Molesworth.

'*Banka, banka*,' said the man.

'He wants us to get change.'

'This is a dollar,' I said. 'Take the whole thing.'

'He won't wear it,' said Molesworth. 'Where's your *banka*, eh?'

The bald man pointed to the station. We ran in the direction his finger was pointing and found a teller's cage where a long line of disconsolate people stood clutching pieces of paper and kicking their luggage as the line inched forward.

'I think we'll have to give this up as a bad job,' said Molesworth.

'I'm dying for one of those sausages.'

'Unless you want to get duffilled,' said Molesworth, 'you should get back on the train. I think I shall.'

We did and minutes later the whistle blew and the Bulgarian darkness swallowed Sofia. Enrico, seeing us empty-handed, got Italian crackers from his sister, the nun, and gave them to us; the Armenian lady presented a slab of cheese and even sat with us and had a drink, until her son wandered in wearing a pair of pyjamas. He saw his mother laughing; he burst into tears. 'Now I go,' she said, and went. Monique had gone to bed; so had Enrico. Car 99 was asleep, but we were picking up speed. 'And we're not badly off,' said Molesworth, slicing the cheese. 'Two more bottles of wine – that's one apiece – and still some Orvieto to finish. Cheese and biscuits. We can call it a late supper.' We went on drinking, and Molesworth talked of India, how he had gone out for the first time on a P & O liner with thousands of enlisted men, tough mineworkers from the Durham coal fields. Molesworth and his fellow officers had plenty to drink, but the lower ranks were battened down. After a month they ran out of beer. There were fights, the men were mutinous, 'and by the time we reached Bombay most of them were in chains. But I got an extra pip on my shoulder for behaving myself.'

'This is the idea,' said Molesworth. The train was racing, and he was uncorking the last bottle. 'It's usually a good rule to drink the wine of the country you're passing through.' He glanced out the window into the blackness. 'I suppose that's still Bulgaria. What a great pity.'

Large grey dogs, a pack of seven, presumably wild, were chasing across the harsh steppes of northwestern Turkey, barking at the train. They woke me in Thrace, which Nagel calls 'rather unattractive', and when the wild dogs slackened their pace and fell behind the fleeing train there was little else to see but a dreary monotony of unambitious hills. The occasional army posts, the men shovelling sugar beets made the dreariness emphatic. And I couldn't bear those hairless hills. Edirne (Adrianople) was to the north, Istanbul still four hours away; but we travelled over the steppes, stopping at only the smallest stations, an unremarkable journey across a barren landscape: featurelessness is the steppes' single attribute, and, having said that, and assigned it a shade of brown, there is nothing more to say.

And yet I hung by the window, hoping to be surprised. We passed another station. I searched it for a detail; it repeated fifty previous stations and this repetition kept it out of focus. But just past it was a garden plot and, next to that, three turkeys, moving with that clockwork bustle characteristic of fowl.

'Look!' Molesworth had seen them.

I nodded.

'Turkeys. In *Turkey!*' he exclaimed. 'I wonder if that's why they're called –'

But it isn't. These birds got their name from African guinea fowl which, imported through Istanbul, were called turkey cocks. We discussed this over our morning drink for the next hour or two, and it struck me that, for a man with a wife and children, I was embarked on a fairly aimless enterprise, the lazy indulgence of travel for its own sake.

The great express from Paris became a doubtful and irritating Turkish local once it got to Istanbul's outskirts, stopping at every station simply to give conductors a chance to fool with notebooks in the Turkish Clapham Junctions and Scarsdales.

On the right-hand side of the train was the Sea of Marmara, where freighters with rusty hulls and fishing boats with the contours of scimitars lay surrounded by caïques in the glittering water. On our left the suburbs were passing, altering every fifty yards: scattered tent settlements and fishing villages gave way to high-rise apartment houses, with shacks at their ankles; then a shantytown on an outcrop of rock, bungalows where it levelled out, and an uneven terrace of wooden houses toppling grandly from a cliff – a style of building (the falling, unpainted, three-decker house) favoured in Somerville, Massachusetts, as well as in Istanbul. It takes a while to realize that what are represented in these vastly different building styles are not social classes, but rather centuries, each style an example of its own age – Istanbul has been a city for twenty-seven centuries – and getting older and more solid (shingle to timber, timber to brick, brick to stone) as you get closer to the Seraglio.

Istanbul begins as the train passes the city wall at the Golden Gate, the Arch of Triumph of Theodosius – built in 380 but not appreciably more decrepit than the strings of Turkish laundry that flap at its base. Here, for no apparent reason, the train picked up speed and rushed east along Istanbul's snout, past the Blue Mosque and the Topkapi Sarayi, and then circled to the Golden Horn. Sirkeči Station is nothing compared to its sister station, Haydarpasa, just across the Bosporus, but its nearness to the busy Eminönu Square and one of the prettiest mosques in the city, Yeni Valide Camii, not to mention the Galata Bridge (which accommodates a whole community of hawkers, fish stalls, shops, restaurants, and pickpockets disguised as peddlers and touts), gives to one's arrival in Istanbul by the Direct-Orient Express the combined shock and exhilaration of being pitched headfirst into a bazaar.

'It all looks absolutely hideous,' said Molesworth. But he was smiling. 'I think I'm going to like it.' He was off to the high-priced fishing village of Tarabya. He gave me his telephone number and said I should ring if I got bored. We were still on the platform at Sirkeči. Molesworth turned to the train. 'I must say I'm not sad to see the back of that train, are you?' But he said it in a tone of fussy endearment, in the way a person who calls himself a fool really means the opposite.

Vignettes of Travel

Farley Mowat

The Mowat family was a restless one – or at least my father was a restless one. Mother would have been content to stay quietly in almost any of the places that were temporarily home to us, but Father always yearned for far horizons.

During the Saskatoon period of our lives we travelled widely, from Churchill on Hudson Bay, to Vancouver on the Pacific shores. We travelled the hard way, too, for a librarian is always underpaid. However, the lessons I learned from the vicissitudes of those journeys have stood me in good stead on my own travels, for writers too are always underpaid.

In examining my memories of those excursions I am struck by the way Mutt looms so large in all of them. There was our journey to the Pacific, for example. Looking back on it now, I can recall a string of vignettes in each of which Mutt was the centre of attention – while for the rest, there is nothing but an amorphous blur.

We began that journey on the June day in 1934 when I finished my last school examination paper. I still possess a snapshot taken of us as we pulled away down River Road, and when I look at it I am appalled at the manner in which we burdened Eardlie. None of your pregnant glass-and-chrome showcases of today could have carried that load for a single mile. Eardlie could do so only because he was the ultimate result of five thousand years of human striving to devise the perfect vehicle. For there is no doubt at all but that the Model A stands at the apex of the evolution of the wheel. And it is a matter of sorrow to me – as it should be to all men – that this magnificent climax should have been followed by the rapid and terrible degeneration of the automotive species into the effete mechanical incubi which batten off human flesh on every highway of the world today.

The load that Eardlie shouldered when he set bravely forth to carry us across far mountains to the sea almost defies belief. There was a large

umbrella tent tied to the spare tyre; there was *Concepcion* supported high
above us on a flimsy rack; there were three folding wooden cots lashed to
the front mudguards; on the right-hand running board (an invaluable
invention, long since sacrificed to the obesity of the modern car) were two
wooden crates of books – most of them about the sea; on the other running
board were two trunk-suitcases, a five-gallon gasoline can, and a spare spare-
tyre. In addition, there were the canoe masts, sails, and leeboards; Father's
Newfoundland-pattern oilskins and sou'wester; a sextant; a schooner's binnacle
compass; Mother's household implements, including pots and pans and a
huge gunny sack containing shreds of cloth for use in making hooked rugs;
and, not least, a canvas bag containing my gopher traps, .22 rifle, and other
essential equipment.

As Eardlie arched his back under the strain and carried us out of the city
past the town slough, where the ducks were already hatching their young,
we would have done justice to Steinbeck's descriptions of the dispossessed.

Mutt enjoyed travelling by car, but he was an unquiet passenger. He
suffered from the delusion, common to dogs and small boys, that when he
was looking out the right-hand side, he was probably missing something far
more interesting on the left-hand side. In addition, he could never be quite
sure whether he preferred the front seat – and looking forwards – or the
rumble seat – and looking backwards. Mutt started out up front with Mother
and Father, while I had the rumble seat; but we had not gone five miles
before he and Mother were at odds with one another. They both wanted the
outside berth, and which ever one was temporarily denied it would growl
and mutter and push, until he or she gained his or her ends.

Before we had been driving for an hour Mother lost her patience and Mutt
was exiled to the rumble seat.

Riding in the rumble did strange things to him, and I have a theory that
his metabolism was disturbed by the enforced intake of air under pressure
from the slipstream, so that he became oxygen-drunk. He would grow wild-
eyed and, although not normally a drooling dog, he would begin to salivate.
Frequently he would stand up with his front feet on the back of Mother's
neck, and he would drool on her until, driven to extremes, she would poke
him sharply on the chin, whereupon he would mutter, and come back to
drool on me.

But his favourite position, when he became really full of oxygen, was to
extrude himself gradually over one of the rear mudguards until there was
nothing of him remaining in the car except his hind feet and his tail. Here

he would balance precariously, his nose thrust far out into the slipstream and his large ears fluttering in the breeze.

The prairie roads were indescribably dusty, and his nose and eyes would soon become so clogged that he would be almost blind, and incapable of smelling a dead cow at twenty paces. He did not seem to mind, but like a misshapen and misplaced figurehead he would thrust farther outwards until he passed the point of balance. Then only my firm grip on his tail could prevent disaster, and on one occasion, when my grip relaxed a little, he became airborne for a moment or so before crashing to the road behind us.

When this happened we thought we had lost him forever. By the time Father got the car stopped, Mutt was a hundred yards in the rear, spread-eagled in the centre of the road, and screaming pitifully. Father assumed the worst, and concluded that the only thing to do was to put the poor beast out of his misery at once. He leaped out of the car and ran to a blacksmith's shop that stood by the roadside, and in a few minutes returned waving the blacksmith's old revolver.

He was too late. While he had been out of sight, Mutt had spotted a pair of heifers staring at him over the fence, and had hastily picked himself up to give vociferous chase.

Although he suffered no lasting injuries from this mishap, there was one minor consequence that allowed me to make a place for myself in the family annals by subsequently reporting that 'Mutt was so scared he went to the bathroom in his pants'.

Because of the dust we three human travellers were equipped with motorcyclists' goggles. Father decided one evening that this was favouritism, and that Mutt should have the same protection. We were then entering the outskirts of a place called Elbow, a typical prairie village with an unpaved main street as wide as the average Ontario farm, and with two rows of plank-fronted buildings facing each other distantly across this arid expanse. The drugstore was the only place still open when we arrived.

Father, Mutt, and I entered the shop together, and when an aged clerk appeared from the back premises, my father asked him for driving goggles.

The old fellow searched for a long time and finally brought us three pairs that had been designed and manufactured in the first years of the automobile era. They seemed to be serviceable and without more ado Father began trying them on Mutt.

Happening to glance up while this was going on, I met the clerk's gaze. He was transfixed. His leathered face had sagged like a wet chamois cloth and his tobacco-stained stubs seemed ready to fall from his receding lower jaw.

Father missed this preliminary display, but he was treated to an even better show a moment later when he got briskly to his feet, holding the second pair of goggles.

'These will do. How much are they?' he asked. And then suddenly remembering that he had forgotten to pack his shaving kit before leaving Saskatoon, he added, 'We'll want a shaving brush, soap, and a safety razor too.'

The old man had retreated behind his counter. He looked as if he was going to begin weeping. He pawed the air with one emaciated hand for several seconds before he spoke.

'Oh, Gawd!' he wailed – and it was a real prayer. 'Don't you tell me that dawg *shaves*, too!'

We had to improvise a special harness for the goggles because of the unusual shape of Mutt's head, but they fitted him tolerably well, and he was pleased with them. When they were not in use we would push them up on the lift of his brow, but in a few days he had learned how to do this for himself, and he could pull them down again over his eyes in time of need. Apart from the effect they had on unimaginative passers-by, Mutt's goggles were an unqualified success. However, they did not give him protection for his nose and one day he met a bee at forty miles an hour. The left side of Mutt's already bulbous nose swelled hugely. This did not inconvenience him too severely, for he simply moved to the other side of the car. But luck was against him and he soon collided with another bee, or perhaps it was a wasp this time. The total effect of the two stings was bizarre. With his goggles down, Mutt now looked like a cross between a hammerhead shark and a deep-sea diver.

Our second night on the western road was spent at Swift River in southern Saskatchewan. Swift River was almost the centre of the dust-bowl country and it had a lean and hungry look. We were very hot, very dusty, and very tired when we drove into its northern outskirts and began searching for the municipal tourist camp – for in those times there were no motels, and the only alternative to a tent of one's own was a tiny cubicle in a crematorium that bore the sardonic title of 'hotel'.

Swift River was proud of its municipal tourist camp, which was located in a brave but pathetic attempt at a park, near the banks of an artificial slough.

We set about pitching the tent, which was a patented affair and not easily mastered. Soon a policeman came along and eyed us suspiciously, as if convinced that we were undesirable vagrants masquerading as bona fide tourists. He became quite grumpy when called upon to help with the tent.

We were all in a taut temper when we finally crawled into our blankets that night. It did not ease our mood that the night's rest was fragmentary due to the influx of clouds of mosquitoes from the nearby slough, and due also to the sad moanings of a pair of emaciated elk who lived in a nearby wild-life enclosure.

We tossed and muttered in the hot and crowded tent, and were not disposed to rise with the dawn. We were still abed, still partly comatose, when voices near at hand brought us unwillingly back to the new day.

The voices were feminine, spinsterish, and indignant. I was too drugged with fatigue to catch the gist of the conversation at first, but I was sufficiently conscious to hear Father's sudden grunt of anger, and Mother's whispered attempts to soothe him. Things seemed interesting enough to warrant waking fully, so I sat up in bed and gave the voices my attention.

The dialogue went like this:

From outside: 'It's a shame – that's what it is. A regular public nuisance! I can't imagine what the officials are thinking of to allow it.'

Mutterings from Father, who seemed to know what this was all about: 'Old harridans! Who the devil do they think they are?'

Mother, soothingly: '*Now*, Angus!'

Outside again: 'What a perfectly *poisonous* smell ... Do you think it really *is* a god?'

At this my father jerked convulsively, and I remembered that Mutt had abandoned the dubious comforts of the tent in the early dawn and had walked all over me, seeking the doorway. I began to share my father's annoyance. No stranger had the right to speak of Mutt in terms like these. And they were growing worse.

'It looks like a dog – but how it stinks!' the disembodied and waspish voice continued. 'Phew! Whoever owns it should be put in jail.'

This was more than Father could bear. His bellow shook the tent.

'*I* own that dog,' he cried, 'and what do you intend to do about it?'

He had already begun to stumble about, looking for his clothes, when one of the voices responded in a manner that unhinged him completely.

'Well!' it said scathingly. 'Why don't you bury it – or is that too much to expect from – from drifters!'

It was at this point that Father burst out of the tent, clad only in his pyjama tops, and so angry that he was incoherent. Wordless he may have been, but his tone of voice was sufficient to send the two bird watchers – for that is what they were – skittering to their car. They vanished with a clash of gears, leaving us alone with the unhappy elk – and with a dog.

It was not Mutt. It was a strange dog, and it floated belly up in a backwater of the slough not more than twenty feet away. It had been dead a long, long time.

Mother was triumphant. 'There, you *see*?' she told my father. 'You never *look* before you leap.'

She was undeniably right, for if Father had looked we would have been spared the half-hour that followed when the grumpy policeman returned and demanded that we haul our dog out of the slough and bury it at once. He was really more truculent than grumpy, and he did not have a sympathetic ear for our attempts at explanation. It would perhaps have been easier to convince him that the whole affair was a misunderstanding had Mutt been present, but Mutt had gone off in the early dawn to examine the quality of Swift River's garbage cans, and he did not return until Eardlie stood packed and ready to flee. Mutt never understood why Father was so short with him for the rest of the day.

The remainder of our journey through the prairies passed without undue excitement, and this was as well, for it was a time of mounting fatigue, and of tempers strained by days of heat, by the long pall of dust, and by the yellowed desert of the drying plains. The poplar bluffs were few and far between and their parched leaves rustled stiffly with the sound of death. The sloughs were dry, their white beds glittering in the destroying heat. Here and there a tiny puddle of muck still lingered in a roadside ditch, and these potholes had become death traps for innumerable little families of ducks. Botulism throve in the stagnant slime, and the ducks died in their thousands, and their bodies did not rot, but dried as mummies dry.

It was a grim passage, and we drove Eardlie hard, heedless of his steadily boiling radiator and his labouring engine. And then one morning there was a change. The sky that had been dust-hazed for so long grew clear and sweet. Ahead of us, hung between land and air, we saw the first blue shadows of the distant mountains.

We camped early that night and we were in high spirits at our escape from drought and desert. When the little gasoline stove had hissed into life and Mother was preparing supper, Mutt and I went off to explore this new and living land. Magpies rose ahead of us, their long tails iridescent in the setting sun. Pipits climbed the crests of the high clouds and sang their intense little songs. Prairie chickens rose chuckling out of a green pasture that lay behind a trim white farmhouse. We walked back to the tent through a popular bluff whose leaves flickered and whispered as live leaves should.

We crossed through most of Alberta the next day, and by evening were climbing the foothills. It had been a day for Mutt to remember. Never had he suspected that cows existed anywhere in such vast numbers. The size of the herds bewildered him so much that he lost all heart for the chase. He was so overwhelmed (and so greatly outnumbered) that he stayed in the car even when we stopped for lunch. In that evening we made our camp near a little roadside stand that sold gasoline and soda pop, and here Mutt tried to recover his self-respect by pursuing a very small, very lonely little cow that lived behind the garage. His cup of woe was filled to overflowing when the little cow turned out to be a billy goat – Mutt's first – and retaliated by chasing him back to the tent, and then attempting to follow him inside.

We began the passage of the mountains in the morning, and we chose the northern route, which at that time was no easy path even for a Model A. The roads were narrow, precipitous, and gravel-surfaced. There were no guard rails, and periodically we would find ourselves staring over the edge of a great gorge while Eardlie's wheels kicked gravel down into the echoing abyss.

We seemed to undergo a strange shrinking process as the mountains grew higher and more massive. I felt that we were no more than four microorganisms, dwarfed almost to the vanishing point. The mountains frightened me, because I knew them as the last of the Terrible Things – the immutable survivors that alone remained unaltered by the human termites who have scarred the face of half a world.

Mutt too was humbled at first, and he showed his awe of the mountains in an odd way. He refused to use them for mundane purposes, and since there was nowhere else to cock a leg, except against a mountain, he was in agony for a time. Fortunately for him his awe was transitory. It was eventually replaced by the urge to climb, for the desire to seek high places had always been his, and it had taken him first to the top of fences, then up ladders, and finally high into the trees. Now he saw that it could take him to the clouds, and he was no dog to miss an opportunity.

We lost Mutt, and two days from our itinerary, when he set out on his own to reach the peaks of the Three Sisters. We never knew for certain if he achieved his goal, but when he arrived back at our impatient camp, his paw pads were worn almost to the flesh and he had a cocky air about him as of one who has stood upon a pinnacle and gazed across the world.

This mountain-climbing was an infernal nuisance to the rest of us, for he would sneak away whenever we stopped, and would appear high on the face of some sheer cliff, working his way steadily upwards, and deaf to our commands that he return at once.

One day we paused for a drink of spring water near the face of a forbidding cliff, and of course Mutt was unable to resist the challenge. We did not notice that he was gone until a large American limousine drew up alongside us and from it four handsome women and two well-fed men emerged. They were all equipped with movie cameras and binoculars, and some of them began staring at the cliff with their glasses, while the rest levelled their cameras. The whirr of the machines brought me over to see what this was all about. I asked one of the woman.

'Hush, sonny,' she replied in a heavy whisper, 'there's a real live mountain goat up there!' And with that she too raised her camera and pressed the button.

I spent a long time looking for that goat. I could see Mutt clearly enough, some three hundred feet up the cliffside; but no goat. I supposed that Mutt was on the goat's trail, and it irked me that I was blind while strangers were possessed of such keen eyes.

After some ten minutes of intent photography the Americans loaded themselves back into the limousine and drove away, engaging in much congratulatory backslapping at their good luck as they went.

I had caught on by then. That night we discussed the anomaly of a piebald mountain goat with long black ears, and I am afraid we laughed outrageously. Yet in point of fact no genuine mountain goat could have given a more inspired demonstration of mountaineering techniques than could Mutt.

Leaving the mountains temporarily, we descended into the Okanagan valley, where we hoped to see a fabulous monster called the Ogo Pogo that dwells in Lake Okanagan. The monster proved reluctant, so we solaced ourselves by gorging on the magnificent fruits for which the valley is famous, and for which we had often yearned during the prairie years. To our surprise – for he could still surprise us on occasion – Mutt shared our appetites, and for three days he ate nothing at all but fruit.

He preferred peaches, muskmelon, and cherries, but cherries were his undoubted favourites. At first he had trouble with the pips, but he soon perfected a rather disgusting trick of squirting them out between his front teeth, and as a result we had to insist that he point himself away from us and the car whenever he was eating cherries.

I shall never forget the baleful quality of the look directed at Mutt by a passenger on the little ferry in which we crossed the Okanagan River. Perhaps the look was justified. Certainly Mutt was a quaint spectacle as he sat in the rumble seat, his goggles pushed far up on his forehead, eating cherries out of a six-quart basket.

After each cherry he would raise his muzzle, point it overside, and nonchalantly spit the pip into the green waters of the river.

The Burglary

Arnold Bennett

I

Lady Dain said: 'Jee, if that portrait stays there much longer, you'll just have to take me off to Pirehill one of these fine mornings.'

Pirehill is the seat of the great local hospital; but it is also the seat of the great local lunatic asylum; and when the inhabitants of the Five Towns say merely 'Pirehill', they mean the asylum.

'I do declare I can't fancy my food nowadays,' said Lady Dain, 'and it's all that portrait!' She stared plaintively up at the immense oil-painting which faced her as she sat at the breakfast-table in her spacious and opulent dining-room.

Sir Jehoshaphat made no remark.

Despite Lady Dain's animadversions upon it, despite the undoubted fact that it was generally disliked in the Five Towns, the portrait had cost a thousand pounds (some said guineas), and, though not yet two years old, it was probably worth at least fifteen hundred in the picture market. For it was a Cressage – it was one of the finest Cressages in existence.

It marked the summit of Sir Jehoshaphat's career. Sir Jehoshaphat's career was, perhaps, the most successful and brilliant in the entire social history of the Five Towns. This famous man was the principal partner in Dain Brothers. His brother was dead, but two of Sir Jee's sons were in the firm. Dain Brothers were the largest manufacturers of cheap earthenware in the district, catering chiefly for the American and Colonial buyer. They had an extremely bad reputation for cutting prices. They were hated by every other firm in the Five Towns, and, to hear rival manufacturers talk, one would gather the impression that Sir Jee had acquired a tremendous fortune by systematically selling goods under cost. They were hatred also by between eighteen and nineteen hundred employees. But such hatred, however virulent, had not marred the progress of Sir Jee's career.

He had meant to make a name, and he had made it. The Five Towns might laugh at his vulgar snobbishness. The Five Towns might sneer at his calculated philanthropy. But he was, nevertheless, the best-known man in the Five Towns, and it was precisely his snobbishness and his philanthropy which had carried him to the top. Moreover, he had been the first public man in the five Towns to gain a knighthood. The Five Towns could not deny that it was very proud indeed of this knighthood. The means by which he had won this distinction were neither here nor there – he had won it. And was he not the father of his native borough? Had he not been three times mayor of his native borough? Was not the whole northern half of the country dotted and spangled by his benefactions, his institutions, his endowments?

And it could not be denied that he sometimes tickled the Five Towns as the Five Towns likes being tickled. There was, for example, the notorious Sneyd incident. Sneyd Hall, belonging to the Earl of Chell, lies a few miles south of the Five Towns, and from it the pretty Countess of Chell exercises that condescending meddlesomeness which so frequently exasperates the Five Towns. Sir Jee had got his title by the aid of the Countess – 'Interfering Iris', as she is locally dubbed. Shortly afterwards he had contrived to quarrel with the Countess; and the quarrel was conducted by Sir Jee as a quarrel between equals, which delighted the district. Sir Jee's final word in it had been to buy a single tract of land near Sneyd village, just off the Sneyd estate, and to erect thereon a mansion quite as imposing as Sneyd Hall, and far more up to date, and to call the mansion Sneyd Castle. A mighty stroke! Iris was furious; the Earl speechless with fury. But they could do nothing. Naturally the Five Towns was tickled.

It was apropos of the housewarming of Sneyd Castle, also of the completion of his third mayoralty, and of the inauguration of the Dain Technical Institute, that the movement had been started (primarily by a few toadies) for tendering to Sir Jee a popular gift worthy to express the profound esteem in which he was officially held in the Five Towns. It having been generally felt the gift should take the form of a portrait, a local dilettante had suggested Cressage, and when the Five Towns had inquired into Cressage, and discovered that that genius from the United States was celebrated throughout the civilized world, and regarded as the equal of Velazquez (whoever Velazquez might be), and that he had painted half the aristocracy, and that his income was regal, the suggestion was accepted and Cressage was approached.

Cressage haughtily consented to paint Sir Jee's portrait on his usual conditions; namely, that the sitter should go to the little village in Bedfordshire where Cressage had his principal studio, and that the painting should be exhibited at the Royal Academy before being shown anywhere else. (Cressage was an R.A, but no one thought of putting R.A. after his name. He was so big that, instead of the Royal Academy conferring distinction on him, he conferred distinction on the Royal Academy.)

Sir Jee went to Bedfordshire and was rapidly painted, and he came back gloomy. The Presentation Committee went to Bedfordshire later to inspect the portrait, and they, too, came back gloomy.

Then the Academy Exhibition opened, and the portrait, showing Sir Jee in his robe and chain and in a chair, was instantly hailed as possibly the most glorious masterpiece of modern times. All the critics were of one accord. The Committee and Sir Jee were reassured, but only partially, and Sir Jee rather less so than the Committee. For there was something in the enthusiastic criticism which gravely disturbed them. An enlightened generation, thoroughly familiar with the dazzling yearly succession of Cressage portraits, need not be told what this something was. One critic wrote that Cressage had displayed even more than 'his customary astounding insight into character. . . .' Another critic wrote that Cressage's observation was, as usual, 'calmly and coldly hostile.' Another referred to the 'typical provincial mayor, immortalized for the diversion of future ages.'

Inhabitants of the Five Towns went to London to see the work for which they saw a mean, little, old man, with thin lips and a straggling grey beard and shifty eyes, and pushful snob written all over him; ridiculous in his gewgaws of office. When you looked at the picture close to, it was a meaningless mass of coloured smudges, but when you stood fifteen feet away from it the portrait was absolutely lifelike, amazing, miraculous. It was so wondrously lifelike that some of the inhabitants of the Five Towns burst out laughing. Many people felt sorry – not for Sir Jee, but for Lady Dain. Lady Dain was beloved and genuinely respected. She was a simple, homely, sincere woman, her one weakness being that she had never been able to see through Sir Jee.

Of course, at the presentation ceremony the portrait had been ecstatically referred to as a possession precious for ever, and the recipient and his wife pretended to be overflowing with pure joy in the ownership of it.

It had been hanging in the dining-room of Sneyd Castle about sixteen months when Lady Dain told her husband that it would ultimately drive her into the lunatic asylum.

'Don't be silly, wife,' said Sir Jee. 'I wouldn't part with that portrait for ten times what it cost.'

This was, to speak bluntly, a downright lie. Sir Jee secretly hated the portrait more than anyone hated it. He would have been almost ready to burn down Sneyd Castle in order to get rid of the thing. But it happened that on the previous evening, in conversation with the magistrates' clerk, his receptive brain had been visited by a less expensive scheme than burning down the castle.

Lady Dain sighed.

'Are you going to town early?' she inquired.

'Yes,' he said. 'I'm on the rota today.'

He was chairman of the borough Bench of Magistrates. As he drove into town he revolved his scheme, and thought it wild and dangerous, but still feasible.

II

On the Bench that morning Sir Jee shocked Mr Sheratt, the magistrates' clerk, and he utterly disgusted Mr Bourne, superintendent of the borough police. (I do not intend to name the name of the borough – whether Bursley, Henbridge, Knype, Longshaw, or Turnhill. The inhabitants of the Five Towns will know without being told; the rest of the world has no right to know.) There had recently occurred a somewhat thrilling series of burglaries in the district, and the burglars (a gang of them was presumed) had escaped the solicitous attentions of the police. But on the previous afternoon an underling of Mr Bourne's had caught a man who was generally believed to be wholly or partly responsible for the burglaries. The Five Towns breathed with relief, and congratulated Mr Bourne; and Mr Bourne was well pleased with himself. The *Staffordshire Signal* headed the item of news, 'Smart Capture of a Supposed Burglar'. The supposed burglar gave his name as William Smith, and otherwise behaved in an extremely suspicious manner.

Now, Sir Jee, sitting as chief magistrate in the police-court, actually dismissed the charge against the man! Over-ruling his sole colleague on the Bench that morning, Alderman Easton, he dismissed the charge against

William Smith, holding that the evidence for the prosecution was insufficient to justify even a remand. No wonder that that pillar of the law, Mr Sheratt, was pained and shocked. At the conclusion of the case Sir Jehoshaphat said that he would be glad to speak with William Smith afterwards in the magistrates' room, indicating that he sympathized with William Smith and wished to exercise upon William Smith his renowned philanthropy.

And so, about noon, when the Court majestically rose, Sir Jee retired to the magistrates' room, where the humble Alderman Easton was discreet enough not to follow him, and awaited William Smith. And William Smith came, guided thither by a policeman, to whom, in parting from him, he made a rude, surreptitious gesture.

Sir Jee, seated in the arm-chair which dominates the other chairs round the elm table in the magistrates' room, emitted a preliminary cough.

'Smith,' he said sternly, leaning his elbows on the table, 'you were very fortunate this morning, you know.'

And he gazed at Smith.

Smith stood near the door, cap in hand. He did not resemble a burglar, who surely ought to be big, muscular, and masterful. He resembled an undersized clerk who has been out of work for a long time, but who has nevertheless found the means to eat and drink rather plenteously. He was clothed in a very shabby navy-blue suit, frayed at the wrists and ankles, and greasy in front. His linen collar was brown with dirt, his fingers were dirty, his hair was unkempt and long, and a young and lusty black beard was sprouting on his chin. His boots were not at all pleasant.

'Yes, governor,' Smith replied lightly, with Manchester accent. 'And what's your game?'

Sir Jee was taken aback. He, the chairman of the borough Bench, and the leading philanthropist in the county, to be so spoken to! But what could he do? He himself had legally established Smith's innocence. Smith was free as air, and had a perfect right to adopt any tone he chose to any man he chose. And Sir Jee desired a service from William Smith.

'I was hoping I might be of use to you,' said Sir Jehoshaphat diplomatically.

'Well,' said Smith, 'that's all right, that is. But none of your philanthropic dodges, you know. I don't want to turn over a new leaf, and I don't want a helpin' hand, nor none o' those things. And what's more, I don't want a situation. I've got all the situation as I need. But I never refuse money, nor beer neither. Never did, and I'm forty years old next month.'

'I suppose burgling doesn't pay very well, does it?' Sir Jee boldly ventured.

William Smith laughed coarsely.

'It pays right enough,' said he. 'But I don't put my money on my back, governor; I put it into a bit of public-house property when I get the chance.'

'It may pay,' said Sir Jee. 'But it is wrong. It is very anti-social.'

'Is it, indeed!' Smith returned drily. 'Anti-social, is it? Well, I've heard it called plenty o' things in my time, but never that. Now, I should have called it quite sociable-like – sort of making free with strangers, and so on. However,' he added, 'I came across a cove once as told me crime was nothing but a disease, and ought to be treated as such. I asked him for a dozen of port, but he never sent it.'

'Ever been caught before?' Sir Jee inquired.

'Not much!' Smith exclaimed. 'And this'll be a lesson to me, I can tell you. Now, what are you getting at, governor? Because my time's money, my time is.'

Sir Jee coughed once more.

'Sir down,' said Sir Jee.

And William Smith sat down opposite to him at the table, and put his shiny elbows on the table precisely in the manner of Sir Jee's elbows.

'Well?' he cheerfully encouraged Sir Jee.

'How should you like to commit a burglary that was not a crime?' and Sir Jee, his shifty eyes wandering round the room. 'A perfectly lawful burglary?'

'What *are* you getting at?' William Smith was genuinely astonished.

'At my residence, Sneyd Castle,' Sir Jee proceeded, 'there's a large portrait of myself in the dining-room that I want to have stolen. You understand?'

'Stolen?'

'Yes. I want to get rid of it. And I want – er – people to think that it has been stolen.'

'Well, why don't you stop up one night and steal it yourself, and then burn it?' William Smith suggested.

'That would be deceitful,' said Sir Jee gravely. 'I could not tell my friends that the portrait had been stolen if it had not been stolen. The burglary must be entirely genuine.'

'What's the figure?' said Smith curtly.

'Figure?'

'What are you going to give me for the job?'

'*Give* you for doing the job?' Sir Jee repeated, his secret and ineradicable meanness aroused. '*Give* you? Why, I'm giving you the opportunity to honestly steal a picture that's worth two thousand pounds – I daresay it would be worth two thousand pounds in America – and you want to be paid into the bargain! Do you know, my man, that people come all the way from Manchester, and even London, to see that portrait?' He told Smith about the painting.

'Then why are you in such a stew to be rid off it?' queried the burglar.

'That's my affair,' said Sir Jee. 'I don't like it. Lady Dain doesn't like it. But it's a presentation portrait, and so I can't – you see, Mr Smith?'

'And how am I going to dispose of it when I've got it?' Smith demanded. 'You can't melt a portrait down as if it was silver. By what you say, governor, it's known all over the blessed world. Seems to me I might just as well try to sell the Nelson Column.'

'Oh, nonsense!' said Sir Jee. 'Nonsense! You'll sell it in America quite easily. It'll be a fortune to you. Keep it for a year first, and then send it to New York.'

William Smith shook his head and drummed his fingers on the table; and then, quite suddenly, he brightened and said:

'All right, governor. I'll take it on, just to oblige you.'

'When can you do it?' asked Sir Jee, hardly concealing his joy. 'Tonight?'

'No,' said Smith mysteriously. 'I'm engaged tonight.'

'Well, tomorrow night?'

'Nor tomorrow. I'm engaged tomorrow too.'

'You seem to be very much engaged, my man,' Sir Jee observed.

'What do you expect?' Smith retorted. 'Business is business. I could do it the night after tomorrow.'

'But that's Christmas Eve,' Sir Jee protested.

'What if it is Christmas Eve?' said Smith coldly. 'Would you prefer Christmas Day? I'm engaged on Boxing Day, *and* the day after.'

'Not in the Five Towns, I trust?' Sir Jee remarked.

'No,' said Smith shortly. 'The Five Towns is about sucked dry.' The affair was arranged for Christmas Eve.

'Now,' Sir Jee suggested, 'shall I draw you a plan of the castle, so that you can –'

William Smith's face expressed terrific scorn. 'Do you suppose,' he said, 'as I haven't had plans o' your castle ever since it was built? What do you take me for? I'm not a blooming excursionist, I'm not. I'm a business man – that's what I am.'

Sir Jee was snubbed, and he agreed submissively to all William Smith's arrangements for the innocent burglary. He perceived that in William Smith he had stumbled on a professional of the highest class, and this good fortune pleased him.

'There's only one thing that riles me,' said Smith in parting, 'and that is that you'll go and say that after you'd done everything you could for me I went and burgled your castle. And you'll talk of the ingratitude of the lower classes, I know you, governor!'

III

On the afternoon of the 24th of December, Sir Jehoshaphat drove home to Sneyd Castle from the principal of the three Dain manufactories, and found Lady Dain superintending the work of packing up trunks. He and she were to quit the castle that afternoon in order to spend Christmas on the other side of the Five Towns, under the roof of their eldest son, John, who had a new house, a new wife, and a new baby (male). John was a domineering person, and, being rather proud of his house and all that was his, he had obstinately decided to have his own hearth. Grandpapa and Grandmamma, drawn by the irresistible attraction of that novelty, a grandson (though Mrs John *had* declined to have the little thing named Jehoshaphat), had yielded to John's solicitations, and the family gathering, for the first time in history, was not to occur round Sir Jee's mahogany.

Sir Jee, very characteristically, said nothing to Lady Dain immediately. He allowed her to proceed with the packing of the trunks, and then tea was served, and the time was approaching for the carriage to come round to take them to the station when at last he suddenly remarked:

'I shan't be able to go with you to John's this affternnon.'

'Oh, Jee!' she exclaimed. 'Really, you are tiresome. Why couldn't you tell me before?'

'I will come over tomorrow morning – perhaps in time for church,' he proceeded, ignoring her demand for an explanation.

He always did ignore her demand for an explanation. Indeed, she only asked for explanations in a mechanical and perfunctory manner – she had long since ceased to expect them. Sir Jee had been born like that – devious, mysterious, incalculable. And Lady Dain accepted him as he was. She was somewhat surprised, therefore, when he went on:

'I have some minutes of committee meetings that I really must go carefully through and send off tonight, and you know as well as I do that there'll be no chance of doing that at John's. I've telegraphed to John.'

He was obviously nervous and self-conscious.

'There's no food in the house,' sighed Lady Dain. 'And the servants are all going away except Callear, and *he* can't cook your dinner tonight. I think I'd better stay myself and look after you.'

'You'll do no such thing,' said Sir Jee decisively. 'As for my dinner, anything will do for that. The servants have been promised their holiday, to start from this evening, and they must have it. I can manage.'

Here spoke the philanthropist, with his unshakable sense of justice.

So Lady Dain departed, anxious and worried, having previously arranged something cold for Sir Jee in the dining-room, and instructed Callear about boiling the water for Sir Jee's tea on Christmas morning. Callear was the undercoachman and a useful odd man. He it was who would drive Sir Jee to the station on Christmas morning, and then guard the castle and the stables thereof during the absence of the family and the other servants. Callear slept over the stables.

And after Sir Jee had consumed his cold repast in the dining-room the other servants went, and Sir Jee was alone in the castle, facing the portrait.

He had managed the affair fairly well, he thought. Indeed, he had a talent for chicane, and none knew it better than himself. It would have been dangerous if the servants had been left in the castle. They might have suffered from insomnia, and heard William Smith, and interfered with the operations of William Smith. On the other hand, Sir Jee had no intention of leaving the castle, uninhabited, to the mercies of William Smith. He felt that he himself must be on the spot to see that everything went right and that nothing went wrong. Thus the previously arranged scheme for the servants' holiday fitted perfectly into his plans, and all that he had had to do was to refuse to leave the castle till the morrow. It was ideal.

Nevertheless, he was a little afraid of what he had done, and of what he was going to permit William Smith to do. It was certainly dangerous – certainly rather a wild scheme. However, the die was cast. And within twelve hours he would be relieved of the intolerble incubus of the portrait.

And when he thought of the humiliations which that portrait had caused him, when he remembered the remarks of his sons concerning it, especially Johns remarks; when he recalled phrases about it in London newspapers, he squirmed, and told himself that no scheme for getting rid of it could be too wild and perilous. And, after all, the burglary dodge was the only dodge, absolutely the only conceivable practical method of disposing of the portrait – except burning down the castle. And surely it was preferable to a conflagration, to arson! Moreover, in case of fire at the castle some blundering fool would be sure to cry: 'The portrait! The portrait must be saved!' And the portrait would be saved. He gazed at the repulsive, hateful thing. In the centre of the lower part of the massive gold frame was the legend: 'Presented to Sir Jehoshaphat Dain, Knight, as a mark of public esteem and gratitude,' etc. He wondered if William Smith would steal the frame. It was to be hoped that he would not steal the frame. In fact, William Smith would find it very difficult to steal that frame unless he had an accomplice or so.

'This is the last time I shall see *you!*' said Sir Jee to the portrait.

Then he unfastened the catch of one of the windows in the dining-room (as per contract with William Smith), turned out the electric light, and went to bed in the deserted castle.

He went to bed, but not to sleep. It was no part of Sir Jee's programme to sleep. He intended to listen, and he did listen.

And about two o'clock, precisely the hour which William Smith had indicated, he fancied he heard muffled and discreet noises. Then he was sure that he heard them. William Smith had kept his word. Then the noises ceased for a period, and they recommenced. Sir Jee restrained his curiosity as long as he could, and, when he could restrain it no more, he rose and silently opened his bedroom window and put his head out into the nipping night air of Christmas. And by good fortune he saw the vast oblong of the picture, carefully enveloped in sheets, being passed by a couple of dark figures through the dining-room window to the garden outside. William Smith had a colleague, then, and he was taking the frame as well as the canvas. Sir Jee watched the men disappear down the avenue, and they did not reappear. Sir Jee returned to bed.

Yes, he felt himself equal to facing it out with his family and friends. He felt himself equal to pretending that he had no knowledge of the burglary.

Having slept a few hours, he got up early and, half-dressed, descended to the dining-room just to see what sort of a mess William Smith had made.

The canvas of the portrait lay flat on the hearthrug, with the following words written on it in chalk: 'This is no use to me.' It was the massive gold frame that had gone.

Further, as was soon discovered, all the silver had gone. Not a spoon was left in the castle.

A Fine Romance

Bob Larbey

Laura and Mike are made for each other – at least that's
what Laura's younger sister Helen thinks. They aren't so
sure – especially when nothing in their romance seems to
go quite right.

Selway Landscape Gardening. The very name conjured up vistas of softly
rolling lawns, intricately planned rockeries and colourful flower-beds. In
reality, things were – to coin a gardening phrase – rather more down to
earth. The Selway Landscape Gardening centre consisted of a ramshackle
wooden shed, standing forlornly in a cluttered yard. It was a shoestring
enterprise and, although Mike was a good gardener, he had neither the time
nor the money for window-dressing. He worked long, hard hours aided by
the redoubtable Charlie, an irascible old Cockney who was constantly
threatening to unionize the business. As Charlie was the only worker Mike
could afford to employ, these threats of unionization were never carried out
and Charlie had to content himself with dark mutterings about tea-breaks,
job demarcation and rates of pay.

Luckily, the majority of Mike's clients did their business by phone; if they
had called round in person they might conceivably have had second thoughts.
There was a time when the 'office' or shed was virtually indistinguishable
from the yard outside: giant bags of peat and compost sagged over the floor,
gardening tools littered the desk top, and the filing cabinet was full of assorted
flower-pots and seed propagators. Since Laura had come into his life, Mike's
premise had taken on a more ordered existence. She and Helen had spent a
whole day happily reorganizing things – much to Charlie's disgust – and
now the place was almost presentable, in a homely sort of way.

It was one of those Mondays when nothing seemed to be working – Charlie certainly wasn't, and Mike was trying to cope on his own. For the last ten minutes he had been struggling to lift a heavy motor mower from the back of his van. His makeshift ramps of two boards had snapped under the weight and he had improvised, rather cleverly he thought, with two large bales of peat. After a massive effort, he'd managed to bump the mower down from the van on to the bales and was psyching himself up to heave it down the rest of the way when Laura arrived at the yard.

'What are you doing?' she asked, looking at the mower wedged awkwardly on top of the peat bags.

'Oh, it's a sort of initiative test,' Mike explained wearily.

'Come inside and have some tea,' she said. 'That's a better idea altogether,' Mike said with evident relief and, giving the mower one last warning look, he followed her into the office.

As Laura busied herself with the tea things, Mike slumped down on the chair behind the desk.

'Tired?' Laura asked.

'A little bit.'

'Hungry?'

'Yes, I am actually.'

Laura delved deep into her shopping bag and brought out a large tin. 'I've made a cake,' she said, easing it out of the tin and setting it down gingerly on the desk in front of Mike. He eyed it warily. 'Not *that* hungry?' she said, looking at his face.

As with the rest of Laura's cooking, her cake-making left a great deal to be desired. One thing was sure – Laura's cakes were never dull. No two were quite the same, and they constantly surprised with their flavour and texture.

'No,' Mike protested, 'they're getting better all the time, your cakes, all the time. Really.'

Laura cut two generous slices and handed one to Mike. Anxiously she looked on as he took an experimental bite. He nodded appreciatively at first, but the chewing seemed to take rather longer than it should.

'Does it go on a bit?' she asked after a full minute had passed.

'A bit,' Mike mumbled, chewing doggedly. He eventually managed to wash it down with some tea and Laura braved a bite out of her slice. Her 'appreciation' was slightly more honest than Mike's.

'I could be sent to prison for experimenting on you like this,' she declared grimly. She pushed the remains of the cake away and then said anxiously, 'Mike, there's a weekend course I'd like to go on.'

'You don't need to go on a course,' he protested. 'I'm not really that fond of cake, anyway.'

'Not a cookery course. Well, it's a seminar really on "Efficiency Principles in Stock Control" – and it's international and they need interpreters and I've been offered a job,' she said in one breath.

'Where is it?'

'Worthing. It would mean a weekend away, but the money's good. What do you think?'

'You don't have to ask my permission.'

'I'm not asking your permission. I'm asking you what you think.'

'Well, if the money's good,' he said.

'You don't want me to go, do you?'

This was slightly dodgy territory and Mike was being very careful not to venture a firm opinion either way. 'It's up to you,' he said vaguely.

'I don't have to go.'

'All right, don't go.'

'I knew you didn't want me to,' she said with just a trace of satisfaction.

Mike looked heavenwards. There was no winning sometimes where women were concerned. 'I said it's up to you,' he repeated.

'All right. I'll go, then,' she said, but without any real conviction.

'Fine.'

'More tea?' she asked, picking up the teapot.

'Yes please.'

'Mostly blokes, I suppose, at this seminar?' Mike asked casually.

'Mostly. I can't see "Efficiency Principles in Stock Control" really fascinating a lot of women.'

An idea occurred to him. 'Well, why don't I come with you? I could do with a couple of days at the seaside.'

'But I'd be working during the day,' she warned.

'I could bring my bucket and spade.'

'It's pebbles at Worthing.'

'All right. Just my bucket. I could collect pebbles.'

Laura considered the prospect for a while. The idea had its good points. Hotels could be lonely places for a single woman. On the other hand, there were definitely pitfalls – particularly with Mike around. 'I wouldn't want you to be bored,' she said.

It was his turn to be difficult now. 'You don't want me to come, do you?' he said.

'I do, I do. I think it's a lovely idea. I've been on this type of thing before and I've never had company.'

'You did when you went to Brussels,' Mike said darkly. 'You met that Ben.'

She didn't really need to be reminded of this unhappy episode in her life. 'Oh. Yes. That was before we . . .'

Mike felt a bit mean dragging this up. 'Yes, I know.'

'That was a shambles.'

'Won't be this time,' he said cheerfully. 'You'll have Mr Smooth along.'

There was a loud crash from the yard and they both jumped.

'What was that?' Laura asked.

Mike got up and looked out of the window. 'Mr Smooth's mower has just fallen off two bales of peat,' he said.

The hotel where the conference was being staged was an impressive Victorian buiding facing the sea front, and when Mike and Laura trundled up to the entrance in the van they were greeted by an impressively disdainful uniformed flunkey.

Mike climbed out of the van on the passenger side. 'Afternoon.' he said casually.

'Good afternoon, sir – madam,' the doorman said grudgingly. 'Do you have any luggage?' The tone of voice clearly implied that the doorman was expecting, at the very best, a pathetic carrier bag containing a toothbrush and assorted nightwear.

'In the back,' Mike said.

Opening up the back of the van with a flourish, the doorman was confronted by a bewildering array of gardening impedimenta and by peering into the gloom he was just able to discern two suitcases wedged in between a couple of bags of John Innes potting compost. Assuming a suitably disgusted look, he gave a lofty signal to the porter, who hauled out the cases and carried them into the hotel. Mike and Laura started to follow but were called back.

'Excuse me, sir,' the doorman said, indicating the van with a gloved finger. 'This.'

'Yes?'

'The car park is at the rear of the hotel.'

'Good. Stick it round there for me, would you?' Mike said, tossing him the keys with a grin.

Laura looked at Mike approvingly and then turned to the doorman to offer some advice. 'And you have to get in the passenger side and climb across, so mind your hat,' she said airily.

Feeling rather pleased with the way they'd handled things, Mike and Laura swept up the steps into reception. Mike was about to register at the desk when Laura tugged him back by the sleeve of his jacket.

'Mike,' she whispered, looking around nervously, 'when I made the reservation I thought ... Well, we're Mr and Mrs Selway.'

'Why?'

'Well,' she said, and gave him a meaning look.

He immediately caught her drift. 'Yes. Probably better.'

Together, they walked up to the desk where the porter was waiting with their suitcases.

The middle-aged male receptionist greeted them efficiently. 'Good afternoon, sir. Good afternoon, madam.'

'Afternoon,' Mike said breezily. 'We have a reservation – Mr and Mrs Selway.'

'Yes, sir. If you'd care to register,' the receptionist said smoothly, handing him a pen.

Mike signed them both in. To his surprise, he was feeling rather giggly by this time and Laura, who had also caught the mood, was fighting hard not to laugh out loud. They were extremely careful not to catch each other's eye.

'Room 504,' the receptionist said to the porter. Then he turned to Mike and Laura. 'May I ask if either or both of you are here for the seminar?'

'Yes, I am actually,' Laura said.

'Ah. Then we have a lapel badge and an itinerary for you,' he told her, sorting through a box file containing several official envelopes. After a few seconds, a thought occurred to Laura. The same thought also occurred to Mike: 'Mrs Selway' was not going to be among the names. They looked at each other guiltily. Unaware of this complication, the receptionist was still busy searching for the non-existent envelope. 'Selway ... Selway ...' he muttered. 'That's strange ...' He started to go through the file once more.

Laura cleared her throat. 'I ... I might be there as Laura Dalton, actually.'

He looked up. 'Laura Dalton?' he queried.

'Yes.'

He looked at Mike and then looked at Laura. 'I see,' he said, and smiled.

'It's a name I use sometimes ... a professional name,' Laura said, feeling herself blushing stupidly.

'Yes, of course,' the receptionist said smoothly, and smiled again. 'Ah, there we are,' he said, finding the envelope and handing it to Laura. 'Mrs Selway. Laura Dalton.'

Laura Dalton, alias Mrs Selway, smiled weakly. The receptionist suddenly winked at Mike who couldn't resist looking suitably roguish. Laura was by now very keen to get away from this embarrassing scene and started to walk towards the lifts. As Mike followed, he gave her a proprietary pat on her bottom – solely for the benefit of the receptionist.

Upstairs in their room, the porter set down the cases and opened up the curtains. Mike fished in his pocket for a tip. He found a fifty-pence piece and tried to flick it casually to the porter but his aim was badly out and the coin shot straight up in the air and landed somewhere over his own head. Feeling suitably foolish, he fumbled in his pocket for another coin. This time he played it safe and handed it over. The porter thanked him, gave him an odd look, and then left. As soon as the door had closed behind him, Mike got down on his hands and knees to look for the first coin. Laura stood by the bed, hands on hips, looking down at him.

'All right, what was that about?' she demanded.

'Well, he obviously knew,' Mike said.

Laura tapped her foot impatiently. 'I'm aware that he obviously knew. I just don't enjoy that sort of male sniggery stuff, that's all.'

'I thought it was very discreet.'

'You, I mean.'

'Oh. Well, I don't know why you should feel aggrieved. You're the one who's here on business, so what does that make me? A bit of fun for the weekend? I'm the one they'll be sniggering at, I'm the one they'll whisper about.'

She saw the funny side of this. 'Fool,' she smiled.

Mike found the missing coin and stood up. 'Ah! Now – shall I slip into something more comfortable?' he asked provocatively.

'I'd sooner you turned that muzak off,' Laura said. The strains of 'Viva España' were beginning to get to her.

'Right,' Mike sprawled across one of the twin beds in order to reach the controls of the console. After switching several lights on and off, he finally managed to put a stop to the music.

'Are you sure you're not going to be bored, Mike?' Laura said, checking through her working itinerary for the weekend.

'Me? No.'

'It's a pretty intensive schedule, you see. Nearly all day tomorrow, then half a day Sunday.'

'You don't have to eat with them, do you?'

'Oh, no.'

'Well, then. I'll see you for meals – see you in the evenings – nights.'

'You're making this sound like a dirty weekend.'

'Well, it doesn't have to be totally clean, does it?'

Laura smiled at him. 'I'm glad you came,' she said.

There was a knock on the door and a waiter entered. 'You rang for service, sir?' he inquired.

Mike looked puzzled. 'No,' he replied.

The waiter indicated the console. 'Are you sure, sir?'

Mike looked across at the console and noticed a tell-tale red light.

'Oh – rang,' he said guiltily. 'Yes, I did. Sorry, I did ring.'

There was a pause, and the waiter looked confused. 'Is there something I can get you, sir?' he finally asked.

Mike considered this for a moment or two, then, believing himself to be on fairly safe ground, said: 'I don't suppose you could get hold of a bottle of very good champagne at this hour of the afternoon, could you?'

'Certainly, sir,' the waiter said deferentially.

'Oh. Fine,' Mike said, unhappily.

After the waiter had scurried away to fetch the champagne, Laura turned to Mike and pointed out, 'You could have simply told him you pressed the wrong button.'

'Yes, I know, but we've already dropped one clanger. We don't want to get a reputation for it, do we?'

'I wonder how much a bottle of very good champagne costs?' Laura mused.

There was that to consider, of course. 'I'll do something cheap tomorrow,' Mike promised.

Laura smiled grimly. 'You may have to.'

The following morning after a walk – or rather a hobble – along the beach, Mike thought he'd pass a pleasant half-hour or so amusing himself on the Crazy Golf course. The first hole was straightforward enough but the second was proving difficult. The idea was to get the ball through the door of a little house, round the gully inside and then out of the back door where it should, preferably, end up near the hole. Mike struck the ball confidently and watched it shoot neatly into the little house. He was just about to walk round the other side when it rolled back out again – the way it had entered. Painstakingly, Mike placed the ball for another shot, aware by this time that he had collected an audience – a solemn little boy with glasses who was watching him owlishly. Mike hit the ball once more and it disappeared inside the house, paused and then rolled back out again. The owl sidled up in order to get a better view. Self-consciously, Mike tried again, this time giving the ball a firmer tap. The ball went into the little house. There was a longer and more significant pause and Mike was convinced he'd cracked it. He hadn't. The ball reappeared and rolled relentlessly back towards his feet. He sighed and handed his putter to the little boy. The budding Ballesteros hit the ball firmly and expertly. It rolled into the house and shot out the other side before plopping neatly in the hole. The little boy allowed himself a smile of satisfaction before handing the putter back to Mike. It was a childish game anyway, Mike thought, as he called it a day and walked off the course.

After a brisk and chilly walk around the floral gardens, Mike decided to return to the hotel and wait in the bar for Laura. It was still rather early and the place was deserted except for a couple of men sitting at a table and chatting quietly. As he approached the bar Mike noticed that the barman was the waiter from whom he had ordered the expensive bottle of champagne the previous day.

'Good morning, sir,' the waiter said, recognizing the big spender instantly. 'Did you enjoy the champagne yesterday?'

'Yes, very much,' Mike said, trying to give the impression that it wasn't anything out of the ordinary for him to be sipping vintage champagne in the afternoon.

'What'll it be today, sir?'

For a wild moment, Mike considered ordering something exotic. Thinking better of it, he said, 'Half a bitter, please.' He looked idly round the bar and nodded politely to the only other occupants – the two men. The waiter passed Mike his humble beer and Mike took a sip. Beginning to feel rather hungry, he looked at his watch to see how much longer Laura would be.

One of the men noticed this and said cheerily, 'About ten minutes, old man.'

'Sorry?'

'They break for lunch in about ten minutes.'

'Oh. How did you know I was waiting?'

'Experience. Veterans of a hundred seminars, aren't we, Chris?' he said, turning to his companion, who nodded sagely, and said:

'Scarred – scarred veterans.'

'Come and join us,' the first man invited.

Mike wasn't too keen on the idea, but, not wanting to seem stand-offish, he picked up his beer and went to sit with the scarred veterans at their table.

'Mike Selway,' he said, introducing himself.

'David Payne. Chris Grover,' David said.

Chris looked around the bar forlornly. 'Why do we do it?' he said.

'Do what?' Mike asked.

'Let our wives talk us into coming to these things. They're the interpreters – it's their job – but "We'll get bored when we're not working," they say. "We'll have the evenings together," they say. And we fall for it and here we sit – off-season ghosts, wishing we were stronger-willed.'

At this juncture, Mike realized that both Chris and Dave had taken it for granted that he was also married.

'Oh, I see. Yes,' he nodded.

'Did yours wheedle?' Dave asked.

'My ... well, actually no. I volunteered.'

The two old hands shook their heads sadly at this basic beginner's mistake.

'You can't have been married long,' David deduced, smiling sympathetically.

'No,' Mike said, beginning now to wish he'd stayed aloof.

'Why do we do it?' Chris repeated, staring moodily into his lager.

'Men of straw,' David said.

'Mike volunteered,' Chris pointed out.

Mike shuffled about in his seat. It was too late now to change his story. It was one thing lying to hotel receptionists, but maybe Chris and David would think it rather odd.

'Ah, here they come,' David said, as some of the convention members, wearing their badges, started to make their way eagerly towards the bar. David turned to Mike. 'Look here, why don't we all have lunch together – perhaps some of your marital bliss will rub off.'

Mike could have kicked himself. He knew that he'd idiotically lied himself into a tight corner. Just then he spotted Laura, who had entered the bar and was looking around for him among the sea of thirsty conference members.

He jumped up quickly. 'No thanks. We'd love to, but we're going somewhere. Out,' he said, keeping it deliberately vague in case they should invite themselves along.

Laura had seen him by now and was making her way towards his table. Mike strode over to her and, taking her firmly by the elbow, propelled her out of the bar. They reached their room in thirty seconds flat, both badly out of breath.

As soon as they were inside their room, Laura snatched her arm away. 'Will you stop bundling me about?' she complained. 'I don't want to get my coat and I don't want to go out and eat.'

'The fresh air will do you good.'

'It's blowing a gale. The fresh air will do you good.'

'It's blowing a gale. The fresh air will probably blow us both into the sea. What's so wrong eating here?'

'It's very expensive,' Mike lied.

'My lunch is already paid for.'

He quickly changed tack. 'I don't think the food's that good.'

'You said the breakfast was delicious.'

'Yes, but that was breakfast. That doesn't mean to say they won't serve an awful lunch.' He was beginning to flounder and knew it. He opted for action: he crossed to the wardrobe, took out Laura's coat and started to force her into it. 'Now come on – get your coat on.'

'I will not get my coat on!' she said, and, shrugging herself loose, she sat on the bed, her arms folded grimly across her chest.

Mike knew he was beaten. He threw the coat on the other bed and sat down beside her. 'Oh, what's the use!'

'Mike, what *is* the matter with you?'

'All right. Well, I got chatting to a couple of blokes in the bar who are married to two of the girls who are interpreting here and they somehow assumed I was as well.'

She looked at him severely. 'And you somehow didn't tell them otherwise?'

'Well, there's no need to go around shouting it from the roof-tops, is there?'

'I didn't mention roof-tops.'

'Or I could drive up and down the prom with a loudspeaker on top of the van,' he said, beginning to get silly.

'All I'm saying, Mike, is, if the subject comes up, why pretend?'

That was rich, he thought. He couldn't resist this one. 'Like booking us in as Mr and Mrs Selway,' he remarked.

'That was different,' she said huffily.

'I thought it might be.' You really couldn't win.

'Well it was. I booked us in as Mr and Mrs to avoid any ... complications.'

'That's why I went along with these blokes – to avoid complications.'

'Which is why we're stuck up here instead of having lunch in the dining-room like normal people.'

They sat in silence, morosely staring at their reflections in the wardrobe mirror.

'This whole thing is turning into a farce, isn't it?' Mike said. He got up, crossed to the wardrobe and looked carefully inside. 'No.'

'No what?'

'Well, the way things are going there should be a vicar or a French maid in there. Why doesn't anything go in a straight line for us? Everything is loops and jumbles and messes.'

'Oh, cheer up. I don't suppose our exact relationship is vitally interesting to that many people, anyway. Look, we'll have lunch up here – quite cosy, really – and, from now on, if anyone wants to know we just tell the truth. How about that?'

This pep talk seemed to make a difference somehow, and Mike started to cheer up. 'Why not?' he said.

'Good.'

Laura picked up the telephone by the bed. 'Room service, please. No, I don't know which button to press. Thank you. Room service? This is Mr Selway's mistress in Room 504. Do you think we could have lunch in our room?' Confidently, she replaced the receiver.

Mike couldn't believe his ears. He stared at her in exasperation. He could just picture the scene in the kitchens – they'd be having a field day. In fact, they were probably tossing a coin to see who would be the lucky one to serve them the meal. For a moment, he seriously considered hiding in the wardrobe.

The next morning, Mike found himself back on the Crazy Golf course. Like a true golfer, he was determined not to let the old 'Devil Hole' beat him. With practised expertise he struck the ball. With practised expertise the ball rolled into the house and straight back out again – to land at Mike's feet. Mike looked around – luckily the would-be Ballesteros was not there to witness his humiliation a second day running. One more go, he thought. This time the ball seemed to stay inside the little house for much longer and, believing he had cracked it, Mike marched victoriously round to the other side, swinging his club nonchalantly. The ball was nowhere to be seen. Puzzled, he returned to the front of the house. No sign of it. Presumably it was stuck inside. Mike looked around once more to see if anyone was watching and then gave the house a sharp kick. Nothing. Another kick landed on the little whitewashed walls. Nothing. Mike decided that the time had come to retire for good. He walked away. Behind him, his ball rolled out on the right side of the house and plopped neatly into the hole. Unaware of this hole in one, Mike continued his long walk back to the clubhouse.

By the time he reached the hotel, he was in a foul mood. He needed a drink and decided to venture into the bar. It was with some considerable relief that he saw the two world-weary conference veterans, Chris and David, were not in evidence. He ordered half a bitter from the barman, who looked at his watch and said, 'You've got about half an hour if you're waiting for your lady, sir.'

It was a perfectly innocent remark but Mike was, by this time, highly sensitive when it came to the subject of mistresses, wives and girlfriends. He glared at the barman. 'What's that supposed to mean?' he asked, instantly hostile.

'The seminar, sir. The afternoon session has got about half an hour to go.'

'Not that. What's this "your lady" supposed to mean?'

The barman shrugged. 'Just an expression.'

'Why use it on me?'

'I'm sorry, sir,' he apologized. 'I always say it.'

'Well, it's a damn silly thing to say.'

The barman looked hurt. 'I beg your pardon,' he said stiffly. 'I'll say "wife" in future, sir.'

'Look, it's not really any of your business, is it?' Mike said, and turned away. His day was complete when he saw David and Chris walking into the bar.

'Hello there,' David said, spotting him immediately. 'Mind if we join you?'

'No.' Mike was beginning to regret his rather churlish attitude towards the barman and he turned to him. 'Look, I'm sorry about that. It wasn't really fair.'

'That's all right, sir.' He smiled magnanimously.

'What was all that about?' David inquired, sitting down beside Mike.

'That? Oh just … nothing, really.'

'Getting to you, is it?' Chris sympathized. 'Still, so long as you don't start hallucinating.'

'Did you find anywhere decent open for lunch, by the way? I've never been able to,' David said.

'No. We decided to eat in our room in the end.'

'Good Lord!' David said. 'How very romantic! You don't write books like "How to Keep Your Marriage Fresh", do you?'

Mike decided it was time to bite the bullet. 'Laura and I aren't married,' he said apologetically.

'Oh.'

'I should have said,' Mike mumbled, looking fixedly into his beer.

'Jan and I aren't married, either,' David admitted.

Mike looked up. 'But you said ...'

'I know. Nonconformists trying to conform.'

Mike turned to Chris. 'What about you?'

'Me. Oh yes, I'm married. I'm married all right.' He paused and then added: 'Not to the girl I'm here with, though.'

The afternoon session had finished early and Laura was looking for Mike. She stopped at the desk to ask the receptionist. 'Excuse me. Have you seen my ...' she began, and then realized it was the same receptionist who had booked them both in. 'Mr Selway?' she said, beginning to feel herself blushing.

'I'm sorry, madam, I haven't.'

'Never mind,' she said, backing away.

A handsome, middle-aged man who had been standing nearby had reacted positively to the sound of her voice and, as she turned away from the desk, he approached her confidently. 'Excuse me, but I heard you speaking,' he said in perfect English only slightly tinged with a French accent.

Instantly jumping to the conclusion that she was being accosted by some sex freak, Laura backed away. 'What do you mean?' she asked suspiciously. 'I don't know what you're talking about. What do you mean?'

The handsome stranger smiled down at her. 'Your voice. It is the voice that has been talking into my ear in the conference.'

'Oh, I see. Yes,' Laura said, relaxing her attitude.

'A very attractive voice,' the Frenchman said, his deep blue eyes holding hers in a hypnotic stare.

Laura blushed. 'Thank you.'

'Could I ask you a small favour? Would you say *"peut-être"* for me?'

She looked around the crowded lobby. 'What, now?'

'Please.' He smiled. It was an irresistible smile.

'It seems a bit silly,' she said, hesitating. She gave in. 'All right. *Peut-être* – there you are.'

'Aha!' he said, with a deep sigh. 'You know, I have imagined during those very boring speeches how your lips would form the word. They form it beautifully.'

This unexpected and unlooked-for compliment made Laura acutely aware of her lips.

'Would you favour me further by saying *"Produit"*?' he begged.

Laura immediately started to comply but then something odd struck her. 'Just a minute. Why have I been translating English into French for you?' she asked suspiciously. 'You speak English perfectly.'

He was completely unabashed at this accusation. 'Oh, these conferences,' he shrugged, as only the French know how to, 'they can be very tiresome. I prefer to close my eyes and listen to the voice in my ear.' Laura found herself closing her eyes dreamily but stopped herself just in time. 'To imagine the lips forming the words – the face that encircles the lips, the body ...'

Somehow she was aware only of this man and, as though in a trance, she felt herself drawn instinctively towards him, her lips ... Someone pushed past and she realized just where she was and who she was. 'I don't think we should go on with this,' she said weakly.

'But why not, Miss' – he looked at her badge – 'Dalton.'

'It's Mrs – Mrs Dalton,' she said quickly and firmly.

'Miss Dalton!' the receptionist called out to her.

'Yes?' Laura responded, giving herself away without thinking.

'I've just been told that Mr Selway is in the bar.'

'Thank you,' she said foolishly.

The Frenchman smiled regretfully. Feeling very much like a silly schoolgirl, Laura quickly turned on her heels and walked away, not even daring to look over her shoulder.

As she entered the bar, her heart still beating wildly, she saw with some dismay that Mike was engrossed in amiable conversation with David and Chris and their two female companions. Laura tried, unsuccessfully, to attract Mike's attention. Noticing her urgent signals, the barman stepped forward.

'Can I help you, madam?' he asked.

'Yes. Could you ask' – she covered her badge with her hand before continuing – 'Mr Selway to come over, please?'

'Yes, of course,' the barman said, and turned away.

Laura, who was keeping an eye on Mike, was not aware that the Frenchman had followed her into the bar. Seeing her standing alone, he approached her and spoke softly into her ear. 'And where is your Mr Selway? Is he perhaps a phantom?'

Laura jumped guiltily. 'No. He is not a phantom. He's just coming – and he's got a very nasty temper,' she added, for good measure.

Mike came towards her. He was smiling and looking not at all like a man with a very nasty temper.

'Especially when he's smiling,' Laura said quickly.

'The French have a word for this,' he said, shrugging beautifully: 'Defeat' – and he walked away.

'Hello,' Mike said. 'Who was that?'

'Nobody. Just a man who likes the way I say "*peut-être*".'

'*Peut-être*? That means "perhaps", doesn't it?'

'Yes,' she said, thinking secret thoughts.

'Perhaps to what?' Mike asked.

'I didn't say "perhaps" to anything.'

'How is it he likes the way you say it, then?' Mike asked suspiciously.

'I was interpreting for him.'

Mike glared along the bar in the Frenchman's general direction.

'There's no need to glare,' she said.

'Well, who does he think he is?'

'Casanova.'

'And who does he think you are?'

'Your mistress.'

'Oh, he does, does he?'

By this stage, they were so caught up with their discussion that they were forgetting to lower their voices, and the barman was able to hear every word.

'Well, I am your mistress,' Laura said, matter-of-factly.

'Yes. Well, I don't like the word. See over there' – and he pointed to the women sitting with Chris and David – 'they're mistresses.'

Laura had a good look. Both women were younger than her and very attractive. 'I don't know whether to feel insulted or flattered,' she said.

The barman could no longer remain silent on the subject. 'Flattered, madam. That's how I'd feel,' he said.

'Would you?' Laura asked, genuinely interested.

'Oh, yes.' He turned to Mike. 'Would your lady like a drink, sir?' he inquired politely.

Mike suddenly realized that he liked the sound of the word as well. 'Yes. Thank you. My lady would like a drink,' he said, smiling.

'Champagne?' the waiter suggested.

'Half a bitter,' Laura said.

'Worth a try,' the barman said regretfully.

'They were the ones who said they were married,' Mike said.

'Oh.'

'Do you know, I'm getting the distinct feeling that we're the only respectable couple here.'

Laura looked round the bar and then pointed out a grey-haired elderly couple sitting by the door.

'Well, almost.'

'Shall we go out to dinner tonight?' she asked.

'Well, I look at it this way. We've already blown half your pay on one bottle of good champagne. Why not blow the other half on another bottle and have dinner in our room?'

Mike was looking decidedly cheeky and Laura quickly got the message. She looked at him and smiled slowly. '*Peut-être,*' she said, relishing the pout.

Mrs Packletide's Tiger

Saki (H. H. Munro)

It was Mrs Packletide's pleasure and intention that she should shoot a tiger. Not that the lust to kill had suddenly descended on her, or that she felt that she would leave India safer and more wholesome than she had found it, with one fraction less of wild beast per million of inhabitants. The compelling motive for her sudden deviation towards the footsteps of Nimrod was the fact that Loona Bimberton had recently been carried eleven miles in an aeroplane by an Algerian aviator, and talked of nothing else; only a personally procured tiger-skin and a heavy harvest of Press photographs could successfully counter that sort of thing. Mrs Packletide had already arranged in her mind the lunch she would give at her house in Curzon Street, ostensibly in Loona Bimberton's honour, with a tiger-skin rug occupying most of the foreground and all the conversation. She had also already designed in her mind the tiger-claw brooch that she was going to give Loona Bimberton on her next birthday. In a world that is supposed to be chiefly swayed by hunger and by love Mrs Packletide was an exception; her movements and motives were largely governed by dislike of Loona Bimberton.

Circumstances proved propitious. Mrs Packletide had offered a thousand rupees for the opportunity of shooting a tiger without overmuch risk or exertion, and it so happened that a neighbouring village could boast of being the favoured rendezvous of an animal of respectable antecedents, which had been driven by the increasing infirmities of age to abandon gamekilling and confine its appetite to the smaller domestic animals. The prospect of earning the thousand rupees had stimulated the sporting and commercial instinct of the villagers; children were posted night and day on the outskirts of the local jungle to head the tiger back in the unlikely event of his attempting to roam away to fresh hunting grounds, and the cheaper kinds of goats were left about with elaborate carelessness to keep him satisfied with his present quarters. The one great anxiety was lest he should die of old age before the date appointed for the memsahib's shoot. Mothers carrying their babies home through the jungle after the day's work in the fields hushed their singing lest they might curtail the restful sleep of the venerable herd-robber.

The great night duly arrived, moonlit and cloudless. A platform had been constructed in a comfortable and conveniently placed tree, and thereon crouched Mrs Packletide and her paid companion, Miss Mebbin. A goat, gifted with a particularly persistent bleat, such as even a partially deaf tiger might be reasonably expected to hear on a still night, was tethered at the correct distance. With an accurately sighted rifle and a thumb-nail pack of patience cards the sportswoman awaited the coming of the quarry.

'I suppose we are in some danger?' said Miss Mebbin.

She was not actually nervous about the wild beast, but she had a morbid dread of performing an atom more service than she had been paid for.

'Nonsense,' said Mrs Packletide; 'it's a very old tiger. It couldn't spring up here even if it wanted to.'

'If it's an old tiger I think you ought to get it cheaper. A thousand rupees is a lot of money.'

Louisa Mebbin adopted a protective elder-sister attitude towards money in general, irrespective of nationality or denomination. Her energetic intervention had saved many a rouble from dissipating itself in tips in some Moscow hotel, and francs and centimes clung to her instinctively under circumstances which would have driven them headlong from less sympathetic hands. Her speculations as to the market depreciation of tiger remnants were cut short by the appearance on the scene of the animal itself. As soon as it caught sight of the tethered goat it lay flat on the earth, seemingly less from a desire to take advantage of all available cover than for the purpose of snatching a short rest before commencing the grand attack.

'I believe it's ill,' said Louisa Mebbin, loudly in Hindustani, for the benefit of the village headman, who was in ambush in a neighbouring tree.

'Hush!' said Mrs Packletide, and at that moment the tiger commenced ambling towards his victim.

'Now, now!' urged Miss Mebbin with some excitement; 'if he doesn't touch the goat we needn't pay for it.' (The bait was an extra.)

The rifle flashed out with a loud report, and the great tawny beast sprang to one side and then rolled over in the stillness of death. In a moment a crowd of excited natives had swarmed on to the scene, and their shouting speedily carried the glad news to the village, where a thumping of tomtoms took up the chorus of triumph. And their triumph and rejoicing found a ready echo in the heart of Mrs Packletide; already that luncheon-party in Curzon Street seemed immeasurably nearer.

It was Louisa Mebbin who drew attention to the fact that the goat was in death-throes from a mortal bullet-wound, while no trace of the rifle's deadly work could be found on the tiger. Evidently the wrong animal had been hit, and the beast of prey had succumbed to heart-failure, caused by the sudden report of the rifle, accelerated by senile decay. Mrs Packletide was pardonably annoyed at the discovery; but, at any rate, she was the possessor of a dead tiger, and the villagers, anxious for their thousand rupees, gladly connived at the fiction that she had shot the beast. And Miss Mebbin was a paid companion. Therefore did Mrs Packletide face the cameras with a light heart, and her pictured fame reached from the pages of the *Texas Weekly Snapshot* to the illustrated Monday supplement of the *Novoe Vremya*. As for Loona Bimberton, she refused to look at an illustrated paper for weeks, and her letter of thanks for the gift of a tiger-claw brooch was a model of repressed emotions. The luncheon-party she declined; there are limits beyond which repressed emotions become dangerous.

From Curzon Street the tiger-skin rug travelled down to the Manor House, and was duly inspected and admired by the county, and it seemed a fitting and appropriate thing when Mrs Packletide went to the County Costume Ball in the character of Diana. She refused to fall in, however, with Clovis's tempting suggestion of a primeval dance party, at which every one should wear the skins of beasts they had recently slain. 'I should be in rather a Baby Bunting condition,' confessed Clovis, 'with a miserable rabbit-skin or two to wrap up in, but then,' he added, with a rather malicious glance at Diana's proportions, 'my figure is quite as good as that Russian dancing boy's.'

'How amused every one would be if they knew what really happened,' said Louisa Mebbin a few days after the ball.

'What do you mean?' asked Mrs Packletide quickly.

'How you shot the goat and frightened the tiger to death,' said Miss Mebbin, with her disagreeably pleasant laugh.

'No one would believe it,' said Mrs Packletide, her face changing colour as rapidly as though it were going through a book of patterns before post-time.

'Loona Bimberton would,' said Miss Mebbin. Mrs Packletide's face settled on an unbecoming shade of greenish white.

'You surely wouldn't give me away?' she asked.

'I've seen a week-end cottage near Dorking that I should rather like to buy,' said Miss Mebbin with seeming irrelevance. 'Six hundred and eighty, freehold. Quite a bargain, only I don't happen to have the money.'

Louisa Mebbin's pretty week-end cottage, christened by her 'Les Fauves', and gay in summer-time with its garden borders of tigerlilies, is the wonder and admiration of her friends.

'It is a marvel how Louisa manages to do it,' is the general verdict.

Mrs Packletide indulges in no more big-game shooting.

'The incidental expenses are so heavy,' she confides to inquiring friends.

Gorilla Suit

John Shepley

Man with gorilla suit or gorilla to help publicize newest
Bing Crosby – Bob Hope – Dorothy Lamour Technicolor
comedy 'Road to Bali.' 1 day's employment. Apply Bali-
Bally Dept, Paramount Pictures, 11th floor, 1501 Broadway,
Monday AM.

– Classified Advertisement in the New York *Times*
Sunday, January 25, 1953.

Toto judged it a very dull issue of the Sunday *Times*. He had read the theater
section, admitting himself reluctantly in agreement with the critics: Broadway
was having another disappointing season. He had not been impressed by any
of the book reviews; the news was the usual alternating succession of horrors
and trivia; the articles in the magazine section had left him cold. Finally,
glumly, he had begun the crossword puzzle, much to the amusement of the
crowd on the other side of the bars. They always distracted and irritated
him particularly, these familial Sunday crowds, the mournful dutiful fathers,
the stout women in hats, the noisy children with candy-smeared faces and
sticky pointing fingers, but nevertheless he had become fairly absorbed ...
until he came to 143 Across: '*U.S. experimental $4 gold pieces, 1879–80.*' A seven-
letter word, the sixth 'A.' But who but a financial historian could be expected
to know what it was? Specialization was creeping even into the simplest
Sunday pastimes – it was unfair. Standing to the front of the crowd and
holding the string of a pink balloon was a kind-looking lady with dim blue
eyes. Perhaps *she* was a financial historian – Toto earnestly approached her.
She shrieked, letting go of the balloon, and as it floated upwards, the children
twittered in chorus and some cried. Toto gave up, threw down pencil and

puzzle, and took refuge on the topmost perch of the cage, where he clung
sulkily until the crowd, bored by his inactivity, moved away. Then he
dropped back to the floor, and, consumed by a sense of futility, began leafing
through the Classified Advertisements.

And there he came across it. Incredulous, he blinked his eyes, scratched
his head and sides, read it through a second, then a third, time ... but no,
it was no mistake: there in cold print was a job opening for a man with a
gorilla suit *or a gorilla* to help publicize Dorothy Lamour's latest picture.
Toto pulled himself up, reflecting that he didn't need a job, that in a sense
he had one already, but the implications contained in the little boxed
announcement would not be silenced, the fun it would be, the glory (he
might even be photographed with Dorothy Lamour!), though only for one
day. He found himself skipping and swinging all over the cage.

But when, with a certain critical caution, he returned to peruse the ad for
a fourth time, subtle qualms began to arise in his mind. Perhaps what they
wanted was a man with a gorilla suit or *a man with* a gorilla – in which case,
there was no point in *his* applying. It was really rather obscure, just what
they thought they wanted, and Toto, trying to figure it out, scratched himself
for a long time. Yet, if the idea was to have a gorilla, simulated or otherwise,
why shouldn't one apply? And indeed, there was a simple solution: if they
insisted that the gorilla be humanly escorted, why not show the ad to his
keeper, Mr McCready, while pointing with especial emphasis to '*11th floor,
1501 Broadway, Monday AM*'?

But no, that wouldn't do, he immediately recognized the impracticality of
it. It wasn't that Mr McCready would refuse – he wouldn't – but he wouldn't
agree either. He would be doubtful; he would give a pompous little laugh,
a nervous cough; he would look puzzled and hurt; until Toto, feeling guilty,
would withdraw his request altogether. Or, on the off-chance that Mr
McCready did agree, it would be only with the understanding that he must
first ask the directors, and he would so procrastinate in doing so that (even
assuming that the directors ultimately gave their approval) it would then be
too late to apply for the job. Someone else would already have enjoyed the
brief, glorious limelight was Dorothy Lamour. No, the only thing to do, Toto
decided, was to present Mr McCready and the zoo authorities with a *fait
accompli*.

He could hardly wait for closing time, when the visitors would vanish and
the doors be locked, so that he might have a little quiet in which to think
out a plan. Surely, he reasoned, as he watched the attendants sweeping up

the trash left by the departed crowd, surely he would be hired in preference
to any man dressed up like a gorilla. It shouldn't be difficult to beat out *that*
kind of competition. But suppose *other gorillas* applied, ones with previous
experience in the theater or public relations? This prospect so frightened him
that he decided to abandon the whole idea. He curled himself up in a fetid
darkness, sadly carressing his toes and listening to familiar noises, metal
somewhere scraping against cement, mechanical rumblings in an underground
distance, the nightly asthmatic wheezing of his neighbor, an old prowling
mandrill. Toto closed his eyes, covered his ears, went on arguing to himself
... what was there to lose? Nothing, really. It wasn't even as though he were
risking anything, for the worst that could happen was that he simply wouldn't
get the job. All the same, it wouldn't be easy to get out of the cage.

Nothing ventured, nothing gained. It was tiresome having to bolster oneself
with truisms – still, cheerfully enough, he set about testing the bars, one by
one. He went all over the cage, without finding a single loose bar. He
groaned, realizing how much time he had already wasted, for not only must
he be out of the cage and away from the zoo before Mr McCready arrived
in the morning, but he must be at 1501 Broadway in time to be among the
first in line. Now, painfully, he tried to squeeze himself between the bars,
aware that the mandrill had stopped his prowling, was crouching there on
his haunches, his eyes a phosphorescent green, watching it all with the
bemused curiosity of the senile. Toto went on pushing and lunging, but all
he succeeded in doing was to scrape some patches of fur from his forearms
and sides. And it was so important to look his best!

It was useless, the space between the bars was too small. In a final,
despairing, almost whimsical gesture, he tried the door – it opened easily.
But that showed that they *trusted* him! Astonished, he could only stand there
holding the catch of the door, wondering if it would not be ungrateful to
take advantage of such trust. Ah, but if he got the job, how proud Mr
McCready would be! Or would he? Toto wavered ... the mandrill resumed
wheezing ... familiar sounds. And then he heard an unfamiliar sound, a
rustling of jungle leaves, and the bright image of Dorothy Lamour stepped
out into the sunlight. Toto leapt confidently out of the cage.

But he had forgotten that the door of the building itself would be locked.
He kicked it, pulled it, beat on it with his fists, which only awoke the spider
monkeys, spiteful little creatures who tumbled and gibbered and pointed
their fingers at him. Then the most fearful racket broke out – the chimpanzees
woke up and began screaming, a chorus of baboons howled, even the mandrill

joined in. *'What's going on in there?'* – and the door opened, pressing Toto behind it, as the night guard came in, cursing softly and flashing his light about the cages. Everybody, blinking, became silent, and Toto had just enough time to slip around the door and hide himself behind a low cement wall before the guard re-emerged and turned the lock. Toto held his breath, but the guard merely went away whistling, swinging his extinguished light.

He rested, until the pounding of his heart subsided and the guard was out of sight. Then, happily, cutting a little caper, he set out across the park.

It was quarter to nine when he took the elevator to the eleventh floor at 1501 Broadway. Again he was feeling worried and uncomfortable. For one thing, he was hungry, and he was afraid he had caught cold during two hours of furtive slumber in some bushes near the skating rink. And all the way from the park, down Broadway to 44th Street, he had reproached himself for forgetting to bring along the Classified Advertisements Section of the *Times*. It would have been most helpful in explaining his presence on the streets had a policeman or anyone else stopped him. But fortunately no one had stopped him. The people in the street had all passed him by with Monday-morning expressions on their faces.

In the crowded elevator, he tried to spruce himself up, brushing from his shoulders and legs the bits of dried grass that clung there from his sleeping in the park. But a murmur of protest arose – 'Hey, quit y'r shovin', Mac,' said a man on his right, who, Toto suddenly saw, had a rolled-up gorilla suit under his arm. He resigned himself to standing quietly, fervently hoping that he had got rid of most of the grass.

The elevator emptied itself at the eleventh floor, they all streamed out together, and to Toto's amazement, each of his fellow passengers was carrying a gorilla suit – some in a neat bundle with the jaws gaping out from under the owner's arm, some draped across human shoulders with a gorilla head bobbing along ludicrously a few inches from the floor, some apparent only by the patches of fur sticking out from the apertures of shabby cardboard suitcases or corrugated boxes. He had not expected so much competition, but there was at least one cause for relief – neither getting out of the elevator nor in the crowd waiting at the door of the Bali-Bally Department was there a single other real gorilla. He joined the increasing throng milling about the unopened office.

Although he knew it was not quite fair to do so, he could not help feeling a little contemptuous. Not only were they not gorillas, they were a sorry lot of men – wan, and thin, and old. He overheard a bit of conversation, one man saying to another, 'Hey, I seen you before! Wasn't you a Santa Claus in Herald Square last Christmas?'

'Yeah. But I don't remember seein' you.'

'I was there awright, Mac, you shoulda looked. I tried to get into Macy's, Gimbel's, anyplace warm, but the best I could get was one of them street jobs. It's a tough racket.'

'Sure is,' the other agreed. 'I got an Easter Bunny job lined up maybe, but I don't know what I'll do till then if I don't get this thing.' And he patted his gorilla suit, while the first man eyed him jealously. 'Even if it *is* just one day.'

And now Toto began to feel sorry for them, wondering if it was not grasping and presumptuous of him to be there at all. He, for whom food and shelter had been generously provided, who had even a recognized social function, had descended to trying to take work away from individuals who really needed it. Perhaps he should turn back ... but at that point the elevator opened again, another mob of men with gorilla suits poured out, and they were followed by a young woman, who, after fumbling in her purse, produced a key and unlocked the door of the Bali-Bally Department.

'Come in, all of you,' she said. 'Take seats along the wall. Mr Phineas will be here any minute to conduct the interviews.'

Toto thought her very attractive, in her hard blond way, though by no means so beautiful as Dorothy Lamour. Even so, it occurred to him, it might be fun to whisk her away for a weekend atop the Empire State Building while crowds gathered and the police hovered in helicopters; but he quickly suppressed this whimsical idea, and filed respectfully into the office along with the other applicants.

There were not enough chairs for all of them. Toto joined a nervous little group standing by the wall, while the blond secretary busied herself at her desk. 'I might as well start the ball rolling,' she announced, 'while we're waiting for Mr Phineas. I certainly didn't expect so many. Let me make it clear at the beginning that we want somebody experienced and responsible, preferably with references. There's every chance that Miss Lamour will ask to be photographed with the successful applicant.'

Toto's heart trembled, beat faster. He had no experience to offer, and no references, but he took pride in thinking he was responsible. And how could they possibly not prefer *him* over these wretched fakes? And to be photographed with ... with ... 'I'll take your names,' he heard the secretary saying. 'You first.' The man next to him started forward. 'No no, the other one. The one that's already got his suit on.' Slowly, fearfully, Toto approached the desk.

'Name?' she said, pencil poised.

. . .

'Speak up. Don't mumble so. What is it?'

. . .

She threw down the pencil. 'Oh, never mind! I can't take everybody's name anyway – there are too many. Why the hell didn't that stupid Phineas do all this through an employment agency?'

Toto, ashamed of his failure to communicate with her, desperately racked his brain. He might, of course, establish for her his authenticity by performing some of the indelicate little antics that so unfailingly delighted visitors to the zoo ... But no, that would probably do more harm than good, would, in fact, quite ruin his chances of being thought responsible. It was better to retire and wait for Mr Phineas.

'I can't say your costume is very convincing,' she called after him as he backed away from the desk. 'Still, it's up to Phineas to decide – Oh, *Mr Phineas!*'

A little bowlegged man had bounded in, breathlessly throwing off his hat and overcoat. 'I'm terribly sorry, Eloise honey,' he cried, 'to have dumped all this on you. Honestly, I didn't *realize*. Next time, sweetie, I'll do it all through an employment agency and let *them* screen people first.'

'Oh, I don't mind, Mr Phineas,' she said, with a brave smile.

'That's the spirit, girl!' He patted her on the shoulder. 'All right, all you Tarzans, let's have a look at you! Into the monkey suits and make it snappy!' And glancing at Toto, he added aside to Eloise, 'A-ha, a real eager beaver!'

A real eager *gorilla*. But he stood patiently, waiting while all the men clambered into their suits. 'Line up!' commanded Mr Phineas, and they all took their places, as he walked along examining them with a shrewd, suspicious eye.

'Just look at *this* one!' he shrieked, pointing to an especially seedy individual standing next to Toto. 'The *buttons* even show. He might as well have turned up in his long winter underwear! I'll bet there's not a *zipper* in the whole crowd.' Toto was on the point of stepping forward to demonstrate that he had neither buttons nor zippers – most important of all, didn't need them – but before he could think of a decorous approach, Mr Phineas had moved on.

'*Honest*, Eloise,' he was saying, sauntering up and down with his hands on his hips, 'did you *ever* in your life see such a bunch of mangy, moth-eaten gorillas? That one there' – he flipped a hand in Toto's direction – 'isn't *too* bad, I suppose. What do *you* think, honey?'

'Gee, Mr Phineas, I *just* don't know,' she said, gazing at them all in bewildered disappointment. 'Would you like me to call up one of the employment agencies after all?'

'No, we haven't got time. It'll have to be one of these.' And he gave Toto a long critical look.

Toto's heart was bursting with hope and joy, but he made every effort to contain himself. And then it happened, in all its horror – the door opened, and in came another *real gorilla*, an arrogant creature carrying a shining aluminum suitcase.

'I'm sorry, sir, I think we have *enough* applicants already –' Eloise began, but the newcomer, grinning, merely slavered at her lecherously. He sat down his suitcase, opened it, and – to Toto's stunned mortification – took out a lustrous gorilla suit, into which he deftly proceeded to zipper himself. This process completed, he made a little bow to Mr Phineas and Eloise, offering his arm for their inspection.

'Why, it's not gorilla fur at all,' said Mr Phineas, feeling the suit. 'It's *genuine*, fine-spun, combed, nylon-acetate!'

'It's beautiful,' breathed the secretary. 'It's perfectly divine.'

'And so *chic*,' marveled Mr Phineas. 'Well, that settles it. He's definitely hired. All the rest of you can go now. Leave by the side door, please.'

The men, grumbling and disconsolate, took off their gorilla suits and trooped out. Toto heard Eloise saying to the successful applicant, 'It's just for one day, but you'll still have to fill out a withholding statement. What's your social security –' And then he was in the hallway, shuffling sadly towards the elevator. 'Too bad, eh, Mac?' said the man next to him. 'That's what always happens.' But Toto had no idea whom he might be addressing.

He reached the street and began walking dejectedly up Broadway. Hurrying pedestrians brushed against him, but he hardly noticed them. He tried to take comfort in the knowledge that he hadn't really needed a job, and he only hoped that Mr McCready wouldn't be too angry when he presented himself back at the zoo. At a corner newsstand he suddenly stopped, his attention caught by a screaming headline in the *Daily News:*

DRAGNET OUT FOR ESCAPED GORILLA

And the *Journal-American* announced in bold red letters:

TERROR GRIPS CITY AS KILLER
APE PROWLS!

while underneath was a photograph, *his*, Toto's, with the caption, 'Have You Seen This Gorilla?' and the telephone number to call in case you had. People milled about the newsstand trying to get a look at the picture, a few women clutched their bosoms, and one of them stepped on Toto's foot. 'Oh, excuse me,' she said, looking him right in the face.

Still, someone soon would recognize him – it was only a matter of time. He wondered whether to strike out boldly along Broadway or try to hide in some side-street, and as he stood, hesitating on the corner, a squad car stopped, and a policeman got out and tapped him on the shoulder.

Going Home Time

Joyce Grenfell

Children – it's time to go home, so finish tidying up and put on your hats and coats. Some of our Mummies are here for us, so hurry up.

Billy won't be long, Mrs Binton. He's on hamster duty.

Now let's see if we can't all help each other.

Janey – I said help each other. Help Bobbie carry that chair, don't pin him against the wall with it.

We're having a go at our good neighbour policy here, Mrs Binton, but it doesn't always . . .

Neville, off the floor, please. Don't lie there.

And Sidney, stop painting, please.

Because it's time to go home.

Well, you shouldn't have started another picture, should you. What is it this time?

Another blue man! Oh, I see, so it is.

All right, you can make it just a little bit bluer, but only one more brushful, please, Sidney.

We don't think he's very talented, but we feel it's important to encourage their self-expression. You never know where it might lead . . .

Rachel. Gently – help Teddy *gently* into his coat.

It's a lovely coat. Teddy, what's wrong with it?

Oh. It looks like a boy's coat when you wear it. And lots of boys wear pink.

Poor wee mite, he has three older sisters!

Neville, I said get up off the floor.

Who shot you dead?

David did? Well, I don't suppose he meant to. He may have meant to then, but he doesn't mean it now, and anyhow I say you can get up.

No, don't go and shoot David dead, because it's time to go home.

George. What did I tell you not to do? Well, don't do it.

And Sidney, don't wave that paint-brush about like that, you'll splash somebody. LOOK OUT, DOLORES!

Sidney! ... It's all right, Dolores, you aren't hurt, you're just surprised. It was only a nice soft brush. But you'd better go and wash your face before you go home.

Because it's all blue.

Sidney, I saw you deliberately put that paint-brush up Dolores's little nostril.

No, it wasn't a jolly good shot. It was ... I don't want to discuss it, Sidney. Now go and tell Dolores you're sorry.

Yes, now.

Thank you, Hazel, for putting the chairs straight for me.

You are a great helper.

Thank you.

And thank you, Dicky, for closing the cupboard door for me.

Dicky, is there somebody *in* the cupboard?

Well, let her out at once.

Are you all right, Peggy? What did you go into the cupboard for?

But we don't have mices – I mean mouses – in our toy cupboard. Mouses only go where there is food, and we don't have any food in our toy cupboard.

When did you hide a bicky in there?

Every day!

Well, perhaps we have got mices in our toy cupboard. I'll have to look.

No, you go and get your coat on.

Dicky – We never shut people in cupboards.

Because they don't like it.

What do you mean, she's puggy? Peggy's puggy?

Oh, she's got puggy hands. But you don't have to hold her hand ...

Well, you must ask her nicely to let go.

Well, if she won't let go ...

You'll have to work it out for yourself, Dicky.

Edgar and Timmy – your knitted caps are not for playing tug-of-war with Look, now the pom-pom's come off.

Whose is it?

Well, give it back to Sidney.

Where are your caps?

Well, go and ask Sidney to give them back to you.

Turn round, Geoffrey. You've got your wellingtons on the wrong feet.

Yes, you have. You'll have to take them off and start again.

Why can't you reach?

Well, undo your coat and then you can bend.

Take off your woolly gloves.

And your scarf.

You can keep your balaclava on. How many jerseys are you wearing?

Heavens. No wonder you can't bend.

Caroline, come and help Geoffrey.

Don't kick her, Geoffrey. She's come to help.

Sidney, I told you to put that paint-brush down ... LOOK OUT, DOLORES!

Well, *that* wasn't a very good shot, was it? You didn't mean to put it in her ear, did you?

Well, you shouldn't have.

You're all right Dolores. It was just a bit of a surprise, but you'll have to go and wash again.

Because you've got a blue ear.

Sidney, I'm ashamed of you, a big boy of four, and she's only just three.

And Sidney, what have you done with Timmy and Edgar's caps?

No, I'm not going to guess.

And I don't want to know they are hidden in a special secret place, I want to know exactly where they are.

No, I'm not going to try and find them. You're going to tell me where they are.

Well, go and get them out of the waste-paper basket at once. Waste-paper baskets aren't for putting caps in.

Now go and say you are sorry to Dolores.

Yes, again.

We think his aggression is diminishing, but we do have setbacks.

Lavinia, is that your coat you've got on? It looks so enormous.

Oh, you're going to grow into it. I see.

Hazel, thank you for helping Betty into her jacket.

Just zip her up once. Not up and down.

No, Neville, you can't have a turn.

No, children, you can't all zip Betty.

Jenny, come here.

Jenny, when we have paid a visit to the littlest room, what do we do?

We pull our knickers up again.
Good-bye, Hazel, Good-bye, Bobbie. Good-bye, everybody.
Good-bye, Mrs Binton.
Hurry up, Sidney, because you'll keep your Mummy waiting.
Well, your Granny then.
Somebody is coming to take you away, aren't they, Sidney?
Good.
No, you won't see me tomorrow, Sidney.
Tomorrow is Saturday, thank heaven.

Opera Interval

Joyce Grenfell

Bravo ... Bravo.

(*Applauding*) Oh, how lovely.

Wasn't it heavenly?

Bravo ... Bravo.

Isn't she marvellous? That voice. It really is celestial. And he was *so* good, wasn't he? The one in the middle. The one in blue. You know, the main man. *Lovely* voice.

(*Gets up to let people pass*) Can you manage?

Do you want to go out and mingle a little and see who is here – or shall we stay here and digest what we've just heard? All right – let's digest now and mingle later.

Do you know, I think that when I was very very young I heard Belushkin sing that part, only he sang it lower.

I must confess I got a little confused in the story, did you? I know she's a twin and there was a muddle, but I can't *quite* remember why she starts off in that pretty white dress, and then when she comes in again later she's dressed as a Crusader. It's probably a disguise. But one wonders why?

She's the daughter of the man in black, I suppose. The one who sang at the top of the stairs with that lovely voice. Let's look it up and see who is who.

'Don Penzalo, a wealthy landowner.' (That's probably her father.) 'Mildura ...' that's her I think ... 'daughter to the Duke of Pantilla.' Oh, not Don Penzalo then. No ... 'The Duke of Pantilla, father of Mildura.' Well, there we are.

'Zelda, an old nurse.' Yes, we have seen her. She's the one with two sticks and rather a rumbly voice, remember?

'Fedora, a confidante.'

'Boldoni, a bodyguard.'

'Don Alfredo, a general in the Crusaders.' Ah, Crusaders.

'Chorus of Fisherfolk, Villagers, Haymakers, Courtiers and Crusaders.' We haven't seen the Courtiers and Crusaders yet, but we've seen the fisherfolk, villagers and haymakers – yes, we have. They were the ones with fishing-nets and rakes and things.

You know, one ought to do one's homework before one goes to the opera. I've got a little book that tells you all the stories, but I never can remember to look it up till I get home, then it's too late.

Let's see what we have just seen:

Oh, it was a market place – I thought so.

'Act I. The Market Place of Pola.'

'As dawn breaks over the sleepy village of Pola in Pantilla fisherfolk on their way to work join with villagers and haymakers to express their concern over the Royalist cause.'

Oh ... *that's* what they were doing.

'Mildura pines for her lover, Don Alfredo, who is preparing to leave for the Crusades' ... ah, there you are ... 'and disguises herself in order to join him in Malta.'

Oh, Malta. Dear Malta. How I love it.

Do you know it well?

I used to go there a great deal when I was a gel, and one had such fun. I used to go and stay with darling old Admiral Sir Cardington Dexter and his wife Nadia. Did you know Nadia? She was a *little* strange! He met her in Casablanca! Yes, exactly. But I won't hear a word against her, because she was always very kind to me. Oh, it was such fun in those days. So gay. Parties, parties and more parties. Heavenly young men in uniform – white naval uniform, quite irresistible, and you know, honestly, one hardly noticed the Maltese at all.

Now, 'Mildura disguises herself in order to join Don Alfredo, but Don Penzalo' (I'm sure he's the one in blue) 'seeks revenge for a slight done him by the Duke and plans to abduct Mildura, whom he suspects of political duplicity, and flee with her to Spain.' Oh, Spain. Very *mouvementé*! Do you know Spain well?

No, Italy is my passion. *Bella Italia*. I always feel very hard done by if I don't get my annual ration of *Bella Italia*. It's so nourishing.

'Zelda, an old nurse, reads warnings in the stars and begs Mildura to delay her departure until the harvest is gathered in. Don Penzalo does not recognize

Mildura and challenges her to a duet.' That's what it says: 'Challenges her to a du –' Oh, I am idiotic. The light's so bad in here.

(Gets up to let people pass back to their seats)

I'm so sorry. Can you get by? Ow – No, it's all right, only a tiny little ladder ...

One really ought to come to the opera more often. I do love it so. My mother used to go a great deal. She loved it, and, of course, she was very musical. Oh, very. She had a most enchanting gift, she played the piano entirely by heart, well I suppose you could call it by ear. She never had a lesson in her life. She would go to an opera, hear it, and then come home and play the entire thing (oh, I'm so sorry, did I hit you?). She'd play the entire thing from memory without a note of music. So, of course, I grew up knowing all the lovely, lovely tunes one knows so well. It is such an advantage – one step ahead of everyone else.

No, alas, I don't play.

(Sighs) Now, let's see what the next act holds in store for us. 'Act II. The Cloisters of San Geminiani Cathedral.'

I wonder if I've been there. So many lovely *Cathedrale* all over *Bella Italia*.

'Mildura, no longer disguised (oh, good), is on her way to Mass with her confidante, Fedora, and Boldoni, a faithful bodyguard. Playfully she takes off her chaplet of roses and puts it on Boldoni, who laughs.' That sounds rather fun.

'Don Alfredo, forewarned of Penzalo's plot, arrives unannounced at the Cathedral with a band of Crusaders, ostensibly to celebrate the Feast of Saint Ogiano.'

Are you getting hungry?

It's a very long opera, three more acts. Are you sure you aren't hungry? I should have fed you better. A boiled egg isn't enough for opera. I do hope you won't wilt.

No, I *love* it. I'm afraid its all food and drink to me. Oh, there the lights are going down – its too exciting – I'm like a child at the theatre.

(Applauds) I don't know who the conductor is, but he's supposed to be very well known.

Oh dear, we don't know where we are, do we. Well, we do. We're in the Cloisters of the Cathedral of St Geminiano. *(Turns to hush other talkers)* Sh. Sh. Sh.

Soaked in Seaweed

or

Upset in the Ocean

(*An Old-fashioned Sea-story*)

Stephen Leacock

It was in August in 1867 that I stepped on board the deck of the *Saucy Sally*, lying in dock at Gravesend, to fill the berth of second mate.

Let me first say a word about myself.

I was a tall, handsome young fellow, squarely and powerfully built, bronzed by the sun and the moon (and even copper-coloured in spots from the effect of the stars), and with a face in which honesty, intelligence, and exceptional brain-power were combined with Christianity, simplicity, and modesty.

As I stepped on the deck, I could not help a slight feeling of triumph as I caught sight of my sailor-like features reflected in a tar-barrel that stood beside the mast, while a little later I could scarcely repress a sense of gratification as I noticed them reflected again in a bucket of bilge-water.

'Welcome on board, Mr Blowhard,' called out Captain Bilge, stepping out of the binnacle and shaking hands across the taffrail.

I saw before me a fine, sailor-like man from thirty to sixty, clean-shaven except for an enormous pair of whiskers, a heavy beard, and a thick moustache, powerful in build, and carrying his beam well aft, in a pair of broad duck trousers, across the back of which there would have been room to write a history of the British Navy.

Beside him were the first and third mates, both of them being quiet men of poor stature, who looked at Captain Bilge with what seemed to me an apprehensive expression in their eyes.

The vessel was on the eve of departure. Her deck presented that scene of bustle and alacrity dear to the sailor's heart. Men were busy nailing up the masts, hanging the bowsprit over the side, varnishing the lee-scuppers, and pouring hot tar down the companion-way.

Captain Bilge, with a megaphone to his lips, kept calling out to the men in his rough sailor fashion:

'Now, then, don't over-exert yourselves, gentlemen. Remember, please, that we have plenty of time. Keep out of the sun as much as you can. Step carefully in the rigging there, Jones; I fear it's a little high for you. Tut, tut, Williams, don't get yourself so dirty with that tar; you won't look fit to be seen.'

I stood leaning over the gaff of the mainsail and thinking – yes, thinking, dear reader, of my mother. I hope that you will think none the less of me for that. Whenever things look dark, I lean up against something and think of mother. If they get positively black, I stand on one leg and think of father. After that I can face anything.

Did I think, too, of another, younger than mother and fairer than father? Yes, I did. 'Bear up, darling,' I had whispered, as she nestled her head beneath my oilskins and kicked out backward with one heel in the agony of her girlish grief; 'in five years the voyage will be over, and, after three more like it, I shall come back with money enough to buy a second-hand fishing-net and settle down on shore.'

Meantime the ship's preparations were complete. The masts were all in position, the sails nailed up, and men with axes were busy chopping away the gangway.

'All ready?' called the Captain.

'Aye, aye, sir.'

'Then hoist the anchor on board and send a man down with the key to open the bar.'

Opening the bar! The last rite of departure. How often in my voyages have I seen it; the little group of men, soon to be exiled from their home, standing about with saddened faces, waiting to see the man with the key open the bar – held there by some strange fascination.

Next morning, with a fair wind astern, we had buzzed around the corner of England and were running down the Channel.

I know no finer sight, for those who have never seen it, than the English Channel. It is the highway of the world, Ships of all nations are passing up and down, Dutch, Scotch, Venezuelan, and even American.

Chinese junks rush to and fro. Warships, motor-yachts, icebergs, and lumbar-rafts are everywhere. If I add to this fact that so thick a fog hangs over it that it is entirely hidden from sight, my readers can form some idea of the majesty of the scene.

We had now been three days at sea. My first seasickness was wearing off and I thought less of father.

On the third morning Captain Bilge descended to my cabin.

'Mr Blowhard,' he said, 'I must ask you to stand double watches.'

'What is the matter?' I enquired.

'The two other mates have fallen overboard,' he said uneasily, and avoiding my eye.

I contented myself with saying, 'Very good, sir,' but I could not help thinking it a trifle odd that both the mates should have fallen overboard in the same night.

Surely there was some mystery in this.

Two mornings later the Captain appeared at the breakfast-table with the same shifting and uneasy look in his eyes.

'Anything wrong, sir?' I asked.

'Yes,' he answered, trying to appear at ease, and twisting a fried egg to and fro between his fingers with such nervous force as almost to break it in two, 'I regret to say we have lost the bo'sun.'

'The bo'sun?' I cried.

'Yes,' said Captain Bilge more quietly, 'he is overboard. I blame myself for it, partly. It was early this morning. I was holding him up in my arms to look at an iceberg, and – quite accidentally, I assure you – I dropped him overboard.'

'Captain Bilge,' I asked, 'have you taken any steps to recover him?'

'Not as yet,' he replied uneasily.

I looked at him fixedly, but said nothing.

Ten days passed.

The mystery thickened. On Thursday two men of the starboard watch were reported missing. On Friday the carpenter's assistant disappeared. On the night of Saturday a circumstance occurred which, slight as it was, gave me some clue as to what was happening.

As I stood at the wheel about midnight, I saw the Captain approach in the darkness, carrying the cabin-boy by the hind leg. The lad was a bright little fellow, whose merry disposition had already endeared him to me, and I watched with some interest to see what the Captain would do to him.

Arrived at the stern of the vessel, Captain Bilge looked cautiously around for a moment and then dropped the boy into the sea. For a brief moment the lad's head appeared in the phosphorus of the waves. The Captain threw a boot at him, sighed deeply, and went below.

Here, then, was the key to the mystery! The Captain was throwing the crew overboard. Next morning we met at breakfast as usual.

'Poor little William has fallen overboard,' said the Captain, seizing a strip of ship's bacon and tearing at it with his teeth as if he almost meant to eat it.

'Captain,' I said, greatly excited, and stabbing at a ship's loaf in my agitation with such ferocity as almost to drive my knife into it, 'you threw that boy overboard!'

'I did,' said Captain Bilge, grown suddenly quiet. 'I threw them all over, and intend to threw the rest. Listen, Blowhard; you are young, ambitious, and trustworthy. I will confide in you.'

Perfectly calm now, he stepped to a locker, rummaged in it a moment, and drew out a piece of faded yellow parchment, which he spread on the table. It was a map or chart. In the centre of it was a circle. In the middle of the circle was a small dot and the letter T, while at one side of the map was a letter N, and against it on the other side a letter S.

'What is this?' I asked.

'Can you not guess?' queried Captain Bilge. 'It is a desert island.'

'Ah!' I rejoined, with a sudden flash of intuition, 'and N is for north, and S is for south.'

'Blowhard,' said the Captain, striking the table with such force as to cause a loaf of ship's bread to bounce up and down three or four times, 'you've struck it. That part of it had not yet occurred to me.'

'And the letter T?' I asked.

'The treasure – the buried treasure,' said the Captain, and, turning the map over, he read from the back of it: 'The point T indicates the spot where the treasure is buried under the sand; it consists of half a million Spanish dollars, and is buried in a brown leather dress-suit case.'

'And where is the island?' I enquired, mad with excitement.

'That I do not know,' said the Captain. 'I intend to sail up and down the parallels of latitude till I find it.'

'And meantime?'

'Meantime, the first thing to do is to reduce the numbers of the crew, so as to have fewer hands to divide among. Come, come,' he added, in a burst of frankness, which made me love the man in spite of his shortcomings, 'will you join me in this? We'll throw them all over, keeping the cook to the last, dig up the treasure, and be rich for the rest of our lives.'

Reader, do you blame me if I said yes? I was young, ardent, ambitious, full of bright hopes and boyish enthusiasm.

'Captain Bilge,' I said, putting my hand in his, 'I am yours.'

'Good,' he said. 'Now go forward to the forecastle and get an idea what the men are thinking.'

I went forward to the men's quarters – a plain room in the front of the ship, with only a rough carpet on the floor, a few simple arm-chairs, writing-desks, spittoons of a plain pattern, and small brass beds and blue-and-green screens. It was Sunday morning, and the men were mostly sitting about in their dressing-gowns.

They rose as I entered, and curtseyed.

'Sir,' said Tompkins, the bo'sun's mate, 'I think it my duty to tell you there is a great deal of dissatisfaction among the men.'

Several of the men nodded.

'They don't like the way the men keep going overboard,' he continued, his voice rising to a tone of uncontrolled passion. 'It is positively absurd, sir, and, if you will allow me to say so, the men are far from pleased.'

'Tompkins,' I said sternly, 'you must understand that my position will not allow me to listen to mutinous language of this sort.'

I returned to the Captain. 'I think the men mean mutiny,' I said.

'Good,' returned Captain Bilge, rubbing his hands; 'that will get rid of a lot of them, and of course,' he added musingly, looking out of the broad, old-fashioned porthole at the stern of the cabin, at the heaving waves of the South Atlantic, 'I am expecting pirates at any time, and that will take off quite a few of them. However' – and there he pressed the bell for a cabin-boy – 'kindly ask Mr Tompkins to step this way.'

'Tompkins,' said the Captain, as the bo'sun's mate entered, 'be good enough to stand on the locker and stick your head through the stern porthole and tell me what you think of the weather.'

Tompkins stood on the locker and put his head and shoulders out of the port.

Taking a leg each, we pushed him through. We heard him plump into the sea.

'Tompkins was easy,' said Captain Bilge. 'Excuse me as I enter his death in the log.'

'Yes,' he continued presently, 'it will be a great help if they mutiny. I suppose they will, sooner or later. It's customary to do so. But I shall take no step to precipitate it until we have first fallen in with pirates. I am expecting them in these latitudes at any time. Meanwhile, Mr Blowhard,' he said, rising, 'if you can continue to drop overboard one or two more each week, I shall feel extremely grateful.'

Three days later we rounded the Cape of Good Hope and entered upon the inky waters of the Indian Ocean. Our course lay now in zigzags, and, the weather being favourable, we sailed up and down at a furious rate over a sea as calm as glass.

On the fourth day a pirate ship appeared. Reader, I do not know if you have ever seen a pirate ship. The sight was one to appal the stoutest heart. The entire ship was painted black, a black flag hung at the masthead, the sails were black, and on the deck people dressed all in black walked up and down arm-in-arm. The words 'Pirate Ship' were painted in white letters on the bow. At the sight of it our crew were visibly cowed. It was a spectacle that would have cowed a dog.

The two ships were brought side by side. They were then lashed tightly together with bag string and binder twine, and a gang-plank laid between them. In a moment the pirates swarmed upon our deck, rolling their eyes, gnashing their teeth, and filing their nails.

Then the fight began. It last two hours – with fifteen minutes off for lunch. It was awful. The men grappled with one another, kicked one another from behind, slapped one another across the face and in many cases completely lost their temper and tried to bite one another. I noticed one gigantic fellow brandishing a knotted towel, and striking right and left among our men, until Captain Bilge rushed at him and struck him flat across the mouth with a banana skin.

At the end of two hours, by mutual consent, the fight was declared a draw, the points standing at sixty-one and a half against sixty-two.

The ships were unlashed, and, with three cheers from each crew, were headed on their way.

'Now, then,' said the Captain to me, aside, 'let us see how many of the crew are sufficiently exhausted to be thrown overboard.'

He went below. In a few minutes he reappeared, his face deadly pale.

'Blowhard,' he said, 'the ship is sinking. One of the pirates (sheer accident, of course; I blame no one) has kicked a hole in the side. Let us sound the well.'

We put our ear to the ship's well. It sounded like water.

The men were put to the pumps, and worked with the frenzied effort which only those who have been drowned in a sinking ship can understand.

At 6 p.m. the well marked one half an inch of water, at nightfall three-quarters of an inch, and at daybreak, after a night of unremitting toil, seven-eights of an inch.

By noon of the next day the water had risen to fifteen-sixteenths of an inch, and on the next night the sounding showed thirty-one thirty-seconds of an inch of water in the hold. The situation was desperate. At this rate of increase few, if any, could tell where it would rise to in a few days.

That night the Captain called me to his cabin. He had a book of mathematical tables in front of him, and great sheets of vulgar fractions littered the floor on all sides.

'The ship is bound to sink,' he said; 'in fact, Blowhard, she is sinking. I can prove it. It may be six months or it may take years, but if she goes on like this, sink she must. There is nothing for it but to abandon her.'

That night, in the dead of darkness, while the crew were busy at the pumps, the Captain and I built a raft.

Unobserved, we cut down the masts, chopped them into suitable lengths, laid them crosswise in a pile, and lashed them tightly together with bootlaces.

Hastily we threw on board a couple of boxes of food and bottles of drinking fluid, a sextant, a chronometer, a gas-meter, a bicycle pump, and few other scientific instruments. Then, taking advantage of a roll in the motion of the ship, we launched the raft, lowered ourselves upon line, and, under cover of the heavy dark of a tropical night, we paddled away from the doomed vessel.

The break of day found us a tiny speck on the Indian Ocean. We looked about as big as this (.).

In the morning, after dressing and shaving as best we could, we opened our boxes of food and drink.

Then came the awful horror of our situation.

One by one the Captain took from the box the square blue tins of canned beef which it contained. We counted fifty-two in all. Anxiously and with drawn faces we watched until the last can was lifted from the box. A single thought was in our minds. When the end came the Captain stood up on the raft, with wild eyes staring at the sky.

'The can-opener!' he shrieked. 'Just heaven, the can-opener!' He fell prostrate.

Meantime, with trembling hands, I opened the box of bottles. It contained lager-beer bottles, each with a patent tin top. One by one I took them out. There were fifty-two in all. As I withdrew the last one and saw the empty box before me, I shroke out, 'The thing! The thing! Oh, merciful heaven! The thing you open them with!'

I fell prostrate upon the Captain.

We awoke to find ourselves still a mere speck upon the ocean. We felt even smaller than before.

Over us was the burnished copper sky of the tropics. The heavy, leaden sea lapped the sides of the raft. All about us was a litter of corned-beef cans and lager-beer bottles. Our sufferings in the ensuing days were indescribable. We beat and thumped on the cans with our fists. Even at the risk of spoiling the tins for ever we hammered them fiercely against the raft. We stamped on them, bit at them, and swore at them. We pulled and clawed at the bottles with our hands, and chipped and knocked them against the cans, regardless even of breaking the glass and ruining the bottles.

It was futile.

Then day after day we sat in moody silence, gnawed with hunger, with nothing to read, nothing to smoke, and pratically nothing to talk about.

On the tenth day the Captain broke silence.

'Get ready the lots, Blowhard,' he said. 'It's got to come to that.'

'Yes,' I answered drearily, 'we're getting thinner every day.'

Then, with the awful prospect of cannibalism before us, we drew lots.

I prepared the lots and held them to the Captain. He drew the longer one.

'Which does that mean?' he asked, trembling between hope and despair. 'Do I win?'

'No, Bilge,' I said sadly, 'you lose.'

But I mustn't dwell on the days that followed – the long, quiet days of lazy dreaming on the raft, during which I slowly built up my strength, which had been shattered by privation. They were days, dear reader, of deep and quiet peace, and yet I cannot recall them without shedding a tear for the brave man who made them what they were.

It was the fifth day after, that I was awakened from a sound sleep by the bumping of the raft against the shore. I had eaten perhaps over-heartily, and had not observed the vicinity of land.

Before me was an island, the circular shape of which, with its low, sandy shore, recalled at once its identity.

'The treasure island!' I cried. 'At last I am rewarded for all my heroism.'

In a fever of haste I rushed to the centre of the island. What was the sight that confronted me? A great hollow scooped in the sand, an empty dress-suit case lying beside it, and, on a ship's plank driven deep into the sand, the legend, '*Saucy Sally*, October 1867.' So! the miscreants had made good the vessel, headed it for the island of whose existence they must have learned from the chart we so carelessly left upon the cabin table, and had plundered poor Bilge and me of our well-earned treasure!

Sick with the sense of human ingratitude, I sank upon the sand.

The island became my home.

There I eked out a miserable existence, feeding myself on sand and gravel, and dressing myself in cactus plants. Years passed. Eating sand and mud slowly undermined my robust constitution. I fell ill. I died. I buried myself.

Would that others who write sea-stories would do as much.

Animals at Alconleigh

Nancy Mitford

Since the earliest days of her childhood, when her parents separated and went to live abroad, Fanny lived with her Aunt Emily during term time, spending her holidays at Alconleigh with her eccentric cousins, the Radletts. It was always the Christmas holidays which created the greatest excitement . . .

There is a photograph in existence of Aunt Sadie and her six children sitting round the tea-table at Alconleigh. The table is situated, as it was, is now, and ever shall be, in the hall, in front of a huge open fire of logs. Over the chimney-piece plainly visible in the photograph, hangs an entrenching tool, with which, in 1915, Uncle Matthew had whacked to death eight Germans one by one as they crawled out of a dug-out. It is still covered with blood and hairs, an object of fascination to us as children. In the photograph Aunt Sadie's face, always beautiful, appears strangely round, her hair strangely fluffy, and her clothes strangely dowdy, but it is unmistakably she who sits there with Robin, in oceans of lace, lolling on her knee. She seems uncertain what to do with his head, and the presence of Nanny waiting to take him away is felt though not seen. The other children, between Louisa's eleven and Matt's two years, sit round the table in party dresses or frilly bibs, holding cups or mugs according to age, all of them gazing at the camera with large eyes opened wide by the flask, and all looking as if butter would not melt in their round pursed-up mouths. There they are, held like flies in the amber of that moment – click goes the camera and on goes life; the minutes, the days, the years, the decades, taking them further and further from that happiness and promise of youth, from the hopes Aunt Sadie must have had for them, and from the dreams they dreamed for themselves. I often think there is nothing quite so poignantly sad as old family groups.

When a child I spent my Christmas holidays at Alconleigh, it was a regular feature of my life, and, while some of them slipped by with nothing much to remember, others were distinguished by violent occurrences and had a definite character of their own. There was the time, for example, when the servants' wing caught fire, the time when my pony lay on me in the brook and nearly drowned me (not very nearly, he was soon dragged off, but meanwhile bubbles were said to have been observed). There was drama when Linda, aged ten, attempted suicide in order to rejoin an old smelly Border Terrier which Uncle Matthew had had put down. She collected and ate a basketful of yew-berries, was discovered by Nanny and given mustard and water to make her sick. She was then 'spoken to' by Aunt Sadie, clipped over the ear by Uncle Matthew, put to bed for two days and given a Labrador puppy, which soon took the place of the old Border in her affections. There was much worse drama when Linda, aged twelve, told the daughters of neighbours, who had come to tea, what she supposed to be the facts of life. Linda's presentation of the 'facts' had been so gruesome that the children left Alconleigh howling dismally, their nerves permanently impaired, their future chances of a sane and happy sex life much reduced. This resulted in a series of dreadful punishments, from a real beating, administered by Uncle Matthew, to luncheon upstairs for a week. There was the unforgettable holiday when Uncle Matthew and Aunt Sadie went to Canada. The Radlett children would rush for the newspapers every day hoping to see that their parents' ship had gone down with all aboard; they yearned to be total orphans – especially Linda, who saw herself as Katy in *What Katy Did*, the reins of the household gathered into small but capable hands. The ship met with no iceberg and weathered the Atlantic storms, but meanwhile we had a wonderful holiday, free from rules.

But the Christmas I remember most clearly of all was when I was fourteen and Aunt Emily became engaged. Aunt Emily was Aunt Sadie's sister, and she had brought me up from babyhood, my own mother, their youngest sister, having felt herself too beautiful and too gay to be burdened with a child at the age of nineteen. She left my father when I was a month old, and subsequently ran away so often, and with so many different people, that she became known to her family and friends as the Bolter; while my father's second, and presently his third, fourth and fifth wives, very naturally had no great wish to look after me. Occasionally one of these impetuous parents would appear like a rocket, casting an unnatural glow upon my horizon. They had great glamour, and I longed to be caught up in their fiery trails and be carried away, though in my heart I knew how lucky I was to have Aunt Emily. By degrees, as I grew up, they lost all charm for me; the cold grey rocket cases mouldered where they had happened to fall, my mother with a major in the South of France, my father, his estates sold up to pay his debts, with an old Rumanian countess in the Bahamas. Even before I was grown up much of the glamour with which they had been surrounded had faded, and finally there was nothing left, no foundation of childish memories to make them seem any different from other middle-aged people. Aunt Emily was never glamorous but she was always my mother, and I loved her.

At the time of which I write, however, I was at an age when the least imaginative child supposes itself to be a changeling, a Princess of Indian blood, Joan of Arc, or the future Empress of Russia. I hankered after my parents, put on an idiotic face which was intended to convey mingled suffering and pride when their names were mentioned, and thought of them as engulfed in deep, romantic, deadly sin.

Linda and I were very much preoccupied with sin, and our great hero was Oscar Wilde.

'But what did he *do*?'

'I asked Fa once and he roared at me – goodness, it was terrifying. He said: "If you mention that sewer's name again in this house I'll thrash you, do you hear, damn you?" So I asked Sadie and she looked awfully vague and said: "Oh, duck, I never really quite knew, but whatever it was was worse than murder, fearfully bad. And, darling, don't talk about him at meals, will you?"'

'We must find out.'

'Bob says he will, when he goes to Eton.'

'Oh, good! Do you think he was worse than Mummy and Daddy?'

'Surely he couldn't be. Oh, you are so lucky, to have wicked parents.'

This Christmas-time, aged fourteen, I stumbled into the hall at Alconleigh blinded by the light after a six-mile drive from Merlinford station. It was always the same every year. I always came down by the same train, arriving at tea-time, and always found Aunt Sadie and the children round the table underneath the entrenching tool, just as they were in the photograph. It was always the same table and the same tea-things; the china with large roses on

it, the tea-kettle and the silver dish for scones simmering over little flames –
the human beings of course were getting imperceptibly older, the babies were
becoming children, the children were growing up, and there had been an
addition in the shape of Victoria now aged two. She was waddling about
with a chocolate biscuit clenched in her fist, her face was smothered in
chocolate and was a horrible sight, but through the sticky mask shone
unmistakably the blue of two steady Radlett eyes.

There was a tremendous scraping of chairs as I came in, and a pack of
Radletts hurled themselves upon me with the intensity and almost the ferocity
of a pack of hounds hurling itself upon a fox. All except Linda. She was the
most pleased to see me, but determined not to show it. When the din had
quieted down and I was seated before a scone and a cup of tea, she said:

'Where's Brenda?' Brenda was my white mouse.

'She got a sore back and died,' I said. Aunt Sadie looked anxiously at
Linda.

'Had you been riding her?' said Louisa, facetiously. Matt, who had recently
come under the care of a French nursery governess, said in a high-pitched
imitation of her voice: '*C'était, comme d'habitude, les voies urinaires.*'

'Oh, dear,' said Aunt Sadie, under her breath.

Enormous tears were pouring into Linda's plate. Nobody cried so much
or so often as she; anything, but especially anything sad about animals, would
set her off, and, once begun, it was a job to stop her. She was delicate, as
well as a highly nervous child, and even Aunt Sadie, who lived in a dream
as far as the health of her children was concerned, was aware that too much
crying kept her awake at night, put her off her food, and did her harm. The
other children, and especially Louisa and Bob, who loved to tease, went as
far as they dared with her, and were periodically punished for making her
cry. *Black Beauty, Owd Bob, The Story of a Red Deer*, and all the Seton Thompson
books were on the nursery index because of Linda, who, at one time or
another, had been prostrated by them. They had to be hidden away, as, if
they were left lying about, she could not be trusted not to indulge in an orgy
of self-torture.

Wicked Louisa had invented a poem which never failed to induce rivers
of tears:

> *A little, houseless match, it has no roof, no thatch,*
> *It lies alone, it makes no moan, that little houseless match.*

When Aunt Sadie was not around the children would chant this in a gloomy chorus. In certain moods one had only to glance at a match-box to dissolve poor Linda; when, however, she was feeling stronger, more fit to cope with life, this sort of teasing would force out of her very stomach an unwilling guffaw. Linda was not my favourite cousin, but, then and for many years, my favourite human being. I adored all my cousins, and Linda distilled, mentally and physically, the very essence of the Radlett family. Her straight features, straight brown hair and large blue eyes were a theme upon which the faces of the others were a variation; all pretty, but none so absolutely distinctive as hers. There was something furious about her, even when she laughed, which she did a great deal, and always as if forced to against her will. Something reminiscent of pictures of Napoleon in youth, a sort of scowling intensity.

I could see that she was really minding much more about Brenda than I did. The truth was that my honeymoon days with the mouse were long since over; we had settled down to an uninspiring relationship, a form, as it were, of married blight, and, when she had developed a disgusting sore patch on her back, it had been all I could do to behave decently and treat her with common humanity. Apart from the shock it always is to find somebody stiff and cold in their cage in the morning, it had been a very great relief to me when Brenda's sufferings finally came to an end.

'Where is she buried?' Linda muttered furiously, looking at her plate.

'Beside the robin. She's got a dear little cross and her coffin was lined with pink satin.'

'Now Linda darling,' said Aunt Sadie, 'if Fanny has finished her tea why don't you show her your toad?'

'He's upstairs asleep,' said Linda. But she stopped crying.

'Have some nice hot toast, then.'

'Can I have Gentleman's Relish on it?' she said, quick to make capital out of Aunt Sadie's mood, for Gentleman's Relish was kept strictly for Uncle Matthew, and supposed not to be good for children. The others made a great show of exchanging significant looks. These were intercepted, as they were meant to be, by Linda, who gave a tremendous bellowing boo-boo and rushed upstairs.

'I wish you children wouldn't tease Linda,' said Aunt Sadie, irritated out of her usual gentleness, and followed her.

The staircase led out of the hall. When Aunt Sadie was beyond earshot,

Louisa said: 'If wishes were horses beggars would ride. Child hunt tomorrow, Fanny.'

'Yes, Josh told me. He was in the car – been to see the vet.'

My Uncle Matthew had four magnificent bloodhounds, with which he used to hunt his children. Two of us would go off with a good start to lay the trail, and Uncle Matthew and the rest would follow the hounds on horseback. It was great fun. Once he came to my house and hunted Linda and me over Shenley Common. This caused the most tremendous stir locally, the Kentish week-enders on their way to church were appalled by the sight of four great hounds in full cry after two little girls. My uncle seemed to them like a wicked lord of fiction, and I became more than ever surrounded with an aura of madness, badness, and dangerousness for their children to know.

The child hunt on the first day of this Christmas visit was a great success. Louisa and I were chosen as hares. We ran across country, the beautiful bleak Cotswold uplands, starting soon after breakfast when the sun was still a red globe, hardly over the horizon, and the trees were etched in dark blue against a pale blue, mauve and pinkish sky. The sun rose as we stumbled on, longing for our second wind; it shone, and there dawned a beautiful day, more like late autumn in its feeling than Christmas-time.

We managed to check the bloodhounds once by running through a flock of sheep, but Uncle Matthew soon got them on the scent again, and, after about two hours of hard running on our part, when we were only half a mile from home, the baying slavering creatures caught up with us, to be rewarded with lumps of meat and many caresses. Uncle Matthew was in a radiantly good temper; he got off his horse and walked home with us, chatting agreeably. What was most unusual, he was even quite affable to me.

'I hear Brenda has died,' he said; 'no great loss I should say. That mouse stank like merry hell. I expect you kept her cage too near the radiator, I always told you it was unhealthy, or did she die of old age?'

'She was only two,' I said, timidly.

Uncle Matthew's charm, when he chose to turn it on, was considerable, but at that time I was always mortally afraid of him, and made the mistake of letting him see that I was.

'You ought to have a dormouse, Fanny, or a rat. They are much more interesting than white mice – though I must frankly say, of all the mice I ever knew, Brenda was the most utterly dismal.'

'She was dull,' I said, sycophantically.

'When I go to London after Christmas, I'll get you a dormouse. Saw one the other day at the *Army & Navy*.'

'Oh Fa, it *is* unfair,' said Linda, who was walking her pony along beside us. 'You know how I've always longed for a dormouse.'

'It is unfair' was a perpetual cry of the Radletts when young. The great advantage of living in a large family is that early lesson of life's essential unfairness. With them I must say it nearly always operated in favour of Linda, who was the adored of Uncle Matthew.

To-day, however, my uncle was angry with her, and I saw in a flash that this affability to me, this genial chat about mice, was simply designed as a tease for her.

'You've got enough animals, miss,' he said sharply. 'You can't control the ones you have got. And don't forget what I told you – that dog of yours goes straight to the kennel when we get back, and stays there.'

Linda's face crumpled, tears poured, she kicked her pony into a canter and made for home. It seemed that her dog Labby had been sick in Uncle Matthew's business-room after breakfast. Uncle Matthew was unable to bear dirtiness in dogs, he flew into a rage, and, in his rage, had made a rule that never again was Labby to set foot in the house. This was always happening, for one reason or another, to one animal or another, and, Uncle Matthew's bark being invariably much worse that his bite, the ban seldom lasted more than a day or two, after which would begin what he called the Thin End of the Wedge.

'Can I bring him in just while I fetch my gloves?'

'I'm so tired – I can't go to the stables – do let him stay just till after tea.'

'Oh I see – the thin end of the wedge. All right, this time he can stay, but if he makes another mess – or I catch him on your bed – or he chews up the good furniture (according to whichever crime it was that had resulted in banishment), I'll have him destroyed, and don't say I didn't warn you.'

All the same, every time sentence of banishment was pronounced, the owner of the condemned would envisage her beloved moping his life away in the solitary confinement of a cold and gloomy kennel.

'Even if I take him out for three hours every day, and go and chat to him for another hour, that leaves twenty hours for him all alone with nothing to do. Oh, why can't dogs read?'

The Radlett children, it will be observed, took a highly anthropomorphic view of their pets.

To-day, however, Uncle Matthew was in a wonderfully good temper, and,

as we left the stables, he said to Linda, who was sitting crying with Labby
in his kennel:

'Are you going to leave that poor brute of yours in there all day?'

Her tears forgotten as if they had never been, Linda rushed into the house
with Labby at her heels. The Radletts were always either on a peak of
happiness or drowning in black waters of despair; their emotions were on no
ordinary plane, they loved or they loathed, they laughed or they cried, they
lived in a world of superlatives. Their life with Uncle Matthew was a sort of
perpetual Tom Tiddler's ground. They went as far as they dared, sometimes
very far indeed, while sometimes, for no apparent reason, he would pounce
almost before they had crossed the boundary. Had they been poor children
they would probably have been removed from their roaring, raging, whacking
papa and sent to an approved home, or, indeed, he himself would have been
removed from them and sent to prison for refusing to educate them. Nature,
however, provides her own remedies, and no doubt the Radletts had enough
of Uncle Matthew in them to enable them to weather storms in which
ordinary children like me would have lost their nerve completely.

Behind the Scenes

Arthur Marshall

Nobody in their youth can ever have been a keener amateur actor than hopelessly stage-struck I. Year after year, audiences sighed and flinched and fidgeted and looked at their watches as I strode the boards and boomed disastrously away in plays by Barrie and Shaw and Sheridan, to name the most reputable. Nor was that all. In lighter vein, I was perfectly ready to rig up in pierrot costume and, a revolting spectacle, dispense and ruin musical items by Coward and Farjeon. Nothing and nobody was safe from me, though it was not until I was nineteen that I was able to get my hands, so to speak, on Shakespeare and mess him about. This was at Cambridge when the Marlowe Society, a distinguished band of skilled and seasoned performers, part dons and part undergraduates, decided to do Henry IV Part II, a work with which I was unfamiliar, and kindly allotted to me the role of the Earl of Surrey.

Hastening to a copy of the text and searching eagerly through the Dramatis Personae, I instantly spied the name of the Earl of Surrey, proudly listed with two other earls, Westmorland and Warwick, described as being 'Of the King's Party', and clearly a person of note. It was with considerable excitement, and wondering whether my talents would be equal to the strain of this exacting part, that I turned the pages, seeking my big speeches, my moments of high drama, my sword fights and, with luck, my eventual death in the King's cause with somebody saying, over my dead body and as the curtain fell, 'What courteous nobility was here! Sleep on, sweet Sir, and take thy well-won rest.' Or something. Great heavens, I could hear the cheers already.

I do not know how recently you have seen or read Henry IV Part II but just in case it hasn't come your way in the last month or so, let me tell you that you have to be pretty nippy even to spot the Earl of Surrey. There is no chance at all of actually hearing him utter for he does not speak. The

Bard has provided for him no words. Moody silence is his. His entrance is certainly saved excitingly up, with the audience on the alert for him, until the very beginning of Act III when, accompanied by the Earl of Warwick, he enters a room in the Palace of Westminster and finds there the night-gowned King who has wound up a long and self-indulgent soliloquy about the great benefits of sleep by saying that he himself cannot sleep and then adding a line that one has heard before somewhere – 'Uneasy lies the head that wears a crown'. Meanwhile, Surrey just stands there and, with him speechless, pushful Warwick greets the King with 'Many good morrows to your majesty!', and when the insomniac old dodderer replies 'Is it good morrow, lords?', Warwick presses on with a time check – ''Tis one o'clock and past.'

This seemed to me to be an immensely unfair distribution of lines and I refused to put up with it. The undergraduate cast to play the Earl of Warwick was an agreeable friend of mine in Trinity. Hurrying speedily round to his rooms in the Great Court, I found him – it was about eleven a.m. – drinking, as was his sensible mid-morning custom, a healing glass of cointreau and deciding not to attend any lectures that day or, indeed, any day. He kindly poured me out a generous measure (we went the pace in those days, I can tell you) and, in the heady fumes of the delicious liqueur, he sportingly agreed to see things my way and to allow me to say his line, ''Tis one o'clock, and past.' I gave it, both in rehearsal and performance, everything I'd got. The experience gained from fourteen years of amateur acting was lavished upon it. Sometimes I said it boldly. Sometimes I said it wistfully. Sometimes I said it reproachfully, implying that we had been kept up long after our bedtime. The line never actually got a round of applause but it kept audiences, I felt, on their toes, wondering among themselves when it was going to be that nice Earl of Surrey's turn to speak again.

At one of our matinées of the play there was for all of us a great thrill. A very famous actress, Irene Vanbrugh, later, and in 1941, to be Dame Irene and who had, I think, a young relative in the cast, came to a performance and sat, splendidly visible to all, in the third row. It was my day for saying my line boldly and I directed it straight at her. ''Tis one o'clock, and past,' I trumpeted, every word a jewel of clarity and superb elocution. It could, I felt, hardly fail to impress her and when, some years later, she wrote her agreeable autobiography, *To Tell My Story*, I hurried to it to see what she had to say about that memorable afternoon. There would, surely, be a reference to the performance and to my line, perhaps in diary form ('Thursday.

Rain morning. Lunched hotel and went afternoon to production by Cambridge Marlowe Society. Was much struck by Earl of Surrey'). But no mention of the matinée or me was made. Odd.

And then, in the strange way that things happen, four years later I had the good fortune to meet Miss Vanbrugh. She was appearing, in a very starry cast, at the Palace Theatre under the banner of C. B. Cochran and in the successful American comedy, *Dinner At Eight* by George Kaufman and Edna Ferber and in which she played Millicent Jordan, the hardboiled New York hostess whose snobbish social aspirations (Lord and Lady Fernecliffe are invited to dine but fail to turn up) assemble round her table a rum collection of ill-assorted guests, every one of them worried and unhappy in some way or other. The piece was in eleven scenes and had to be played at great speed, with lines thrown away or trampled on, a relatively recent technique to which American actors and actresses were at that time more accustomed than English ones, and least of all Miss Vanbrugh. She had been brought up in the excellent stage tradition of clear, measured speech. You waited to speak until the other person had stopped speaking. She had created the part of Gwendolen in *The Importance of Being Earnest*, Pinero wrote plays specially for her, and she was the original Lady Mary in *The Admirable Crichton*. Search the plays of Wilde and Pinero as you may, there are no lines that can either be hurried or thrown away. The same applies to Barrie, apart from a few that one would wish, for other reasons, excised. Miss Vanbrugh was at the time 61 years old, a latish age for learning new tricks and so the engagement was in the nature of a challenge.

I had become very friendly with a delightful niece-by-marriage of the Vanbrughs and together we saw the play (and a splendid theatrical evening it made) and afterwards went round to see and congratulate Miss Vanbrugh. Playing against the grain every inch of the way (tough and nasty women were never her line), she had given a remarkable performance, and in her dressing-room she displayed all the charm and tact and modesty that made her so much loved. And she had, heaven knows, needed them when trying to cope with Mr Kaufman and Miss Ferber, both of them formidable characters who had come over to London after having triumphantly launched the piece in New York and who plainly did not regard the somewhat solid and statuesque Miss Vanbrugh as ideal casting. She told us that when, on one occasion at rehearsal when he was attempting to get extra pace on the dialogue, she had said 'You know, Mr Kaufman, you are asking me to speak quicker than I can think', his reply had been a crisp one: 'Then don't think'.

Meanwhile Miss Ferber, snugly housed at Claridge's, was, as she tells us in her autobiography, disenchanted with everything. There were fogs, she disliked London, she hated the Palace Theatre and, when her spirits were at their nadir, news came to her from rehearsals that Miss Vanbrugh was planning, in the last scene of the second act, to wear 'pink lace lounging pyjamas'. She then, to cap all, caught influenza and was somewhat startled to hear her English maid announcing this misfortune to Mr Kaufman down the telephone wires and in the accepted phrase of the time, 'Miss Ferber's very queer today'. The phrase held a different meaning for Mr Kaufman who, the soul of loyalty, is said to have replied, 'Not when you really know her.'

Parents

John Aye

'There was a young fellow named Tommy,
Well known for his fun and bonhomie,
But he made a faux pas
With his young lady's ma,
Which landed him in the consommé.'

F. W. Thomas.

The interference of parents in the love affairs of their children is now almost a thing of the past. At one time the male parent filled quite an important place in both the comedy and the drama of love. In those days his very appearance struck terror into the breast of the youthful aspirant to his daughter's hand, he was approached with fear and trembling, he turned the unsatisfactory wooer from his door with curses loud and deep, he frustrated elopements and, where all was satisfactory, was generous with his blessing, but not so much with his dowries, and generally bossed around as if he was the principal character in the show. As regards the female parent – this was of course before the days of woman's emancipation – she stood silently in the background, mutely acquiescent in the decrees of her lord and master, and usually weeping tears of sympathy with her son or daughter until sternly ordered by the lord of the household to 'stop that snivelling.'

But, during the last ten to twenty years a change has come over the scene, and the one-time domestic tyrant has, in most cases, been relegated by his up-to-date daughter to a very secondary position. For the future he may consider himself lucky if he is even introduced to the latest young man on whom she has conferred the freedom of his house and garden, together with such gratuitous board, light and heat as may be found necessary. 'You'll be coming round tonight, Bertie, old top?' said Muriel to her latest attaché.

'Rather! But I say, old bean, I wish you'd get rid of that sour, bad-tempered, antiquated old bird that works in the garden and sometimes drives the car. He's no ornament, and whenever I turn up he gives me such a nasty look.' 'Oh, don't worry about that,' laughed the sweet young thing, 'that's only father.'

According to all the best books, together with the most learned authorities on the subject, the custom in the good old days was for the girl, directly she felt any unusual flutterings in the cardiac region, to rush to mother and tell her all about it, and mother, from the depths of her experience and her more mature wisdom, would give sage and goodly counsel. At the same time, by a little adroit cross-examination, she would elicit some information as to the desirability of the suitor, apart from the fact, so emphasized by the girl, that he was a modern combination of a Greek god and a knight *sans peur et sans reproche*. But today youth thinks and gets ahead more rapidly. Doris had apparently good hopes of securing what looked like a quite eligible young man, and mother was giving advice as to the best means of getting him for keeps. This was largely founded on the good idea of ganging warily. 'If that young man asks for a kiss,' she said, 'you must refuse to give him one for the present.' 'Yes,' replied Doris thoughtfully, 'but suppose he doesn't ask for it?'

Mabel had been out to dinner and on her return was full of what a good time she had had, so much so that mother had become suspicious. 'Was it really so very enjoyable?' she asked. 'Rather! Why the menu was great.' 'My dear,' replied her wise mamma, 'it isn't the menu that makes a good dinner, it's the men you sit next to.'

With a little pressing, and a good deal of blushing, Maisie had admitted that there was a young man who meant a good deal to her, whereupon mother at once proceeded to give a little advice. 'If you ever have a quarrel,' she said, 'whatever you do don't give in. Start as you mean to go on.' 'Yes, mother,' replied the girl, 'but what if someone has given Bill the same advice?'

Moreover, in this watching over her daughter's future the old-time mother would frequently display the shrewdness and the perception of a Sherlock Holmes. 'Did you walk all the way from the house to the village and back again alone?' asked one fond mamma. 'Yes, mother,' replied the dutiful daughter, 'every step.' 'Good, but how is it that you went out with a lady's umbrella and came back with a gentleman's walking-stick?'

Lily had taken a job in London and, coming home for a short holiday, proudly announced that she was engaged to be married. Of course there was a flood of inquiries, with the result that the fiancé, as portrayed by Lily, would appear to have been something nearly approaching an archangel. 'But has he got any money?' asked her mother finally. 'Well,' said the girl triumphantly, 'look at the splendid ring he has given me?' 'Yes, I know,' said her shrewd mamma, 'but what I mean is, has he got any left?'

Nor, so far as the parents are concerned, can this question of means ever be considered anything but a dominating factor, and, much to the girl's disgust, they usually think it of far more importance than Charlie's good looks, his charm of manner, or his prowess at tennis. Mother had been calling her daughter's attention to the fact that it was quite evident that Mr Williams had serious intentions. 'But, mother,' complained the young lady, whose desires were in another direction, 'I can't stand him. He's such an awful flat.' 'Yes, I know, my dear,' said her worldly-wise mamma, 'But he has a car, a house, and an income of £1,000 a year. What you might call a flat with all modern conveniences.'

On the other hand it is not unusual in these days for the modern girl to make no announcement to her people until affairs are approaching completion, and when she does condescend to do so she brooks neither argument nor discussion. A flapper of the very newest school had announced to the household that she proposed to get married very shortly. 'But, my dear,' protested her mother, 'you are very young. Are you fitted for such a solemn undertaking?' 'Rather, old bean,' was the dutiful retort, 'I've fixed up to be fitted this afternoon.'

Sometimes it happens that, no matter how desirable he may be in other respects, the young man's first appearance before her mother does not tend to the furtherance of his suit. Cynthia had brought home her latest boy, and proudly introduced him to mamma. 'Your face seems strangely familiar. Have we met before?' inquired the young man. 'Yes,' said mamma grimly, 'we met yesterday. It was in the Tube. You were sitting and I was standing; all the way from Oxford Circus to Shepherd's Bush.'

As a general rule the modern father interferes very little with the love affairs of his sons and daughters until they reach the point of an engagement, but sometimes he steps in prematurely, and then generally to his own undoing. One of this type, who objected very much to his daughter having a boy, because in the event of her getting married she would be compelled to give up a very good job, concluded a long tirade against rushing into matrimony by quoting the words of St Paul, 'Those who marry do well; but they who do not, do better.' 'Quite so,' replied the girl, 'I love to do well and let those do better who can.'

'When that fellow asked you to go out with him,' said one old supporter of the things-that-had-been, 'why didn't you tell him to come and see me?' 'I did, Daddy,' said the girl quietly, 'but he said that he had already seen you once, and so far as he could see there was nothing about you to which he need take objection.'

'When you get married,' said another stern old gentleman to his very modern daughter, 'I'm going to take good care that you don't throw yourself away on one of those long-haired tailors's dummies, without a brain in his head, that one sees about nowadays. What do you say now to a quiet, staid, sensible, middle-aged man of about fifty?' 'Well, Dad,' replied the young lady, 'if it's all the same to you, I'd rather have two of about twenty-five.'

Another perplexed father had been giving his daughter a lecture on her varied little incursions into Love's kingdom with especial reference to the unsuitability of the most recent. 'What you want, Dad,' said the girl at length, 'is a courting salad.' 'A courting salad! What's that?' 'Lettuce alone,' said the girl sweetly as she gently faded from the room.

Nor is the young lady at times above using father for her own purposes, and making him an unwilling partner in her love adventures. One parent had given his daughter a long lecture on her flagrant flirtations. The girl heard him quietly to the end and then remarked, 'Now you've got that off your chest I want your help. I want you to pretend you've failed in business.' 'I don't understand,' said the puzzled father. 'What's the idea?' 'Well,' explained the girl, 'I've got engaged to nine men, and I must find some means of getting rid of some of them.'

When it comes to advising or questioning the boy on the same subject the father stands on more familiar and therefore safer ground, though even in this case he sometimes meets more than his match, while in others he often gets in a pretty telling blow. The dear old man had been enlarging at some length on the absolute absurdity of any young fellow getting tied up to a girl before he'd had the time or opportunity to look around. 'Think of the future, my boy,' he concluded. 'I can't Dad,' replied the young hopeful, 'it's her birthday next week and I've got to think of the present.'

'It's not the original cost of the motor cycle that runs away with the money,' complained the young son, 'it's all the cycle attachments.' 'Yes,' said his father grimly, 'especially those with short skirts and bobbed hair.'

'Where were you last night?' asked his father of young Horace. 'Oh, just riding round in the car with some of the lads.' 'Very good, but please tell them next time not to leave their powder puffs behind them in the car.'

The young son had returned from London to the old homestead, and proudly announced that the prettiest girl in all that great city had promised to marry him one day. The old farmer listened quietly till the end of the eulogy. 'So you've picked up a lass in London?' he said. 'Yes, father.' 'What can she do? Can she sew on buttons, milk the cows, make porridge or bake cakes?' 'No, I'm afraid not, father, but she is a lovely singer; she has the finest voice you ever heard.' 'Voice,' said the indignant old man, 'why, guid sakes, laddie, could ye not get a canary in London?'

The Jewish boy had serious thoughts of looking out for a life partner, but before committing himself was considering the subject from every side. In the course of such investigation he approached his father. 'Fader,' he inquired, 'is it true what they say that marriage is a failure?' 'Vell, my poy,' was old Isaac's reply, 'if you marry a woman that has lots and lots of cash marriage is almost as good as a failure.'

Unfortunately when the time arrives that the young female has more or less permanently attracted to her side the male bird then the troubles of the father really begin, for, if he plays his part properly, no matter how tired he may be, he has to sit up, usually in the kitchen, until the enamoured youth sees fit to take his departure. It was getting on towards the witching hour when the wearied parent popped his head into the room where the two were sitting and asked, 'Do you know what the time is?' Without a word the young man reached for his hat and bolted. 'What's the matter with him?' asked the old man in amazement. 'I just wanted to know the time because my watch has stopped.'

They had been taking a very, very long goodnight in the hall and every moment made it seem harder to break away. At length this 'lingering sweetness long drawn out' was interrupted by a wearied voice from the kitchen. 'Mabel,' it said, 'doesn't that young man of yours know how to say "goodnight"?' 'Doesn't he!' replied Mabel from the darkness of the hall. 'Well, I should rather say he does!'

'I don't think your father entirely approves of me,' he complained. 'Oh yes he does,' replied the girl, 'but he was annoyed because he thought I had not treated you with proper courtesy.' 'How absurd! Whatever did he mean?' 'He said that I had behaved rudely in allowing you to go away last night without offering you breakfast.'

Even when father does go off to bed and leaves the lovers in undisputed possession of the ground floor he cannot always be sure of an undisturbed rest. The two young things had been saying good night for about two hours on the doorstep when the sweet quietude of the night was rudely broken by a voice like the bellowing of an irate bull from the top of the stairs. 'Look here,' it roared, 'I have no objection to your sitting up half the night with my daughter, or spending two hours saying good-bye on the doorstep, but for heaven's sake have pity on those of us who have gone to bed and take your elbow off the bell-push.'

'Look here, young man,' said another angry father, 'I wish you could manage to leave the house a little earlier sometimes. When you stand at the gate bidding my daughter good night does it ever dawn upon you –' 'Oh, no, sir,' replied the enamoured one, 'I'm quite sure I've never stayed as late as that.'

'I'm afraid,' complained one good mother, 'that Mabel's young man has taken offence at something. He hasn't been round for nearly a fortnight. Have you said anything to him?' 'No,' replied her husband, 'I've neither heard nor seen him since I posted him last quarter's bill for electric light.'

With the arrival of the time when the young couple have made the great and wonderful discovery that life without each other would be one long, drab, unendurable wilderness comes the necessity of breaking the news to father. In most cases the young man is of opinion that this will be a great and sudden shock to the paternal relative, and, to avoid dire consequences, either to the old man or himself, will sometimes make a few preliminary inquiries from the girl herself before plunging his head into the lion's jaws. They had fixed it all up, and he was throwing out a few feelers as to what his reception would be. 'Do you think your dad will say much when I tell him we are going to be married?' he asked. 'I don't know,' said the girl, 'but I fancy he would say something if you told him we weren't.'

'What will your father say when he learns we are engaged?' another asked tremulously. 'Oh, he'll be simply delighted,' was her artless reply. 'He always is.'

He had been sounding her about the reception he might expect from her father. 'Yes,' she said. 'Daddy will be awfully pleased to hear you are a poet.' 'Does he like poetry?' asked her lover eagerly. 'Not at all. Looks on it as awful tosh. But the last boy friend of mine he tried to kick out was a first-rate amateur boxer.'

He was endeavouring to make a few inquiries about his probable reception, but she seemed to think that he should be only too happy to dare anything for her sake, and that any hanging back was a sign that his love was none too strong. 'But how shall I know that you love me?' she wailed. 'Well I can't sleep at night for thinking of you,' he said. 'That doesn't prove anything. Father says he can't sleep at night for thinking of you, but I know it isn't through love.'

She was the daughter of a wealthy man, and, being no beauty, everyone but herself knew in what direction lay the attraction to the somewhat needy suitor. For some time he had been looking for a chance to sound her as to the possibilities of financial aid from the old man, and at last he considered that a suitable moment had arrived. With a wealth of language he had told her how his one desire in life was that they should speedily be united, but that unfortunately the state of his finances did not permit of that happy event taking place for some time. 'Do you think your father would be willing to help me in the future?' he asked anxiously. 'Well,' replied his adored one sadly, 'I heard him say the other night that he felt like kicking you into the middle of next week.'

However, when the time arrives for the prospective son-in-law to present himself in person before father and there make a formal declaration of his intentions, there comes the inevitable question of ways and means. The young lover's financial reputation was not good, and when he asked for Mavis' hand the old man was not exactly pleased, and made a few remarks about debts and such like. 'Oh,' said the young man airily, 'I've turned over a new leaf. I mean to settle down now.' 'Yes,' said her father grimly, 'but how long will it be before you want me to settle up for you?'

Having spent a considerable part of his time and cash at the King's Arms young Hardup decided that he might do worse than enter the business, and Molly, the landlord's pretty daughter, having declared that she was by no means indifferent to him he ventured to approach the old man. 'What!' roared the latter, 'want to marry my daughter, why, hang it, man, you ain't able to keep yourself!' 'No,' replied the undaunted aspirant, 'but I nearly can, and I reckon she'll be able to help a bit.'

'It seems to me rather presumptuous for a youth in your position to ask for my daughter's hand,' said the purse-proud father. 'Well, sir,' replied the suitor, 'I am modest and economical in my personal expenditure and I think that altogether you will find me less costly to maintain than almost any other son-in-law you could select.'

But when it comes to the case of the purse-proud man the answer is often very crushing. A wealthy profiteer, who had made money during the war, was determined that such money should not be spent in the support of sons-in-law. He was interviewing a suitor who had expounded at some length his great love for the old man's youngest daughter. 'But how much money have you?' came the leading question. 'About £300.' 'Good gracious, man,' snorted the old boy, 'I said money – not loose change.'

Prosaic as such inquiries into the financial position may be, and almost as it were throwing a shadow across the primrose path of youthful love, yet when we consider how often the poor father-in-law is let down we must admit that it would be criminal of him not to make the strictest investigation. A dear easy-going old gentleman was being congratulated by a friend on the engagement of his youngest daughter. 'So all your daughters are now married except the last one, and she's engaged?' 'That's so.' 'It must be nice to get them all off your hands?' 'I don't know so much about that. It's nice to get them off your hands, but it's darned hard luck having to keep your sons-in-law on their feet.'

Still, if the young wooer feels that his means are quite adequate, the questions hold no terrors, and he may sometimes even venture on a reply that is not strictly on the orthodox lines. 'Before I give my consent to your engagement to my daughter,' said a careful father, 'I must ask if you are able to support her.' 'I often have,' replied the lover with a tender smile of reminiscence.

Though fortunately the specimen is rare, there is the type of father who will put these questions more for his own benefit than that of his daughter. 'Did Dad seem pleased when you told him about the £200 you had saved?' asked the girl. 'I think so,' replied her lover mournfully, 'he borrowed it.'

In some cases, although the financial position of the suitor may be quite satisfactory, there are other and good reasons why the father cannot give his consent. 'Yes,' said the man of Big Business who was anxious that his daughter should marry a title. 'I regret I cannot see my way to allow you to marry my daughter at present. However, perhaps you will kindly leave your name and address, and if nothing better turns up in the near future we may communicate with you again.'

Following an interview with George her father informed Enid that he could not accept him as a son-in-law, and that she must give him up at once. 'But,' protested the girl, 'he's a man of splendid character, and of a very old family. His ancestors came over with the Normans.' 'Normans,' said the old gentleman, 'why doesn't the fellow speak up? I thought he said Mormons.'

According to that well-known humorous writer, Ashely Sterne, many a man has sought a maiden's hand only to find her father's foot, and certainly in the following cases the suitor would have richly deserved it. 'Your daughter has promised to marry me,' said a pert and conceited young man, 'but before going any further may I inquire if there is any insanity in the family?' 'There must be,' said the old man quietly.

'Sir,' said a very pompous young man, 'I wish to marry your daughter.' 'And I absolutely forbid it,' was the paternal answer. 'Why, what's the matter with her?' asked the young egoist in astonishment.

He was a very young member of the Ultra Bright Young People, and, with all the assurance of an unbroken and ill-mannered young pup, approached an aristocrat of the old school and asked permission 'to marry one of his girls.' 'Certainly,' was the courteous reply, 'which do you prefer, the cook or the housemaid?'

Harry had spoken to her father, and the anxious girl was endeavouring to elicit from her mother what had happened at the interview. 'Daddy wouldn't listen to him,' explained mamma. 'Was Harry much cast down?' asked the anxious girl. 'Yes, down the front door steps into the garden.'

'Have you seen father yet, darling, about our engagement?' asked the anxious girl. 'No,' said the young man, 'I haven't seen him, but I told him by telephone.' 'And what did he say?' 'I couldn't tell; I don't know whether he replied or the line was struck by lightning.'

On the other hand where the refusal by the father is couched in language not conspicuous for its politeness, and contains a decided element of finality, an opening is often given for the rejected suitor to reply with a fairly nasty come-back. 'What!' shouted the Big Business Man, 'You, a mere clerk on a few pounds a week, have the impudence to come to my private office and ask me for my daughter's hand? You might as well have saved yourself the journey.' 'Oh, that's all right,' said the applicant coolly, 'I had another message to deliver in the same block of buildings.'

'You marry my daughter!' roared the apoplectic old colonel (Indian Army, retired). 'Why, dammit, man, it's only a few years ago since you were caddying for me.' 'Quite so,' said the young man, 'but I don't intend to allow that to influence me against you. I think I have sufficient sense to know that a very bad golfer may make quite a decent father-in-law.'

'You, a man like you, wishes to marry my daughter!' said a stern parent, 'I wonder if before putting such an impertinent request you have ever for one moment considered her family?' 'Certainly I have,' was the reply, 'but I love your daughter so much that I am prepared to put up with almost anything.'

'You wish to marry my daughter!' said the rich old man almost bursting with anger at the youth's presumption. 'Do you know, sir, what you are asking? She's my only child.' 'Yes, I know that,' said the young man quietly, 'but one is all I want.'

Diplomatic as well as truthful, however, was the lover who, when her father superciliously sniffed, 'What possible reason can a fellow like you bring forward for wanting to marry my daughter?' replied, 'I have no reason, sir, I am in love.'

In these days of woman surplus it would seem that the timid lover has little to fear from father, since that poor man is only too glad to shift the responsibility for the board and lodging of his daughters onto someone else. 'Is it not beautiful,' says one writer, 'to behold at a wedding the sorrow-stricken air of the parent as he gives the bride away, when you know that for the last ten years he has been trying his best to get her off his hands?' If further evidence of this change of outlook is required it is to be found in one of Ashley Sterne's short sketches. It is the young suitor who is speaking. 'the fact is,' he says, 'if you promise to keep it a secret I've got rather dippy on a girl. Practically engaged, you know. Nice girl, but rather old-fashioned about those things. Said I had to ask father. So I dolled myself up in my soberest rags to give the impression I was an earnest sort of fellow, straightened my knees, cleared my throat, and asked the old fruit for her hand. Did the venerable parent cast a spell on me, cleave me to the chin, or cast me into the moat? He did not. He just said, "That's all right, my boy. What'll you have? I only hope something will come of it this time. Chin, Chin!" And that was that!'

The pretty daughter of the old professor had just received her first proposal, and, as soon as she could tear herself from her lover's arms, rushed off to the study to tell the glad news to Daddy. The old man listened to her in silence, and then scribbling something on a piece of paper pinned it on her back and pushed her out of the room. Returning to her sweetheart the latter read the message, 'With the author's compliments.'

In one case the timid and bashful lover had approached her stern parent in fear and trembling. 'Sir,' he faltered, 'your daughter has promised to become my wife.' 'Has she?' snapped the old man, 'then it's no good coming to me expecting sympathy. You might have known something would happen, hanging round her as you have done six nights a week.'

Much as he may appreciate her, the average father is not blind to the faults of his very modern daughter, though usually he refrains from saying anything about them to her future husband – at any rate until after the wedding. One young lover was so pleased at getting the paternal approval that in the excess of his joy he burst out with, 'If ever I make your angelic daughter unhappy may I suffer tortures!' 'She will see to it that you do,' replied her father grimly.

Moreover the extravagant language to which the loved one will listen with eagerness does not always go down with her parent. 'You say you love my daughter,' said a father to the aspiring and perspiring youth. 'I would die for her,' was the fervid reply. 'For her I would gladly hurl myself from some tall cliff and perish in the waves.' 'Look here,' said the practical father, 'cool it down. I'm a bit of a liar myself, and one in the family at a time is enough.'

A somewhat laughable situation that sometimes arises in this business of asking father is where the young man is too timid to approach his future father-in-law and the young couple decide to elope, while all the time the old man is really simply panting to hand over the girl. Further, he will probably welcome the young couple taking such a course, as by so doing they will save him the expense of a wedding and reception. In one such case the father had called the young man into his study. Trembling the young fellow waited for the storm that would soon break over his devoted head. 'It has come to my notice,' said the old man, 'that you propose to elope with my daughter. Is that so?' 'Yes, sir.' 'Then in that case I want to give you fair warning that you should not use the ladder in the garage because it's cracked.'

In another case the elopement had been carried out successfully while the old father sat at home smiling. 'Did her father catch you?' asked a friend meeting the bridegroom about six months later. 'Yes,' was the sad reply, 'and the old boy is living with us still.'

Unfortunately from time to time the lover is somewhat slow in coming to the point, and since the girl, in spite of her many wiles, is unable to extract any specific offer, it devolves on father to take a hand in the game. 'Look here, Mr Dilly,' said one father who had been placed in this awkward position, 'you've been coming after Nelly for about two years now, taking her out to pictures and that sort of thing, and yet up to the present nothing has come of it. Now, as man to man, the time has come when I must ask you what are your intentions?' 'Well, Mr Brown,' was the answer, 'there's no need for you to get into a stew about it. As regards my intentions they are honourable but remote.'

But where the young lover comes along in good time, without keeping the family too long in doubt as to 'whether anything will come of it,' and where

his income and manners are such as to recommend him, then the course of
true love does, for a time, run smooth. 'Take her, my boy,' said a fond father,
'and my blessing with her. You will find her a particularly generous, large-
hearted girl.' 'Then may I venture to hope,' said the future son-in-law, 'that
she inherits these fine feelings from her father?'

'Yes,' said a fond mother, 'we ain't 'alf pleased with Mord Emily's young
man. She's got a gentleman, she 'as. I knows cos I tried 'im. The first time
'e came to our 'ouse I gave 'im a cup o' tea – biling 'ot. When 'e poured it
out into 'is saucer did 'e blow on it like an ordinary common fellow would?
Betcher life 'e didn't. No, 'e's a torf, got manners, 'e 'ave. 'E fanned it wiv'
is 'at.'

Once his consent has been obtained, however, only too often the poor
paterfamilias has to fade away into the background and become a mere
nonentity until the time when it is necessary for him to emerge once more
and contribute his quota towards the starting of the young couple. In the
interim, so far as they are concerned, he does not exist. Ralph and May had
been engaged about three weeks, when one evening the former turned up at
the trysting place looking rather distressed. 'What's the matter, dear?' asked
the girl anxiously. 'An absolutely rotten bit of luck. I ran over your pater
with my new car,' was the reply. 'Good gracious! What happened?' 'Nothing
serious, thank goodness. Just a bent mudguard and the paint off in one or
two places.'

One case is recorded, however, where the process of time only seemed to
increase the respect and admiration of the future son-in-law for her father,
and nearly every night the young man sacrificed himself by acceding to the
old gentleman's request to have a hand at cards. At length the girl was
moved to expostulation. 'I believe you would sooner play cards with father
than make love to me,' she complained. 'No, darling, I wouldn't,' was his
reply, 'but we must have money to get married on.'

A much quicker and surer way of making certain that pa-in-law had
contributed an adequate amount to the setting up of the new home was that
adopted by another prospective bridegroom. 'I suppose that you quite
understood, Jim, that the cheque for £100 that I put among your wedding
presents was purely for effect?' said her father. 'Oh, rather,' said the happy
bridegroom, 'and the effect was excellent. The bank cashed it without a
word.'

Unfortunately when all the preliminaries are settled it frequently happens
that the young man finds that the sweet and kindly lady who made him so

welcome during his wooing has now developed into the embryo mother-in-law in whose eyes the daughter's intended can do nothing right. 'My girl's mother,' declared one young lover, 'is driving me silly. In her opinion I can't do anything right. The only thing in me of which she approves is my choice of a girl.'

The usher was showing people to their seats at the wedding. 'Are you a friend of the bridegroom?' he asked of one stern and determined old lady. 'No,' was the grim reply, 'I'm the bride's mother.'

'Well, George,' said a friend, 'is it true what I hear, that your engagement is broken off?' 'It is.' 'Why, whatever for?' 'Well you see we were looking over our new house one day when her mother remarked that it would be rather small for three of us, so I gracefully retired.'

'Yes, dear,' said the girl, 'I'm afraid mother doesn't like you very much.' But he was tired of mother and her likes and dislikes. 'Don't bother about that, darling. The whole of my family object to you.'

In the following case, too, the young man was evidently wise in time. 'Mother never goes out, you know,' said the girl. 'She simply hates visiting.' Without a moment's delay the young man made up his mind. 'Splendid,' he said, 'will you marry me, darling?'

In this matter of the future mother-in-law one's sympathy must of necessity go out to the man, for, as Max O'Rell says, 'If you have to choose between living with your mother-in-law and shooting yourself do not hesitate a moment – shoot her.' From the literature of all countries it is clear that everywhere she has been the bar to marital happiness. As evidence to this is the old Hampshire proverb, 'There is but one good mother-in-law and she is dead,' and the German one, 'There is no good mother-in-law but she that wears a green gown.' (i.e., is covered with the grass of the churchyard), or the alternative version, 'The best mother-in-law is she on whom the geese feed.' Of this mind must have been the suitor who was asking papa for permission to marry his daughter. 'Hadn't you better see her mother first?' inquired the hen-pecked father. 'I have,' came the do-or-death reply, 'but I still wish to marry her.'

Another lover thought he was on safe ground as he had been told by his fiancée that her mother was no longer living. Subsequently he learned to his horror that the lady in question was in prison. Naturally he at once taxed his lady-love with deceiving him. 'Why,' he stormed, 'you told me she wasn't living, and I find she is in prison!' 'Quite so,' said the girl calmly, 'you don't call that living, do you?'

PS. – In reading this chapter through after completion the author was at first uncertain whether he had not been a little unkind in his portrayal of the modern girl's outlook on marriage in relation to her parents. At that moment he picked up the current number of *Punch* and there found a drawing illustrating a very up-to-date young lady, followed by a vacuous, simpering youth, rushing up to her parents and announcing with great glee, 'Darlings, I'm engaged. This damfool wants to marry me.'

A Trip to Brighton

Graham Greene

Recently retired from his job as a bank manager, Henry
Pulling is looking forward to a restful old age cultivating his
dahlias. But he has reckoned without his Aunt Augusta,
whose bizarre adventures take him on many memorable
journeys – of which a trip to Brighton is only the first . . .

I was weeding the dahlias, the Polar Beauties and the Golden Leaders and
the Requiems, when my telephone began to ring. Being unused to the sound
which shattered all the peace of my little garden, I assumed that it was a
wrong number. I had very few friends, although before my retirement I
boasted a great many acquaintances. There were clients who had stayed with
me for twenty years, who had known me in the same branch as clerk, cashier
and manager, and yet they remained acquaintances. It is rare for a manager
to be promoted from the staff of a branch in which he will have to exercise
authority, but there were special circumstances in my case. I had been acting
manager for nearly a year owing to my predecessor's illness, and one of my
clients was a very important depositor who had taken a fancy to me. He
threatened to remove his custom if I did not remain in charge. His name
was Sir Alfred Keene: he had made a fortune in cement and my father,
having been a builder, gave us an interest in common. He would invite me
to dinner at least three times a year and he always consulted me on his
investments, though he never took my advice. He said it helped him to make
up his mind. He had an unmarried daughter called Barbara who was
interested in tatting, which I think she must have given to the church bazaar.
She was always very kind to me, and my mother suggested I might pay her
attentions, for she would certainly inherit Sir Alfred's money, but the motive
seemed to me a dishonest one and in my case I have never been greatly

interested in women. The bank was then my whole life, and now there were my dahlias.

Unfortunately Sir Alfred died a little before my retirement, and Miss Keene went to South Africa to live. I was intimately concerned, of course, with all her currency difficulties: it was I who wrote to the Bank of England for this permit or that and reminded them constantly that I had received no reply to my letters of the 9th ult.; and on her last night in England, before she caught her boat at Southampton, she asked me to dinner. It was a sad occasion without Sir Alfred, who had been a very jovial man, laughing immoderately even at his own jokes. Miss Keene asked me to look after the drinks and I chose an Amontillado, and for dinner Sir Alfred's favourite Chambertin. The house was one of those big Southwood mansions surrounded by rhododendron bushes which dripped that night with the steady slow November rain. There was an oil painting of a fishing boat in a storm after Ven de Velde over Sir Alfred's place at the dinning-room table, and I expressed the hope that Miss Keene's voyage would be less turbulent.

'I have sold the house as it stands with all the furniture,' she told me. 'I shall live with second cousins.'

'Do you know them well?' I asked.

'I have never seen them,' she said. 'They are once removed. We have only exchanged letters. The stamps are like foreign stamps. With no portrait of the Queen.'

'You will have the sun,' I encouraged her.

'Do you know South Africa?'

'I have seldom been out of England,' I said. 'Once when I was a young man I went with a school friend to Spain, but my stomach was upset by the shell-fish – or perhaps it was the oil.'

'My father was a very overpowering personality,' she said. 'I never had friends – except you, of course, Mr Pulling.'

It is astonishing to me now how nearly I came to proposing marriage that night and yet I refrained. Our interests were different, of course – tatting and dahlias have nothing in common, unless perhaps they are both the interests of rather lonely people. Rumours of the great bank merger had already reached me. My retirement was imminent, and I was well aware that the friendships I had made with my other clients would not long survive it. If I had spoken would she have accepted me? – it was quite possible. Our ages were suitable, she was approaching forty and I would soon be half-way through the fifth decade, and I knew my mother would have approved. How different everything might have been if I had spoken then. I would never have heard the disturbing story of my birth, for she would have accompanied me to the funeral and my aunt would not have spoken in her presence. I would never have travelled with my aunt. I would have been saved from much, though I suppose I would have missed much too. Miss Keene said, 'I shall be living near Koffiefontein.'

'Where is that?'

'I don't really know. Listen. It's raining cats and dogs.'

We got up and moved into the drawing-room for coffee. There was a Venetian scene copied from Canaletto on the wall. All the pictures in the house seemed to represent foreign parts, and she was leaving for Koffiefontein. I would never travel so far, I thought then, and I wished that she was staying here, in Southwood.

'It seems a very long way to go,' I said.

'If there was anything to keep me here ... Will you take one lump or two?'

'No sugar, thank you.' Was it an invitation for me to speak? I have always asked myself since. I didn't love her, and she certainly didn't love me, but perhaps in a way we could have made a life together. I heard from her a year later; she wrote, 'Dear Mr Pulling, I wonder how Southwood is and whether it's raining. We are having a beautiful sunny winter. My cousins have a small (!) farm of ten thousand acres and they think nothing of driving seven hundred miles to buy a ram. I am not quite used to things yet and I think often of Southwood. How are the dahlias? I have given up tatting. We lead a very open air existence.'

I replied and gave her what news I could, but I had retired by then and was no longer at the centre of Southwood life. I told her of my mother's failing health and how the dahlias were doing. There was a rather gloomy variety in royal purple called Deuil du Roy Albert which had not been a success. I was not sorry. It was an odd name to give a flower. My Ben Hurs were flourishing.

I had neglected the telephone, feeling so sure that it was a wrong number, but when the ringing persisted, I left my dahlias and went in.

The telephone stood on the filing cabinet where I keep my accounts and all the correspondence which my mother's death caused. I had not received as many letters as I was receiving now since I ceased to be manager: the solicitor's letters, letters from the undertaker, from the Inland Revenue, the crematorium fees, the doctor's bills, National Health forms, even a few letters of condolence. I could almost believe myself a business-man again.

My aunt's voice said, 'You are very slow to answer.'

'I was busy in the garden.'

'How was the mowing-machine by the way?'

'Very wet, but no irreparable damage.'

'I have an extraordinary story to tell you,' my aunt said. 'I have been raided by the police.'

'*Raided* . . . by the police?'

'Yes, you must listen carefully for they may call on *you*.'

'What on earth for?'

'You still have your mother's ashes?'

'Of course.'

'Because they want to see them. They may even want to analyze them.'

'But Aunt Augusta . . . you must tell me exactly what happened.'

'I am trying to, but you continually interrupt with unhelpful exclamations. It was midnight and Wordsworth and I had gone to bed. Luckily I was wearing my best nightdress. They rang the bell down below and told us through the microphone that they were police officers and had a warrant to search the flat. "What for?" I asked. Do you know, for a moment I thought it might be something racial. There are so many rules now for races and against races that you don't know where you stand.'

'Are you sure they were police officers?'

'Of course I asked to see their warrant, but do you know what a warrant looks like? For all I know it might have been a reader's ticket to the British Museum library. I let them in, though, because they were polite, and one of them, the one in uniform, was tall and good-looking. They were rather surprised by Wordsworth – or perhaps it was the colour of his pyjamas. They said, "Is this your husband, ma'm?" I said, "No, this is Wordsworth." The name seemed to ring a bell with one of them – the young man in uniform – who kept on glancing at him surreptitiously, as though he were trying to remember.'

'But what were they looking for?'

'They said they had reliable information that drugs were kept on the premises.'

'Oh, Aunt Augusta, you don't think Wordsworth . . .'

'Of course not. They took away all the fluff from the seams of his pockets, and then the truth came out. They asked him what was in the brown-paper package which he was seen handing to a man who had been loitering in the street. Poor Wordsworth said he didn't know, so I chipped in and said it was my sister's ashes. I don't know why, but they became suspicious of me at once. The elder, who was in plain clothes, said, "Please don't be flippant, ma'am. It doesn't exactly help." I said, "As far as my sense of humour goes, there is nothing whatever flippant in my dead sister's ashes." "A sort of powder, ma'am?" the younger policeman asked – he was the sharper of the two, the one who thought he knew the name of Wordsworth. "You can call it that if you like," I said, "grey powder, human powder," and they looked as though they had won a point. "And who was the man who received this powder?" the man in plain clothes asked. "My nephew," I said. "My sister's son." I saw no reason to go into that old story which I told you yesterday with members of the Metropolitan Police. Then they asked for your address and I gave it to them. The sharp one said, "Was the powder for his private use?" "He wants to put it amongst his dahlias," I said. They made a very thorough search, especially in Wordsworth's room, and they took away samples of all the cigarettes they could find, and some aspirins I had left in a cachet box. Then they said, "Goodnight, ma'am," very politely and left. Wordsworth had to go downstairs and open the door for them, and just before he left the sharp one said to him, "What's your first name?" "Zachary," Wordsworth told him and he went out looking puzzled.'

'What a very strange thing to have happened,' I said.

'They even read some letters and asked who Abdul was.'

'Who was he?'

'Someone I knew a very long time ago. Luckily I had kept the envelope and it was marked Tunis, February, 1924. Otherwise they would have read all sorts of things into it about the present.'

'I am sorry, Aunt Augusta. It must have been a terrifying experience.'

'It was amusing in a way. But it did give me a guilty feeling ...'

There was a ring from the front door and I said, 'Hold on a moment, Aunt Augusta.' I looked through the dining-room window and saw a policeman's helmet. I returned and said, 'Your friends are here.'

'Already?'

'I'll ring you back when they've gone.'

It was the first time I had ever been called on by the police. There was a short middle-aged man in a soft hat with a rough but kindly face and a broken nose and the tall good-looking young man in uniform. 'Mr Pulling?' the detective asked.

'Yes.'

'May we come in for a few moments?'

'Have you a warrant?' I asked.

'Oh no, no, it hasn't come to that. We just want to have a word or two with you.' I wanted to say something about the Gestapo, but I thought it wiser not. I led them into the dining-room, but I didn't ask them to sit down. The detective showed me an identity card and I read on it that he was Detective-Sergeant Sparrow, John.

'You know a man called Wordsworth, Mr Pulling?'

'Yes, he's a friend of my aunt's.'

'Did you receive a package from him in the street yesterday?'

'I certainly did.'

'Would you have any objection to our examining the package, Mr Pulling?'

'I most certainly would.'

'You know, sir, we could easily have obtained a search warrant, but we wanted to do things delicately. Have you known this man Wordsworth a long time?'

'I met him for the first time yesterday.'

'Perhaps, sir, he asked you as a favour to deliver that package and you seeing no harm at all in that and him being an employee of your aunt ...'

'I don't know what you are talking about. The package is mine. I had accidentally left it in the kitchen.'

'The package is yours, sir? You admit that.'

'You know very well what's in the package. My aunt told you. It's an urn with my mother's ashes.'

'Your aunt has been in communication with you, has she?'

'Yes, she has. What do you expect? Waking up an old lady in the middle of the night.'

'It had only just gone twelve, sir. And so those ashes ... They are Mrs Pulling's?'

'There they are. You can see for yourself. On the bookcase.'

I had put the urn there temporarily, until I was ready to bed it, above a complete set of Sir Walter Scott which I had inherited from my father. In his lazy way my father was a great reader, though not an adventurous one. He was satisfied with possessing a very few favourite authors. By the time he had read the set of Scott through he had forgotten the earlier volumes and was content to begin again with *Guy Mannering*. He had a complete set too of Marion Crawford, and he had a love of nineteenth-century poetry which

I have inherited – Tennyson and Wordsworth and Browning and Palgrave's *Golden Treasury*.'

'Do you mind if I take a look?' the detective asked, but naturally he couldn't open the urn. 'It's sealed,' he said. 'With Scotch tape.'

'Naturally. Even a tin of biscuits ...'

'I would like to take a sample for analysis.'

I was becoming rather cross by this time. I said, 'If you think I am going to let you play around with my poor mother in a police laboratory ...'

'I can understand how you feel, sir,' he said, 'but we have rather serious evidence to go on. We took some fluff from the man Wordsworth's pockets and when analyzed it contained pot.'

'Pot?'

'Marijuana to you, sir. Likewise cannabis.'

'Wordsworth's fluff has got nothing to do with my mother.'

'We could get a warrant, sir, easily enough, but seeing how you may be an innocent dupe, I would rather take the urn away temporarily with your permission. It would sound much better that way in court.'

'You can check with the crematorium. The funeral was only yesterday.'

'We have already, sir, but you see it's quite possible – don't think I'm presuming to suggest your line of defence, that's a matter entirely for your counsel – that the man Wordsworth took out the ashes and substituted pot. He may have known he was being watched. Now wouldn't it be much better, sir, from all points of view to know for certain that these are your mother's ashes? Your aunt told us you planned to keep it in your garden – you wouldn't want to see that urn every day and wonder, are those really the ashes of the dear departed or are they an illegal supply of marijuana?'

He had a very sympathetic manner, and I really began to see his point.

'We'd only take out a tiny pinch, sir, less than a teaspoonful. We'd treat the rest with all due reverence.'

'All right,' I said, 'take your pinch. I suppose you are only doing your duty.' The young policeman had been making notes all the time. The detective said, 'Take a note that Mr Pulling behaved most helpfully and that he voluntarily surrendered the urn. That will sound well in court, sir, if the worst happens.'

'When will I get the urn back?'

'Not later than tomorrow – if all is as it should be.' He shook hands quite cordially as if he believed in my innocence, but perhaps that was just his professional manner.

Of course I hastened to telephone to my aunt. 'They've taken away the urn,' I said. 'They think my mother's ashes are marijuana. Where's Wordsworth?'

'He went out after breakfast and hasn't come back.'

'They found marijuana dust in the fluff of his suit.'

'Oh dear, how careless of the poor boy. I thought he was a little disturbed. And he asked for a CTC before he went out.'

'Did you give him one?'

'Well, you know, I'm really very fond of him, and he said it was his birthday. He never had a birthday last year, so I gave him twenty pounds.'

'Twenty pounds! I never keep as much as that in the house.'

'It will get him as far as Paris. He left in time for the Golden Arrow, now I come to think of it, and he always carries his passport to prove he's not an illegal immigrant. Do you know, Henry, I've a great desire for a little sea air myself.'

'You'll never find him in Paris.'

'I wasn't thinking of Paris. I was thinking of Istanbul.'

'Istanbul is not on the sea.'

'I think you are wrong. There's something called Sea of Marmara.'

'Why Istanbul?'

'I was reminded of it by that letter from Abdul the police found. A strange coincidence. First that letter and then this morning in the post another – the first for a very long time.'

'From Abdul?'

'Yes.'

It was weak of me, but I did not then realize the depth of my aunt's passion for travel. If I had I would have hesitated before I made the first fatal proposal: 'I have nothing particular to do today. If you would like to go to Brighton ...'

Brighton was the first journey I undertook in my aunt's company and proved a bizarre foretaste of much that was to follow.

We arrived in the early evening, for we had decided to spend the night. I was surprised by the smallness of her luggage which consisted only of a little white leather cosmetics case which she called her *baise en ville*. I find it difficult myself to go away for a night without a rather heavy suitcase, for I am uneasy if I have not at least one change of suit and that entails also a change of shoes. A change of shirt, a change of underclothes and of socks are almost an essential to me, and taking into consideration the vagaries of the English climate I like to take some woollens just in case. My aunt looked askance at my suitcase and said, 'We must take a cab. I had hoped we could walk.'

I had booked our rooms at the Royal Albion because my aunt wished to be near the Palace Pier and the Old Steine. She told me, incorrectly I think, that this was named after the wicked marquess of *Vanity Fair*. 'I like to be at the centre of all the devilry,' she said, 'with the buses going off to all those places.' She spoke as though their destinations were Sodam and Gomorrah rather than Lewes and Patcham and Littlehampton and Shoreham. Apparently she had come first to Brighton when she was quite a young woman, full of expectations which I am afraid were partly fulfilled.

I thought I would have a bath and a glass of sherry, a quiet dinner in the grill, and an early bedtime, so that we would both be rested for a strenuous morning on the front and in the Lanes, but my aunt disagreed. 'We don't want dinner for another two hours,' she said, 'and first I want you to meet Hatty if Hatty's still alive.'

'Who is Hatty?'

'We worked together once with a gentleman called Mr Curran.'

'How long ago was that?'

'Forty years or more.'

'Then it seems unlikely ...'

'*I* am here,' Aunt Augusta said firmly, 'and I got a card from her the Christmas before last.'

It was a grey leaden evening with an east wind blowing on our backs from Kemp Town. The sea was rising and the pebbles turned and ground under the receding waves. Ex-President Nkrumah looked out at us from the window of the waxworks, wearing a grey suit with a Chinese collar. My aunt paused and regarded him, I thought, a little sadly. 'I wonder where Wordsworth is now,' she said.

'I expect you'll hear from him soon.'

'I very much doubt it,' she said. 'My dear Henry,' she added, 'at my age one has ceased to expect a relationship to last. Think how complicated life would be if I had kept in touch with all the men I have known intimately. Some died, some I left, a few have left me. If they were all with me now we would have to take over a whole wing of the Royal Albion. I was very fond of Wordsworth while he lasted, but my emotions are not as strong as they once were. I can support his absence, though I may regret him for a while tonight. His knackers were superb.' The wind took my hat and tossed it against a lamp-post. I was too surprised by her vulgarity to catch it, and my aunt laughed like a young woman. I returned, brushing it down, but Aunt Augusta still lingered at the waxworks.

'It's a kind of immortality,' she said.

'What is?'

'I don't mean the waxworks here in Brighton, they are rather a job lot, but in Madame Tussaud's. With Crippin and the Queen.'

'I'd rather have my portrait painted.'

'But you can't see all round a portrait, and at Tussaud's they take some of your own clothes to dress you in, or so I've read. There's a blue dress of mine I could easily spare ... Oh well,' she said with a sigh, 'it's unlikely I'll ever be famous like that. Idle dreams ...' She walked on, I thought a little cast down. 'Criminals,' she said, 'and queens and politicians. Love is not highly regarded, except for Nell Gwynn and the Brides in the Bath.'

We came to the saloon doors of the Star and Garter and my aunt suggested that we take a drink. The walls were covered with inscriptions of a philosophic character: 'Life is a one-way street and there's no coming back'; 'Marriage is a great Institution for those who like Institutions'; 'You will never persuade a mouse that a black cat is lucky'. There were old programmes too and photographs. I ordered a sherry and my aunt said she would like a port and brandy. When I turned round from the bar I saw her examining a yellowed photograph. There was an elephant and two performing dogs drawn up in front of the Palace Pier behind a stout man in a tail-coat wearing a top hat and a watch chain, and a shapely young woman in tights stood beside him carrying a carriage whip. 'There's Curran,' my aunt said. 'That's how it all began.' She pointed at the young woman. 'And there's Hatty. Those were the days.'

'Surely you never worked in a circus, Aunt Augusta?'

'Oh no, but I happened to be there when the elephant trod on Curran's toe, and we became very close friends. Poor man, he had to go to hospital, and when he came out, the circus had gone on without him to Weymouth. Hatty too, though she came back later when we were established.'

'Established at what?'

'I'll tell you one day, but now we have to find Hatty.' She drained her port and brandy, and out we went into the cold blow of the wind. Just opposite was a stationer's which sold comic postcards and she stopped there to inquire: the metal stands for the cards rattled and strained and turned like a windmill. I noticed a card with a bottle of Guinness on it, and a fat woman in a snorkel floating face down. The legend read 'Bottoms Up!' I was looking at another of a man in hospital saying to a surgeon, 'But I said circumcision, doctor', when my aunt came out. 'It's just here,' she said. 'I knew I wasn't far wrong,' and in the window of the very next house a card in front of some net curtains read 'Hatty's Teapot. By Appointment Only'. There were photographs by the door of Marilyn Monroe and Frank Sinatra and the Duke of Edinburgh which seemed to have been signed by their subjects, although it seemed unlikely in the case of the Duke.

We rang the bell and an old lady answered it. She was wearing a black evening dress and a lot of jet objects jangled when she moved. 'You're too late,' she said sharply.

'Hatty,' said my aunt.

'I close at six-thirty sharp except by special appointment.'

'Hatty, It's Augusta.'

'Augusta!'

'Hatty! You haven't changed a bit.'

But remembering the young girl in tights carrying the whip and looking sideways at Curran I thought there had been greater changes than my aunt made out.

'This is my nephew Henry, Hatty. You remember about *him*.' They exchanged a look which I found disturbing. Why should I have been discussed all those years ago? Had she led Hatty into the secret of my birth?

'Come on in, the two of you. I was just going to have a cup of tea – an unprofessional cup of tea,' Hatty added and giggled.

'In here?' my aunt asked, opening a door.

'No dear, that's the waiting-room.' I just had time to see an engraving by Sir Alma Tadema of a lot of tall naked ladies in a Roman bathhouse.

'Here's my den, dear,' Hetty said, opening another door. It was a small over-crowded room, and everything seemed to be covered with fringed mauve shawls, the table, the backs of chairs, the mantel – there was even a shawl dangling from a studio portrait of a stout man whom I recognized as Mr Curran.

'The Revered,' Aunt Augusta said, looking at it.

'The Revered,' Hatty repeated, and then they both laughed at some secret joke of their own.

'The Rev. for short,' Aunt Augusta said, 'but that, of course, was only a coincidence. You remember how we explained it to the police. They've still got a photo of him, Hatty, stuck up in the Star and Garter.'

'I haven't been there for years,' Hatty said. 'I'm off the hard liquor.'

'You are there and the elephant too,' Aunt Augusta said. 'Can you remember the elephant's name?'

Hatty was putting out two more cups from a china cabinet. There was a fringed shawl over that too. She said, 'It wasn't a common name like Jumbo. Something classical. How one forgets things, Augusta, at our age.'

'Was it Caesar?'

'No, it wasn't Caesar. Do you take sugar, Mr – ?'

'Call him Henry, Hatty.'

'One lump,' I said.

'Oh dear, oh dear, I had such a good memory once.'

'The water's boiling, dear.'

The kettle was on a spirit ring close to a big brown teapot. She began to pour out.

'Oh, I quite forgot the strainer,' she said.

'Never mind, Hatty.'

'It's because of my clients. I never strain theirs, so I forget when I'm alone.'

There was a plate of ginger-snaps and I accepted one for politeness' sake. 'From the Old Steine,' Aunt Augusta told me. 'Ye Olde Bunne Shoppe. You don't get ginger-snaps like that anywhere else in the world.'

'And now they have turned it into a betting shop,' Hatty said. 'Pluto, dear? Was it Pluto?'

'No, I'm sure it wasn't Pluto. I think it began with a T.'

'I can't think of anything classical beginning with T.'

'There was a point to his name.'

'There certainly was.'

'Historical.'

'Yes.'

'You remember the gods, dear. They are in the photo too.'

'It was them gave Curran the idea.'

'The Revered,' Aunt Augusta repeated again, and they laughed in unison at their private memory. I felt very much alone, so I took another ginger-snap.

'The boy has a sweet tooth,' Hatty remarked.

'To think that little shop in the Old Steine survived two great wars.'

'We've survived,' Hatty replied, 'but they aren't turning us into betting shops.'

'Oh, it will need an atom bomb to destroy *us*,' Aunt Augusta said.

I thought it was time to speak. 'The situation in the Middle East is pretty serious,' I said, 'judging from today's *Guardian*.'

'You can never tell,' Hatty said, and they were both for a while buried in thought. Then my aunt picked out a tea leaf, put it on the back of her hand and slapped it with the other; it clung obstinately to a vein which was surrounded by what my mother used to call grave-marks.

'Can't get rid of the fellow,' Aunt Augusta said. 'I hope he's tall and handsome.'

'That isn't a stranger,' Hatty corrected her. 'That's the thought of a departed you can't get out of your mind.'

'Living or dead?'

'It could be either. How stiff does he feel?'

'If he's living I suppose it could be poor Wordsworth.'

'Wordsworth is dead, dear,' Hatty said, 'a very long time ago.'

'Not my Wordsworth. It's stiff as wood. I wonder who a dead one could be.'

'Poor Curran perhaps.'

'I have thought a lot about him since I came to Brighton.'

'Would you like me to do a professional cup, dear, for you and your friend?'

'Nephew,' Aunt Augusta corrected Hatty in her turn. 'It would be fun, dear.'

'I'll make another pot. The leaves have to be fresh and I use Lapsang Souchong professionally, though I drink Ceylon – Lapsang gives big leaves and good results.'

When she came back after washing the pot and our cups my aunt said, 'You must let us pay.'

'I wouldn't dream of it, dear, not after all we've been through together.'

'With the Revered.' They giggled again.

Hatty poured in the boiling water. She said, 'I don't let the pot draw. The leaves speak better fresh.' She filled our cups. 'Now toss the tea away, dear, in this basin.'

'I've got it,' my aunt said. 'Hannibal.'

'Who's Hannibal?'

'The elephant that trod on Curran's toe.'

'I do believe you're right, dear.'

'I was watching the tea and it came to me suddenly in a flash.'

'I often notice that with the leaves. Things come back. You are watching the leaves and things come back.'

'I suppose Hannibal's dead too.'

'You can't tell, dear, with elephants.'

She picked up my aunt's cup and studied it closely. 'It's interesting,' she said, 'very interesting.'

'Bad or good?'

'A bit of both.'

'Just tell me the good.'

'You are going to do a bit of travelling. With another person. You are going to cross the ocean. You are going to have many adventures.'

'With men?'

'That the leaves don't say, dear, but knowing you as I do, it wouldn't surprise me. You will be in danger of your life and liberty on more than one occasion.'

'But I'll come through?'

'I see a knife – or it might be a syringe.'

'Or it could be something else, Hatty – you know what I mean?'

'There is some mystery in your life.'

'That's nothing new.'

'I see a lot of confusion – a lot of running about this way and that. I'm sorry, Augusta, but I can't see any peace at the close. There's a cross. Perhaps you find religion. Or it could be a double-cross.'

'I've always been interested in religion,' my aunt said, 'ever since Curran.'

'Or it could be a bird, of course – a vulture perhaps. Keep away from deserts.' Hatty gave a sigh. 'Things don't come to me so easily as they once did. I exhaust myself with strangers.'

'But you'll take one look at Henry's cup too, dear, won't you? Just one look.'

She poured my tea away and looked in the cup. 'Men are difficult,' she said. 'They have so many occupations beyond a woman's knowledge and that affects the interpretation. I had a client once who said he was a bevel-edger. I don't know what he meant. Are you an undertaker?'

'No.'

'There's something that looks like an urn. Do you see it there? On the left of the handle. That's the recent past.'

'It might be an urn,' I said, looking.

'You will do a lot of travelling.'

'That's not very likely. I've always been rather stay-at-home. It's quite an adventure for me coming as far as Brighton.'

'It's in the future you're going to travel. Across the ocean. With a lady friend.'

'Perhaps he's coming with me,' Aunt Augusta said.

'It's possible. The leaves don't lie. There's a round thing like a target. There's a mystery in your life too.'

'I've only just discovered that,' I said.

'I see a lot of confusion too and running about. Just like in Augusta's cup.'

'That's most unlikely,' I said. 'I lead a very regular life. A game of bridge once a week at the Conservative Club. And my garden, of course. My dahlias.'

'The target might be a flower,' Hatty admitted. 'Forgive me. I'm tired. I'm afraid it was not a very good reading.'

'It was most interesting,' I told her for politeness' sake. 'But of course, I'm no believer.'

'Have another ginger-snap,' Hatty said.

Pages from a Private Diary

Kenneth Williams

Stories, reminiscences, bizarre incidents, encounters with friends and celebrities – all these find their way into the edited highlights from a year in the life of a household name.

1 January

The start of another year. Walking through Regent's Park this morning, past the barren trees, I reflected that I couldn't turn over a new leaf since there wasn't one to be seen. A passer-by, wearing a radio head-set, called out, 'Hello, how's it going, Kenny?' I smiled mutely, not knowing *what* was supposed to be going, nor where it was going to, unless it was humanity going up to the Gates of Heaven in a formless din. Perhaps we should all start wearing head-sets.

In the evening to Barry Wade's party in his new flat. Everyone murmured admiration for the bric-à-brac. Miriam Karlin told me about her own house-warming party. 'I invited quite a lot of people for drinks in the new house,' she said, 'and Fenella Fielding went all over the place inspecting every room. Finally she returned and pronounced judgement: "It's a great success, darling, when are you going to bring it into town?"'

My sinus congestion got worse during the party, the remnants of the Christmas cold. 'I suppose I'll have to go back to that ENT man,' I said despairingly to Barry, 'and have it cauterized.'

'How on earth do they do that?' he asked.

'They burn through the nasal passages to allow the air in,' I said. 'It's a dreadful, painful process. They bore right through both nostrils.'

'Get some menthol and shove a couple of pipe cleaners up instead,' he laughed, 'then you won't be paying through the nose.'

On the way home I reflected that Barry always did have very little understanding of rhinology.

4 January

Bronchial condition still painful. Must have been mad to look for electric food-mixers in the afternoon, especially as the shops were bedlam with sales customers. The noise in Harrods merely increased the agony.

Met Michael for dinner at The Hungry Horse. He talked about a company trip to the Far East. 'It's going to be a lot of fun, with a lot of parties,' he said.

'If you're going to meet people in the East and have any kind of adventures with them,' I told him, 'you'll really need someone to teach you the techniques required for oriental love-making. They're quite different from European styles. You'll need to find some Mandarin expert on all the social and sexual customs of the East.'

'Yes, I suppose I'd need to,' he said pensively, 'otherwise I'd be a bull in a china shop.'

I laughed immoderately, but he seemed totally unaware that he had made a witticism. Odd that a lot of the best lines are unconsciously funny – like the French lady who said, 'I wish for a penis,' until she was enlightened by a friend, who said 'In English, it's pronounced *happiness.*'

5 January

In Dr Clarke's waiting-room I sat next to a man with a Sherlock Holmes hat and a very nasty cold. When I went in to see Bertie (Clarke) I said, 'That man in the deer-stalker has been giving me his germs.'

'Don't worry,' he said. 'I've filled him so full of penicillin that every time he sneezes, he cures everyone in the room.' *Very* droll I thought – for a doctor.

I told him the bronchitis had left me feeling tired and wan. 'Only the other night, I fell asleep watching television,' I said.

'I'm not surprised,' he said, 'watching all that rubbish.' He then gave me a prescription for iron tablets. 'In the old days you got iron naturally in black bread. But now everyone eats the white stuff.'

Taking his tip I stopped on the way home at the health shop. A sympathetic assistant sold me a loaf made with real wheatgerm. 'These modern bakers', she said, 'take all the good things out of the flour and sell them on the side. They call them by-products and flog what's left over, but it's all soggy rubbish that tastes like blotting paper. They publicize white bread as being pure. The English have always had a thing about purity and whiteness. Have you noticed how we put our brides in white, how our underwear's white, our hospitals are white – it's no wonder we end up looking white ourselves. We walk around as white as sheets. If anyone takes a holiday in France, where you can still get black bread, they come back and get stared at. People cry out, "Oh, you do look brown! Have you been on holiday?" It's finally got through to the British that if you look well, you must have been abroad, enjoying the sunshine and natural food.'

'Very perceptive,' I said. 'You should be lecturing on nutrition.'

'Ah,' she smiled, 'but then I'd never meet charmers like you!'

'Flattery will get you anywhere,' I said, repressing my blushes.

7 January

Heard Bernard Cribbins on LBC. I telephoned the station and they broadcast our chat together. I reminded him of the time when the cordite singed him on the behind in *Carry on Spying*. That reminded him in turn of a sketch he did in revue. He had to sit on a throne in great magnificence as four trumpeters appeared and played a fanfare which went on and on. When it finally stopped Bernard said, 'You fools, I ordered crumpets.'

I wished him a Happy New Year, and rang off.

10 January

To Brian and Molly Dobson for dinner. Richard Williams was there, too. He directed me in my first animation film called *Love Me, Love Me*: I remember seeing it at the Academy some years ago.

I commented on the fact that Molly had given her children their meal earlier, on the grounds that it was better for children to eat before the adults.

Richard remarked, 'It's ridiculous, they're adults really. They've just shrivelled a bit, that's all.'

An animated wit, too, I see.

12 January

Bumped into Johnny Koon, the restaurateur, and we talked about the time when I'd been stranded in Gibraltar en route for Morocco. I was staying at the Queen's Hotel and having a drink in the bar when I met two men, whom I assumed at first were fellow-travellers, stranded as I was. When we got talking, however, one turned out to be a signalman on the aircraft-carrier *Eagle*, and the other a leading stoker. As they were dressed in civvies, I'd mistaken them for holidaymakers. While we were chatting the page came up and said, 'You're wanted on the phone.'

It was Johnny Koon: 'I'm opening my new Chinese restaurant', he said, 'and I'd love it if you would come and cut the ribbon and make a little speech. *The Times of Gibraltar* will be taking pictures and I've invited the Governor and the C-in-C Troops, Gibraltar.'

I told him I'd just met two chums in the bar and he said, 'Bring them along – the more the merrier!'

We arrived at this grand restaurant opening. I spoke a few words of welcome to everyone, with a passing reference to the exotic nature of the East coming to Gibraltar, and then we were shown to our tables.

I found myself seated, with my signalman and stoker, opposite the Governor, the Admiral and their captain. I asked him the name of his ship. When he replied, 'The *Eagle*', I said 'Well, you'll know Sylvester and James here.'

The captain looked rather coldly at me and said, 'There are over two thousand men under my command, and it's hardly likely I would remember every face.'

I said, 'No, but as Dr Johnson rightly remarked, "When it comes to lapidary inscriptions, no man is upon oath".'

'Yes, that is very true,' he said uncertainly. 'How very wise, how very apt.' I secretly thought it wasn't apt at all, but it had filled what could have been an embarrassing gap.

A drink or two later, the page from the hotel rushed in to tell me that my plane was at last ready to go, and that my luggage had already been taken to the airport. I leapt up and bade a hasty farewell to my fellow-guests. But the Admiral stopped me and asked, 'What about transport?'

'Well, I assume I'll get a taxi in the street,' I said.

'No, don't worry,' he said, 'use my car.'

So I arrived at the airport in a huge Rolls Royce, flying the Admiral's pennant. The car drove straight onto the tarmac by the stairs up to the plane. The BEA staff were on the steps as the limousine arrived. Their faces were eager with expectation and awe at this unexpected VIP, and then I stepped out.

'Oh, it's that twit from the *Carry On's*,' a steward said. 'I suppose you'll want the gin and tonic.'

I doubt if even Dr Johnson would have had an answer to that one.

14 January

The Lyric, Hammersmith, rang about casting the part of the father in my production of *Entertaining Mr Sloane*. 'See if you can get David Blake Kelly,' I said. Within a few minutes they rang back to say that David would be delighted to accept. So that's more or less fixed all the casting for the play – except for the part of Cathy.

I mentioned this to Barbara Windsor, since I think she'd be marvellous in it. In discussing the kind of clothes that Cathy would wear Barbara had the temerity to reprove me, saying, 'I saw you the other day from the window of Hartnell's where I get my clothes. You were passing by and several of the assistants commented on your awful appearance – going around in that terrible, dirty old raincoat and filthy cap. You look like some old flasher. Can't you buy yourself some decent gear? You look as though you're dressed by Oxfam. If you tried, you could look quite smart.'

'Dressing smartly is not my style, Barbara.'

'As far as clothes are concerned, Kenneth, you haven't got *any* style,' she said.

Just as well Barbara and I are old chums. Anyway, we've fixed a meeting to discuss the part. When I said, 'Don't worry, I'll wear the right dress,' she said, 'Hang on, I think I prefer the raincoat.'

15 January

Hearing a radio talk today on the ludicrous nature of lines taken out of context made me remember the actor who took part in a documentary programme apropos of Regency Brighton and the Prince Regent's lavish entertaining in that daft pavilion. He had to say the line, 'The Prince Regent's balls were the largest in Europe.' He told me afterwards that there wasn't one note of complaint.

Trevor Baxter once told me about playing Robert Burns in an ill-fated production, where his opening gambit was, 'You'll excuse my crutch, Miss Maclehose?'

The Listener once printed a piece from a broadcast by the scientist, Brian Ford, who said, 'In Delhi I was taken to Dikshit University and passed by Phuket Island on my way through Malaysia, and in the South Pacific I learned that the Tongan for beautiful is "U-fukofa'ofa".'

Obviously, in the Orient, beauty is in the ear of the beholder – and the genteel will be supplied with ear-plugs.

16 January

Went to the Lyric, Hammersmith. Odd to think I shall be directing a play in the refurbished theatre where I made my debut in a musical, *The Buccaneer*, by Sandy Wilson. The place is full of curious memories for me. I was once taken by Eric Portman to see a revue there. During the interval I went to the lavatory, fell asleep on the seat, and woke up just in time to return for the National Anthem. 'Sorry' I whispered to E.P. 'I went right off!' 'Don't worry,' he returned drily, 'so did the show', which left me feeling quite guiltless.

The only other time I played the Lyric was in *Share My Lettuce*, before it transferred to the West End. In the 'Wallflower Waltz' scene, all the men danced with pieces of chiffon which floated down from the flies, while the girls stood apart, singing an accompaniment. On the first night, my piece of chiffon got caught on a spot-bar and I had nothing to dance with, so I spent the entire scene trying to steal pieces of material belonging to the others. They kept pushing me off, and I ran round from one to another muttering, 'I haven't got a bit!' It provoked so much laughter from the audience that this hitherto plaintive number in the show became a comedy item.

I told Roy Castle about this experience when I did 'Record Breakers' with him on television. We agreed that the unexpected can sometimes have very funny results in the theatre. 'I remember being on a bill with Tommy Cooper', Roy said, 'and commenting on the shortness of his turn that evening. Tommy said it was because he'd built the act round a walking stick, which was an essential prop, but the preceding artists had bolted their equipment to the floor and unbeknown to him there were now several holes in the stage. His walking stick fell through one of these and he was left with nothing to finish his act. Tommy didn't worry, though. He did a brilliant ad-lib, he said. He walked off!'

Then I told Roy about the funny ad-lib which occurred during the Equity AGM at the Victoria Palace when Dulcie Gray rose to complain, 'Mister Chairman, I must protest! There is no paper in the ladies' lavatory!' When someone grumbled, 'This is holding up the motion!' a wag shouted from the back, 'So is the lack of loo paper!'

In the evening to Richard Williams's studio to work on his new animated film, *The Thief and the Cobbler*. Richard said he'd got Vincent Price for the King and I told him how brilliant Vincent had been in *Champagne for Caesar*. 'If you ever get a chance to see that film, don't miss it!' I said. 'It's a marvellous satire on commercialism and sponsored broadcasting. In it there's a splendid line when, during a quiz game, Ronald Colman is asked: "What is the Japanese for goodbye?" and he says "Sayonara, not to be confused with Cyanide, which is goodbye in any language!"'

17 January

Dinner with John Schlesinger and Noel Davis. It seems extraordinary that my friendship with John stems from the transit camp at Nee Soon in Malaya in 1946. Even then John's flair for direction and his imaginative grasp of stage settings were obvious. We talked endlessly about our time with CSE (Combined Services Entertainment) in Singapore and I reminded him of the occasion when the sergeant-major committed suicide because he'd been discovered embezzling the funds and splitting the proceeds with the Chinese tailors who made the costumes.

The commanding officer paraded us and said, 'You've all heard the news. The sergeant-major's killed himself and now the man's more bloody trouble dead than he was alive. We've got to bury him. All those over six feet, stand forward for pall-bearing.' People shrank visibly in the ranks.

The colonel went down the line and stopped in front of Stanley Baxter, 'You'll do,' he said. 'Stand forward.'

'Ah, I'm sorry,' said Stanley, 'Church of Scotland.'

'Oh, I beg your pardon – of course,' said the colonel, and went on down the line. When he'd got past a few more the penny dropped. He turned back and said, 'Just a minute. What are you talking about, Church of Scotland? You bury people, don't you?'

Stanley spluttered, 'We-ell, yes, but...'

'You'll do,' said the colonel. 'You'll go.'

So Stanley and the other members of the burial party were sent off to the British Military Cemetery in the midst of a tropical downpour. It was an ill-assorted group to lower a coffin. As well as Stanley, there was a pianist, a dancer, a pipe-major and a couple of others. They were all quite unmilitary. When they got there, they draped the coffin with a Union Jack, but the chaplain whispered, 'Get the flag off. It's ignominious death, no battle honours are given.'

Hurriedly the monsoon-sodden flag was removed and the service began. As the chaplain came to the passage about life being brief and full of misery, with the colonel standing, saluting reverently, a huge Cadillac drew up. A Chinese chauffeur got out and held up an umbrella for an attractive woman, visibly tearful, who came and stood alongside Stanley and the others.

'My dear,' whispered the Colonel, 'are you a friend of the deceased?'

'Friend?' she said in a pronounced American accent. 'I'm his wife.'

Stanley said they were all taken aback at the dead sergeant-major's secret nuptials. But the colonel sized up the situation promptly. At the end of the funeral he said, 'Dismiss your chauffeur, my dear. You are obviously distressed and in need of comfort. I will take you back to Nee Soon in my jeep.' And off they drove together.

I asked Stanley about the outcome. 'When I went in to see the Colonel for orders the next morning,' he said, 'there was the late sergeant-major's wife sitting in a kimono, sipping coffee! Never had the effects of mourning evaporated so rapidly.'

18 January

I'm reading the John Lahr biography of Joe Orton. Strange how Lahr's accounts of events I thought I'd remembered well are not at all as I had imagined them. Recalling my conversations with Joe during the tour of *Loot* I'd have said that we got on very well with each other, but Lahr has found a letter from Orton complaining about my being temperamental! Can you imagine? Certainly Joe conveyed nothing of the kind to me. Of course one knows that people say contradictory things the moment one's back is turned, but it's still a shock to find that people one thinks of as constant and consistent are really mercurial and changeful. Perhaps we always expect too much of other people and are always disappointed by them. It's in the nature of humanity. That's why we need faith so much: the unaltering, the everlasting and the endlessly forgiving. I think of Wilfred Owen's line about 'the eternal reciprocity of tears.' The mind that can resolve contented thought is just as capable of harbouring discontent and despair.

I remember visiting Tony Hancock in hospital and finding the bed covered with books by Leibnitz, Nietzsche and Bertrand Russell. He said, 'I'm trying to discover the purpose of it all. Have you ever thought, Kenny, what if there's no point to existence at all? What if there's no one up there? Sometimes I think it's all a joke.'

'Well, in that case,' I said, 'you must try and make it a good one.'

'Oh, that's just evading the issue,' he said, and he went on to talk about the fictitious line we draw between subjectivity and objectivity. It's weird how people love definitions and labels; yet they so often turn out to be spurious – like the Motorist and the Pedestrian. Both labels are invalid; when the motorist gets out of his car he becomes a pedestrian and vice versa.

It's like the man searching under the lamp-post. A policeman asks what he's lost, and the man tells him he's dropped a coin 'over there', pointing to a spot in the darkness. 'Then why aren't you looking there?' asks the policeman.

'Because this is where the light is.'

25 January

With Michael to the Chanterelle restaurant. It was 12.15, but it was closed, so I banged on the door and the boy who admitted us said, quite distantly. 'We don't open until one on Sundays.' I swept him aside. We had a fairly good meal at all events, certainly a lot better than the disastrous one we had there the last time. Michael took me through a car-wash afterwards, which was quite an adventure. Barbara Windsor telephoned with the good news that she's going to play Cathy in *Sloane*. She told me she'd got three more weeks' panto in Newcastle and that business was marvellous. 'We're Harry Packers,' she said. She's staying at the Holiday Inn up there and said that she had done one length in its swimming pool.

'Rather you than me,' I said. 'You can pick up things in those places.'

'I've never heard that.'

'Well, you wouldn't. The p is silent as in pneumonia.'

We went on to discuss characterizations in general and how one approaches a role. Whenever I get on to that subject I'm always reminded of the person who rang up Alec Guinness, when he was rehearsing *Hamlet*, and said he'd discovered a completely original conception of the role in a wonderful book. Alec said, 'I'd be interested to read it. What is the book?'

'I can't remember the author,' said the caller.

'What's the title?'

'Well, I can't remember that either, but it was a red book.'

I related this to Barbara, who snorted derisively: 'Yes, advice like that is about as effective as a fart in wet blancmange.'

26 January

Hearing a Liszt recital on the radio today my mind drifted back to a revue I once did at the Duke of York's and to one night in particular when the stage-box was occupied by a gentleman who fell about laughing every time I was on. He laughed so much and so loudly that he nearly had us all giggling on the stage. The crisis came with the barber's sketch in which I was supposed to do elaborate things with Lance Percival's hair, while he expostulated, 'Nothing fancy, you understand. Just short back and sides.'

I had to rant on saying, 'Oh, I've had them all in here. I've had bishops in here. They all wanted the gold rinse to match the mitre.' At this point the man in the box laughed so loudly that it set us both off and we could hardly act the rest of the sketch. Luckily I could walk upstage and pretend to get scissors and hair-spray, but Lance was stuck in the chair, in full view of the house, and he went through an agony of mirth.

I still laugh whenever I think of it. There was a terrible row afterwards and the stage manager came round and berated us. 'You ruined the performance by corpsing on stage. It's a disgrace.' At that point the stage-door man came in and announced the occupant of the box. In walked one of the greatest American exponents of Liszt, George Bolet. I'd heard him play in the film *Song Without End*. I was staggered that a concert pianist of his stature should stroll into my dressing-room and say he was a fan.

'I want to congratulate you on a wonderful show,' he said, and he sang our praises fulsomely. 'Gentlemen, it's a triumph!' he concluded.

The stage-manager sycophantically concurred. 'I was just telling Mr Williams, sir, what a wonderful performance it had been.'

Afterwards I said to the stage-manager, 'Well, that was a fine *volte face*. You said at first we were disgraceful, but then you told George Bolet it was marvellous.'

'Ah, my dear,' he countered, 'the customer's always right.'

27 January

Health warnings appear on everything these days and I see in a letter to *The Times* today someone has written that, 'Since health warnings appear on cigarettes and people are now telling us we mustn't drink coffee because it contains caffeine, that tea contains tannin, and butter contains cholesterol, the government should print on our birth certificates, "Life is about dying".' Quite right.

The Times has got another piece about the dangers of alcohol. It's actually claimed that whisky kills more people than bullets. It's all quite ridiculous, because, as any child knows, bullets don't drink whisky.

At least it's an easy crossword today – no hazard to health there.

31 January

My confidante at the health food shop was in one of her didactic moods today.

'You'd be amazed at the ignorance of the general public,' she said. 'I had a customer in the other day who didn't even know that vinegar was sour wine.'

I said, 'I didn't know that myself.'

'There you are, and you'd call yourself a knowledgeable man, wouldn't you?'

'Well, ye...'

'Exactly. Vinegar is a natural astringent. You might as well put after-shave on your salad. It shrinks the stomach.'

I shuddered. 'Then I shall certainly avoid it. I don't want to walk round with a shrunken stomach.'

I fled into the street grasping my wheat loaf and thinking for some extraordinary reason of Mahatma Gandhi.

Heard a lovely story at the Cosmo restaurant tonight. The owner said he'd overheard one mittel-European lady tell her friend she'd paid five-fifty to see *Dr Zhivago*.

The other woman exploded, 'Five-fifty! What is he, some sort of specialist?'

The Dentist and the Gas

Stephen Leacock

'I think,' said the dentist, stepping outside again, 'I'd better give you gas.'

Then he moved aside and hummed an air from a light opera, while he mixed up cement.

I sat up in my shroud.

'Gas!' I said.

'Yes,' he repeated, 'gas or else ether or a sulphuric anaesthetic or else beat you into insensibility with a club or give you three thousand volts of electricity.'

These may not have been his exact words. But they convey the feeling of them very nicely.

I could see the light of primitive criminality shining behind the man's spectacles.

And to think that this was *my* fault – the result of my own reckless neglect. I had grown so used to sitting back dozing in my shroud in the dentist's chair, listening to the twittering of the birds outside, my eyes closed in the sweet half sleep of perfect security, that the old apprehensiveness and mental agony had practically all gone.

He didn't hurt me, and I knew it.

I had grown – I know it sounds mad – almost to like him.

For a time I had kept up the appearance of being hurt every few minutes, just as a precaution. Then even that had ceased, and I had dropped into vainglorious apathy.

It was this, of course, which had infuriated the dentist. He meant to reassert his power. He knew that nothing but gas could rouse me out of my lethargy and he meant to apply it – either gas or some other powerful pain stimulant.

So as soon as he said *gas*, my senses were alert in a moment.

'When are you going to do it?' I said in horror.

'Right now, if you like,' he answered.

His eyes were glittering with what the Germans call Blutlust. All dentists have it.

I could see that if I took my eye off him for a moment he might spring at me, gas in hand, and throttle me.

'No, not now, I can't stay now,' I said, 'I have an appointment, a whole lot of appointments, urgent ones, the most urgent I ever had.' I was unfastening my shroud as I spoke.

'Well then, tomorrow,' said the dentist.

'No,' I said, 'tomorrow is Saturday. And Saturday is a day when I simply can't take gas. If I take gas, even the least bit of gas, on a Saturday, I find it's misunderstood.'

'Monday, then.'

'Monday, I'm afraid, won't do. It's a bad day for me, worse than I can explain.'

'Tuesday?' said the dentist.

'Not Tuesday,' I answered, 'Tuesday is the worst day of all. On Tuesday my church society meets, and I *must* go to it.'

I hadn't been near it in reality for three years, but suddenly I felt a longing to attend it.

'On Wednesday,' I went on, speaking hurriedly and wildly, 'I have another appointment, a swimming club, and on Thursday two appointments, a choral society and a funeral. On Friday I have another funeral. Saturday is market day. Sunday is washing day. Monday is drying day –'

'Hold on,' said the dentist, speaking very firmly. 'You come tomorrow morning, I'll write the engagement for ten o'clock.'

I think it must have been hypnotism.

Before I knew it, I had said 'Yes.'

I went out.

In the street I met a man I knew.

'Have you ever taken gas from a dentist?' I asked.

'Oh, yes,' he said. 'It's nothing.'

Soon after I met another man.

'Have you ever taken gas?' I asked.

'Oh, certainly,' he answered, 'it's nothing, nothing at all.'

Altogether I asked about fifty people that day about gas and they all said that it was absolutely nothing. When I said that I was to take it tomorrow, they showed no concern whatever. I looked in their faces for traces of anxiety.

There weren't any. They all said that it wouldn't hurt me, that it was nothing.

So then I was glad because I knew that gas was nothing.

It began to seem hardly worth while to keep the appointment. Why go all the way down town for such a mere nothing?

But I did go.

I kept the appointment.

What followed was such an absolute nothing that I shouldn't bother to relate it except for the sake of my friends.

The dentist was there with two assistants. All three had white coats on, as rigid as naval uniforms.

I forget whether they carried revolvers.

Nothing could exceed their quiet courage. Let me pay them that tribute.

I was laid out in my shroud in a long chair and tied down to it – I think I was tied down; perhaps I was fastened with nails – this part of it was a mere nothing. It simply felt like being tied down by three strong men armed with pinchers.

After that a gas tank and a pump were placed beside me and a set of rubber tubes fastened tight over my mouth and nose. Even those who have never taken gas can realize how ridiculously simple is this.

Then they began pumping in gas. The sensation of this part of it I cannot, unfortunately, recall. It happened that just as they began to administer the gas, I fell asleep. I don't quite know why. Perhaps I was overtired. Perhaps it was the simple home charm of the surroundings, the soft drowsy hum of the gas pump, the twittering of the dentists in the trees – did I say in the trees? – No, of course they weren't in the trees – imagine dentists in the trees – ha! ha! – here, take off this gas pipe from my face till I laugh – really I just want to laugh – only to laugh –

Well, that's what it felt like.

Meanwhile, they were operating.

Of course I didn't *feel* it. All I felt was that someone dealt me a powerful blow in the face with a sledge-hammer. After that somebody took a pick-axe and cracked in my jaw with it. That was all.

It was a mere nothing. I felt at the time that a man who objects to a few taps on the face with a pick-axe is over critical.

I didn't happen to wake up till they had practically finished. So I really missed the whole thing.

The assistants had gone and the dentist was mixing up cement and humming airs from light opera just like old times. It made the world seem a bright place.

I went home with no teeth. I only meant them to remove one, but I realized that they had taken them all out. Still, it didn't matter.

Not long after I received my bill. I was astounded at the nerve of it; for administering gas, debtor, so much; for removing teeth, debtor, so much – and so on.

In return I sent in my bill: –

Dr William Jaws

Debtor:

To mental agony	$ 50.00
To gross lies in regard to the nothingness of gas	100.00
To putting me under gas	50.00
To having fun with me under gas	100.00
To Brilliant Ideas, occurred to me under gas and lost	100.00
Grand Total	$400.00

My bill has been contested and is in the hands of a solicitor. The matter will prove, I understand, a test case, and will go to the final courts. If the judges have toothache during the trial, I shall win.

Flashback Country

J. H. Irving

> Schmovie-buffs are the people who go to the cinema not
> only to watch the film but also to enjoy the wealth of mis-
> takes and blunders with which every movie seems to be
> blighted ...

As audiences go, schmovie-buffs are a pushy and inquisitive lot. Before we
can really settle down to pick holes in a picture, there are certain facts we
insist on knowing – the end, for a start. Most people want to know how a
film will end, but are quite content to wait until they get there to find out.
Not us. By that time, as you'll see, it may be too late. We want this
information well in advance. To spot mis-takes properly, it is helpful if we
can discover right at the beginning the direction a story is going to take,
which of the characters will be lovers, which of them are cheats or heroes or
double-dealers; who will die halfway through, and so on – if only to release
us from having to follow the plot too closely while we're out fishing for goofs.

Fortunately, in many schmovies most of these details are dropped
deliberately into the storyline like dead weights early on – usually in the first
15 minutes – equipping you with all the facts you will need to know in one
cumbersome dollop.

For instance, keep a close watch on the old man in disaster movies, who
mentions in passing, when we meet him initially, that he was once a key
member of the Belgrano Brothers highwire act until he lost his nerve, and
mark it well, because towards the end, when this guy and his wife are trapped
alone on the roof of a burning skyscraper, and when the sole way to fetch
help is for *someone* to walk 200 yards across a thin steel cable to the
neighbouring building, he will miraculously come into his own. 'I'll go,' he'll

say, chalking his feet and leaping to the cable with his arms outstretched, having suddenly regained his pluck.

And that is what we call a plot device: a seed planted in that first quarter of an hour, which can be harvested later on before they reach the closing credits. You could almost put money on it!

'But Johnnie ... I can't swim!' is another. Anyone who chances to slip this into the conversation will sooner or later find himself diving into rapids off a 60-foot ledge, or thrashing helplessly about in the foam after a shipwreck. You can see it coming. Nobody prepared to admit to any sort of incapacity in films can do so without suffering for it in due course. Phobias and infirmities are milked for all they are worth. Dizziness, black-outs, heart trouble, you name it – each will be fully exploited before the picture is through. Asthma sufferers are an absolute menace for this. When a character announces he is asthmatic he is telling you two things: one, that he has asthma, and two, that he will have one of his attacks at the worst possible moment – during a siege maybe, or while he is stuck in a crowded elevator between floors, or as the jet-engines on an aeroplane cut out and it starts to bank over and descend rapidly. Only then will he slump into a corner, clutching at his collar and wrestling to pull the cap off his inhaler.

Because time is short, a writer daren't waste a split-second of it telling you something you do not need to know, which makes the task of writing rubbish a tough one; tougher, in some cases, than writing quality stuff.

Pity, then, the frustrated schmovie-author sitting at his typewriter at 4.30 in the morning with an ugly 10 o'clock deadline to beat. Waist-deep in waste-paper after trying to work the same set of facts into the first scene in 400 different ways, and down to his last Mogadon, he has slipped into the sort of trance that comes from staring at an empty vodka bottle for too long. The whole situation can lead him into very serious temptation. The urge is soon upon him to unlock his desk and pull out that battered copy of the Cliché Code he keeps there for emergencies. He knows full well that inside it he will find a wealth of answers to his problems – a list of Ten Little Helpers that the struggling idea-less writer may recruit at any time to assist him in carrying his story forward; tips on how to alter the texture of his script for effect, how other authors before him have coped with the problems facing him right now, and, maybe most importantly, how best to cram his plot devices into the opening 15 minutes of the film: little touches that, if applied diligently, are sure to make his movie no different from anyone else's.

Sadly, it is a temptation that few are able to resist – even expert scriptwriters succumb occasionally.

The Ten Little Helpers are as old as the hills, each one wearing thin after constant use, but none of them any the less popular for that. Again, it feeds on examples drawn from half a century of popular film-making.

Little Helper Number One: The Letter

No one in a film who opens a letter or finds a message left pinned to his bedroom mirror is able to keep the content of it to himself for very long. He automatically assumes we want to know what it says. Just as well he does, too, because a lot of basic plot information can be passed on in letters, telegrams, ransom demands and goodbye notes – 'Dearest Kip, I have gone. Please do not come after me. We shall never meet again, my love. You see, I have found another. It is much bigger than the first. Thank you for everything. Affectionately, Isabel.'

Either the message will be held up to the camera, probably with the vital part illuminated to catch our eye, in which case it must be typed, or written in clear, bold, together handwriting. (People with squiggly, illegible, untogether handwriting never have a letter of theirs held up to the camera.) Or, and this is more popular, it will be read aloud to us. The recipient may read it himself, first of all, or he may pass it on to someone else, making a weak excuse: 'I can't read without my glasses. Will you read it to me?' (*The Way to the Stars*, 1945); 'I can't read it. I'm too nervous.' (*Little Women*, 1949); or, equally, he may imagine that the voice of whoever wrote it is reading it to him.

Take care with this last one. If you do hear the voice of the author, make sure that what he says is what is actually written on the paper.

The Bermuda Triangle (1978) An astronomer receives a letter from a fellow scientist. 'My dear Jessop' – the sender's voice – 'in our responsibility to science, can we forget our humanity?' But if you pay close attention to the page being held up to the camera, what that sentence really says is, 'Anyway, I think this is an interesting angle worth ... experimentation, do you?'

Little Helper Number Two: The Flashback

Flashbacks enjoyed the greatest popularity back in the 1960s when it was all the rage to make those stern but colourful adaptations of H. G. Wells' and Jules Verne's classic science-fantasy novels – *The Time Machine, 20, 000 Leagues* ... you know the sort of thing.

Out of the relatively small batch that were made about that time, a 'best way' of introducing the story evolved, and has been taken up in many other films and television series since. The picture should open in a country nursing home. An elderly explorer sits smothered in blankets and padlocked to a wheelchair, from where he recounts to a gawping reporter the fantastic adventure he had when he 'accidentally went to the Moon', or when his diving bell slipped through a fissure in some ocean trench or other, and he discovered a lost civilization, the remains of Atlantis, or Captain Nemo, presumed dead but still alive and working.

'It all began in the year of our Lord eighteen hundred and ninety-three – June the 24th. I found a curious note stuck to the door of my carriage. At first I paid it little heed, but subsequent events soon conspired to change my mind ...' Then comes the flashback. Present action merges with the past by way of a queazy-ripple effect, as though a stage-hand is standing out of shot tipping honey down the screen. (A similar effect can be achieved at home, if you wear a pair of goggles in the shower. Try it.) The ripple transports us back 40 years, and only now do we find out why we were introduced to this old windbag in the first place – so that he can spend the rest of the film rambling on and on about his bloody expedition. We get to see the Moon, the civilization, Captain Nemo, Atlantis, and then, after 90 minutes, more honey is tipped down the screen, bringing us quickly to the present again, as he tails off with, 'So you see, young man, there are worlds other than our own ... worlds we can reach if we only hhhhhh ...' Then he dies.

The same actor plays both roles – the youthful as well as the demented professor. All make-up artists have their own 'senile old git' kit and, in a couple of hours, a young actor can be given the white, wispy toupée, stick-on silver eyebrows, latex wrinkles and cysts that have come to be the trademark of old age in the movies.

Flashbacks will rarely creep up on you by surprise, you'll find. They are usually well-signposted in the story. The three standard lead-in lines to listen out for are:

1. '... it happened on Tuesday ... I was on my way to the office as usual ... when ...' and the scene switches swiftly to the Houses of Parliament with Big Ben chiming the quarter-hour (*School for Scoundrels*, 1960). This one is reserved for the retelling of a joky tale, or for the evidence given by a murder-witness.

2. 'Where did it all begin? I suppose it was when I was at school ...' (*Curse of Frankenstein*, 1957) – kept for mental patients under psychiatric examination, or prisoners on the night before their execution.

3. 'As long as I live, no matter how far I go from the scene, I shall never forget how it all began ...' (*Moss Rose*, 1947). A sure indication that whoever can't forget whatever it is, is determined that we won't forget it either. These films usually open halfway through the story, or even at the end, so that by the time you drop in on the characters, hearts have been broken, families wrenched apart, lives lost or shattered, leaving nothing but despair. A house so run-down that water drips relentlessly on to the bed; Papa sits alone in a wicker chair, saying nothing; Momma cries quietly into her dish-flannel; Carol has a leg missing, and gazes broodily into the fire. Something privately cataclysmic has happened to these sorrowful souls, but what? Admittedly, you are *slightly* intrigued as to how they came to be in such a state, but not overly so – not to the extent that you want to sit in an uncomfortable seat for two hours to find out. However, just as you're feeling relieved that all the misery is behind you, and that from now on their plight can only improve, up comes a flashback, dragging you into the past again, and you have to endure the whole history of their torment right from the beginning.

Little Helpers Numbers Three and Four: Narration and the Caption

Linked because they amount in essence to the same thing, these two are the simplest devices at a writer's disposal, and the most boring, too, in many ways, so I shall dispose of them fairly quickly myself.

They are used largely as scene-setters. A caption will tell you in which country or city a film is set. The usual stock-shot Eiffel Tower at the opening of the picture is not enough for some. The Dimwit Element tend to require a caption that says 'Paris', before they can fully grasp what they're being told. 'Paris 1914', superimposed over a panorama of the city rooftops, is even better for us, especially if the film was made entirely in the studio in England or America (as is invariably so when you see a caption like this), since, first, it lets us know that this is going to be a period picture, which is Good News, and, second, it acts as our cue to be on the look-out for TV aerials, fast-moving commuter traffic and Boots le Chemists signs.

Narration, for its part, is little more than a caption read aloud. The best you can do as a schmovie-buff is ensure that what the narrator tells you agrees with what you can see on the screen.

The Bermuda Triangle (1978) A formation of American P51 Mustangs locates a UFO in the skies over Kentucky. Their flight leader, Captain Mantel, radios in to Godman Tower at Fort Knox to report the sighting – message timed at 3 p.m. according to a clock on the wall. After which, the narrator blurts out, 'Then at 2.45, Mantel contacted the Tower ...'

Little Helper Number Five: Time

Time oils the cogs of a film. Skilfully manipulated, a story can span several decades, if necessary. The writer may shift the action from day to day in his script, or from millennium to millennium. Characters can grow old and die, new generations spring up, poor men become rich and rich men tumble, all in three reels. This capacity to dodge carefreely between centuries and seasons, to hop from here to there without restraint, is the writer's joy. To see his efforts grind inadvertently on to the rocks and break up is the schmovie-goer's joy. A discrepancy may be measured in many ways. It could take minutes ...

Kiss Me Deadly (1955) Mike Hammer (Ralph Meeker) passes a street-vendor, buys some popcorn off him and walks away with it – a brief sequence lasting nine seconds – if that. Yet, watching the clock in the window behind him, you'll see that he walks up to the vendor at 2.10 p.m., buys the popcorn at 2.15, and carries on up the street immediately – at 2.20!

The Master of Ballantrae (1953) At the point where Errol Flynn is having an argument with his brother in the film, the candle on the table *grows* four inches while they shout at each other.

... or hours ...

The Corn Is Green (1945) Prim schoolma'am Bette Davis arrives in a Welsh village with her housemaid. When the maid walks in through the door of their new home, the time on the grandfather clock is 12.10. She announces to the people waiting inside that Miss Davis is following right behind and, sure enough, five minutes later, the lady herself strides in through the door – at 5.15, according to the same clock.

... or months ...

On the Fiddle (1961) Staff Sergeant Graham Stark has been keeping a full dossier on a couple of new recruits at an Air Force base. Having earmarked them as loafers, his file maps out their doings and whereabouts 'since they joined us in October ...' that is, October 1944. But earlier in the film, when we see the two of them signing up to join the RAF, the calendar on the wall says '5th April'.

Jaws (1975) The Amity Swimming Regatta on 4 July is terrorized by a great white shark, which scares most of the holiday-makers off the beach, and all the leaves off the trees as well. The shark scenes were filmed in the spring, the rest of it during the summer, and when the two sets of shots are joined up, the effect is quite jarring.

By far the most vulnerable time for mis-takes to happen is between day and night. For a writer to set a scene at night is one thing, but for his instructions to be translated on to the screen is another entirely.

For Your Eyes Only (1981) Roger Moore is exploring an old warehouse in Corfu after dark when it explodes. The man who set the charges makes a swift getaway by car and speeds off into the night. Moore takes a short cut to head him off: he climbs a flight of steps, runs along a tunnel, up another flight of steps, and then another, and finally reaches the top of the hill before the car does, by which time – ta-raaaaa! – it's daylight and the sun is shining!

A night scene may be created quite easily in the controlled conditions of the studio, as the lights can be dimmed on demand. But studio night is not without its own little problems.

Carry on Spying (1964) Three British secret agents interrogate a stabbed enemy spy under the beam of a hand-held torch. The man dies before he can tell them anything, so they stand up and go – taking the torch with them, but leaving the beam behind.

Spooks Run Wild (1941) A young girl with a torch in her hand stands so close to the man in front of her that the beam casts a small circle of light on to his shirt. Yet, rather curiously, the beam that came into the room when she walked in carrying the torch, is still bobbing merrily away on the back wall of the set, all on its own.

The glow from a battery-operated torch or a lantern is rarely strong enough to light up the whole room in a film. It needs to be boosted by an extra light, shone from behind the camera and moved, as required, to correspond with the movement of the one in shot. Sad to say, this normally works quite well. But when you are checking these things, don't forget to make sure that there is one beam *per* lamp.

Blood From the Mummy's Tomb (1971) An archaeology expedition penetrates deep into an unlit Egyptian tomb. The members of the team file through the door, each with his own lantern, but apparently sharing one 'glow' between them. The guy standing at the back of the camera with his booster-light trains it on one man at a time, keeping it there long enough for him to scramble into the chamber, before bouncing it on to the next lantern, leaving the first guy stumbling around in the dark.

At times, shadows and silhouettes can be more trouble than they are worth, too.

Circus of Horrors (1960) One of the circus performers eavesdrops on a conversation going on in a sideshow tent by hiding behind a notice board outside. From where she is standing, she casts a clear shadow across the canvas wall of the tent. But when you see her silhouette from inside the tent, it is of her only – no notice-board.

The Intelligence Men (1965) During a performance of *Swan Lake* by a Russian ballet troupe, members of the cast are being knocked off by a mystery killer. His next victim is the lead male dancer in his dressing-room. When the door is pushed open, the dancer is out of sight, sitting at a table around the corner, shaving. All we can see is his shadow against the back wall. The killer takes his gun by the butt, creeps up behind the dancer and slugs him over the head. But look closer. Before the attack, when the door swings back, the killer's shadow is already in the room! It is standing to one side, waiting for the man to pass through the door. Once he is out of the way, the shadow takes over and does the rest.

If it ever happens that they have to film a night-time sequence, but they wish to do it during the day, then they do it by hanging a special filter over the lens – enough to subdue the sunshine, darken the picture overall, and so give a rough impression of gloom. The filter only tends to work on overcast days, when there are no obvious shadows. If it is done in bright sunshine, it merely throws a thick blue fug across the picture, and creates much the same effect as when you hold a boiled-sweet wrapper up to your eye. They keep on telling you it's midnight, when you can see for yourself that it is mid-afternoon. They think we're fooled, they think we don't notice. But we're not and we do.

The lousy blue fug effect is known to schmovie-goers as 'broad daynight', and accounts for many a strange hiccup. It explains how Dracula, who only moves about at night, can be found wandering through a wood in the daytime, apparently unbothered by the sunshine (*Dracula Has Risen From the Grave*, 1968); and how a young girl can leave her bedroom at the dead of night, run off into the local village seemingly on a sunny day, then reach the vicar's house two minutes later at the dead of night again (*Captain Clegg*, 1962); and how a secret agent can break into a prison building at night, and burst out five minutes after in brilliant sunlight (*Jaguar Lives*, 1979).

In many cases, they try to pass the effect off as very, very strong moonlight, just like they used to do in Westerns 40 years ago. The sort of very, very strong moonlight that makes you screw up your eyes at the glare, that sparkles on water (*Vera Cruz*, 1953) and glints fiercely off anything metallic (*Sea of Sand*, 1958).

In *Jaguar Lives*, it looks as though they didn't bother using a filter at all. And they certainly didn't in:

The Wonderful World of the Brothers Grimm (1962) In the fairy-tale episode about the princess and the woodman, the king hires a happy-go-lucky woodcutter to find out where his daughter goes to at night, and how she manages to wear holes in her shoes. As it turns out, when the princess leaves the palace on these nocturnal jaunts, she merely pops down to the forest to groove with the gypsies, toe-heeling around their camp through the small hours and returning before dawn. The thing you will notice is that it is as bright and sunny when she sneaks away at midnight, as it is when she gets back in the morning.

Little Helper Number Six: Language

As a rule, audiences in Western cinemas do not warm to films in which the actors speak an alien language. Pictures in Hindustani or any one of the 200 Cameroonic dialects, or French, may be all-time blockbusters back home, but will not be terribly popular where it matters most – in the West, which you can take in this context to mean west of the English Channel.

To be a widespread success, a film must be understood in Britain and America without subtitles or dubbed voices being added: subtitles because they are an inconvenience – reading them while you follow the story is rather like trying to dig the garden and retile the roof at the same time; whereas dubbed dialogue, even when it is done well, makes for an infuriating distraction, since the voices never tie in exactly, or even remotely, with the mouth movements. This was proved over and over again in pictures such as *Godzilla versus the Smog Monster*, *Tidal Wave*, *Matango*, *Fungus of Terror*, and dozens of other cinematic suppositories inserted into our culture in the 1960s by the Japanese film industry, in which a four-minute monologue spoken with passion and conviction and urgency would be interpreted simply by the one caption: 'Come on – let's go!'

So if a scene is set in distant parts, and foreign tongues are involved, the writer must somehow twist the conversation round and introduce into it a good excuse for everyone to abandon their own language and speak ours instead.

Red Planet Mars (1952) The Martians have somehow come by a copy of the New Testament and are sending religious messages to Earth, causing alarm among the Super Powers, not least in the Soviet Union where top level talks at the Kremlin are continually drowned by communal hymn-singing from the streets, as Communist chants and slogans are quickly ditched in favour of a Thanksgiving Day knees-up. Inside a committee room, as one chap is making a crucial point to his comrades in Russian, the chairman stops him abruptly. 'Speak English – fool!' after which, everyone in the room speaks English, for no reason I could readily discern, save that if they hadn't, the whole point of the scene would have been lost on us.

The Half-Breed (1952) An Indian squaw runs to her brother, babbling in their native tongue: 'Shickoshen yor-ash tahayo ...' she pleads, which I roughly translate as, 'Quick, do something! Nobody understands a word I'm saying!' To this he replies in a flash, 'When you speak to me, little sister, try to speak in English – then you know *two* proud languages.' Brilliant! Pure mastery of the technique.

Little Helper Number Seven: The Journalist

Since an audience usually joins a story when it is partly over, in that we enter people's lives having missed everything that has happened to them before we paid our money and sat down, the things we ought to know have to be explained to us in full so that the story can develop from there. They could, if they chose to, let you try and work it out for yourself. But we can't be left in the dark for too long in the vague hope that we'd deduce it all for ourselves. Also, they have the Dimwit Element to consider again here. It would only take one of *them* to lose the thread, to tell his friends that the film is a muddle and not worth seeing, and soon everybody would be staying at home. This is too great a risk for a director to take, and therefore everything that is important is said clearly, out loud, at length, in earshot and, to this end, characters quite often go out of their way to give each other information of which they are already fully aware.

The Guns of Navarone (1961) Anthony Quayle tells Gregory Peck, 'Before the war you were the greatest mountain-climber in the world.' Something that Peck knows already, of course, and doesn't need to be reminded of, though we do. Since they are about to embark on an impossible climbing mission, this fairly major point needs to be cleared up before they start.

The Battle of the Bulge (1965) Colonel Hessler (Robert Shaw) has the full Nazi air-attack capacity of V1s and V2s explained to him in considerable detail, with models and visual aids, even though he is a high-ranking German officer to whom all of this must surely be old ground. But in the circumstances, he suffers in silence for our benefit, in order that we can learn how lethal the German arsenal is.

These are essentially one-off examples. The task of reminding us of the story-so-far is usually left to journalists. Any obscure plot-detail or matters of background can be sorted out in no time at all, by letting the leading characters cross the path of a reporter before the story starts in earnest.

Torn Curtain (1966) Paul Newman is a physicist who appears to be defecting from the West with his latest invention. He arrives in East Berlin under escort, to face a pack of wild journalists. 'Sir,' begins one of them, 'is it true you're defecting because Washington abandoned your anti-missile project?' Not bad as an opening thrust. Neat, well-written and concise. 'Professor,' a second hack says, 'is that the anti-missile missile? The one that's supposed to make nuclear defence obsolete?' Needless to say, it is. Ten minutes of exposition condensed into 25 seconds. And now you know everyth ... 'Does that mean ...?' A *third?* '... that you plan to hand over your secret to a Communist country?'

Yes, yes, yes! This device will carry on indefinitely and take over if something isn't done to put an end to it. So usually the interviewee will wind up by being bundled into a waiting car. Either that, or an official will step in from the sidelines and usher the journalists away with 'That's enough ... no more questions,' which means they've told us all we need to know for the moment, and isn't it about time we got on with the goddamned story?

Little Helper Number Eight: The Stock Character

Once a director has fully identified his principal characters, and worked on their backgrounds, attitudes and behaviour, he must then turn to consider the peripheral roles – barmaids, waiters, postmen, whoever, satellites orbiting around the central figures, whose personalities and histories need only a light dusting of detail – nothing too specific. This is where the Cliché Code comes in very handy, by providing both writer and director with a range of ready 'stock' characters which an audience will have seen 100 times before in other films and will therefore recognize instantly.

Regular appearances over the years have invested these people with a number of well-established characteristics and mannerisms. So stock drunks behave the way stock drunks behaved in other pictures, stock doctors behave like stock doctors, stock farmers like stock farmers, and the same goes for any of the hundreds of other screen stereotypes, from whores to shop-assistants, gay hairdressers to crotchety aunts, ageing manservants right through to frightened Malaysian guides on lost river expeditions. You can picture for yourself, approximately, what any one of them looks like, and how they might walk and speak, long before they ever appear on the screen. Their backgrounds are filled in effortlessly using the viewer's own memory and imagination.

This makes sound sense. Why should a director be original and fritter away precious dialogue explaining who some new characters are and what they are like when he can take these neatly-rounded people 'off-the-peg', and kill two clichés with one stone?

To get you started with stock characters, I have picked out three from the many listed in the Code as a taste of what you can expect.

The Stock Biddy

Wherever this woman goes in films, disaster erupts in her wake. Once she decides to board a ship, then you know that the voyage is doomed. It could capsize, strike an iceberg, spring a leak, ram a trawler or have a homicidal maniac somewhere in the upper deck. If you find her strapping herself into a seat on an aircraft then, sure as anything, the whole flight will be marked by incident – either the plane will develop engine trouble and be forced to put down on water, or it will plunge out of the sky into a mountainside. But you'll also find her at the head of a queue in a bank, making a complaint just before an armed robbery that leaves 70 per cent of the customers and staff dead, and the rest held hostage; or walking her hairless chihuahuas down Rodeo Drive when her bag is snatched. What's more, she's even worse than an asthmatic in any kind of seige.

Likely as not, all the script called for was 'an old lady', with no further qualifying remarks. But the experienced director knows what it means and immediately he will invoice the casting agent for a 'stock biddy', a lively, chuckling widow, cute, irresistibly lovable, neatly dressed, freshly washed and powdered, with her hair thrown up into a bob and a square of cream lace at her cuff, ready to pull out whenever she gets round – as she surely will, believe me – to relating brief episodes from her normally quite horrific past to the 'young man' in the next seat: her first husband drowned in a freak white-water rafting accident in Vermont; or her only daughter was brutally slaughtered by Bedouin tribesmen on her honeymoon – that kind of thing. It follows the same routine every time – first the memories, then the sniffles, then the handkerchief, then the distress and horror, but she does it with such well-practised ease and a charm that is sweet enough to sicken.

This is strictly Tinseltown senility, you understand, perpetuated by too many cosy television commercials portraying old age as fun, the way it ought to be – carefree, warm, comfortable and healthy to the last gasp. Nothing like reality, in fact. No mention of inflamed joints or wet patches on sheets, or special walking frames or 'homes'; and so far removed from all those ga-ga grannies with buckled spines and shabby overcoats who sit with their legs wide open in supermarket doorways, talking to their groceries and smelling like a stevedore's vest.

The Brains-in-Her-Bristols Blonde

A standard feature of those swinging comedies and cheap, seedy thrillers produced in the sixties, the era in film history when the cinema first became chest-conscious, was the Brains-in-Her-Bristols Blonde.

There was never any more to her than met the eye; her intelligence was minimal, though I don't doubt that she had more than the producer who hired her to play in his films. Rather, what she had was immaculate lacquered hair – a tribute to the topiarist's art – held back with a wide white headband, full lips, shiny, red and fixed permanently into a half-pout; smoothly-tapered sapling legs; generous hips packed into a mini-skirt three sizes too small, with just a smile of buttock peeking out from underneath; and, of course, the boobs, the giant boobs, apportioned so that they fell in perfect symmetry. She was supposed to represent Mr Average's idea of Miss Wonderful, his unattainable dream-girl, but when these films are re-run on television today, all of a sudden she looks so terribly plain.

The B-I-B Blonde is possibly the least amusing and most offensive of all the stock characters. What makes it worse is that she never died out; the girl is still around today, still unable to act, but nevertheless taking that first step in the profession using her figure as a passport to a big break. For her, success is just a matter of being in the right bed at the right time. To land the part and to catch the producer's eye, she has done everything the agency told her to do: She has Ryvita'd her body, Slimcea'd it, Nivea'd it and Jane Fonda'd

it until her waist is within a hair's breadth of being . . . well, a hair's breadth.
It may have been acceptable in the sixties. Now, it's humiliating and sad.

If you discount the current rash of successful High School 'growing up and
doing it for the first time' movies, the B-I-B blonde turns up in seven clearly-
definable situations:

1. The stereotypist: the vain and fabulously-titted personal secretary. Bearing
   a tray of coffee or a sheaf of papers, she teeters into the office on impossible
   heels, teeth, hair, lips and chest, all in synch, the lines she has been given
   to say – 'Here's the Feldman Contract you asked for, Jeff' – obviously
   playing on her mind. When the words actually arrive, each syllable
   screams, 'Hey, look, everybody, I'm *acting*!' After a glorious 55 seconds in
   shot, she edges out again, but slowly – careful not to snag her breasts on
   the door knob as she leaves, pulling the door to behind her, never to be
   heard of again.

2. The busty hitchhiker in the bright red hugger shorts, found tinkering
   cluelessly under the bonnet of the car at the roadside, waiting for a man,
   such as Leslie Phillips, Kenneth Connor or any one of the other faded
   British comedy actors with well-practised leers, to stop by and help her –
   and note, it is always a man who stops, never a woman.

3. The attractive girlie motorist sitting at the traffic lights in her open-topped
   Spitfire, applying lipstick or eye-shadow in the rear-view mirror, to the
   gloating delight of the lorry driver in the next lane. In this situation, the
   cameraman rarely misses an opportunity to high-dive into her cleavage
   with his lens.

4. Anyone to this day who surveys the view through a telescope or binoculars
   will find one of these girls undressing in her bedroom, or easing out of the
   bath, unaware she is being spied on.

5. Whenever a man has to climb out of his hotel window, inch along the
   ledge outside and climb through the window of the room next door, he
   always stumbles upon one of these girls, standing half-naked, clipping on
   her bra, or in bed with her lover. All she has to do for this is sit with her
   mouth open and pull the duvet up over her acting ability.

6. She is one of the first people to be invited to one of Leo's far-out opium
   parties, and spends the whole evening twisting to old Johnny Dankworth
   EPs.

7. Big-budget spy films are full of B-I-B blondes, though, strangely, she need
   not be blonde – this is merely a tag of convenience, and it is the mammarial

complement that counts, not the shade of dye she has dipped her hair in. B-I-Bs stroll around laboratories in white coats, gripping a clipboard, twiddling knobs knowingly, peering into blinking monitor screens and making note of what they see. The most despicably evil villains seem to employ a steady turnover of these girls in their homes and missile bases. The film's publicity usually calls them 'a bevy of beauties', but they can't hoodwink us with hype. We know who they really are.

The Stock Scientist

It is not enough for a cinema audience merely to be told that a man is a scientist, or so runs the reasoning; nobody is going to believe he truly is one unless he goes out of his way to prove it, by making pointed remarks, dropping king-sized hints and ramming the point home at every available opportunity. On this score, film-makers see you, the viewer, as a cynical, unyielding adversary. They figure that no matter what lengths they go to to persuade you otherwise, you will still be sitting out there in the darkness, staring at the screen and muttering, 'I'm sure that guy's not *really* a scientist!'

But with audience opinion weighted against them, and the battle as good as lost before it's begun, do film-makers give up? Not a bit of it. Instead, they simply double their efforts: they include remarks that are even more pointed than normal, drop bigger and bigger hints, and ultimately call upon a well-established three-phase plan, set out in full in the Code, which answers the question, 'Is there a doctor in the script?'

Phase One: Dress

You can tell a lot about a doctor by the way he dresses.

1. A white-coat-and-spectacles image means reliable, it means informed, an all-round serious thinker who can be trusted to impart the very gravest news at any time – a vital member of the cast may have slipped into a coma (her saline drip came unplugged in the night); he is going to have to operate; the baby is hideously deformed, may even be a mutant. He walks as he talks, taking off his glasses and slipping them into his top pocket, stopping and turning now and then to pose for a close-up shot when the news gets worse – 'There's no hope. I'm sorry.' 'Only one chance in a million that he'll survive. It doesn't look good.' 'She may never regain

consciousness. I'm sorry.' He's always sorry, but can never do anything to help.

On the other hand, it is quite rare for a patient to die if the doctor treating him is carrying a clipboard. A clipboard says 'progress', it indicates reassuring news, a change for the better, the possibility of complete recovery, although there are two important exceptions to this. The first is when the doctor is a woman.

Stock characters are only useful so long as the audience recognizes them immediately for what they are. You have to remember that well into the 1950s, many women were being tied to sofas, and were still tripping, falling and getting rescued for a living. To the movie industry, women were always housewives first, glamour-pusses second, plates of meat third, and women a poor fourth – purely functional items, cast to play the love interest rather than the principal character. Girls were made to love and kiss, and that was about it. So this is why, when a space mission needed a touch of romance, and a woman, however regrettably, had to be cast as an astronaut or explorer, she seemed to fit her duties at mission control in between doing the shopping and dusting the house.

War of the Satellites (1958) Only half an hour before the latest satellite is due to be launched to the Spiral Nebular Gann, the one female member of the crew, Sybil, is still at home, putting her coat on and chatting socially to a friend on the telephone.

For these reasons, among others, women have lost a lot of ground over the years, and cannot be taken seriously as doctors on the screen. So to fill the credibility gap in the viewer's mind, women scientists are not only given the white coat and specs, but a clipboard too. It doesn't make their news any better, it simply means they are more acceptable in the role.

Mind you, if you thought women were badly placed in the cinema's Inconsequentiality League, then you should consider the plight of black people. They are so far down the table that there is nothing below them but horses and cockroaches, and after that you drop off it altogether.

Although they managed to shrug off the zip-a-dee-doo-dah image of broad-beaming 'Yus, Masser!' butlers, handymen, cooks and shoeshine boys a long time ago, and although big-name actors such as Richard Prior and Eddie Murphy have made it to the top on pure talent, and in spite of any natural prejudice they may have encountered on the way up, as yet black people do not fit so easily into a film that the whole story can go by without at least some reference being made to their colour. What change there has been, was spearheaded as far back as 1955 by *The Blackboard Jungle*, and then *The Defiant Ones, The World, The Flesh and the Devil* and others, when attitudes in films began to reflect social change. As discrimination against blacks became a topical issue, so a small coterie of talented black actors rose to prominence and became much in demand. One apocryphal message from those days, sent by a Hollywood mogul to his casting agent, read:

I told you on the telephone,
T'hire me Harry Belafonte;
If he's busy or away,
Get me Sidney Poitier!

Even now black actors cannot comfortably be cast as scientists. In schmovie-terms, this means that the credibility gap is practically unbridgeable, and consequently, to be convincing as doctors, they must not only have the standard-issue white coat, the glasses and the clipboard tucked tightly under the arm, but also, to round it off and kill any last nagging worry you may have that they are just pretending, a stethoscope!

A stethoscope, you'll find, is the piece of apparatus carried by any doctor whose identity is in doubt.

2. The second style of dress is the brown tweed suit and crushed plaid fishing hat, worn by ageing country doctors on call, plus a few scatty college professors. From this you can tell he will turn out to be a doddery guessworker. He works purely off hunches, and rants and gibbers breathlessly about things that nobody, not even he, understands. As a doctor, he only ever carries with him the one piece of equipment he is likely to need for the next scene.

The Beast From Twenty Thousand Fathoms (1953) In this, the doctor says, 'Bring me my bag!' When he opens it up, all he has inside is one stethoscope, and nothing else.

His favourite part of any film is when he gets to stand by a bedside, shaking his head as he pulls the sheet up across the patient's face and says, 'There was nothing I could do. I'm sorry.' He is usually a good deal sorrier than the other guy, if only because most of his patients seem to die long before he has finished with them. The knowledge that he is attending to their case seems only to exacerbate the condition. The reason he gets away with it so often is that he treats people quietly at home. The white-coat-and-glasses chap can't do that, because all his patients have to be rushed down hospital corridors on a trolley while they watch the lights flash by on the ceiling above them. This means they are treated much sooner, and therefore survive.

Phase Two: Science

While the clothing they wear is important, that is just the start of it. Once a scientist looks the part, he must next try and convince you that he is qualified to do the job. So with this in mind, the writer tends to throw various dabs of information into the dialogue, a few rogue technical terms and references to vaguely sciencey things that have little bearing on the story, but that are the sort of topics real scientists might refer to in conversation. Isotopes have always been a big favourite here; gravity is another, but also in the running are neutrons, molecules, fall-out, forceps, vortex and the all-purpose scientific fobbing-off term – gamma rays. A bogus scientist will blame everything he can on gamma rays in the confidence that no one watching will know sufficient about them to contradict what he says.

These key words and phrases are traditionally worked into the script by way of a fairly facile conversation held early on, in which he and another similarly sham professor set about telling each other things that, if the pair of them were genuine, they would know anyway. Ideally, this should be conducted against a background that serves to reinforce the overall suspicion you may be harbouring by this time that they *are* scientists, after all: posters of 'The Earth' and 'The Moon' on the wall maybe (*The Terrornauts*, 1967); or a detailed diagram of 'The Human Ear' (*The Curse of Frankenstein*, 1957); or if the set is meant to be a biology lab, there ought to be stacks of wire cages with rats snuffling about inside them, a rather manky-looking spider in a jar, and the now-compulsory human skeleton hanging from a stand in the corner.

Finally, to keep up the pretence, schmovie scientists usually have the most elementary school textbooks littered about their study or office. One laboratory in *The Great Spider Invasion* (1975), has a book carefully placed in shot, entitled *Physics*, while in *The Bermuda Triangle* (1978) an internationally respected astronomer sits over breakfast with a copy of a book called *The Stars* prominently nestling on the table in front of him.

Phase Three: The Disregardables

You'll find there are broadly four types of screen scientist you can happily disregard:

1. Don't put your faith in any scientist (or indeed anyone else, for that matter) who says 'According to my calculations ...' when there's no possible way he could know what he is about to tell you. It's another fobbing-off phase that means that, having no real facts to hand on the subject, they have made some up. And this applies to the doctor or professor who, when asked a question, replies with, 'Oh, that would take far too long to explain.' Or 'Take my word for it – I'm a scientist' or 'Trust me!' Needless to say, you shouldn't.

2. Be especially cautious, too, of any scientist whose laboratory is packed to the walls with first-year chemistry equipment: flasks, tubes, bell-jars, rubber hosing, burners, tripods, pestles, curly pipes and glass beakers filled with gaily-coloured liquids, bubbling erratically and letting off faint wisps of gas. It's all for show and, pound to a penny, he won't know what half of it is for.

3. Beware of the doc-meet! I don't normally use abbreves myself, but this is a fairly well-known piece of schmovie jargon. The doc-meet is a device used by film-makers, as an alternative to the journalist, for relating the story-so-far. It involves a roomful of concerned scientists, each with half-moon spectacles and a clipboard, sitting with their legs crossed, mumbling and nodding knowingly as another concerned scientist, who is just as phoney as they are, addresses them with the most inflammatory wildspeak. 'Gentlemen, there is a crack in the world!' or 'Gentlemen, we have a confirmed sighting of a UFO!' or 'Gentlemen, the world as we know it will cease to exist in precisely six days from today!' If the film opens with this kind of assembly, then you may well be heading for a flashback, and the complete set of circumstances leading up to that statement will be shown in full. None of them is to be trusted. All are just performers pretending to be profs and can once again, be disregarded, as can the last sort.

4. The white-haired genius who seems to be taken along on all voyages to

distant uncharted isles, forgotten plateaux or lost worlds inhabited by Stone Age tribes and a number of jerky rubber dinosaurs. This is the man who runs across rhinoceros-sized hornets, or plants that suck his arm in up to the shoulder, and wheezes, 'Most interesting.'

Permanently out of breath with excitement, he will pick up a peculiar creature that the props department knocked together at short notice the night before out of three grapefruit segments, two cotton-bobbins and a set of joke rubber udders, and will gasp: 'A species of lepimolluscrodipodicus. Fascinating.' Next, he will trip over a bush that shoots poisoned feelers around his ankles and flings him into a lake. After struggling to the surface by catching his umbrella on a well-placed rock, he'll splutter: 'Well, I never! Absolutely fascinating. Wait until the institute hears about this!' And so it goes on. He tackles all the awaiting perils benignly and methodically, each one more dangerous than the last – and at least one of which is bound to be a fight to the death between two colossal lizards that are really only two tiny lizards magnified with a special lens – and each forgotten the moment it is past, to be replaced by an even greater calamity around the next inlet. 'Fascinating. This incredible ...' Ignore this man. He is a nonsense and a troublemaker.

A Love-Match

A. G. Macdonell

The annual cricket match between Eldersley Towers and Limberfold Hall is a desperately serious affair, for the two great country-houses are deadly rivals. It was in March 1925 that Lord Sigg, the famous financier, bought the Hall, and it was in April of the same year that Sir Jerusha Dibble, the famous financier, bought the Towers, and the flames of rivalry sprang up at once. Sir Jerusha, mortified at finding that he had missed being the senior squire of the district by a paltry fortnight, redressed the balance somewhat by adding an Elizabethan wing to his fine old Georgian mansion and buying four Rolls-Royce cars. Lord Sigg countered smartly with a Gothic annexe, somewhat in the style of the Scott Memorial in Edinburgh, to his Carolean house, and six Daimlers.

Sir Jerusha built a village-hall for the village of Eldersley Porcorum. Lord Sigg presented a cricket pavilion with lecture-room, shower-bath, and skittle-alley to Limberfold St Eustace. His lordship gave a tenner to the local branch of the British Legion. Sir Jerusha made it guineas. And so it was in everything.

The rivalry was not confined to the two great men. It spread vertically in the good old feudal fashion.

The butlers, of course, never met (county butlers never do) except on the one day in each year of the cricket match, when they bowed in a dignified silence that would have marked them out as men of the *haute noblesse* in a Louis Quinze *salon*. The valets and footmen, however, were less concerned with their dignity, and they took part in many crisp bouts of repartee in the local pubs (for the two villages were only a mile apart), while the boot-boys frankly attacked each other on sight. The chauffeurs added to the gaiety of the district by trying to crowd each other into ditches and, whenever a rival was behind, by driving as slowly as possible in the middle of the road.

As for the villages, they had detested each other with the passionate hatred of the peaceful countryside ever since, so far as can be authoritatively ascertained, about A.D. 920, and they simply continued to do so.

The cricket match only added to the tenseness of the situation. For the six months from July to December in each year the recently played match was the sole topic of conversation in the pubs and the collection of outstanding bets one of the main activities. From January to July the forthcoming match and the laying of fresh wagers occupied everyone.

The match of 1938 was an unusually critical one, even in such a series of critical matches, and by about the first week of May the tension between the two great houses was acute.

There were several reasons for this. For instance, the second valet at Limberfold was walking out with the eleventh housemaid of Eldersley, and the Eldersley valets took it as a personal affront.

Then Lord Sigg was known to have sold International Buttons at the wrong moment, whereas Sir Jerusha was known to have held on and cleaned up very nicely, and then Sir Jerusha had written a civil little note to his lordship, condoling with him on his losses and offering to advise him in future transactions in the stock markets. Lord Sigg, in a cold fury, at once ordered a few Bentleys, and asked Sir Jerusha if he was thinking of selling the Towers, as he was looking about for a cosy little place for one of his grand-aunts who was an old lady and did not get about much.

And then on top of all that, what must those young fools Dick Dibble, heir to the Hall, and the Hon. Angela Tripp, heiress to the Towers, do but pull the Montague-and-Capulet stuff and get engaged to be married a fortnight before the great match.

They were a tough young brace of eggs, and they had no illusion about what their beloved, but not very much respected, parents would say about it. And the parents said it, in no uncertain terms. 'No,' they both said, very firmly and in a whole variety of different ways, and with a remarkable wealth of expletive even for gentlemen who had been connected with the Stock Exchange.

Lord Sigg, of course, soon gave in. He had been giving in to Angela now for so long – for twenty-two years in fact, for she was born in 1916 – that it had become a habit. Indeed, by this time neither of them ever noticed whether he had given in or not, such a meaningless formality had it become. Sir Jerusha's task was easier. It was not with a lovely, dark-haired, green-eyed, graceful daughter that he had to be firm, but with a rather ordinary, pleasant-faced boob of a son who refused to bother about earning a living. So Sir Jerusha was firm, very firm indeed, firm almost to the point of nastiness, and talked a good deal about altering his will.

Dick, whose mental equipment was not up to the task of combating his formidable sire, went off gloomily and reported progress to Angela. Fortunately Angela had more than enough intelligence for two, and within an hour the young man was back in his father's presence with a new proposition.

'Will you give me enough money to get married on, Father,' he said, 'if I fix it so that we beat old Sigg in the cricket match?'

Sir Jerusha started visibly.

'Nobble 'em, eh?' he said, putting his finger on the spot unerringly.

'Sort of,' replied Dick.

'Can't be done,' said the knight.

'How do you know, Father?'

Sir Jerusha's ruddy countenance went even ruddier, and he coughed self-consciously.

'Anyway it can't be done,' he said at last, walking over to the window and looking out at the seven under-gardeners who were at that moment weeding the approach to the southern, or lesser, heronry.

'Why, did you ever try it, Dad?' inquired Dick.

'There was no proof,' cried Sir Jerusha sharply, wheeling round.

'Well, listen to this,' said Dick. 'If Angela invites the Sigg team this year, and if she invites a crowd so bad that we can't help winning, what about it, eh?'

'What about it?' shouted Sir Jerusha. 'I'll tell you what about it. If that girl will nobble her own father, and do a thing like that, then by crikey, she's the girl for me, and you can marry her the day after we win. But will she do it?' he went on anxiously.

'She'll do it, Dad. It was her own suggestion.'

'What a girl!' said Sir Jerusha, sinking his voice to a reverent whisper. 'What a peach of a girl.'

There was a pause, and then the veteran financier went on more briskly: 'Well, I'd better ring up Sigg and get a bet on with the old crook. No harm in making a little money on the side, eh, my boy? Eh, my boy? What?'

And Sir Jerusha, beaming delightedly, smacked Dick on the back and almost danced his way to the telephone.

Next day the Hon. Angela Sigg took out her sports Alvis and proceeded to Chelsea, Bloomsbury, Fleet Street, and Hampstead, in search of eleven really bad cricketers. Sir Jerusha, on the other hand, having concluded a satisfactory wager with Lord Sigg, took the precaution of strengthening his team by inviting Mr John Pobblewick, the famous amateur who had bowled for England against Australia at Lord's some years before, to play for Eldersley in the great match.

The great day was windless, blue-skied and sunny – a perfect day for cricket.

It was the turn of Eldersley to be the hosts, and the staff of the Towers had been busy for days before, pitching the marquees, rolling out the beer and cider barrels, painting the boundary flags and the numbers for the score-board, and mowing and rolling the pitch.

Sir Jerusha was in high good-humour. His team had all arrived the night before, and a cleaner-limbed, better-tubbed body of young men he had seldom had the pleasure of clapping eyes upon. After an abstemious dinner they had practised their catching on the lawn for half an hour, and had all retired to bed at ten o'clock sharp. Very different had been the scene over at the Hall, according to information received by Sir Jerusha from his butler, who had got it from the eleventh housemaid, who had got it from her boy friend, the second Limberfold valet. His lordship's team, it appeared, was very different from his former teams. This year it consisted of men with longish hair and red faces, men with loud voices and gusts of roof-shaking laughter, men who all talked simultaneously, and, above all, men with truly stupendous thirsts.

'Twenty-seven bottles of his lordship's best champagne,' the butler reported with awe in his voice, 'and they broke into the cellar and got the last fifteen themselves, because his lordship thought a dozen was enough, and one of them fell over a bin of '96 port and smashed the lot, sir, and they all sat down on the floor of the cellar and cried. And then it appears, sir, that they found his lordship's old Napoleon brandy and they drank a couple of magnums of that and started laughing again.'

'When did they go to bed, Parker?' asked Sir Jerusha, chuckling and rubbing his podgy hands together.

'I am informed, sir, that four of them were carried upstairs at 3.30 A.M., that three others retired at 5 A.M., and that the remaining four were found this morning by the gardeners, sir, climbing in his lordship's new rock-garden. They were in full evening dress and were roped together, sir, being under the impression that they were climbing the Matterhorn. I understand, sir, that the frequent ice-steps, as it were, which they thought it necessary to dig, or cut, as you might say, sir, have not materially improved his lordship's rock-garden.'

'Good lads, good lads!' exclaimed Sir Jerusha, and then he added, greatly to the butler's mystification, 'What a girl, what a peach of a girl!'

The butler coughed discreetly. 'I may say, sir,' he said, 'that, news of these events having spread in the neighbourhood, the betting is now eighteen to one on us, sir.'

'And I've got an even ten thousand with the old fool,' roared Sir Jerusha in an ecstasy of glee. 'Serve champagne at luncheon, Parker, and plenty of it. None of your miserly dozen. We'll fix 'em.'

Dick smiled a quiet smile when he heard the news. Brains and beauty! What a marvellous girl!

Punctually at eleven o'clock the house team was waiting outside the pavilion, resplendent in beautifully creased flannels, blazers, scarves, and caps. Mr Pobblewick was wearing his England cap. The deck-chairs on the edge of the ground near the pavilion were rapidly filling up with elegant frocks, parasols, and silk stockings, while on the other side two large separate groups of spectators, lying on the grass or sitting on long benches, showed that the village partisans were in strong force. Everything, in fact, was ready except the visiting team.

At 11.15 the Eldersley team began to bowl to each other in a desultory sort of way, but by 11.30 they were beginning to look at wrist-watches and to scan the horizon. Finally, at 11.40 Lord Sigg, with a face of thunder, arrived in a huge motor with four of his daughter's eleven.

They were Sir William Biffington, the famous poet, Messrs Belton and Drury, dramatic critics, and Mr Whistle, an actor. Sir William was wearing an ancient pair of linen trousers, Mr Belton's pair were grey with a thin white stripe, and Mr Drury took off his coat and revealed an elegant blue-and-yellow football shirt which fastened at the throat with a string arrangement. Mr Whistle was immaculate but rather drunk, and he gazed round with a sort of owlish benevolence and invariably addressed Lord Sigg as 'laddie'.

The Eldersley team were aghast. Never before had they seen such fearful clothes. Pobblewick took Dick aside and whispered, 'Make them bat first if you win the toss. Let's get it over quickly.' Dick nodded. He would have agreed to anything that morning. The match was as good as won and Angela was as good as his.

There was, however, a considerable delay before the coin could be spun, for first of all the visiting quartet caught a glimpse of a champagne bottle in one of the marquees, and they disappeared with miraculous rapidity. Then, after they had been run to earth, they all claimed the captaincy of the team, and a warm wrangle was soon in full swing, and then the wrangle resolved itself into an academic discussion about the priority of the Arts. Sir William and Mr Whistle agreed that criticism was not an Art at all, but disagreed between Poetry and Drama; the two critics held together for their profession, but quarrelled about their respective newspapers. Then Mr Belton suggested that Dick should toss against his own vice-captain, but Sir William pointed out rather shrewdly that that would materially reduce the Limberfold chance of winning the toss, and the deadlock was only settled by the arrival of a fifth member of the Limberfold team, Mr Twigg, a distinguished novelist. Mr Twigg was in full evening dress, complete with silk hat, and the other four, dazzled by his appearance, instantly elected him captain. The coin was spun. Mr Twigg called wrongly, and Dick asked him to bat first.

'Certainly,' said Mr Twigg, turning to his men. 'Two of you bat, a third hold himself in readiness, a fourth go out to umpire, while I will endeavour to find more suitable apparel. I appear to have mistaken the nature of this jamboree.' He looked down at his costume with an air of surprise. 'My attire seems only suitable,' he added, 'for dining, waiting at table, or being married in France.'

'The essence of our position,' continued Mr Twigg to his team, after they had got back into the champagne tent, 'is to hold the fort until such time as reinforcements arrive. I take it that reinforcements will arrive, by the way?'

'Sammy and young Pie-Face are up,' said Sir William. 'I saw them throwing billiard-balls at the swans on the lake as we came along. Old Sigg was crazy about it.'

'Why? They weren't hitting them, were they?' asked Mr Whistle in surprise.

'Oh no,' replied Sir William.

'Well, we must do the best we can,' said Mr Twigg. 'Out you go and try to hold the fort till lunch.'

Ten minutes later, that is to say sharp at 12.25, the great match began.

Sir William prepared to receive the first ball, Mr Pobblewick of Cambridge, Surrey, and England, to bowl it, and the first of the many strange incidents which made this match so extraordinary took place at once. The first ball was loudly 'no-balled' by the umpire. Mr Pobblewick was surprised.

'Was I over the crease or outside it?' he asked mildly.

'Neither,' said the umpire, who was none other than Mr Whistle, the actor. 'You were throwing.'

'What!' cried the outraged Test Match player.

'You were throwing,' replied Mr Whistle with dignity.

Mr Pobblewick, white with rage, bowled again and was no-balled again. This time he said nothing, but handed the ball to his captain, and walked off the field. Dick Dibble ran after him and tried to soothe the outraged warrior, but all his blandishments were in vain, and he was forced to return and depute his first-change bowler to take up the attack. The new bowler, a medium-paced left-hander who had played for Northamptonshire, took a little time in rearranging his field, and Sir William took a little more in taking new guard, and then Mr Whistle intervened again with the blandest possible smile.

'I'm sorry,' he said, addressing Dick, 'but I am afraid you can't do this. The bowler who began the over must finish it.'

'He's not going to play any more,' explained Dick.

'He must finish the over,' replied the adamantine umpire, and so Dick had to go off and persuade Mr Pobblewick, who had already half changed out of his flannels, to come back so that the game might continue.

It was 12.45 before the third ball of the match was delivered by a very sulky England bowler, and it was a very slow underhand full-pitch to leg which Sir William hit out of the ground with his well-known flail-stroke.

The remaining five balls of the over were identical and were dispatched into the same field by the delighted knight. Mr Pobblewick, his duty done, then retired from the field for good, accompanied by the good-natured, jovial cat-calls of the Limberfold villagers and the savage boos and hisses of the Eldersleyites, who were appalled to see thirty-eight runs being scored against them in the very first over of the match. Their spirits rose, however, when Mr Belton was dismissed by the third ball of the second over and when Mr Drury fell backwards over his wicket in attempting to play the fourth ball.

After a short pause Mr Twigg himself came in, having borrowed some flannels and a shirt, but still wearing his suède-topped, pearl-buttoned boots, and there was a long delay while he insisted on having the sight-screen moved, backwards and forwards, an inch or two at a time. He succeeded in stopping the last two balls of the over, and, as it was now one o'clock, luncheon was announced. The fort had been held, and the six stragglers of the Limberfold team, consisting of two journalists, a painter, a playwright, another poet, and another novelist, arrived at that precise moment in an ancient wagonette drawn by a cart-horse and a small patient donkey, and they were singing an old French marching song at the tops of their not inconsiderable voices.

Luncheon was a painful affair. One team sat in dead silence at one end of the long trestle table, the other roared and sang at the other. Amid the noice could be heard sometimes the silvery laughter of Angela.

After luncheon was over, Lord Sigg made his last appeal to his by now hilarious eleven. He took them aside and began, almost with tears in his eyes: 'I know it isn't any use with literary gentlemen like you offering you money –'

'What!' Exclaimed the eleven literary gentlemen simultaneously. Lord Sigg wrung his hands. 'I knew it would be an insult,' he moaned.

'Insult, my eye,' exclaimed Sir William, who, being a poet, had a very competent grasp of worldly affairs. 'How much?'

Lord Sigg was bewildered. 'Do you mean to say that you would accept a present of twenty-five pounds apiece if you win this match?'

'We do,' was the emphatic and simultaneous reply. 'The only question is: how are we going to do it?' added Sir William thoughtfully, and 'Why the devil didn't you tell us before?' said Mr Twigg with some petulance. 'We could have collected Larwood and Voce or someone.'

'My daughter said you were all county players and that you were certain to win,' bleated Lord Sigg.

'Look here,' said Sir William Biffington abruptly, 'have your villages and retainers and what-nots been betting on us?'

'Heavily,' said his lordship, 'and so have I,' he added plaintively.

'Very well,' replied the poet. 'I declare our innings closed.'

'Hey!' cried Mr Twigg, 'You're not the captain. I am.'

'If we're to get this money,' answered Sir William gravely, 'you must do as I tell you.'

The remainder of the team, with a sad fickleness, instantly voted for the deposition from the captaincy of Mr Twigg and the election of Sir William, while Lord Sigg sat down on a bench and buried his face in his hands.

The news spread like wildfire. Limberfold had declared at thirty-eight for two wickets after two overs. Things began to happen at once. Firstly, three of the star Eldersley batsmen announced that they had never been so damnably treated in their lives, and that if anyone thought they were going to waste a Saturday afternoon clowning about with a lot of mountebanks they were jolly well mistaken, and they collected their cricket-bags, got into their motor-cars and drove away. Dick made little effort to detain them. He wanted to get the match over as soon as possible and he still had seven (for Pobblewick had also departed) perfectly good cricketers to score thirty-nine runs on a plumb wicket.

The second result of the premature declaration was, as the crafty Sir William, poet and therefore expert in psychology, had anticipated, a wild burst of fury among the Limberfold supporters, who jumped to the conclusion that the whole thing was a put-up job on the part of their hated rivals to cheat them on their wagers. It required, therefore, but little encouragement from Sir William, acting as *agent provacateur* in a disguise of a raincoat and a bowler, belonging to one of the butlers, which he had found hanging in the pavilion, for them to invade the ground and start kicking their heels into the wicket. The sight of this was too much for the lads of Eldersley, and they rushed to the rescue, and in a moment there was a very pretty free-for-all in full swing on the pitch.

While it was in progress, and all eyes were either fixed on the fight or being blacked in it, Sir William might have been seen talking earnestly to Mr Jaggin, the Limberfold policeman, and a close observer might even have seen a piece or two of paper passing surreptitiously from the knightly to the constabulary hand. However that may be, it is certain that a few minutes later P. C. Jaggin accosted one of the Eldersley players, a minor-counties batsman of some distinction, and requested him to accompany him to Limberfold police-station to give an account of his movements on the morning of the 27th ult. Protesting vehemently, but nevertheless bowing, in true British fashion, to the Majesty of the Law, the player departed with Mr Jaggin, and Dick suddenly found that he had only six players, of whom two were bowlers pure and simple, with which to make thirty-nine runs on a wicket that now looked, after the fracas had been quelled and the combatants persuaded to retire across the boundary, as if a whippet tank had been dragging a harrow backwards and forwards over it. He hastened up to Mr Twigg.

'I say, sir, we must change the pitch,' he said. Mr Twigg shook his head. 'I am no longer captain of our eleven,' he observed mournfully. 'Bill Biffington is captain now.'

Somewhat surprised at this novel change of leadership, Dick went in search of the poet, and at last found him sitting under an elm-tree writing a ballade on the lining which he had torn out of a Free Forester straw hat that someone had carelessly left lying on a deck-chair.

Dick made his proposal, but Sir William was immovable. 'I would do it if I could,' he kept on saying, 'but it's against the Rules, and we must keep to the Rules.'

'But the pitch is in a terrible state,' cried Dick in consternation. 'If you've got a fast bowler it will be simple murder.'

'I myself am a bowler of exceptional speed,' replied the knight modestly, and he added another line to his poem.

'Well, I suppose I must do the best I can with the heavy roller,' said Dick gloomily. He was not quite so happy about the outcome of the match now. Sir William sprang to his feet and hauled an enormous watch out of his trouser-pocket.

'Sorry,' he said, 'I'm afraid there isn't time for that. Already more than the statutory forty minutes for luncheon have elapsed. We must start as soon as the umpire calls "Play". The side refusing to play within two minutes loses the match. Rule 45.' He made a cup of his hands and roared, 'Whistle, out you go and umpire and call "Play" at once.'

Dick sprinted to the pavilion and got into pads and gloves in time to reach the wicket with a colleague before the two minutes had elapsed after Mr Whistle had called 'Play'.

Sir William was the bowler. Now Sir William had never bowled in his life, but one glance at the torn and scarred wicket showed him that this was no occasion for orthodox methods. It was a case, as in warfare, for what the experts call the Weapon of Surprise, and he ambled up to the wicket and bounced the ball in the neighbourhood of his feet. The ball, when it started off on its long journey towards the other wicket, was going comparatively straight. On its fourth and fifth bounces, however, it turned sharply to leg and was ultimately retrieved by the square-leg umpire. The second ball, conversely, started towards point and gradually worked its way inwards over the furrows and pits until Dick felt that he ought to pay some attention to it. He blocked it, therefore, with his bat, picked it up and politely returned it to Sir William.

'How's that?' roared the entire fielding side. Mr Whistle's finger pointed inexorably to the heavens, and the Eldersley mob sprang into action once again in a frantic burst of rage. But before the jubilant Limberfoldians had time to mobilize in defence, Mr Whistle had stalked across the field and announced to the Eldersleyites, in tones which Henry Irving might have envied, 'Out for handling the ball without being requested to by the opposite side. Rule 29.'

The next batsman was a wary player, and he watched the erratic approach of the ball with a hawk-like eye, and struck it beautifully past cover for an easy single. But most unfortunately as he was running towards the other wicket he somehow, quite inexplicably, bumped into Sir William, who fell heavily to the ground.

'How's that?' roared the fielding side, and again Mr Whistle's finger pointed heavenward, and he shook his head sadly. 'Rule 309,' he said dreamily, 'Obstructing the field.'

The silence that settled down like thunder over the Eldersley partisans was more eloquent of approaching storms than any vocal demonstrations could have been. Limberfold, on the other hand, were wildly jubilant.

Sir William's next ball was a strange one. Elated by his success at capturing two cheap wickets, he attempted to bowl a much faster one, and, employing a sort of slinging, round-arm action, he hurled the ball violently at the opposing batsman. Unfortunately he let go of it a little too soon, and it soared high over the wicket and landed on the fourth waistcoat-button of an elderly J.P. who was taking a comfortable nap in a deck-chair on the boundary. Mr Whistle reluctantly had to perform the unique ceremony of signalling six wides.

Sir William was undaunted, and slung down another tremendous ball. This time, however, he held on much too long, and the ball struck the ground almost at once. But it did not bounce. It must have hit some very odd contour, for it shot straight forward at a high rate of speed along the ground, and then, just as it reached the batsman, it must have hit another very odd contour, for it reared straight up into the air and connected precisely upon the point of the batsman's nose. Whimpering in agony, the unfortunate man retired to the pavilion and refused to take any further part in the game.

But his agony was as nothing compared with the agony of Dick and Angela. Talking in frenzied whispers behind the score-tent, they discussed the calamitous situation. 'We've only got two more men,' muttered Dick hoarsely, 'and Hobbs himself wouldn't make thirty on that pitch against those fiends and their damned umpire. Dad will lose ten thousand quid and I'll be cut off with a farthing. Oh, Angela, what are we to do?' He almost wrung his hands, but being a British public school boy, he just managed to refrain from this hideous solecism.

Angela tapped her shoe thoughtfully with her parasol and gazed at the sky. Dick gazed at Sir Jerusha, who was striding up and down with his hands behind his back and his face purple.

'Dad's bribed them, of course,' she remarked, still gazing at the sky.

'But poets don't care about money,' expostulated Dick.

'Oh, yeah?' replied Angela inelegantly.

A great roar from the Eldersley partisans interrupted them. They turned and saw the ball being thrown back from the boundary. The next moment there was a Limberfold roar as the next ball broke sharply from the off, thence twice in succession from the leg, and then once again from the off, and shot against the foot of the middle stump.

Dick groaned. 'Only one more man and twenty-eight still to get. We're done.'

'Listen,' said Angela urgently. 'Our only chance now is to get a draw out of it. That's better than losing outright. Look at that storm coming up,' and she pointed with her parasol to a mass of black clouds that were advancing rapidly. 'If we can only delay the game for a quarter of an hour we will be saved yet.'

'But how?' asked Dick helplessly.

'By taking champagne out to the fielding side, of course,' said Angela.

'Darling, you're a genius,' he cried, and raced off to the refreshment tent.

The fielding side were enchanted with such hospitality. It was barely three o'clock, and here was the Roederer coming out again.

Forgetting all about the game, they clustered round the trays and fell to with zest. Nor did they pay the slightest attention to the furious exhortations of the weather-wise Limberfoldians to 'get on with the game'. Those old farmers knew what that storm-cloud meant.

Sir Jerusha, into whose ear Angela had been melodiously whispering, looked up at the sky, and his face brightened. 'If I don't win, at least I won't lose,' he muttered.

'And do I get Dick if it's a drawn match?' inquired Angela.

'I didn't say so,' said Sir Jerusha cautiously.

'If I don't,' said Angela casually, 'I'll tell the world how you bribed me to fake the match.'

Sir Jerusha started violently. 'Blackmail, eh, you hussy?'

Angela nodded and smiled a sweet smile.

'Well, damme, if you aren't a peach of a girl,' exclaimed the former finance-pirate in admiration.

'All right. You shall have him.'

At that moment there was a flash of lightning, a clap of thunder, and the rain came down in sheets.

So ended one of the most remarkable cricket matches in history. Play lasted from 12.25 until 3.40, and, in spite of that, only three overs were bowled, and in spite of that again the match was within an ace of being brought to a definite conclusion.

The two teams dined together at Eldersley Hall, and Dick and Angela announced their engagement. After tumultuous cheering, Sir William Biffington proposed their health in an impromptu speech that was so full of poetry and grace that it moved even Lord Sigg to tears. 'Dammit,' he said to the poet after he had sat down, 'you didn't win my match for me, but you shall all get your twenty-five pounds all the same.'

'What twenty-five pounds?' said Sir William. 'Pass the champagne.'

The Standard of Living

Dorothy Parker

Annabel and Midge came out of the tea room with the arrogant slow gait of the leisured, for their Saturday afternoon stretched ahead of them. They had lunched, as was their wont, on sugar, starches, oils, and butter-fats. Usually they ate sandwiches of spongy new white bread greased with butter and mayonnaise; they ate thick wedges of cake lying wet beneath ice cream and whipped cream and melted chocolate gritty with nuts. As alternatives, they ate patties, sweating beads of inferior oil, containing bits of bland meat bogged in pale, stiffening sauce; they ate pastries, limber under rigid icing, filled with an indeterminate yellow sweet stuff, not still solid, not yet liquid, like salve that has been left in the sun. They chose no other sort of food, nor did they consider it. And their skin was like the petals of wood anemones, and their bellies were as flat and their flanks as lean as those of young Indian braves.

Annabel and Midge had been best friends almost from the day that Midge had found a job as stenographer with the firm that employed Annabel. By now, Annabel, two years longer in the stenographic department, had worked up to the wages of eighteen dollars and fifty cents a week; Midge was still at sixteen dollars. Each girl lived at home with her family and paid half her salary to its support.

The girls sat side by side at their desks, they lunched together every noon, together they set out for home at the end of the day's work. Many of their evenings and most of their Sundays were passed in each other's company. Often they were joined by two young men, but there was no steadiness to any such quartet; the two young men would give place, unlamented, to two other young men, and lament would have been inappropriate, really, since the newcomers were scarcely distinguishable from their predecessors. Invariably the girls spent the fine idle hours of their hot-weather Saturday afternoons together. Constant use had not worn ragged the fabric of their friendship.

They looked alike, thought the resemblance did not lie in their features. It was in the shape of their bodies, their movements, their style, and their adornments. Annabel and Midge did, and completely, all that young office workers are besought not to do. They painted their lips and their nails, they darkened their lashes and lightened their hair, and scent seemed to shimmer from them. They wore thin, bright dresses, tight over their breasts and high on their legs, and tilted slippers, fancifully strapped. They looked conspicuous and cheap and charming.

Now, as they walked across to Fifth Avenue with their skirts swirled by the hot wind, they received audible admiration. Young men grouped lethargically about newsstands awarded them murmurs, exclamations, even – the ultimate tribute – whistles. Annabel and Midge passed without the condescension of hurrying their pace; they held their heads higher and set their feet with exquisite precision, as if they stepped over the necks of peasants.

Always the girls went to walk on Fifth Avenue on their free afternoons, for it was the ideal ground for their favourite game. The game could be played anywhere and, indeed, was, but the great shop windows stimulated the two players to their best form.

Annabel had invented the game; or rather she had evolved it from an old one. Basically, it was no more than the ancient sport of what-would-you-do-if-you-had-a-million dollars? But Annabel had drawn a new set of rules for it, had narrowed it, pointed it, made it stricter. Like all games, it was the more absorbing for being more difficult.

Annabel's version went like this: You must suppose that somebody dies and leaves you a million dollars, cool. But there is a condition to the bequest. It is stated in the will that you must spend every nickel of the money on yourself.

There lay the hazard of the game. If, when playing it, you forgot, and listed among your expenditures the rental of a new apartment for your family, for example, you lost your turn to the other player. It was astonishing how many – and some of them among the experts, too – would forfeit all their innings by such slips.

It was essential, of course, that it be played in passionate seriousness. Each purchase must be carefully considered and, if necessary, supported by argument. There was no zest to playing wildly. Once Annabel had introduced the game to Sylvia, another girl who worked in the office. She explained the rules to Sylvia and then offered her the gambit 'What would be the first thing you'd do?' Sylvia had not shown the decency of even a second of hesitation. 'Well,' she said, 'the first thing I'd do, I'd go out and hire somebody to shoot Mrs Gary Cooper, and then . . .' So it is to be seen that she was no fun.

But Annabel and Midge were surely born to be comrades, for Midge played the game like a master from the moment she learned it. It was she who added the touches that made the whole thing cozier. According to Midge's innovations, the eccentric who died and left you the money was not anybody you loved, or, for the matter of that, anybody you even knew. It was somebody who had seen you somewhere and had thought, 'That girl ought to have lots of nice things. I'm going to leave her a million dollars when I die.' And the death was to be neither untimely nor painful. Your benefactor, full of years and comfortably ready to depart, was to slip softly away during sleep and go right to heaven. These embroideries permitted Annabel and Midge to play their game in the luxury of peaceful consciences.

Midge played with a seriousness that was not only proper but extreme. The single strain on the girl's friendship had followed an announcement once made by Annabel that the first thing she would buy with her million dollars would be a silver-fox coat. It was as if she had struck Midge across the mouth. When Midge recovered her breath, she cried that she couldn't imaging how Annabel could do such a thing – silver-fox coats were common! Annabel defended her taste with the retort that they were not common, either. Midge then said that they were so. She added that everybody had a silver-fox coat. She went on, with perhaps a slight toss of head, to declare that she herself wouldn't be caught dead in silver-fox.

For the next few days, though the girls saw each other as constantly, their conversation was careful and infrequent, and they did not once play their game. Then one morning, as soon as Annabel entered the office, she came to Midge and said that she had changed her mind. She would not buy a silver-fox coat with any part of her million dollars. Immediately on receiving the legacy, she would select a coat of mink.

Midge smiled and her eyes shone. 'I think,' she said, 'you're doing absolutely the right thing.'

Now, as they walked along Fifth Avenue, they played the game anew. It was one of those days with which September is repeatedly cursed; hot and glaring, with slivers of dust in the wind. People drooped and shambled, but the girls carried themselves tall and walked a straight line, as befitted young

heiresses on their afternoon promenade. There was no longer need for them
to start the game at its formal opening. Annabel went direct to the heart of
it.

'All right,' she said. 'So you've got this million dollars. So what would be
the first thing you'd do?'

'Well, the first thing I'd do,' Midge said, 'I'd get a mink coat.' But she
said it mechanically, as if she were giving the memorized answer to an
expected question.

'Yes,' Annabel said, 'I think you ought to. The terribly dark kind of mink.'
But she, too, spoke as if by rote. It was too hot; fur, no matter how dark
and sleek and supple, was horrid to the thoughts.

They stepped along in silence for a while. Then Midge's eye was caught
by a shop window. Cool, lovely gleamings were there set off by chaste and
elegant darkness.

'No,' Midge said, 'I take it back. I wouldn't get a mink coat the first thing.
Know what I'd do? I'd get a string of pearls. Real pearls.'

Annabel's eyes turned to follow Midge's.

'Yes,' she said, slowly. 'I think that's kind of a good idea. And it would
make sense, too. Because you can wear pearls with anything.'

Together they went over to the shop window and stood pressed against it.
It contained but one object – a double row of great, even pearls clasped by
a deep emerald around a little pink velvet throat.

'What do you suppose they cost?' Annabel said.

'Gee, I don't know,' Midge said. 'Plenty, I guess.'

'Like a thousand dollars?' Annabel said.

'Oh, I guess like more,' Midge said. 'On account of the emerald.'

'Well, like ten thousand dollars?' Annabel said.

'Gee, I wouldn't even know,' Midge said.

The devil nudged Annabel in the ribs. 'Dare you to go in and price them,'
she said.

'Like fun!' Midge said.

'Dare you,' Annabel said.

'Why, a store like this wouldn't even be open this afternoon,' Midge said.

'Yes, it is so, too,' Annabel said. 'People just came out. And there's a
doorman on. Dare you.'

'Well,' Midge said. 'But you've got to come too.'

They tendered thanks, icily, to the doorman for ushering them into the
shop. It was cool and quiet, a broad, gracious room with panelled walls and

soft carpet. But the girls wore expressions of bitter disdain, as if they stood in a sty.

A slim, immaculate clerk came to them and bowed. His neat face showed no astonishment at their appearance.

'Good afternoon,' he said. He implied that he would never forget it if they would grant him the favour of accepting his softspoken greeting.

'Good afternoon,' Annabel and Midge said together, and in like freezing accents.

'Is there something—?' the clerk said.

'Oh, we're just looking,' Annabel said. It was as if she flung the words down from a dais.

The clerk bowed.

'My friend and myself merely happened to be passing.' Midge said, and stopped, seeming to listen to the phrase. 'My friend here and myself,' she went on, 'merely happened to be wondering how much are those pearls you've got in your window.'

'Ah, yes,' the clerk said. 'The double rope. That is two hundred and fifty thousand dollars, Madam.'

'I see,' Midge said.

The clerk bowed. 'An exceptionally beautiful necklace,' he said. 'Would you care to look at it?'

'No, thank you,' Annabel said.

'My friend and myself merely happened to be passing,' Midge said.

They turned to go; to go, from their manner, where the tumbrel awaited them. The clerk sprang ahead and opened the door. He bowed as they swept by him.

The girls went along the Avenue and disdain was still on their faces.

'Honestly!' Annabel said. 'Can you imagine a thing like that?'

'Two hundred and fifty thousand dollars!' Midge said. 'That's a quarter of a million dollars right there!'

'He's got his nerve!' Annabel said.

They walked on. Slowly the disdain went, slowly and completely as if drained from them, and with it went the regal carriage and tread. Their shoulders dropped and they dragged their feet; they bumped against each other, without notice or apology, and caromed away again. They were silent and their eyes were cloudy.

Suddenly Midge straightened her back, flung her head high, and spoke, clear and strong.

'Listen, Annabel,' she said. 'Look. Suppose there was this terribly rich person, see? You don't know this person, but this person has seen you somewhere and wants to do something for you. Well, it's a terribly old person, see? And so this person dies, just like going to sleep, and leaves you ten million dollars. Now, what would be the first thing you'd do?'

The Waltz

Dorothy Parker

Why, *thank you so much. I'd adore to.*

I don't want to dance with him. I don't want to dance with anybody. And even if I did, it wouldn't be him. He'd be well down among the last ten. I've seen the way he dances; it looks like something you do on Saint Walpurgis Night. Just think, not a quarter of an hour ago, here I was sitting, feeling so sorry for the poor girl he was dancing with. And now *I'm* going to be the poor girl. Well, well. Isn't it a small world?

And a peach of a world, too. A true little corker. Its events are so fascinatingly unpredictable, are not they? Here I was, minding my own business, not doing a stitch of harm to any living soul. And then he comes into my life, all smiles and city manners, to sue me for the favour of one memorable mazurka. Why, he scarcely knows my name, let alone what it stands for. It stands for Despair, Bewilderment, Futility, Degradation, and Premeditated Murder, but little does he wot. I don't wot his name, either; I haven't any idea what it is. Jukes, would be my guess from the look in his eyes. How do you do, Mr Jukes? And how is that dear little brother of yours, with the two heads?

Ah, now why did he have to come around me, with his low requests? Why can't he let me lead my own life? I ask so little – just to be left alone in my quiet corner of the table, to do my evening brooding over all my sorrows. And he must come, with his bows and his scrapes and his may-I-have-this-ones. And I had to go and tell him that I'd adore to dance with him. I cannot understand why I wasn't struck right down dead. Yes, and being struck dead would look like a day in the country, compared to struggling out a dance with this boy. But what could I do? Everyone else at the table had got up to dance, except him and me. There was I, trapped. Trapped like a trap in a trap.

What can you say, when a man asks you to dance with him? I most certainly will *not* dance with you, I'll see you in hell first. Why, thank you, I'd like to awfully, but I'm having labor pains. Oh, yes, *do* let's dance together – it's so nice to meet a man who isn't a scaredy-cat about catching my beri-beri. No. There was nothing for me to do, but say I'd adore to. Well, we might as well get it over with. All right, Cannonball, let's run out on the field. You won the toss; you can lead.

Why, I think it's more of a waltz, really. Isn't it? We might just listen to the music a second. Shall we? Oh, yes, it's a waltz. Mind? Why, I'm simply thrilled. I'd love to waltz with you.

I'd love to waltz with you. I'd love to waltz with you. I'd love to have my tonsils out, I'd love to be in a midnight fire at sea. Well, it's too late now. We're getting under way. *Oh.* Oh, dear! Oh, dear, dear, dear. Oh, this is even worse than I thought it would be. I suppose that's the one dependable law of life – everything is always worse than you thought it was going to be. Oh, if I had any real grasp of what this dance would be like, I'd have held out for sitting it out. Well, it will probably amount to the same thing in the end. We'll be sitting it out on the floor in a minute, if he keeps this up.

I'm so glad I brought it to his attention that this is a waltz they're playing. Heaven knows what might have happened, if he had thought it was something fast; we'd have blown the sides right out of the building. Why does he always want to be somewhere that he isn't? Why can't we stay in one place just long enough to get acclimated? It's this constant rush, rush, rush, that's the curse of American life. That's the reason that we're all of us so – *Ow!* For God's sake, don't *kick*, you idiot; this is only second down. Oh, my shin. My poor, poor shin, that I've had ever since I was a little girl!

Oh, no, no, no. Goodness, no. It didn't hurt the least little bit. And anyway it was my fault. Really it was. Truly. Well, you're just being sweet, to say that. It really was all my fault.

I wonder what I'd better do – kill him this instant, with my naked hands, or wait and let him drop in his traces. Maybe it's best not to make a scene. I guess I'll just lie low, and watch the pace get him. He can't keep this up indefinitely – he's only flesh and blood. Die he must, and die he shall, for what he did to me. I don't want to be of the over-sensitive type, but you can't tell me that kick was unpremeditated. Freud says there are no accidents. I've led no cloistered life, I've known dancing partners who have spoiled my slippers and torn my dress; but when it comes to kicking, I am Outraged Womanhood. When you kick me in the shin, *smile.*

Maybe he didn't do it maliciously. Maybe it's just his way of showing his high spirits. I suppose I ought to be glad that one of us is having such a good time. I suppose I ought to think myself lucky if he brings me back alive. Maybe it's captious to demand of a practically strange man that he leave your shins as he found them. After all, the poor boy's doing the best he can. Probably he grew up in the hill country, and never had no larnin'. I bet they had to throw him on his back to get shoes on him.

Yes, it's lovely, isn't it? It's simply lovely. It's the loveliest waltz. Isn't it? Oh, I think it's lovely, too.

Why, I'm getting positively drawn to the Triple Threat here. He's my hero. He has the heart of a lion, and the sinews of a buffalo. Look at him – never a thought of the consequences, never afraid of his face, hurling himself into every scrimmage, eyes shining, cheeks ablaze. And shall it be said that I hung back? No, a thousand times no. What's it to me if I have to spend the next couple of years in a plaster cast? Come on, Butch, right through them! Who wants to live forever?

Oh, Oh, dear. Oh, he's all right, thank goodness. For a while I thought they'd have to carry him off the field. Ah, I couldn't bear to have anything happen to him. I love him. I love him better than anybody in the world. Look at the spirit he gets into a dreary, commonplace waltz; how effete the other dancers seem, beside him. He is youth and vigor and courage, he is strength and gaiety and – Ow! Get off my instep, you hulking peasant! What do you think I am, anyway – a gangplank? *Ow!*

No, of course it didn't hurt. Why, it didn't a bit. Honestly. And it was all my fault. You see, that little step of yours – well, it's perfectly lovely, but it's just a tiny bit tricky to follow at first. Oh, did you work it up yourself? You really did? Well, aren't you amazing! Oh, now I think I've got it. Oh, I think it's lovely. I was watching you do it when you were dancing before. It's awfully effective when you look at it.

It's awfully effective when you look at it. I bet I'm awfully effective when you look at me. My hair is hanging along my cheeks, my skirt is swaddling about me, I can feel the cold damp of my brow. I must look like something out of 'The Fall of the House of Usher.' This sort of thing takes a fearful toll of a woman my age. And he worked up his little step himself, he with his degenerate cunning. And it was just a tiny bit tricky at first, but now I think I've got it. Two stumbles, slip, and a twenty-yard dash; yes. I've got it. I've got several other things, too, including a split shin and a bitter heart. I hate this creature I'm chained to. I hated him the moment I saw his leering, bestial face. And here I've been locked in his noxious embrace for the thirty-five years this waltz has lasted. Is that orchestra never going to stop playing? Or must this obscene travesty of a dance go on until hell burns out?

Oh, they're going to play another encore. Oh, goody. Oh, that's lovely. Tired? I should say I'm not tired. I'd like to go on like this forever.

I should say I'm not tired. I'm dead, that's all I am. Dead, and in what a cause! And the music is never going to stop playing, and we're going on like this. Double-Time Charlie and I, throughout eternity. I suppose I won't care any more, after the first hundred thousand years. I suppose nothing will matter then, not heat nor pain nor broken heart nor cruel, aching weariness. Well. It can't come too soon for me.

I wonder why I didn't tell him I was tired. I wonder why I didn't suggest going back to the table. I could have said let's just listen to the music. Yes, and if he would, that would be the first bit of attention he has given it all evening. George Jean Nathan said that the lovely rhythms of the waltz should be listened to in stillness and not be accompanied by strange gyrations of the human body. I think that's what he said. I think it was George Jean Nathan. Anyhow, whatever he said and whoever he was and whatever he's doing now, he's better off than I am. That's safe. Anybody who isn't waltzing with this Mrs O'Leary's cow I've got here is having a good time.

Still if we were back at the table, I'd probably have to talk to him. Look at him— what could you say to a thing like that! Did you go to the circus this year, what's your favourite kind of ice cream, how do you spell cat? I guess I'm as well off here. As well off as if I were in a cement mixer in full action.

I'm past all feeling now. The only way I can tell when he steps on me is that I can hear the splintering of bones. And all the events of my life are passing before my eyes. There was the time I was in a hurricane in the West Indies, there was the day I got my head cut open in the taxi smash, there was the night the drunken lady threw a bronze ash-tray at her own true love and got me instead, there was that summer that the sailboat kept capsizing. Ah, what an easy, peaceful time was mine, until I fell in with Swiftly, here. I didn't know what trouble was, before I got drawn into this *danse macabre*. I think my mind is beginning to wander. It almost seems to me as if the orchestra were stopping. It couldn't be, of course; it could never, never be. And yet in my ears there is a silence like the sound of angel voices. ...

Oh, they've stopped, the mean things. They're not going to play any more. Oh, darn. Oh, do you think they would? Do you really think so, if you gave them twenty dollars? Oh, that would be lovely. And look, do tell them to play this same thing. I'd simply adore to go on waltzing.

Trousers Over Africa

Beachcomber (*J. B. Morton*)

Big White Carstairs has been spending a few days at the Residency in Jaboola.
Imagine, then, his chagrin on discovering that his fool of a native servant
has not packed his dress clothes. Being too humiliated to admit this, and too
decent by far to pollute the dinner table by appearing in day clothes, he
stayed in his room last night, pleading a headache. His hostess herself brought
him up some dirtibeeste soup, but he had locked his door, and dared not
open it, lest she should note the absence of the ritual uniform. He pleaded
giddiness. Whereupon the Resident sent Dr Gilmartin up a ladder to break
into the room. Poor Carstairs, half-starved and mortified with shame,
unlatched the window, and confessed the whole truth to the kindly physician,
who promised to keep the secret, and later brought him up a cupful of cold
curry. But what, oh what, will tomorrow bring forth? The native tailor,
perhaps, may come to the rescue.

Meanwhile the hostess tried once more to bring Carstairs some comfort,
this time with light literature. The Resident found her, at 10 p.m., whispering
outside his door, 'Let me in. I have *Life of Livingstone* for you.' 'My dear,'
said the Resident, 'don't you think? I mean to say – the natives – this time
of night – better come away.' Amazed at the scurviness of her husband's
mind, she flounced away from the door, leaving Carstairs to his martyrdom.

Poor Carstairs! Having feigned illness rather than admit that he had no
dress clothes with him, he has had to keep up the pretence and cannot even
appear during the day. His hostess, with diabolical persistence, sends him
dull books by the ton. Yesterday he determined to confess the truth, and
when the Resident called from the veranda, 'How are you today?' Carstairs
began, 'The fact is I –' But he got no further. The words stuck in his throat
like shark-bones. How could a fellow admit that he hadn't got any dress
clothes with him? He would be the laughing-stock of Africa. So he kept his
guilty secret, and remained in his room until – oh joy – a trader who

happened to look in for a drink brought word of a dress suit left in his hut long ago by a political officer. Carstairs confessed his predicament, and the Resident at once sent a native to fetch the suit. But Carstairs, fuming in his room, said to himself, 'It'll be years out of date. Wrong pockets. Stripe down trousers too narrow. What a position to be in!'

A pretty kettle of fish! A beautiful cauldron of mackerel! A fine saucepan of turbot! The dress suit arrived at the Residency yesterday, and Carstairs unpacked it with feverish fingers. Ha! No trousers!

A fellow in the middle of Africa without dress trousers! A tiny cog in the great machine of Empire! A ball-bearing in the skates of the Raj! And no dress trousers!

Poor Carstairs! When the Resident banged on his door and asked if he was dressed, he had to pretend he had had a relapse, and couldn't appear at dinner. The Resident then informed him that on the next night there was a large party, and that it was most important for him to meet a new politcal officer and various high officials.

On rejoining his wife, the Resident said, 'He may be big, he may be white, and his name may be Carstairs, but he's a queer bird. Seems to be always ill.'

In his room Carstairs paced to and fro, almost tempted to envy those backward and superstitious foreigners who dine in ordinary clothes. And that foul thought, against which so many Englishmen have battled successfully, remained with him until he fell asleep.

Once more, last night, Carstairs had his evening meal alone in his bedroom. The Resident, having been once more informed of the truth, feels that the whole situation is becoming rather absurd, and is hinting that the visit has lasted long enough. After dinner both he and his wife talked to their guest through the half-open door of his room, for, of course, he could not appear in day clothes, even after dinner was over. The conversation was stilted and dull, and all three were soon yawning.

'I suppose,' said the Resident's wife, loudly enough for Carstairs to hear, 'I suppose, my dear, he couldn't just wear his dinner jacket and stiff shirt and so on, with ordinary lounge suit or flannel trousers.

'Impossible!' snapped the Resident. 'Nor would he consent to do so.'

'Not for a moment!' said Carstairs indignantly.

For decent men always stick together in a crisis.

So it is stalemate still. All day long Carstairs takes part in the normal life

of the Residency, but the moment it is time to dress for dinner he retires and
is seen no more.

The Resident sat at his desk writing a confidential report to the Colonial
Secretary on the subject of a grant for a local fire brigade in Jamalawoo. A
faint hum in the air made him raise his head. Far above the Residency a
single air machine was circling. It came lower and lower. Carstairs, sunning
himself on the veranda, shaded his eyes to watch it. The machine descended
to about 200 feet above the ground, and the pilot, leaning out, threw a small
object overboard. This object floated down until it got caught on the flagstaff.
The Resident dashed out. 'Saved!' cried Carstairs excitedly, as he waved to
the departing machine.

'What do you mean – "saved"?' asked the Resident peevishly.

Carstairs pointed to the flagstaff. 'My dress trousers,' he said simply, and
he added: 'I hope you will include in your next report to the Colonial Office,
sir, a strong recommendation for the fellow who brought them.'

'That's a personal matter,' said the Resident touchily. 'Your trousers are
not a State affair. And, damn it, we can't have dress trousers up there when
the flag is hoisted at sundown. We must get 'em down.'

They got the trousers down from the flagstaff, and everybody was happy.
Even the natives whistled at their work. The Resident said, 'Now we can
dine together like civilized people.' Old Umtifooti grinned broadly as he
sounded the dressing gong. The household was at peace.

But what is this, dirty reader? In his room Carstairs almost weeps with
rage. For the dress trousers are not his own, and are apparently intended for
a man the size of a house. He tries them on. They are monstrous. And at
that moment the cheery voice of the Resident cries, 'Are you ready, old boy?
Get a move on.' Desperately the empire-builder tries expedients. The trousers
are so big round the waist that he has to wear four shirts, one on top of the
other. They are so long that when he has finished tightening his braces the
trouser-tops shows above the bulging waistcoat. They are bell-bottomed, like
a sailor's, and still so long that his dress shoes are muffled in them. And the
Resident is shouting impatiently. With beads of perspiration twinkling on his
forehead like fairy lights, the miserable Carstairs stumbles and shuffles towards
the drawing-room. His paunch of shirt is so fat that he cannot see the trailing
trousers. But he sets his teeth and enters the room with as jaunty an air as
he can manage.

The appearance of Carstairs in the doorway of the drawing-room was followed by a ghastly hush. The Resident's eyes grew round with horror. His wife wanted to laugh. For Carstairs looked like a circus clown in his enormous billowing trousers and with his padded stomach bulging. He himself, as though conscious of all this, paused on the threshold in some anxiety.

'What – on – earth—?' gasped the Resident. 'Look here, old man, I don't want to be personal but why don't you wear braces?'

'I am wearing braces, sir,' said Carstairs, flushing angrily.

'Well, what the devil is the matter with your trousers? And why have you padded yourself out? This is not a circus, after all.'

The Resident's wife, shaking with mirth, moved away to a window.

'I must apologize, sir,' said Carstairs with ridiculous dignity. 'These trousers aren't mine. They don't fit.'

'So I observe,' remarked the Resident, with an angry glance at the floor, where several inches of trouser obscured each of the empire-builder's feet.

Shrugging his shoulders, the Resident called to his wife to lead the way into dinner.

Stumbling and shuffling, and with one of his four shirts overflowing outside his waistcoat, Carstairs followed.

Dinner was a dreadful meal. Carstairs, owing to the four shirts which he wore to make the enormous trousers fit round his waist, had to sit back from the table, and as he leaned forward to his food the trouser-tops appeared above the straining waistcoat. The Resident affecting not to notice these things, clicked his teeth impatiently. When finally the waistcoat burst with a report like a small airgun, one button hit him on the cheek, another fell into his wife's glass, and a third rebounded from the ceiling on to the head of the native waiter, who fled screaming from the room. 'I'm really most terribly sorry,' said Carstairs.

'Deuced awkward,' said the Resident. And then, very loudly, 'Of course, we can't go on like this. We must get you some proper dress clothes somehow, damn it. Look here, can't you, I mean, tighten up your confounded braces?'

'They're as tight as they'll go,' said Carstairs. 'If they burst –'

'If *they* burst,' roared the Resident, 'the whole show will come tumbling down, and a nice pack of savages we'll all look. Why four shirts should be necessary to hold your trousers up is beyond me. However, things have changed since my young days.'

'I think I'll leave you men to your fun,' said the Resident's wife with a tolerant smile.

The manly conduct of Carstairs at the Residency, while enhancing his popularity, has done nothing to solve the immediate problem. *He had no dress trousers.* The Resident's wife, a kindly lady, said yesterday to her lord and master, 'Look here, old divot, tonight there'll be only a few at dinner. No guests. Couldn't we kind of stretch a point for Carstairs?' 'You mean,' thundered the Resident, 'you mean, *let him dine in day clothes?*'

'Why not?' said the châtelaine.

For a moment the Resident seemed to be about to burst in pieces. His neck swelled. His face turned magenta under its chemical sunburn. Then he shouted:

'Have you gone mad? *What on earth would the natives think?*'

'Ah, I had not thought of that,' said she.

'One must never cease to think of that,' roared the Resident. 'Better he should starve than give a lot of agitators in England a chance to say that Greater England is represented by fellows who can't even dress decently.'

'Yes, dear,' said his wife soothingly.

'Time to dress.'

The voice of the Resident broke in on the despair of our hero. Hot African twilight, guests about to arrive, and he trouserless. Suddenly he shot to his feet. He had thought of a way out. 'Oh, sir,' he shouted, 'I wonder if you'd mind if I wore my kilt tonight. It's the gathering of our clan, back in Busby, tonight, and the old customs, you know....' 'Delighted, old boy,' said the Resident.

In his bedroom he said to his wife, 'That fellow Carstairs is an odd customer. Wants to wear a kilt. Some damned local Scottish nonsense or other.'

Carstairs, meanwhile, was rigging up a bath towel with safety-pins.

The guests were arriving – traders, political officers, agents, *dibris*, a doctor, a missionary, and so on. The entry of Carstairs, in evening dress, save for what looked like a bath towel, caused a stir. 'His clan,' explained the Resident. 'What clan?' queried one of the ladies. 'The Clan Lochjaugh,' said the Resident, on the spur of the moment. 'They have the right to wear a white kilt.' Carstairs hung his head in shame, and when the Resident's wife said loudly, 'The white kilt of the Lochjaughs looks very like the white bath towel of the Resident,' the empire-builder flushed and stammered. There was a ghastly silence.

All were silent at the dining-table, while Carstairs, with rare courage, explained what had occurred.

'My kilt,' he said, 'is a bath towel. I am not a Lochjaugh. I deceived you all. But what was the alternative? I had no dress trousers.'

A murmur of admiration greeted this manly confession, made so simply and quietly.

'Anybody,' said the doctor, rather churlishly, 'could have lent you a spare pair.'

Carstairs lowered his eyes. 'I didn't dare to admit I needed them,' he said.

Here the Resident came to his aid. 'Knew a chap down-country, at Papawatta, who came to dinner in ordinary togs. Sheer ignorance, I suppose. Or damned Bolshevism. He was sent home. Damned good cricketer. Outsider, though. Grammar school or something. Knew another chap, up-country, at Wappapoopa. All right. Top drawer. But *made-up* tie. Tied by some infernal machine. Came off at dance. Picked up by his poor wife. She tried to hide it. No good. Sent home. Plucky little woman. Met 'em last year after Henley. Tie still made-up. Hopeless.'

'A man like that would murder his own grandmother,' said a young political agent.

'Probably did,' said the Resident.

'Look here, sir,' said Carstairs, 'we must settle this. Either I must come in to dinner tonight in ordinary clothes, or else we must go through this farce again, with four shirts and those awful trousers.'

The Resident looked at him icily.

'Are you suggesting,' he asked, 'that I should encourage you not to dress for dinner?'

'Certainly not, sir,' said Carstairs. 'You know what my choice would be. I'm only thinking of you and your wife.'

'Then don't,' said the Resident with a bark. 'Think only of the Raj.'

Carstairs was about to leave the room when the Resident added, 'But, damn it, try to be presentable. Can't you *cut* off the ends of the trousers?'

'By Jove, sir,' said Carstairs, his eyes alight. 'That's the idea.'

That night, happily and carelessly, the scissors were wielded – too carelessly. The trousers became shorts. There was nothing for it but to go in to dinner. The Resident hated unpunctuality. In the doorway appeared Carstairs, still with four shirts to fill up the waistline, and with dress-trousers which ended at the knee. The Resident's wife went into screaming hysterics. The Resident said in his parade voice, 'Major Carstairs, are you a political officer or a – a – some damned kind of fat Boy Scout in mourning?'

And then – oh, joy! a parcel arrived from up-country, addressed to Carstairs. His dress clothes. At last everything was going to be all right again. The Resident, when he heard the news, smiled broadly. 'Now,' he said, 'we can get back to normal decent living.' An American lady explorer was asked to dinner, and Carstairs regained his self-confidence. During the day he inspected the native cricket team, and gave a short lecture on the team spirit. When he went to his room to dress for dinner, he found the dear, well-remembered clothes laid out on the bed. He could have hugged them. He fingered the coat, the waistcoat – and then horror caught him by the throat. There were no trousers! Feverishly he examined every corner of the room. He summoned the native servants. No. No trousers. In a rage he paced his room, ignoring the dressing gong. And when the Resident knocked on the door and shouted cheerfully, 'Get a move on, old man!' he gritted his teeth.

The dinner gong went. The Resident knocked and shouted again. 'What's keeping you?' he cried. 'That parcel,' answered Carstairs in a voice of despair, 'contained everything but my trousers.' Outside the door there was a short, sharp gasp; and then the bellow of a creature mortally wounded. 'Damnation!' shouted the Resident, 'this is more than I can stand!'

It cannot be said that any tears were shed when Carstairs left the Residency at the end of his visit. It has been a nerve-racking time for everybody. The Resident, with bluff good humour, said, 'Next time you come, old boy, I suggest you bring your dress clothes.'

Hardly had he left when the post arrived. Bale after bale of parcels addressed to Carstairs, and all marked, 'Dress Clothes. Handle With Care.' They were offerings from well-wishers all over the Empire, but, alas, they arrived too late.

'One more day,' said the Resident, 'and he'd have had enough trousers to make a sleeping-bag for an elephant.'

'One more day,' said his wife, 'and I should have forgotten my Position and begged him to dine in day clothes.' The Resident glared at her as though she had plunged a dagger into his chest. 'I know you don't mean that, little woman,' he said uncomfortably.

To the Editor,
The Daily Express

Dear Sir,

   I am sure many of your readers will fail to see anything excruciatingly funny in the idea of a gentleman habitually dressing for dinner. 'Beachcomber', like all subversive snobs, probably has no notion of the meaning of self-respect and prestige. I consider the whole Carstairs episode as not only bad manners, but disgracefully bad taste. And it is not the Empire-builders who are made to look absurd, but 'Beachcomber' himself. Of course, the idea of a man without trousers will always raise a cheap laugh from certain types of people, but I am sure it is not on the taste of such as these that your great newspaper has built up its popularity.

Yours faithfully,
'Not Amused.'

I enclose my card.

How to Survive Middle Age

Christopher Matthew

In which I offer a simple office survival guide for executives over forty. Includes a shocking in-depth interview with a big cheese in a top London advertising agency. Also advice on how to suffer the office party, the business trip, the business meeting and the boot, without losing your dignity.

It seems only the other day that the theory: 'If a chap hasn't made it by the age of forty, he's never going to make it at all' was being bandied about in pubs, clubs, dinner parties, office corridors and wherever else it is that people who make such pronouncements habitually meet. Nowadays, it would appear that a more realistic figure would be about twenty-seven. The briefest glance through the Situations Vacant columns shows that they are full of such ominous provisos as: 'If you're in your late twenties or early thirties we'd like to hear from you', and: 'Only applicants between twenty-five and thirty-five need apply.' Only the other day I learned that the world creative supremo of one of Britain's biggest advertising agencies is all of thirty-three. What's more, I distinctly remember him arriving as a callow trainee at an agency where I was doing sterling work on behalf of Kellogg's Ricicles back in the middle sixties. I don't remember him as being particularly great shakes, but then not even I in my creative prime was ever able to conjure up prize-winning copy out of free offers for Noddy Bouncy Balls on the back of cereal packets.

Indeed, it was for this reason as much as any other that I left the business a year or two later and have been unemployed ever since. I was just over thirty at the time – a young man trembling on the brink of life. Nowadays I daresay I'd be considered a pipe and slippers case.

But is this in fact true or am I the unwitting victim of false rumour? Is it just another middle-aged neurosis that convinces me that if the policemen are getting younger, the captains and the kings of the business world are little older than schoolboys? Supposing, just supposing, I had stayed on in the advertising world, would I really now be nothing more than a has-been who never was?

For an answer to these and other questions I rang a contemporary of mine from my last agency. I cannot really remember now exactly what we worked on. Some shoe campaign possibly, but possibly not. Certainly in those days, a dozen years ago, we were both still very much at lieutenant level. I'd bumped into him once or twice since – on the slopes of a Swiss ski resort, in the Crush Bar at Covent Garden where, as a Friend of the Opera House, he was entertaining a client, and at a couple of dinner parties given by mutual friends. I could see he was getting on pretty well in my absence. Even so, I was rather surprised when, having been finally punched through by his secretary and explained what I was after, he told me that he'd be delighted to fix a meeting, but not for another three weeks as he was rather tied up at the moment.

I laughed it off as a blatant attempt to impress me, until, that is, I saw his office. Although perhaps not as spacious as some I have been into in my time, it gave all the appearance of belonging to a man who had come on in the world in no uncertain terms – a corner room overlooking the square, leather button-back sofa, silver-framed prints, the odd carefully placed antique ...

I suppose I should have guessed that by now he'd be one of the top six men who actually run the whole caboodle. Looking at his expensive suit, his real leather briefcase with combination locks, his poised and confident air, the elegant way in which he tossed his secretary a bunch of keys and asked her if she'd be very sweet and do something with his car, it was just outside the front door on a double yellow line ... it made me wonder if perhaps I'd been a fool to throw it all up so soon. Had I stuck it out, I'd surely have been up at the top there with him by now.

'Actually,' he said, lying back against the dark brown leather and sipping at his coffee, 'there aren't any old copywriters these days. You'd have been well over the hill by now. To give you an idea, the oldest creative man we've hired recently is thirty-seven and he's already been managing director of his own company.'

'But all those young men I started out with ...?' I said. 'That band of gilded youth ... that brilliant generation that helped to fire the white heat

of technology ... the very warp and weft of swinging London ... you mean
to say...?'

'Out,' he said. 'Finished.'

'But where? What...?'

'Freelancing, some of them. Running pubs. Writing restaurant columns.
Who knows? All I can tell you is that in our day there were 30,000 people
in London working in advertising. Now there are half that.'

I suggested that I might have gone across to the executive side.

'You might have made it to the top,' he said, his voice tinged with serious
doubt. 'Three of the men who run this company are under fifty. Mind you,
the other three are forty or less.'

It crossed my mind to enquire why it was that a business that aimed to
catch the attention of so many middle-aged and elderly citizens should be
staffed entirely by people who had no conception of what it was to be a
member of either of those age groups – or, for that matter, had ever known
what it is like to travel on a bus, but I let it pass. Doubtless, in the view of
advertising people, those over the age of forty just don't have the spending
power. They're certainly right in my case.

I said, 'But just supposing I had turned out to be so brilliant and
indispensable and good at office politics that I had managed to pass the age
of forty without getting the chop and was still in there with a chance at
forty-three...?'

He said, 'Well, we almost certainly wouldn't be able to sit here chatting
like this in a chummy sort of way, and I'm afraid I'd have to turn you down
for lunch and squash and that sort of thing. Drinkies after work in the pub
and so on. Socially we'd have to take care we didn't meet outside the office
either. No more dinner parties and what not.'

I said coldly, 'In my day, the whole point about advertising was that there
was none of the dreadful seniority business you get in big old firms. Everyone
mucked in together. It was always Christian names all round. You make it
sound like public school, except that at least at school you could meet up
with a chap in the hols even if he was in a junior study to you.'

He said, 'It would be for the good of both of us. Just in case I had to give
you the sack, you see. So embarrassing if our wives had become bosom pals.'

I laughed and said, 'But you wouldn't sack someone with a good lively
mind like mine would you?'

His face hardened. 'Everyone's worried about unemployment these days,
but that still doesn't stop people of a certain age getting complacent. You

never know. It is possible to remotivate someone over forty, but there are always exceptions. Besides, you might suddenly decide to use our friendship in a very unuseful way. Unuseful to the company and unuseful to both of us. When you get to my position, the masterly touch to objectivity is all-important. People after all have got to listen to you, and if you can't be tough when you need to be tough, it'll show a year later. It may be all an act, but one has to have an edge if one wants to stay at the top.'

I told him that at his salary I could probably handle it.

He said, 'The salary is not important. It's the fringe benefits that count at my level. But it's true you'd expect to earn about £25,000 a year, plus a car, plus expenses. On the other hand, would you be able to sleep at night, knowing that you were responsible for £100,000,000 worth of business? And, more importantly, have you actually got it in you to lead? Remember the older you get, the more important self-motivation becomes. Infectious enthusiasm is what makes a company successful and when you're at the top it's all got to come from you. There's no one else.'

Having spent the past twelve years training myself against all the odds to get the bum on to the chair, the fingers on to the typewriter keys and the mind on to the business in hand – viz: knocking out a thousand words a day and keeping the children in socks – I felt like saying that if anybody wanted to know about self-motivation, then I was their boy. But then I suppose when you're an unemployable has-been of forty-three, it isn't easy to be taken seriously these days.

As I stepped out into the mid-morning sunshine and headed for Hatchard's for a relaxing browse before lunch at Searcy's Wine Bar in Chelsea, I couldn't help reflecting how lucky I was to have been sufficiently unencumbered at the age of thirty with dependants, mortgages, school fees – what one copywriter I used to know always referred to sadly as 'caught on a green hook' – to have escaped regular employment when I did. To say that I would recommend any man who is approaching middle age and still retains a vestige of his sanity to get out before they throw you out (and let's face it, fifty-five is chucking-out time in a lot of big firms these days), smacks badly of smugness. Besides, in ninety-nine cases out of a hundred, it would be a sheer impossibility. At the same time I feel duty bound to report that there is nothing like a spot of self-employment, with all its uncertainties, its lack of pension and paid holidays and its quarterly struggle with the VAT return, to keep the mind young and flexible, if not the body. Apart from anything else, it gets you out of that quaintest of all British tribal rituals ...

The Office Party

Like all tribal rites, its origins are buried deep in the mists of time. All that anthropologists and sociologists can say with any degree of certainty is that, for some arcane reason, every year, about a week or two before Christmas, thousands of office workers willingly and apparently cheerfully submit themselves to several hours of indignity and torture at the hands of their fellow workers, in the sure and certain knowledge that if at any point in the proceedings they put so much as a small toe wrong, they could place themselves, their families and their whole lives in jeopardy.

For what may appear to the untutored eye to be nothing more than a jolly good knees up and, with a bit of luck, a hand up, too, is often nothing more than a thinly disguised appraisal board, and one's behaviour during that period of gay abandon could well decide one's future with the company. Indeed, the *on dit* is that some companies deliberately put off their New Year salary review until after the office party.

It is at times like this that the middle-aged man, his natural inhibitions loosened and the memory of his wife's disapproving features clouded by a liberal intake of Carafino Bianco, is at greater risk than at any other time in his professional year. Many's the executive who has found himself lured into all manner of hanky-panky by an unscrupulous secretary and wished he'd gone home after one quick drink as he said he would.

More anxious-making still is being reminded the following morning of behaviour of which one has not the faintest recollection.

A middleweight executive in an advertising agency I once worked in left one office party on his knees and arrived at his desk at lunchtime the following day to be faced by a copy of a letter from a senior colleague to an important client he'd invited along to the party for a drink after a long meeting. In it he apologized for his colleague's appalling behaviour, details of which were outlined at some length and included biting the client sharply on the ankle as he was leaving.

The fellow lived for the next week in mortal dread of the inevitable telephone call summoning him on high, until he discovered the whole thing was a hoax, dreamed up by the junior members of the staff to pay him back for some high-handed act or other from which they were still smarting.

If you must make a complete idiot of yourself by having it off with the relief receptionist behind, or indeed inside, the filing cabinet, for goodness' sake wait until the big cheeses have tactfully withdrawn and you have made your number with whoever it is who holds your future in his or her hands – preferably while you are still capable of coherent thought.

There are no hard and fast rules about how this delicate manoeuvre should be executed: with the minimum of palaver and the maximum of impact is probably as good a rule of thumb as any.

The moment your quarry is obviously at a loose end (why is it that everything one writes in this context seems to be fraught with double entendre and innuendo?), present yourself to him in as casual a way as possible, remind him of your name and department, chuck in a couple of complimentary remarks about the friendliness and generosity of the company and leave it at that. You cannot, and should not, do more.

Any attempt at part chitchat must be considered ill-advised in situations of this kind. Ditto name-dropping and attempts to place yourself socially.

A friend of mine, finding himself face to face with the chairman at an office party and momentarily at a loss for words, panicked, and for reasons that to this day he still cannot fully explain, heard himself saying, 'I understand you know Rear-Admiral Sandy Woodward?'

'Yes,' said the chairman. 'Why? Do you?'

'No,' he replied lamely, 'I'm afraid I don't myself.'

There is only one sure way to get through these gruesome events with any vestige of dignity and that is by making a firm dinner date with someone first. Anyone. Just so long as it isn't the relief receptionist.

The Business Trip

Happily, I gave up being employed before I became important enough to have to make long aeroplane journeys to Australia or Hong Kong – or, for that matter, short ones to Manchester and Glasgow. I have never known what it is like to find myself alone in a hotel restaurant in Frankfurt or Adelaide working my way through a steak dinner, at the same time trying to counter the waiters' pitying looks with an expression that is meant to imply that I needn't be alone, I just prefer it that way. Or, indeed, lying alone in a hotel room, staring blindly at some programme in a language I don't understand while I fight the temptation to call up the front desk and enquire where the action is in this town.

Those experienced in business travel assure me that at my age all I'd be up to after a day of meetings would be a quiet meal followed by an early night – unless, of course, I happened to work for a firm that did a lot of business in Tokyo, in which case it would be a noisy meal followed by a late night whether I felt like it or not.

I'm also assured that the only way to survive the long-distance flight is by ignoring all those tempting drinks and eats and in-flight movies starring Burt Reynolds, taking a couple of Mogadon, wrapping yourself firmly in a blanket and complimentary sleeping mask and missing the whole thing altogether.

Unfortunately, being temperamentally incapable of refusing a freebie, I sit there cheerfully accepting anything and everything that comes my way, from the flight plan to the complimentary cashews, and as a result, spend the first two days in my destination trying to give the impression of being a sophisticated man of the world with a brain that appears to have assumed the size and substance of a pickled walnut.

Merely another reminder that I was right to espace from the world of big business when I did.

The Business Meeting

In the days when I was a fresh-faced ad man, eccentric behaviour was tolerated and even expected from members of the creative department. Bored brand managers from Watford and Solihull did not come all the way to the West End of London to be bored even further by earnest people no different from the ones they spent every day with back at head office. They came for glamour, for laughs, for showbusiness; and the more talented a creative man was at dreaming up comic diversions to break the monotony of a long marketing presentation, the more likely the agency was to keep the account and the creative man his job.

One creative group head I worked with would not only arrive equipped with an array of stage props which he would whip out at carefully prearranged moments (his false nose and glasses always went down particularly well with the Ford client, I seem to remember), but he would suddenly interrupt a detailed analysis of sales figures in the north-east with the news that he had suddenly remembered an extremely important phone call he had to make. The entire meeting would come to a halt and a hush would descend over the assembled executives as he picked up the telephone and dialled a number.

'Won't keep you a moment longer than necessary,' he would say in a low, conspiratorial voice and then, 'Harry? Is that you? Oh, Roger here. I wonder if you'd be very kind and do me ten pounds each way, Lester Piggott in the three thirty?'

But of course everyone and everything has become much more serious since those days, and such frivolity is now firmly discouraged, or not even considered. Even in my day, and that was twelve years ago now, the man who, in the middle of a client meeting, suddenly turned to the chairman and asked if he could be excused as he had an urgent golf lesson, was not looked upon with favour. Though charm itself at the time, the chairman called him into his office the following morning and enquired politely if his lesson had been a success.

'Yes, thank you, sir,' replied the hapless executive.

'Excellent, excellent,' said the chairman. 'Well you'll certainly have plenty of time to put it all into practice from now on. Goodbye.'

The Boot

There's nothing funny about getting the sack. Certainly not these days and certainly not after the age of forty. It is shocking, humiliating, infuriating and depressing, though not necessarily in that order.

In my parents' day, being fired was only slightly less shaming that being caught in bed with the vicar's wife. It was not a subject fit for discussion in polite society.

In these recessive times, however, when whole firms are being laid off at a stroke, redundancy, as it is now known, is nothing to be ashamed of. Not only do respectable men deliberately get themselves chucked out so they can collect the redundancy pay, but the boot can actually launch some people into wonderful new careers.

More often than not, however, the sack comes like a bolt from the blue and you're the last one to be told. The friend of mine who was told by his boss, 'We wouldn't want to lose the sound of your little piccolo in our big orchestra,' could easily be forgiven for believing the remark was meant as a compliment. He certainly took it as such until the people from Office Services came to take away his desk.

There are various recognized tactics which can be brought into play should the boot appear to be in the wind. If cunningly employed, they might help to fend off the catastrophe that is about to be visited upon you.

Ploy 1: On the principle that it is never easy to sack anyone with whom you enjoy a close personal relationship, get your wife to ring up the boss's wife and ask them both to dinner.

Ploy 2: Devise some brilliant new money-saving efficiency scheme for the firm.

Ploy 3: Carry the war into the enemy's camp. I know of one enraged executive who left a large carving knife on his boss's desk, covered in tomato ketchup. Attached to it was a label with the words, 'I found this in my back. I believe it belongs to you.'

In the event of the sack actually being given, all need not be lost. Try asking, 'May I come back after my operation?' Or simply do as a friend of mine did. Not knowing what the procedure was upon receiving the sack he returned, quiet and uncomplaining, to his office and carried on with his work as if nothing had happened. His colleagues knew nothing about it, so they said nothing. Accounts, not having received notification of his imminent departure, continued to pay him in the normal way. Where it was finally discovered, some weeks later, that he was still there, his boss hadn't the heart to put him through it all over again. As far as I know, he's still at his desk.

I'm only glad I'm not.

The Skin-Game

Cornelia Otis Skinner

It's not that I don't want to be a beauty, that I don't yearn to be dripping with glamour. It's just that I can't see how any woman can find time to do to herself all the things that must apparently be done to make herself beautiful and, having once done them, how anyone without the strength of mind of a foreign missionary can keep up such a regime. To read the accounts in the fashion magazines of the well-known It-girls and all the elaborate pains they take to make themselves a menace to every happy home; how they pat their chins with one kind of cream, rub their temples with another, apply lip-rouge with a Japanese paint brush, and sit for hours with their elbows in fragrant oil is indeed inspiring, but one wonders how they manage to get it all in. Maybe they don't do anything else. Maybe they don't receive urgent phone-calls at the moment they're about to apply an egg-mask. Maybe they don't have husbands who when they're in the midst of a little retiring facial yell out, 'Aren't you ever coming to bed?' And maybe those same husbands on beholding them creamed and anointed for the night don't utter cries of pain and tell them to go wash their faces. Or maybe (a nasty suspicion) they're just natural beauties anyway and don't really do half the things they get the credit for.

I try. I even have a fair supply of the wherewithal to make me beautiful ... all manner of facial junk, most of which, be it known, has been purchased under duress. About three times a year I go in for one of those sybaritic debauches known as a 'facial'. I do it because while it may not lift my face it does my morale. In other words, it makes me feel like a kept woman. To recline on silken cushions in a boudoir fit for Peggy Hopkins Joyce while a creature who might be Miss 1938 slathers and pats and strokes the face with scented creams and lotions is sheer opiate bliss. It is very helpful if the cook has walked out, or if that Englishman you met last summer has just written to say he's coming over with his new wife, or if a Harvard senior tells you he likes you so much because you remind him of his mother. It is when I am in a thus vulnerable state that the young lady who has me in her fingertips starts her sales talk. (She gets a *cum laude* if she sells over twenty dollars' worth.)

She begins by asking me just what I've been using on my face in a tone that implies she suspects it's 'Dutch Cleanser'. She tells me what my skin cells are crying for (the realization is touching) is their new 'Wonder Crème', composed of water lilies and the female glands of South American turtles. She then dabs on something that feels and smells the way Marlene Dietrich looks, explaining how it purifies the pores, turns wrinkles into dimples, and creates such sex-appeal it can be employed only sparingly. It must be used, she insists, in conjunction with their 'Gland Stimulant,' which does everything for you short of teaching you the 'Big Apple'. On learning the price, I croak that I guess I'll just take the 'crème'; but implying, oh, so politely, that I'm a cheap-skate, she explains that the one is no good without the other (like Seidlitz powders). Further to weaken me she suddenly comes across some humiliating blemish, at sight of which she gasps, shakes her head, and makes me feel she's discovered cooties.

'How long,' she asks, 'since you've used our 'Contouration Balm' for spots?' She might as well ask how long since I've used a tree-toad for warts, but she shames me into a further purchase.

Then I'm covered in thick layers of goop and gently mauled until I almost forget myself and fall asleep. But no. She was just waiting to catch me unawares. Sneaking up from behind, suddenly she clamps some pungent cloth over my face, ties it tightly under my chin, over my head, around my ears. I can't swallow. I can't see. There's one fearful moment when I'm afraid I can't breathe. And she cheerfully goes away and leaves me in this strait jacket. In panic I wait. Suppose there's a fire. Suppose she's gone to lunch. Suppose she got a 'phone call that her little sister's sick and she's gone home and won't remember me till late tonight. Suppose she just doesn't care. As I am about to ring bells to summon either manager or fire department, back she comes just as though nothing had happened.

When I leave I take with me a collection of creams, lotions, and fragrant junk that not only costs me a petty penny but that in all probability will remain on my bathroom shelves, decorative but quite unused.

For to give myself a series of home facials requires not only time but strength of mind, and I haven't either. Whenever I do plan to lie down for half an hour with a mud-pack on my face and pads on my eye-lids, the phone rings. There is something about trying to talk on the phone with pads on my eyes that has a disturbing effect upon my powers of speech. Nor is my conversation the only thing that gets tangled. The wires of the telephone, the bedlight, and the electric clock suddenly form themselves into a deep tangled wildwood which ends in one or all three crashing to the floor. Or if the phone doesn't ring somebody drops in to call, or my child enters and on seeing me screams with fright, or my husband returns unexpectedly and says, 'What in the name of sweet gentle God are you doing?' Then I find that a 'complete home beauty treatment' requires a lot of paraphernalia that I haven't always got.

It is all so complicated with the various creams that must be used along with certain others. I once, in the spirit of defiance, used a particularly fiery blotch-cure that apparently had a base of mustard and carbolic without removing it with the specified oil. As a result I turned, and remained for half a day, a deep shade of garnet. At sight of me, mothers drew their children away and I'm not sure that one or two didn't notify the Board of Health. As for those eye-pads, either I don't know how to use them or the skin about my eyes is of the same consistency as those Japanese flowers that swell up when they're wet. After using them I rush to a mirror expecting to see a starry-orbed vision only to be confronted by something that could be considered a beauty only in Lapland.

However, I continue to have spasmodic attacks of beauty culture, brought on, largely, by the cosmetic ads for which I am a complete sucker. These fall into two lines of sales talk, the 'glamour' and the 'scientific'. The former presents the picture of some ravishing creature in an attitude that implies she's about to be yet more ravished. And in the blurb below, which is the 'tropic-seas-night-of-love' sort of thing, the purchaser of the product is assured of romance, seduction, and general hell-raising. In fact, with every jar comes a free ticket down the primrose path. In the 'scientific' and we see an enlargement of the cutaneous and sub-cutaneous layers revealing those hungry little cells clamoring for their morning cosmetic and, below, the photograph of a famous Viennese doctor who has consecrated his life to making a perfect complexion within the reach of every woman. After years of research he has hit upon an ingredient that can be likened in importance only to the discovery of radium ... something with an imposing name like 'ichthyosaurus'. They then give the prescription which might be a prescription for horse liniment for all I know, but it's impressive. And that extra ten bucks meant for the

Savings Bank goes into a jar of 'Viennese Miracle' (or what have you), which in all probability I shall never find time to use.

One never-ending joy about these products is the wording of the directions that accompany them. The face is not cleaned, it is *cleansed*. A skin softener is said to be *satinizing* and an aid to circulation is a *muscle toner*. Rejuvenating has been supplanted by the incredible word *youthifying* and even an old-fashioned pimple is referred to with averted eyes as an *acne condition*. Ah me! It is all very refined and most exquisite and I wish I could manage to fit it all in! Sometime I'll knock off all other activities for a month and try.

Bonny Boating Weather

Cornelia Otis Skinner

The older I get the more difficult I find it is to be sporting. As a matter of truth, I have always found it difficult. What I should say is that with increasing maturity I am beginning to realize that to assume an attitude of splendid animal enjoyment in situations of acute discomfort, not to say of peril, is childish and unnecessary. It is all very well for the very young or for the female who by exhibiting her fine out-door nature hopes to land her man. But for the woman past thirty who no longer goes in for such complicated forms of angling, it is so much easier to come clean and admit she prefers to remain on the chaiselongue in the cabaña.

Take sailing for example. There is no more enthusiastic salt than myself, provided the skies are fair and the boat that carries me is equipped with something a degree more comfortable to sit on than a cleat. But when the weather turns Cape Horny and the conveyance changes from a pleasure-craft into a submarine and there is nothing to hold on to but a scupper and the arm of the helmsman (a form of feminine approach that is not appreciated at the time) I for one prefer the 'Queen Mary'.

Perhaps it's not so much my nature as my anatomy that isn't adapted to the more primitve methods of navigation. I am not one who can sit for hours on a flat surface with my feet straight out before me. In fact, I can't sit that way for even a few seconds. I guess I'm lacking a joint because I don't bend. On the other hand (or rather on the other limb) to sit tailor-fashion on a heaving deck is not only precarious but extremely painful and my ankle-bones can't take it for long. If space permits, you can lie stretched out on the hatch but again the danger of being hurled overboard obviates any degree of relaxation. Then there is the violent alternative of sitting astride the bow-sprit, which is just a picturesque version of the ducking-stool. Of course, you can go back and repose on one of those nice hard seats in the cockpit. Some well-equipped sail-boats have cushions, I am told, but the people who take me sailing either have lost their last one overboard or they're above such decadent luxury. Often as not I find myself sitting on the deck with feet dangling into the cockpit. This position of comparative comfort is ruined by the presence of a viciously sharp little rim that surrounds the edge for no apparent reason other than to give whoever sits on it for long a permanent wave in the wrong place.

Then there's the question of agility. Not only must one be able to spring, crawl, or fall flat at a moment's notice, there is any amount of hazards in the way of ropes that trip, hatches that become oubliettes, and surfaces that grow slippery as skating-rinks. Those sudden crises that arise when somebody, just to be capricious, decides to bring the boat about and you have to bend double or lean out over the brink of eternity to avoid being decapitated by the onrushing boom require a talent or contortionism with which I am not endowed. I have yet to get comfortably settled in a sail-boat when someone hasn't yelled 'Watch your head!' (as if watching it would do any good) and a menacing flail of wood canvas and rigging hasn't rushed past, missing me by inches and tilting me into a position of complete unbalance. In regard to that tipping, too, I guess I'm no true yo-heave-hoer, because when a boat leans at an angle of forty degrees and one side is well under water I have never been able to figure out what in hell keeps the whole works from going all the way under. This feeling gives rise to a good deal of straining on my part to pull the balance in the other direction, which is exhausting to the nerves, to say nothing of the abdominal muscles.

From a feminine point of view sailing is about as unbecoming an activity as woman can pursue. The idea of the wind-blown sweetheart of the crew is all very romantic and looks fine in the travel ads but in reality an hour or more of breeze and spray can turn an attractive well-groomed creature into something pretty alarming if not repellent. Hair, unless bound down with uncompromising severity, soon gets looking like a bunch of old kelp and what the salt air does to make-up is nobody's business, unless possibly Neptune's Powder goes streaked and cakes in patches and under it one's nose acquires the hearty color of a port light while the rest of the face approaches a more starboard shade. One more injustice of a man-made world is that the wetter a man gets the more it adds to his charms, while a wet woman assumes the forlorn aspect of a wet cat.

Another disadvantage for the sea-faring female is that while she is never permitted to take any part in the navigating, when it comes time for food she is expected to do her bit in a gallery that would have turned the stomach of Henry Morgan. I suppose it's traditional to have everything connected with food on a sailing-boat as repulsive as possible but I do wish it weren't considered so darned sporting to keep all utensils in a state of grease, rust spots, and the dried remains of ancient baked beans. Then there seems to be a quaint misconception that a slight flavor of kerosene and wet bathing suits is conducive to appetite. Personally I prefer my butter free from flecks of pipe tobacco and I'm not nuts for bread that for a number of days has been wrapped in oil-skins. Under these distressing circumstances the gallant little woman is expected to let loose her domestic nature, concoct something in the way of a meal for the great bullies in the fresh air above, and come through the ordeal pink and cheerful and not at all in an advanced state of jaundice. I am an annoyingly good sailor. The channel in winter, a Chris-craft in a squall, the 'Ile de France' in any weather fails to down me. But even on land I've never liked the combination of food and sneakers.

There are compensations for growing older. One is the realization that to be sporting isn't at all necessary. It is a great relief to reach this stage of wisdom. Hereafter I go boating only in fair weather when I can loll on soft cushions, sip cooling drinks, and keep up my appearance. All else I leave to the Joan Lowells. Not that anyone will be particularly interested in this announcement. It merely gives me satisfaction to make it.

An Entertainment with Animals

Gerald Durrell

Whe he was ten, Gerald Durrell spent five years with his family on the Greek island of Corfu. He described it as 'living in one of the more flamboyant and slapstick comic operas' – as this extract shows ...

The house was humming with activity. Groups of peasants, loaded with baskets of produce and bunches of squawking hens, clustered round the back door. Spiro arrived twice, and sometimes three times, a day, the car piled high with crates of wine, chairs, trestle tables and boxes and foodstuffs. The Magenpies, infected with the excitement, flapped from one end of their cage to the other, poking their heads through the wire and uttering loud raucous comments on the bustle and activity. In the dining-room Margo lay on the floor, surrounded by huge sheets of brown paper on which she was drawing large and highly coloured murals in chalk; in the drawing-room Leslie was surrounded by huge piles of furniture, and was mathematically working out the number of chairs and tables the house could contain without becoming uninhabitable; in the kitchen Mother (assisted by two shrill peasant girls) moved in an atmosphere like the interior of a volcano, surrounded by clouds of steam, sparkling fires, and the soft bubbling and wheezing of pots; the dogs and I wandered from room to room helping where we could, giving advice and generally making ourselves useful; upstairs in his bedroom Larry slept peacefully. The family was preparing for a party.

As always, we had decided to give the party at a moment's notice, and for no other reason than that we suddenly felt like it. Overflowing with the milk of human kindness, the family had invited everyone they could think of, including people they cordially disliked. Everyone threw themselves into the preparations with enthusiasm. Since it was early September we decided to call it a Christmas party, and, in order that the whole thing should not be too straightforward, we invited our guests to lunch, as well as to tea and dinner. This meant the preparation of a vast quantity of food, and Mother (armed with a pile of dog-eared recipe books) disappeared into the kitchen and stayed there for hours at a time. Even when she did emerge, her spectacles misted with steam, it was almost impossible to conduct a conversation with her that was not confined exclusively to food.

As usual, on the rare occasions when the family were unanimous in their desire to entertain, they started organizing so far in advance, and with such zest, that by the time the day of the festivities dawned they were generally exhausted and irritable. Our parties, needless to say, never went as we envisaged. No matter how we tried there was always some last-minute hitch that switched the points and sent our carefully arranged plans careering off on a completely different track from the one we had anticipated. We had, over the years, become used to this, which is just as well, for otherwise our Christmas party would have been doomed from the outset, for it was almost completely taken over by the animals. It all started, innocently enough, with goldfish.

I had recently captured, with the aid of Kosti, the ancient terrapin I called Old Plop. To have obtained such a regal and interesting addition to my collection of pets made me feel that I should do something to commemorate the event. The best thing would be, I decided, to reorganize my terrapin pond, which was merely an old tin wash-tub. I felt it was far too lowly a hovel for such a creature as Old Plop to inhabit, so I obtained a large, square stone tank (which had once been used as an olive oil store) and proceeded to furnish it artistically with rocks, waterplants, sand and shingle. When completed it looked most natural, and the terrapins and watersnakes seemed to approve. However, I was not quite satisfied. The whole thing, though undeniably a remarkable effort, seemed to lack something. After considerable thought I came to the conclusion that what it needed to add the final touch was goldfish. The problem was, where to get them? The nearest place to purchase such a thing would be Athens, but this would be a complicated business, and, moreover, take time. I wanted my pond to be complete for the day of the party. The family were, I knew, too occupied to be able to devote any time to the task of obtaining goldfish, so I took my problem to Spiro. He, after I had described in graphic detail what goldfish were, said that he thought my request was impossible; he had never come across any such fish in Corfu. Anyway, he said he would see what he could do. There was a long period of waiting, during which I thought he had forgotten, and then, the day before the party, he beckoned me into a quiet corner, and looked around to make sure we were not overheard.

'Master Gerrys, I thinks I can gets you them golden fishes,' he rumbled hoarsely. 'Donts says anythings to anyones. You comes into towns with me this evenings, whens I takes your Mothers in to haves her hairs done, and brings somethings to puts them in.'

Thrilled with this news, for Spiro's conspiratorial air lent a pleasant flavour of danger and intrigue to the acquisition of goldfish, I spent the afternoon preparing a can to bring them home in. That evening Spiro was late, and Mother and I had been waiting on the veranda some considerable time before his car came honking and roaring up the drive, and squealed to a halt in front of the villa.

'Gollys, Mrs Durrells, I'm sorrys I'm lates,' he apologized as he helped Mother into the car.

'That's all right, Spiro. We were only afraid that you might have had an accident.'

'Accidents?' said Spiro scornfully. 'I never has accidents. No, it was them piles again.'

'*Piles?*' said Mother, mystified.

'Yes, I always gets them piles at this times,' said Spiro moodily.

'Shouldn't you see a doctor if they're worrying you?' suggested Mother.

'Doctors?' repeated Spiro, puzzled. 'Whats fors?'

'Well, piles can be dangerous, you know,' Mother pointed out.

'*Dangerous?*'

'Yes, they can be if they're neglected.'

Spiro scowled thoughtfully for a minute.

'I mean them aeroplane piles,' he said at last.

'*Aeroplane* piles?'

'Yes. French I thinks theys are.'

'You mean aeroplane *pilots.*'

'Thats whats I says, piles,' Spiro pointed out indignantly.

It was dusk when we dropped Mother at the hairdressers, and Spiro drove me over to the other side of the town, parking outside some enormous wrought-iron gates. He surged out of the car, glanced around surreptitiously, then lumbered up to the gates and whistled. Presently an ancient and be-whiskered individual appeared out of the bushes, and the two of them held a whispered consultation. Spiro came back to the car.

'Gives me the cans, Master Gerrys, and yous stay heres,' he rumbled. 'I wonts be longs.'

The be-whiskered individual opened the gates, Spiro waddled in, and they both tip-toed off into the bushes. Half an hour later Spiro reappeared, clutching the tin to his massive chest, his shoes squelching, his trouser legs dripping water.

'Theres you ares, Master Gerrys,' he said, thrusting the tin at me. Inside swam five fat and gleaming goldfish.

Immensely pleased, I thanked Spiro profusely.

'That's all rights,' he said, starting the engine; 'only donts says a things to anyones, eh?'

I asked where it was he had got them; who did the garden belong to?

'Nevers you minds,' he scowled; 'jus' you keeps thems things hidden, and donts tells a soul about them.'

It was not until some weeks later that, in company with Theodore, I happened to pass the same wrought-iron gates, and I asked what the place was. He explained that it was the palace in which the Greek King (or any other visiting royalty) stayed when he descended on the island. My admiration for Spiro knew no bounds: to actually burgle a palace and steal goldfish from the King's pond struck me as being a remarkable achievement. It also considerably enhanced the prestige of the fish as far as I was concerned, and gave an added lustre to their fat forms as they drifted casually among the terrapins.

It was on the morning of the party that things really started to happen. To begin with, Mother discovered that Dodo had chosen this day, of all days, to come into season. One of the peasant girls had to be detailed to stand outside the backdoor with a broom to repel suitors so that Mother could cook uninterruptedly, but even with this precaution there were occasional moments of panic when one of the bolder Romeos found a way into the kitchen via the front of the house.

After breakfast I hurried out to see my goldfish and discovered, to my horror, that two of them had been killed and partially eaten. In my delight at getting the fish, I had forgotten that both terrapins and the water-snakes were partial to a plump fish occasionally. So I was forced to move all the reptiles into kerosene tins until I could think of a solution to the problem. By the time I had cleaned and fed the Magenpies and Alecko I had still thought of no way of being able to keep the fish and reptiles together, and it was nearing lunchtime. The arrival of the first guests was imminent.

Moodily I wandered round to my carefully arranged pond, to discover, to my horror, that someone had moved the water-snakes' tin into the full glare of the sun. They lay on the surface of the water so limp and hot that for a moment I thought they were dead; it was obvious that only immediate first aid could save them, and picking up the tin I rushed into the house. Mother was in the kitchen, harassed and absent-minded, tryiing to divide her attention between the cooking and Dodo's followers.

I explained the plight of the snakes and said that the only thing that would save them was a long, cool immersion in the bath. Could I put them in the bath for an hour or so?

'Well, yes, dear; I suppose that would be all right. Make sure everyone's finished, though, and don't forget to disinfect it, will you?' she said.

I filled the bath with nice cool water and placed the snakes tenderly inside; in a few minutes they showed distinct signs of reviving. Feeling well satisfied, I left them for a good soak, while I went upstairs to change. On coming down again I sauntered out on to the veranda to have a look at the lunch table, which had been put out in the shade of the vine. In the centre of what had been a very attractive floral centrepiece perched the Magenpies, reeling gently from side to side. Cold with dismay I surveyed the table. The cutlery was flung about in a haphazard manner, a layer of butter had been spread over the side plates, and buttery footprints wandered to and fro across the cloth. Pepper and salt had been used to considerable effect to decorate the smeared remains of a bowl of chutney. The water-jug had been emptied over everything to give it that final, inimitable Magenpie touch.

There was something decidedly queer about the culprits, I decided; instead of flying away as quickly as possible they remained squatting among the tattered flowers, swaying rhythmically, their eyes bright, uttering tiny chucks of satisfaction to each other. Having gazed at me with rapt attention for a moment, one of them walked very unsteadily across the table, a flower in this beak, lost his balance on the edge of the cloth and fell heavily to the ground. The other one gave a hoarse cluck of amusement, put his head under his wing and went to sleep. I was mystified by this unusual behaviour. Then I noticed a smashed bottle of beer on the flagstones. It became obvious that the Magenpies had indulged in a party of their own, and were very drunk. I caught them both quite easily, though the one on the table tried to hide under a butter-bespattered napkin and pretend he was not there. I was just standing with them in my hands, wondering if I could slip them back in their cage and deny all knowledge of the outrage, when Mother appeared carrying a jug of sauce. Caught, as it were, red-handed I had no chance of being believed if I attributed the mess to a sudden gale, or to rats, or any one of the excuses that had occurred to me. The Magenpies and I had to take our medicine.

'Really, dear, you *must* be careful about their cage door. You know what they're like,' Mother said plaintively. 'Never mind, it was an accident. And I suppose they're not really responsible if they're *drunk*.'

On taking the bleary and incapable Magenpies back to their cage I discovered, as I had feared, that Alecko had seized the opportunity to escape as well. I put the Magenpies back in their compartment and gave them a good telling off; they had by now reached the belligerent stage, and attacked my shoe fiercely. Squabbling over who should have the honour of eating the lace, they then attacked each other. I left them flapping round in wild, disorderly circles, making ineffectual stabs with their beaks, and went in search of Alecko. I hunted through the garden and all over the house, but he was nowhere to be seen. I thought he must have flown down to the sea for a quick swim, and felt relieved that he was out of the way.

By this time the first of the guests had arrived, and were drinking on the veranda. I joined them, and was soon deep in a discussion with Theodore; while we were talking, I was surprised to see Leslie appear out of the olive-groves, his gun under his arm, carrying a string bag full of snipe, and a large hare. I had forgotten that he had gone out shooting in the hope of getting some early woodcock.

'Ah ha!' said Theodore with relish, as Leslie vaulted over the veranda rail and showed us his game bag. 'Is that your own hare or is it ... um ... a *wig*?'

'Theodore! You pinched that from Lamb!' said Larry accusingly.

'Yes ... er ... um ... I'm afraid I did. But it seemed such a good *opportunity*,' explained Theordore contritely.

Leslie disappeared into the house to change, and Theodore and I resumed our conversation. Mother appeared and seated herself on the wall, Dodo at her feet. Her gracious hostess act was somewhat marred by the fact that she kept breaking off her conversation to grimace fiercely and brandish a large stick at the panting group of dogs gathered in the front garden. Occasionally an irritable, snarling fight would flare up among Dodo's boy friends, and whenever this occurred the entire family would turn round and bellow 'Shut up' in menacing tones. This had the effect of making the more nervous of our guests spill their drinks. After every such interruption Mother would smile round brightly and endeavour to steer the conversation back to normal. She had just succeeded in doing this for the third time when all talk was abruptly frozen again by a bellow from inside the house. It sounded the sort of cry the minotaur would have produced if suffering from toothache.

'Whatever's the matter with Leslie?' asked Mother.

She was not left long in doubt, for he appeared on the veranda clad in nothing but a small towel.

'Gerry,' he roared, his face a deep red with rage. 'Where's the boy?'

'Now, *now*, dear,' said Mother soothingly, 'whatever's the matter?'

'Snakes,' snarled Leslie, making a wild gestue with his hands to indicate extreme length, and then hastily clutching at his slipping towel, 'snakes, that's what's the matter.'

The effect on the guests was interesting. The ones that knew us were following the whole sceene with avid interest; the uninitiated wondered if perhaps Leslie was a little touched, and were not sure whether to ignore the whole incident and go on talking, or whether to leap on him before he attacked someone.

'What *are* you talking about, dear?'

'That bloody *boy's* filled the sodding *bath* full of bleeding *snakes*,' said Leslie, making things quite clear.

'Language, dear, language!' said Mother automatically, adding absently, 'I do wish you'd put some cothes on; you'll catch a chill like that.'

'Damn great things like *hosepipes*.... It's a wonder I wasn't bitten.'

'Never mind, dear, it's really my fault. I told him to put them there,' Mother apologized, and then added, feeling that the guests needed some explanation, 'they were suffering from sunstroke, poor things.'

'Really, Mother!' exclaimed Larry, 'I think that's carrying things too far.'

'Now don't *you* start, dear,' said Mother firmly; 'it was Leslie who was bathing with the snakes.'

'I don't know why Larry always has to interfere,' Margo remarked bitterly.

'Interfere? I'm not interfering. When Mother conspires with Gerry in filling the bath with snakes I think it's my duty to complain.'

'Oh, shut up,' said Leslie. 'What I want to know is, when's he going to remove the bloody things?'

'I think you're making a lot of fuss about nothing,' said Margo.

'If it has become necessary for us to perform our ablutions in a nest of hanadryads I shall be forced to move,' Larry warned.

'Am I going to get a bath or not?' asked Leslie throatily.

'Why can't you take them out yourself?'

'Only Saint Francis of Assisi would feel really at *home* here ...'

'Oh, for heaven's sake be quiet!'

'I've got just as much right to air my views ...'

'I want a *bath*, that's all. Surely it is not too much to ask ...'

'Now, now, dears, don't quarrel,' said Mother. 'Gerry, you'd better go and take the snakes out of the bath. Put them in the basin or somewhere for the moment.'

'No!' They've got to go right outside!'

'All right, dear; don't shout.'

Eventually I borrowed a saucepan from the kitchen and put my watersnakes in that. They had, to my delight, recovered completely, and hissed vigorously when I removed them from the bath. On returning to the veranda I was in time to hear Larry holding forth at length to the assembled guests.

'I assure you the house is a death-trap. Every conceivable nook and cranny is stuffed with malignant faunae waiting to pounce. How I have escaped being maimed for life is beyond me. A simple, innocuous action like lighting a cigarette is fraught with danger. Even the sanctity of my bedroom is not respected. First, I was attacked by a scorpion, a hideous beast that dripped venom and babies all over the place. Then my room was torn asunder by magpies. Now we have snakes in the bath and huge flocks of albatrosses flapping round the house, making noises like defective plumbing.'

'Larry, dear, you do *exaggerate*,' said Mother, smiling vaguely at the guests.

'My dear Mother, if anything I am understating the case. What about the night Quasimodo decided to sleep in my room?'

'That wasn't very dreadful, dear.'

'Well,' said Larry with dignity, 'it may give *you* pleasure to be woken at half-past three in the morning by a pigeon who seems intent on pushing his rectum into your eye ...'

'Yes, well, we've talked quite enough about animals,' said Mother hurriedly. 'I think lunch is ready, so shall we all sit down?'

'Well, anyway,' said Larry as we moved down the veranda to the table, 'that boy's a menace ... he's got beasts in his belfry.'

The guests were shown their places, there was a loud scraping as chairs were drawn out, and then everyone sat down and smiled at each other. The next moment two of the guests uttered yells of agony and soared out of their seats, like rockets.

'Oh, dear, *now* what's happened?' asked Mother in agitation.

'It's probably scorpions again,' said Larry, vacating his seat hurriedly.

'Something bit me ... bit me in the leg!'

'There you are!' exclaimed Larry, looking round triumphantly. '*Exactly* what I said! You'll probably find a brace of bears under there.'

The only one not frozen with horror at the thought of some hidden menace lurking round his feet was Theodore, and he gravely bent down, lifted the cloth and poked his head under the table.

'Ah ha!' he said interestedly, his voice muffled.

'What is it?' asked Mother.

Theodore reappeared from under the cloth.

'It seems to be some sort of a ... er ... some sort of a *bird*. A large black and white one.'

'It's that albatross!' said Larry excitedly.

'No, no,' corrected Theodore; 'it's some species of *gull*, I think.'

'Don't move ... keep quite still, unless you want your legs taken off at the knee!' Larry informed the company.

As a statement calculated to quell alarm it left a lot to be desired. Everybody rose in a body and vacated the table.

From beneath the cloth Alecko gave a long, menacing yarp; whether in dismay at losing his victims or protest at the noise, it was difficult to say.

'Gerry, catch that bird up immediately!' commanded Larry from a safe distance.

'Yes, dear,' Mother agreed. 'You'd better put him back in his cage. He can't stay under there.'

I gently lifted the edge of the cloth, and Alecko, squatting regally under the table, surveyed me with angry yellow eyes. I stretched out a hand towards him, and he lifted his wings and clicked his beak savagely. He was obviously in no mood to be trifled with. I got a napkin and started to try to manoeuvre it towards his beak.

'Do you require any assistance, my dear boy?' inquired Kralefsky, obviously feeling that his reputation as an ornithologist required him to make some sort of offer.

To his obvious relief I refused his help. I explained that Alecko was in a bad mood and would take a little while to catch.

'Well, for heaven's sake hurry up; the soup's getting cold,' snapped Larry irritably. 'Can't you tempt the brute with something? What do they eat?'

'All the nice gulls love a sailor,' observed Theodore with immense satisfaction.

'Oh, Theodore, please!' protested Larry, painted; 'not in moments of crisis.'

'By Jove! It does look savage!' said Kralefsky as I struggled with Alecko.

'It's probably hungry,' said Theodore happily, 'and the sight of us sitting down to eat was gull and wormwood to it.'

'*Theodore!*'

I succeeded at last in getting a grip on Alecko's beak, and I hauled him screaming and flapping out from under the table. I was hot and dishevelled by the time I had pinioned his wings and carried him back to his cage. I left him there, screaming insults and threats at me, and went back to resume my interrupted lunch.

'I remember a very dear friend of mine being molested by a large gull, once,' remarked Kralefsky reminiscently, sipping his soup.

'Really?' said Larry. 'I didn't know they were such depraved birds.'

He was walking along the cliffs with a lady,' Kralefsky went on without listening to Larry, 'when the bird swooped out of the sky and attacked them. My friend told me he had the greatest difficulty in beating it off with his umbrella. Not an enviable experience, by Jove, eh?'

'Extraordinary!' said Larry.

What he *should* have done,' Theodore pointed out gravely, 'was to point his umbrella at it and shout – "Stand back or I'll fire".'

'Whatever for?' inquired Kralefsky, very puzzled.

'The gull would have believed him and flown away in terror,' explained Theodore blandly.

'But I don't quite understand ...' began Kralefsky, frowning.

'You see, they're terribly *gullible* creatures,' said Theodore in triumph.

'Honestly, Theodore, you're like an ancient copy of *Punch*,' groaned Larry.

The glasses clinked, knives and forks clattered, and the wine-bottles glugged as we progressed through the meal. Delicacy after delicacy made its appearance, and after the guests had shown their unanimous approval of each dish Mother would smile deprecatingly. Naturally, the conversation revolved around animals.

'I remember when I was a child being sent to visit one of our numerous elderly and eccentric aunts. She had a bee fetish; she kept vast quantities of them; the garden was overflowing with hundreds of hives humming like telegraph poles. One afternoon she put on an enormous veil and a pair of gloves, locked us all in the cottage for safety and went out to try to get some honey out of one of the hives. Apparently she didn't stupefy them properly, or whatever it is you do, and when she took the lid off, a sort of waterspout of bees poured out and settled on her. We were watching all this through the window. We didn't know much about bees, so we thought this was the correct procedure, until we saw her flying round the garden making desperate attempts to evade the bees, getting her veil tangled up in the rose-bushes. Eventually she reached the cottage and flung herself at the door. We couldn't open it because she had the key. We kept trying to impress this on her, but her screams of agony and the humming of the bees drowned our voices. It was, I believe Leslie who had the brilliant idea of throwing a bucket of water over her from the bedroom window. Unfortunately in his enthusiasm he threw the bucket as well. To be drenched with cold water and then hit on the head with a large galvanized-iron bucket is irritating enough, but to have to fight off a mass of bees at the same time makes the whole thing extremely trying. When we eventually got her inside she was so swollen as to be almost unrecognizable.' Larry paused in his story and sighed sorrowfully.

'Dreadful by Jove,' exclaimed Kralefsky, his eyes wide. 'She might have been killed.'

'Yes, she might,' agreed Larry. 'As it was, it completely ruined my holiday.'

'Did she recover?' asked Kralefsky. It was obvious that he was planning a thrilling Infuriated Bee Adventure that he could have with his lady.

'Oh, yes, after a few weeks in hospital,' Larry replied carelessly. 'It didn't seem to put her off bees though. Shortly afterwards a whole flock of them swarmed in the chimney, and in trying to smoke them out she set fire to the cottage. By the time the fire brigade arrived the place was a mere charred shell, surrounded by bees.'

'Dreadful, *dreadful*,' murmured Kralefsky.

Theodore, meticulously buttering a piece of bread, gave a tiny grunt of amusement. He popped the bread into his mouth, chewed it stolidly for a minute or so, swallowed, and wiped his beard carefully on his napkin.

'Talking of fires,' he began, his eyes alight with impish humour, 'did I tell you about the time the Corfu Fire Brigade was modernized? It seems that the Chief of the fire service had been to Athens and had been greatly ... er ... *impressed* by the new fire-fighting equipment there. He felt it was high time that Corfu got rid of its horse-drawn fire engine and should obtain a new one ... um ... preferably a nice, shiny *red* one. There were several other improvements he had thought of as well. He came back here alight with ... um ... with *enthusiasm*. The first thing he did was to cut a round hole in the ceiling of the fire station, so that the firemen could slide down a pole in the correct manner. It appears that in his haste to become modernized he forgot the pole, and so the first time they had a *practice* two of the firemen broke their legs.'

'No, Theodore, I refuse to believe that. It couldn't be true.'

'No, no, I assure you it's perfectly true. They brought the men to my laboratory to be X-rayed. Apparently what had happened was that the Chief had not explained to the men about the pole, and they thought they had to *jump* down the hole. That was only the beginning. At quite considerable cost an extremely ... er ... large fire engine was purchased. The Chief insisted on the *biggest* and *best*. Unfortunately it was so big that there was only one way they could drive it through the town – you know how narrow most of the streets are. Quite often you would see it rushing along, its bell changing like mad, in the *opposite* direction to the fire. Once outside the town, where the roads are somewhat ... er ... broader, they could cut round to the fire. The most curious thing, I thought, was the business about the very modern fire alarm the Chief had sent for: you know, it was one of those ones where you break the glass and there is a little sort of ... um ... telephone inside. Well, there was a great argument as to where they should put this. The Chief told me that it was a very difficult thing to decide, as they were not sure *where* the fires were going to break out. So, in order to avoid any confusion, they fixed the fire alarm on the *door* of the fire station.'

Theodore paused, rasped his beard with his thumb and took a sip of wine.

'They had hardly got things organized before they had their first fire. Fortunately I happened to be in the vicinity and could watch the whole thing. The place was a garage, and the flames had got a pretty good hold before the owner had managed to run to the fire station and break the glass on the fire alarm. Then there were angry words exchanged, it seems, because the Chief was annoyed at having his fire alarm broken so *soon*. He told the man that he should have knocked on the door; the fire alarm was brand new and it would take weeks to replace the glass. Eventually the fire engine was wheeled out into the street and the firemen assembled. The Chief made a short speech, urging each man to do his ... um ... duty. Then they took their places. There was a bit of a fuss about who should have the honour of ringing the bell, but eventually the Chief did the job himself. I must say that when the engine *did* arrive it looked very impressive. They all leapt off and bustled about, and looked very efficient. They uncoiled a very large hose, and then a fresh hitch became apparent. No one could find the key which was needed to unlock the back of the engine so that the hose could be attached. The Chief said he had given it to Yani, but it was Yani's night off, it seems. After a lot of argument someone was sent running to Yani's house, which was ... er ... *fortunately*, not too far away. While they were waiting, the firemen admired the blaze, which by now was quite considerable. The man came back and said that Yani was not at his house, but his wife said he had gone to the fire. A search through the crowd was made and to the Chief's indignation they found Yani among the onlookers, the key in his pocket. The Chief was very angry, and pointed out that it was *this* sort of thing that created a bad impression. They got the back of the engine open, attached the hose and turned on the water. By that time, of course, there was hardly any garage left to ... er ... *put out.*'

Lunch over, the guests were too bloated with food to do anything except siesta on the veranda, and Kralefsky's attempts to organize a cricket match were greeted with complete lack of enthusiasm. A few of the more energetic of us got Spiro to drive us down for a swim, and we lolled in the sea until it was time to return for tea, another of Mother's gastronomic triumphs. Tottering mounds of hot scones; crisp, paperthin biscuits; cakes like snowdrifts, oozing jam; cakes dark, rich and moist, crammed with fruit; brandy snaps brittle as coral and overflowing with honey. Conversation was almost at a standstill; all that could be heard was the gentle tinkle of cups, and the heartfelt sigh of some guest, already stuffed to capacity, accepting another slice of cake. Afterwards we lay about on the veranda in little groups, talking in a desultory, dreamy fashion as the tide of green twilight washed through the olive-groves and deepened the shade beneath the vine so that faces became obscured in the shadow.

Presently Spiro, who had been off in the car on some mysterious expedition of his own, came driving through the trees, his horn blaring to warn everything and everyone of his arrival.

'Why *does* Spiro have to shatter the evening calm with that ghastly noise?' inquired Larry in a pained voice.

'I agree, I agree,' murmured Kralefsky sleepily; 'one should have nightingales at this time of day, not motor-car horns.'

'I remember being very puzzled,' remarked Theodore's voice out of the shadows, with an undertone of amusement, 'on the first occasion when I drove with Spiro. I can't recall exactly what the conversation was about, but he suddenly remarked to me, "Yes, Doctors, peoples are scarce when I drive through a village." I had a ... um ... curious mental picture of villages quite empty of people, and huge piles of corpses by the side of the road. Then

Spiro went on, "Yes, when I goes through the village I blows my horns like Hells and scares them all to death."'

The car swept round to the front of the house, and the headlight raked along the veranda briefly, showing up the frilly ceiling of misty green vine leaves, the scattered groups of guests talking and laughing, the two peasant girls with their scarlet headscarves, padding softly to and fro, their bare feet scuffing on the flags, laying the table. The car stopped, the sound of the engine died away, and Spiro came waddling up the path, clutching an enormous and apparently heavy brown-paper parcel to his chest.

'Good God! Look!' exclaimed Larry dramatically, pointing a trembling finger. 'The publishers have returned my manuscript again.'

Spiro, on his way into the house, stopped and scowled over his shoulder.

'Golly, nos, Master Lorrys,' he explained seriously, 'this is thems three turkeys my wifes cooked for your mothers.'

'Ah, then there is still hope,' sighed Larry in exaggerated relief; the shock has made me feel quite faint. Let's all go inside and have a drink.'

Inside, the rooms glowed with lamplight, and Margo's brilliantly coloured murals moved gently on the walls as the evening breeze straightened them carefully. Glasses started to titter and chime, corks popped with a sound like stones dropping into a well, the siphons sighed like tired trains. The guests livened up; their eyes gleamed, the talk mounted into a crescendo.

Bored with the party, and being unable to attract Mother's attention, Dodo decided to pay a short visit to the garden by herself. She waddled out into the moonlight and chose a suitable patch beneath the magnolia tree to commune with nature. Suddenly, to her dismay, she was confronted by a pack of bristling, belligerent and rough-looking dogs who obviously had the worst possible designs on her. With a yell of fright she turned tail and fled back into the house as quickly as her short, fat little legs would permit. But the ardent suitors were not going to give up without a struggle. They had spent a hot and irritating afternoon trying to make Dodo's acquaintance, and they were not going to waste this apparently Heaven-sent opportunity to try to get their relationship with her on a more intimate footing. Dodo galloped into the crowded drawing-room, screaming for help, and hot on her heels came the panting, snarling, barging wave of dogs. Roger, Puke and Widdle, who had slipped off to the kitchen for a snack, returned with all speed and were horrified by the scene. If anyone was going to seduce Dodo, they felt, it was going to be one of them, not some scrawny village parish. They hurled themselves with gusto upon Dodo's pursuers, and in a moment the room was a confused mass of fighting, snarling dogs and leaping hysterical guests trying to avoid being bitten.

'It's wolves! ... It means we're in for a hard winter,' yelled Larry, leaping nimbly on to a chair.

'Keep calm, keep calm!' bellowed Leslie, as he seized a cushion and hurled it at the nearest knot of struggling dogs. The cushion landed, was immediately seized by five angry mouths and torn asunder. A great whirling cloud of feathers gushed up into the air and drifted over the scene.

'Where's Dodo?' quavered Mother. 'Find Dodo; they'll hurt her.'

'Stop them! Stop them! They're killing each other,' shrilled Margo, and seizing a soda syphon she proceeded to spray both guests and dogs with complete impartiality.

'I believe *pepper* is a good thing for dog-fights,' observed Theodore, the feathers settling on his beard like snow, 'though of course I have never tried myself.'

'By Jove!' yelped Kralefsky, 'watch out ... save the ladies!'

He followed this advice by helping the nearest female on to the sofa and climbing up beside her.

'Water also is considered to be good.' Theodore went on musingly, and as if to test this he poured his glass of wine with meticulous accuracy over a passing dog.

Noting on Theodore's advice, Spiro surged out to the kitchen and returned with a kerosene tin of water clasped in his ham-like hands. He paused in the doorway and raised it above his head.

'Watch outs,' he roared; 'I'll fixes the bastards.'

The guests fled in all directions, but they were not quick enough. The polished, glittering mass of water curved through the air and hit the floor, to burst up again and then curve and break like a tidal wave over the room. It had the most disastrous results as far as the nearest guests were concerned, but it had the most startling and instantaneous effect on the dogs. Frightened by the boom and swish of water, they let go of each other and fled out into the night, leaving behind them a scene of carnage that was breath-taking. The room looked like a hen-roost that had been hit by a cyclone; our friends milled about, damp and feather-encrusted; feathers had settled on the lamps and the acrid smell of burning filled the air. Mother, clasping Dodo in her arms, surveyed the room.

'Leslie, dear, go and get some towels so that we can dry ourselves. The room *is* in a mess. Never mind, let's all go out on to the veranda, shall we?'

she said, and added sweetly, 'I'm so sorry this happened. It's Dodo, you see, she's very *interesting* to the dogs at the moment.'

Eventually the party was dried, the feathers plucked off them, their glasses were filled and they were installed on the veranda where the moon was stamping the flags with ink-black shadows of the vine leaves. Larry, his mouth full of food, strummed softly on his guitar and hummed indistinctly; through the french windows we could see Leslie and Spiro both scowling with concentration, skilfully dismembering the great brown turkeys; Mother drifted to and fro through the shadows, anxiously asking everyone if they were getting enough to eat; Kralefsky was perched on the veranda wall – his body crab-like in silhouette, the moon peering over his hump – telling Margo a long and involved story; Theodore was giving a lecture on the stars to Dr Androuchelli, pointing out the constellations with a half-eaten turkey leg.

Outside, the island was striped and patched in black and silver by moonlight. Far down in the dark cypress trees the owls called to each other comfortingly. The sky looked as black and soft as a mole-skin covered with a delicate dew of stars. The magnolia tree loomed vast over the house, its branches full of white blooms, like a hundred miniature reflections of the moon, and their thick, sweet scent hung over the veranda languorously, the scent that was an enchantment luring you out into the mysterious, moonlit countryside.

Col. Tiger Rashid

Richard Stilgoe

I hadn't seen Uncle Harry for years, so it was quite a surprise when his card arrived. No warning (there never is with Uncle Harry, my mother always says). 'In town for a few days. Come and have dinner on Wednesday. Uncle Harry.' That was all the card said. It was one of those plain white jobs with the sender's address across the top. It said 'From the Endangered Species Club, Pickerings Court, St James's, SW.'

I found the place pretty easily – Pickerings Court isn't very big, and 'Endangered Species Club' was engraved on only the fourth brass pate I read. I gave my name to the porter, and asked for Uncle Harry. The porter scooted off to fetch him. I looked around the dimly lit hall. There was something about it that was different from other clubs I'd been to. I couldn't quite put my finger on it.

Uncle Harry came in. He had lost none of the impressiveness I remembered. Still the shock of hair shooting away from the forehead, the bushy moustache which jockeyed for position with the side-whiskers. And still the brilliant eyes, peeping out from lids which the sun had turned to walnuts, like two small animals hiding in a hollow tree. He wore an immaculate dark blue suit with a wide chalk-stripe, and plimsolls. He moved like a cat. (Well, he moved the way a cat would if it wore plimsolls). 'Tony,' he greeted me. 'Good to see you. How's Mummy? How's Daddy? How's Nanny? Caroline? Pippa? Ned? Wonky?' I replied that they were all well. 'Damned good,' he said. 'Come in and have a drink. Old enough now, aren't you?' I was in fact only seventeen, which he should have known, being my godfather as well as my uncle, but I didn't argue.

The bar of the Endangered Species Club was panelled, and again had that – well, *odd* feeling about it. 'Sherry?' offered Uncle Harry. I nodded. 'Felt I ought to say hello,' said Uncle Harry. 'Godfather and all that. Haven't seen much of you. Thought we'd get to know each other. Thought you might like to see the club. Rum old place, isn't it?' I agreed that it was a rum old place. Uncle Harry went on, 'Notice anything different? Look at the walls, old boy. Notice? No trophies. Not one.'

So that was it! The walls, unlike most of the clubs Daddy had shown me, were completely free of antelope, bison, boar, lion or rhino. The floors as well had no skins on them. There was no sign of the normal elephant's foot waste-paper basket. And in the rexine armchairs, every one of the members sat reading their papers with their feet encased in pumps or slippers. Nowhere in the room was there any evidence that animals' lives were ever taken by man. In fact, the only ornament of any sort was a picture. I don't know what it was a picture of, for it was turned to face the wall so that only the back of the frame, the back of the canvas and the protruding ends of hardwood wedges were visible. Under the frame, on a small plaque on the wall, were the words 'COL. 'TIGER' RASHID 1917–71.'

'The Endangered Species Club,' said Uncle Harry, 'was started by a few of us in 1964. Hunters, all of us. Killers, every one. We hunted, we fished, we shot. If it moved, we shot it. Then – well, I remember it almost exactly. Buffy Charlesworth rang me up one August and said he wasn't going with me to Kenya. Next morning, Dogs Anderson and Gerry Belwether rang up and said the same. And when Reggie Wincanton came on the blower I smelt a rat. I mean Reggie would no more miss a chance of taking a pot at a rhino than fly. So I knew something was up. D'you know what had happened'

I shook my head. Uncle Harry looked thoughtful. 'Ever heard of television?' he asked. I said I had. He looked surprised, and continued. 'These chaps told me they'd seen this television thing, and were giving up killing things. They made me go round to Reggie's house – his man owned one of the receivers – and made me watch it. Only one. But one was enough.' He looked thoughtful again.

'Lots of people say wildlife's one of the best reasons for having television,' I said. 'Was it a chap called Attenborough you saw?'

'No, not Attenborough,' said Uncle Harry. 'Met him since, of course. Nice feller. Kneels down a lot. No, no. Programme we all saw was called – er – Lenny the Lion. That was it. The next day we bought this place and started the club. Saving animals. That kind of thing.'

'But Uncle Harry, why would Lenny the Lion make anyone give up big-game hunting?' I remembered Lenny the Lion from when I was a kid, and it seemed a bit – well, unlikely.

'Tony,' said Uncle Harry seriously. 'You're very young. Reggie and Dogs

and Buffy and Gerry and I had knocked about a bit, but we'd never seen
before a chap sticking his hand up a lion's jaxi and making its mouth move
from inside. It just horrified us. It made us think about what we chaps did
to animals. And so – well, we went the other way. Conservation. But nutty
about it, you may think. Often the case, they say, with converts. Could well
be true! But we do damned good work, though I say it myself. D'you know,
since we started we've persuaded every single big-game hunter the five of us
knew to give up. Well, nearly every one. All except one.'

'Tiger Rashid?' I asked, and wished that I hadn't. For every head in the
club turned towards me, took me in icily, and then remembered its manners
and went back to its paper or its conversation. 'Sorry, Uncle Harry,' I said,
'but it's written on the wall there.'

'Well spotted, young Tony. But keep the voice down. Tell you what, we'll
go in to dinner early. Then I can tell you the story without everyone
earwigging.'

I'm not a great one for vegetarian food normally, but I had to admit that
the club chef did a jolly good job. Not that I had much time to concentrate
on what I was eating, because Uncle Harry did tell me the most astonishing
story during dinner. He started as soon as the *cotelettes aux noix* were served.

'I first met Rashid in Bhagalpur. He was in the army – our army. Odd
how we met, actually. He – well, I suppose, not to beat about the bush, he
saved my life. After a Polo accident. Damned thing went down the wrong
way, and if he hadn't seen me choking and bashed me on the back with a
punkah, I could have turned my toes up there and then. So we got chatting,
the way you do when someone's saved your life, and he was one of those
odd chaps – lot of them in India – who had sort of given up being Indian
and gone overboard the other way. He talked as if he was in an Aldwych
farce – you know, "I say, spiffin' don't y'know, pip-pip, cheerioh, what-
what-what?" – that sort of thing. Sounded odd, coming out of a brown face.
Turned out he had been over here to school, gone to Sandhurst, and was
now a Colonel in the Lancers.

'Well, I didn't see him for a bit, because our lot went up country to
Katihar on a pig-stick, but when we came back to Bihar, there was a tiger-
shoot. The local Nabob organized it. We all climbed on to the old jumbos,
and the Nabob got into his Silver Ghost, and off we went to bag a few rugs.
Now normally tiger-shoots were pretty over-rated. If you found a tiger at all
it usually killed a couple of beaters and ran away before anyone could shoot

it. But this time was different. There was a chap leading us, walking ahead of the first elephant, and he had the most uncanny knack of locating the tigers. Not only locating them, but sort of mesmerising them. They ambled up to him, gave him a friendly sort of look, and then walked down the line of elephants, as if he'd told them where to stand in order to get shot. We got seventeen in the one afternoon. I got one myself. You've got it at home haven't you?'

I told him we had. It used to lie on the floor in the morning room, but had been banished to an attic since my kid brother jumped out of the linen cupboard wearing it and gave Nanny a stroke.

Uncle Harry went on. 'Well, at one point towards the end of the day, this chap at the front turned round and I caught a glimpse of him. And d'you know who it was?'

'Col. Tiger Rashid?' I ventured. Uncle Harry looked at me, surprised.

'Have I told you this story before? No mattter. Col. Tiger Rashid it was, the very same that had helped me spit out peppermints in Bhagalpur. They called him "Tiger", I gather from the Nabob, because – well, obviously because he had this knack with the big cats, but it went deeper than that. Evidently when he was a baby he actually lived with a litter of tiger cubs and was brought up with them, like that boy with the wolves. No-one knew how he got there, but you get a lot of abandoned babies around Bhagalpur. Energetic chap, the Nabob. No one was untouchable to him! Anyway, one day the female got herself shot, and the beaters found this Rashid fellow toddling about with the orphaned cubs. They brought him in, and the Nabob brought him up as if he was his own which, as I say, was a pretty fair assumption. Sent him to school in England. Eton. Then to Sandhurst – well, I told you all that. He'd told me himself when I met him. And of course I met him again that day, after the shoot. I wondered whether I could broach the subject of his, to say the least, unorthodox upbringing. I needn't have bothered. He came right out with it. "Harry, old fruit!" he cried. "Ripping to see you again. Have the chaps given you the lowdown on my stripy kith and kin? All true, old bean. Many have been eaten by tigers, but I'm the only Tiger who's ever been to Eton, what?' and he laughed, sort of cackling – the way your Indian does.

'I was going to ask him more, but again he butted in. "Now, Harry, I can see you're dying to know why I get involved in tiger-shoots and don't I find it a morsel beyond the pale? Every Tom, Dick and Harry asks me that, and you're a Harry so I knew you would, what?" He cackled again, and

went on. "Bullying, Harry. Beastly thing. All I remember about the tigers.
I remember them bullying me in a beastly, rotten way. So I get my own
back. I went to see a trick cyclist about it, don't y'know, and he explained
it to me." Well, that was interesting, but what I wanted to know was how
he did it – how he found the tigers and dominated them, as I'd seen him do
that afternoon. But when I asked him about that he sort of glanced it through
the slips, as it were, and went on about knowing a lot of other chaps who'd
been bullied and would be only too happy to see their big brothers and
sisters on the wrong end of a big-game rifle. His eyes went funny while he
said it. I don't know whether it was being brought up by tigers, or just going
to Eton, but something had certainly made him determined to take his
revenge.

'Anyway – cut a long story short, eh? – we didn't see each other for a few
years, and then the club got started and I thought I'd write to him and ask
him to join. I got the most venomous letter back, full of words like traitor
and turncoat and toad-eater and such; really quite rude. So I didn't pursue
it, but got on with forming the club with the others.'

I looked round at the others. We were back now in the club's bar. All but
two of the other members had gone. One was reading a back number of
Vole, and the other, as he had been since I first came into the club, was fast
asleep in the darkest corner with a newspaper over his face.

Uncle Harry went on. 'One of our first campaigns, funnily enough, was
the tiger. At one time they were down to a hundred in Bengal, where the
best ones are. We got them protected. The Nabobs were very good about it
on the whole, but I got a letter from the one I told you about whose shoot
I'd been on years ago. He said that Rashid, on hearing that the Bengal tiger
was nearly extinct, had seen it as a personal challenge, and had set off
immediately with a rifle and a hundred bullets, his eyes funnier than ever.
Well, I told the other chaps about this, and we had a council of war, as it
were, and decided there was only one thing to do. If the tigers weren't to
become extinct, then Col. Rashid must.

'Six of us set off – myself and five others who'd known him at Eton. We
went up country from Cooch Behar. The locals said he'd passed through
there a few days earlier. And we tracked him through the forest. All of us,
remember, were hunters. We could read a spoor as easily as the *Sporting Life*.
Not that he was difficult to track, for there were traces of him everywhere:
half-smoked Passing Clouds, miniatures of port, copies of the *Tatler*. It was
almost as if he wanted us to find him. And find him we did. At first light,

in a clearing just north of Tikkapore, there he was, drinking tea and fretting over the house prices in *Country Life*. He turned when he saw us and raised himself on his hind legs, his eyes yellow and staring, his teeth bared in a fearsome snarl. We all fired at once, as we'd agreed we would.' Uncle Harry went silent, and I leant forward.

'What happened, Uncle?'

'Oh, I'm afraid the head was ruined. We must all have hit him. But the skin was perfect. Absolutely perfect.'

'The skin, Uncle? Tiger Rashid's skin?'

'Does sound a bit odd to you, young Tony, I suppose. But we were hunters. We were killing something that preyed on other animals. And a hunter's proof of success is the trophy. So we brought him back.'

'Back here?' I looked around, half expecting to see Colonel Rashid spread face down on the floor.

'Of course. As a warning to all of us. As a reminder of our position as part of the animal world. Mind you, not everyone would understand, so we couldn't have him as a rug. And we have ladies' nights now sometimes. So we had to put him somewhere he wouldn't attract attention. Somewhere he could fade into the background. Camouflage, y'know – second nature to a hunter. So we ... well, see for yourself. See if you can spot our only trohpy.'

I followed his eyes as they travelled round the room. Apart from us, there was now only one other occupant. Sitting motionless in the darkest corner, with a newspaper concealing the damage the Endangered Species Club had wrought, were the remains of Col. Tiger Rashid.

'You've got him, Tony,' said Uncle Harry. 'He always was a bit of a stuffed shirt.'

On Eating and Drinking

Jerome K. Jerome

I always was fond of eating and drinking, even as a child – especially eating, in those early days. I had an appetite then, also a digestion. I remember a dull-eyed, livid-complexioned gentleman coming to dine at our house once. He watched me eating for about five minutes, quite fascinated, seemingly, and then he turned to my father, with, 'Does your boy ever suffer from dyspepsia?'

'I never heard him complain of anything of that kind,' replied my father. 'Do you every suffer from dyspepsia, Collywobbles?' (They called me Collywobbles, but it was not my real name.)

'No, pa,' I answered. After which, I added, 'What is dyspepsia, pa?'

My livid-complexioned friend regarded me with a look of mingled amazement and envy. Then in a tone of infinite pity he slowly said, 'You will know – some day.'

My poor, dear mother used to say she liked to see me eat, and it has always been a pleasant reflection to me since, that I must have given her much gratification in that direction. A growing, healthy lad, taking plenty of exercice, and careful to restrain himself from indulging in too much study, can generally satisfy the most exacting expectations as regards his feeding powers.

It is amusing to see boys eat, when you have not got to pay for it. Their idea of a square meal is a pound and a half of roast beef with five or six good-sized potatoes (soapy ones preferred, as being more substantial), plenty of greens, and four thick slices of Yorkshire pudding, followed by a couple of currant dumplings, a few green apples, a pen'orth of nuts, half-a-dozen jumbles, and a bottle of ginger beer. After that, they play at horses.

How they must despise us men, who require to sit quiet for a couple of hours after dining off a spoonful of clear soup and the wing of a chicken!

But the boys have not all the advantages on their side. A boy never enjoys the luxury of being satisfied. A boy never feels full. He can never stretch out his legs, put his hands behind his head, and, closing his eyes, sink into the ethereal blissfulness that encompasses the well-dined man. A dinner makes no difference whatever to a boy. To a man, it is as a good fairy's potion, and, after it, the world appears a brighter and a better place. A man who has dined satisfactorily experiences a yearning love towards all his fellow-creatures. He strokes the cat quite gently, and calls it 'poor pussy,' in tones full of the tenderest emotion. He sympathises with the members of the German band outside, and wonders if they are cold; and, for the moment, he does not even hate his wife's relations.

A good dinner brings out all the softer side of a man. Under its genial influence, the gloomy and morose become jovial and chatty. Sour, starchy individuals, who all the rest of the day go about looking as if they lived on vinegar and Epsom salts, break out into wreathed smiles after dinner, and exhibit a tendency to pat small children on the head, and to talk to them – vaguely – about sixpences. Serious young men thaw, and become mildly cheerful; and snobbish young men, of the heavy moustache type, forget to make themselves objectionable.

I always feel sentimental myself after dinner. It is the only time when I can properly appreciate love stories. Then, when the hero clasps 'her' to his heart in one last wild embrace, and stifles a sob, I feel as sad as though I had dealt at whist, and turned up only deuce; and, when the heroine dies in the end, I weep. If I read the same tale early in the morning, I should sneer at it. Digestion, or rather indigestion, has a marvellous effect upon the heart. If I want to write anything very pathetic – I mean, if I want to *try* to write anything very pathetic – I eat a large plateful of hot buttered muffins about an hour beforehand, and, then, by the time I sit down to my work, a feeling of unutterable melancholy has come over me. I picture heart-broken lovers parting for ever at lonely wayside stiles, while the sad twilight deepens around them, and only the tinkling of a distant sheep bell breaks the sorrow-laden silence. Old men sit and gaze at withered flowers till their sight is dimmed by the mist of tears. Little dainty maidens wait and watch at open casements; but, 'he cometh not,' and the heavy years roll by, and the sunny gold tresses wear white and thin. The babies that they dandled have become grown men and women with podgy torments of their own, and the playmates that they laughed with are lying very silent under the waving grass. But still they wait and watch, till the dark shadows of the unknown night steal up and gather round them, and the world with its childish troubles fades from their aching eyes.

I see pale corpses tossed on white-foamed waves, and death-beds stained with bitter tears, and graves in trackless deserts. I hear the wild wailing of women, the low moaning of the little children, the dry sobbing of strong men. It's all the muffins. I could not conjure up one melancholy fancy upon a mutton chop and a glass of champagne.

A full stomach is a great aid to poetry, and, indeed, no sentiment of any kind can stand upon an empty one. We have not time or inclination to indulge in fanciful troubles, until we have got rid of our real misfortunes. We do not sigh over dead dicky-birds with the bailiffs in the house; and, when we do not know where on earth to get our next shilling from we do not worry as to whether our mistress's smiles are cold, or hot, or lukewarm, or anything else about them.

Foolish people – when I say 'foolish people' in this contemptuous way, I mean people who entertain different opinions to mine. If there is one person I do despise more than another, it is the man who does not think exactly the same on all topics as I do. Foolish people, I say, then, who have never experienced much of either, will tell you that mental distress is far more agonising than bodily. Romantic and touching theory! so comforting to the love-sick young sprig who looks down patronisingly at some poor devil with a white starved face, and thinks to himself, 'Ah, how happy you are compared with me!' so soothing to fat old gentlemen who cackle about the superiority of poverty over riches. But it is all nonsense – all cant. An aching head soon makes one forget an aching heart. A broken finger will drive away all recollections of an empty chair. And when a man feels really hungry, he does not feel anything else.

We sleek, well-fed folk can hardly realise what feeling hungry is like. We know what it is to have no appetite, and not to care for the dainty victuals placed before us, but we do not understand what it means to sicken for food – to die for bread while others waste it – to gaze with famished eyes upon coarse fare steaming behind dingy windows, longing for a pen'orth of pease pudding, and not having the penny to buy it – to feel that a crust would be delicious, and that a bone would be a banquet.

Hunger is a luxury to us, a piquent, flavour-giving sauce. It is well worth while to get hungry and thirsty, merely to discover how much gratification can be obtained from eating and drinking. If you wish to thoroughly enjoy your dinner, take a thirty-mile country walk after breakfast, and don't touch anything till you get back. How your eyes will glisten at sight of the white table-cloth and steaming dishes then! With what a sigh of content you will put down the empty beer tankard, and take up your knife and fork! And how comfortable you feel afterwards, as you push back your chair, light a cigar, and beam round upon everybody.

Make sure, however, when adopting this plan, that the good dinner is really to be had at the end, or the disappointment is trying. I remember once a friend and I – dear old Joe, it was. Ah! how we lose one another in life's mist. It must be eight years since I last saw Joseph Taboys. How pleasant it would be to meet his jovial face again, to clasp his strong hand, and to hear his cheery laugh once more! He owes me fourteen shillings, too. Well, we were on a holiday together, and one morning we had breakfast early, and started for a tremendous long walk. We had ordered a duck for dinner over night. We said, 'Get a big one, because we shall come home awfully hungry'; and as we were going out, our landlady came up in great spirits. She said, 'I have got you gentlemen a duck, if you like. If you get through that, you'll do well'; and she held up a bird about the size of a door-mat. We chuckled at the sight, and said we would try. We said it with self-conscious pride, like men who know their own power. Then we started.

We lost our way, of course. I always do in the country, and it does make me so wild, because it is no use asking direction of any of the people you meet. One might as well inquire of a lodging-house slavey the way to make beds, as expect a country bumpkin to know the road to the next village. You have to shout the question about three times, before the sound of your voice penetrates his skull. At the third time, he slowly raises his head, and stares blankly at you. You yell it at him than for a fourth time, and he repeats it after you. He ponders while you could count a couple of hundred, after which, speaking at the rate of three words a minute, he fancies you 'couldn't do better than –' Here he catches sight of another idiot coming down the road, and bawls out to him the particulars, requesting his advice. The two then argue the case for a quarter of an hour or so, and finally agree that you had better go straight down the lane, round to the right, and cross by the third stile, and keep to the left by old Jummy Milcher's cow-shed, and across the seven-acre field, and through the gate by Squire Grubbin's haystack, keeping the bridle path for a while, till you come opposite the hill where the windmill used to be – but it's gone now – and round to the right, leaving Stiggin's plantation behind you; and you say 'Thank you,' and go away with a splitting headache, but without the faintest notion of your way, the only clear idea you have on the subject being that somewhere or other there is a stile which has to be got over; and, at the next turn, you come upon four stiles, all leading in different directions.

We had undergone this ordeal two or three times. We had tramped over fields. We had waded through brooks, and scrambled over hedges and walls. We had had a row as to whose fault it was that we had first lost our way. We had got thoroughly disagreeable, footsore, and weary. But, throughout it all, the hope of that duck kept us up. A fairy-like vision, it floated before our tired eyes, and drew us onward. The thought of it was as a trumpet call to the fainting. We talked of it, and cheered each other with our recollections of it. 'Come along,' we said, 'the duck will be spoilt.'

We felt a strong temptation, at one point, to turn into a village inn we passed, and have a cheese and a few loaves between us; but we heroically restrained ourselves: we should enjoy the duck all the better for being famished.

We fancied we smelt it when we got into the town and did the last quarter of a mile in three minutes. We rushed upstairs, and washed ourselves, and changed our clothes, and came down, and pulled our chairs up to the table, and sat and rubbed our hands while the landlady removed the covers, when I seized the knife and fork and started to carve.

It seemed to want a lot of carving. I struggled with it for about five minutes without making the slightest impression, and then Joe who had been eating potatoes, wanted to know if it wouldn't be better for someone to do the job that understood carving. I took no notice of his foolish remark, but attacked the bird again; and so vigorously this time, that the animal left the dish, and took refuge in the fender.

We soon had it out of that though, and I was prepared to make another effort. But Joe was getting unpleasant. He said that if he had thought we were to have a game of blind hockey with the dinner, he would have got a bit of bread and cheese outside.

I was too exhausted to argue. I laid down the knife and fork with dignity, and took a side seat: and Joe went for the wretched creature. He worked away, in silence for a while, and then he muttered, 'Damn the duck,' and took his coat off.

We did break the thing up at length, with the aid of a chisel; but it was perfectly impossible to eat it, and we had to make a dinner off the vegetables and an apple tart. We tried a mouthful of the duck, but it was like eating india-rubber.

It was a wicked sin to kill that drake. But there! there's no respect for old institutions in this country.

I started this paper with the idea of writing about eating and drinking, but I seem to have confined my remarks entirely to eating as yet. Well, you see, drinking is one of those subjects with which it is unadvisable to appear too well acquainted. The days are gone by when it was considered manly to go to bed intoxicated every night, and a clear head and a firm hand no longer draw down upon their owner the reproach of effeminacy. On the contrary, in these sadly degenerate days, an evil-smelling breath, a blotchy face, a reeling gait, and a husky voice are regarded as the hall-marks of the cad rather than of the gentleman.

Even now-a-days, though, the thirstiness of mankind is something supernatural. We are for ever drinking on one excuse or another. A man never feels comfortable unless he has a glass before him. We drink before meals, and with meals, and after meals. We drink when we meet a friend, also when we part from a friend. We drink when we are talking, when we are reading, and when we are thinking. We drink one another's healths, and spoil our own. We drink the Queen, and the Army, and the Ladies, and everybody else that is drinkable; and, I believe, if the supply ran short, we should drink our mothers-in-law.

By-the-way, we never *eat* anybody's health, always *drink* it. Why should we not stand up now and then and eat a tart to somebody's success.

To me, I confess, the constant necessity of drinking under which the majority of men labour is quite unaccountable. I can understand people drinking to drown care, or to drive away maddening thoughts, well enough. I can understand the ignorant masses loving to soak themselves in drink – oh, yes, it's very shocking that they should, of course – very shocking to us who live in cosy homes, with all the graces and pleasures of life around us, that the dwellers in damp cellars and windy attics should creep from their dens of misery into the warmth and glare of the public-house bar, and seek to float for a brief space away from their dull world upon a Lethe stream of gin.

But think, before you hold up your hands in horror at their ill-living, what 'life' for these wretched creatures really means. Picture the squalid misery of their brutish existence, dragged on from year to year in the narrow, noisome room where, huddled like vermin in sewers, they welter, and sicken, and sleep; where dirt-grimed children scream and fight, and sluttish, shrill-voiced women cuff, and curse, and nag; where the street outside teems with roaring filth, and the house around is a bedlam of riot and stench.

Think what a sapless stick this fair flower of life must be to them, devoid of mind and soul. The horse in his stall scents the sweet hay, and munches the ripe corn contentedly. The watch-dog in his kennel blinks at the grateful sun, dreams of a glorious chase over the dewy fields, and wakes with a yelp of gladness to greet a caressing hand. But the clod-like life of these human logs never knows one ray of light. From the hour when they crawl from their comfortless bed to the hour when they lounge back into it again, they never live one moment of real life. Recreation, amusement, companionship, they know not the meaning of. Joy, sorrow, laughter, tears, love, friendship, longing, despair, are idle words to them. From the day when their baby eyes first look out upon their sordid world to the day when, with an oath, they close them for ever, and their bones are shovelled out of sight, they never warm to one touch of human sympathy, never thrill to a single thought, never start to a single hope. In the name of the God of mercy let them pour the maddening liquor down their throats, and feel for one brief moment that they live!

Ah! we may talk sentiment as much as we like, but the stomach is the real seat of happiness in this world. The kitchen is the chief temple wherein we worship, its roaring fire is our vestal flame, and the cook is our great high-priest. He is a mighty magician and a kindly one. He soothes away all sorrow and care. He drives forth all enmity, gladdens all love. Our God is great, and the cook is his prophet. Let us drink, and be merry.

Oops!
Conversations of a delicate nature
Richard Briers

I reckon that one of the greatest compensations of being middle-aged is that you stop being embarrassed by things which used to turn you puce at an early age. I was always frightfully shy and this led to me being embarrassing in the worst possible way. I used to speak very fast and loud, and to make matters worse I made wild gesticulations, like a sort of juvenile Magnus Pyke.

Mercifully those days have gone. Today I can spill soup down my front, knock over a pyramid of baked bean tins in Sainsburys and approach any potentially awkward situation without so much as a raised word or a flick of the wrist. But it wasn't so long ago that any conversation of a delicate nature filled me with trepidation and gave the palms of my hands a nasty, clammy feeling.

My nerves used to bring on an aggressive turn in my manner that always achieved exactly the opposite effect to the one I wanted. Instead of easing the situation with my own polished confidence, I almost invariably put other people's backs up and came out of the encounter ruffled, not to say fleeing with my tail between my legs.

Well can I sympathize with the well-meaning blunderer who approached a fellow-passenger on the platform at Euston with:

'Pardon me, but ... um ...'

only to be spurned with:

'No, you've never met me at Biarritz, Cannes or Bognor. I never travel on the Central Line at 8.45. I know that I'm good looking and that I remind you of your sister. I'm not getting off at your station and I wouldn't accept a lift from you if you owned the only car in England. I didn't go to school with you. I'm not waiting for a bus. It's not about to rain and my boy friend is in the SAS. Now, were you about to say something?'

'Yes, damn it, your knickers are falling down.'

Whenever possible, conversations of a delicate nature should not be handled like this. The tactful commuter would have done much better to come straight out with a jolly line like, 'Hey, love, you're losing your drawers', or something like that. Where he, I and, I suspect, most of the male population of this country come a cropper is in the momentary hesitation when our nerve fails. What middle age teaches is how to be prepared at moments like this.

We would all dearly love the practised ease of the smoothy who can come out with lines like this: 'Delightful as all these suggestions sound, I'm afraid that my intentions were far more mundane. As they say in gentlemen's lavatories, kindly adjust your dress.'

This sort of reply is marvellous. It is brief. It says exactly what it is meant to say, and it has the other great merit of giving the silly cow a ticking off for flying off the handle in the first place, by implying that she was showing her knickers deliberately.

Of course this type of situation does offer plenty of other possibilities. Supposing that the chap had really been eyeing her up, the episode with the knickers would give him a perfect reason for trying his luck with her. Then of course he'd have to answer her tirade with something ingratiating like:

'Look, I'm terribly sorry. I know this must look like the most awful pick-up, but I couldn't help noticing you standing by the chocolate machine and I'm afraid I couldn't help seeing that you were having some trouble with your underwear. Please excuse my apparent rudeness, but I was only trying to save your embarrassment. Could I apologize properly over a cup of coffee/a drink/dinner sometime/ in Marks while you're buying another pair?'

Apart from his cowering subservience and his subtly boyish manner the man who can produce a reply like this also has the presence of mind to swap 'knickers' for the more decorous 'underwear' – which shows that he's got breeding. Even if his amorous intentions prove fruitless, he's certainly far less likely to be slapped across the face for his pains.

Anyhow, that's quite enough about knickers. The point is that delicate conversations can occur any time and anywhere. They creep up on us unexpectedly and trip us up if we're not careful. Even if we can't prevent ourselves from falling, we can at least take care that we fall properly and do ourselves the minimum of damage.

So for the sake of simplicity, I have divided the various types of delicate conversations into three broad areas – affairs of the heart, criticism, and awkward and embarrassing situations.

Here goes.

Affairs of the Heart

Without doubt the most important of these is falling in love.

People have been falling in love ever since Adam and Eve, but the formulae of how it happens are as complicated and varied as those that they print on the side of bottles of mineral water. But falling in love is one thing. The real problem is getting the message across, and this is where conversation comes in.

I have always believed that true love is founded on understanding. That may sound like a platitude, probably because it is, but if you get completely the wrong idea of what the other person feels about you right from the start, then things can become horribly confused later on.

If you gaze into a pair of limpid eyes on the Central Line at 5.35 every week-day evening, your tactics clearly must be very different from those of the country swain who has been courting for two years and eventually plucks up courage to pop the question having found out that he won't stand a cat in hell's chance of getting an estate cottage unless he's married.

Making an advance to an absolute stranger is by far the most difficult; about the only advantage it has in fact is the element of surprise. I knew a bloke who had once been asked by a gorgeous cinema usherette, 'Can I show you to your seat, sir?' to which he replied, with great presence of mind, 'Thanks, but I'd far rather be shown to yours.' And he was!

In spite of the inroads of the women's lib brigade, it's still mainly men who have to take it upon themselves to utter the magic words. That's fine if you come from south of Brussels, but for the rest of us it's not that easy. Though speaking of magic words, don't let yourself get off on the wrong foot by an approach like the one overheard to a pretty waitress in a tea-shop:

'Would you like me to whisper to you the three words every girl longs to hear?'

'Yes.'

'Here's your tip.'

Likewise the tired old phrases like, 'Has anyone told you that you're beautiful?', or, 'You must get used to being told that you're an amazingly attractive girl', are only useful opening gambits if they share some connection with reality. If they don't they come out as rather unimaginative flattery. Of course they also leave themselves open to the simple rebuff, 'yes'.

Love strikes us at the most inopportune moment. A colleague of mine was pierced by Cupid's arrow just as a district nurse was dressing his backside following an operation he'd had for a colourful complaint called 'Jeep seat'. There's not a lot you can do to help your cause when you're flat on your face with a pretty girl pouring TCP and baby powder over your bum. He had the idea of asking her out for dinner, but somehow that didn't seem very suitable under the circumstances. So he decided to ask her swimming because that would be good physiotherapy, but in the middle of February that suggestion didn't work out as well as he hoped.

There must be something about women in uniforms that turns on some men. Nurses I can understand, ministering angels and all that, but policewomen, that does take some understanding. But one man's poison is another man's meat, so to speak, though in one instance that springs to mind the two were combined.

I still maintain, mind you, that the driver threw caution to the winds, for he had two endorsements already, but it still took some courage to pick up the officer who was booking him. He was just cruising gently through a 30 mph limit minding his own business at about 45 (well, we all do, don't we?) when a girl popped out from behind a wooden fence and waved him to the side of the road. For one ghastly minute he thought that he'd run over someone and not stopped, and the look on his face must have given him away immediately. But the girl seemed a bit unsure of herself too.

'Excuse me, sir,' she said through the window which was firmly closed. 'Excuse me, sir. Would you mind opening your window and turning off your radio.'

Which the driver duly did.

'I have to inform you that anything you may say – no, sorry, that comes later. I have to inform you that you were picked up on the radar travelling at 46 miles-per-hour in a 30 mile-an-hour limit. I have to warn you that anything you say may be taken down and may be used in evidence against you. Do you have anything to say?'

Quite sensibly the driver said that he had not and the policewoman then asked to see his driving licence and copied down the number of the car. She wrote something down on a piece of paper, tore it up and tried to write it down again. At the third attempt she started to blush and the façade cracked. She started to giggle.

After warning him that he would be receiving a summons in due course she told him that he could drive on and he was just about to pull away when she dashed out from the pavement again saying:

'Oh, wait a minute. I didn't write down your address.'

'I didn't write down yours,' said the driver, 'but I got your number. How about letting me book you one evening?' And the jammy devil did. Mind you his summons came through the post just the same, and he lost his licence.

Then there are those circumstances which are almost too opportune, like finding yourself standing next to the ideal stranger while you're peering into the window of a sex-shop. There's no point in trying to disguise what you're up to. That runs the terrible risk of giving the idea that you're less than normal. All you can do is to brazen it out, bearing in mind that whoever you're interested in is looking at the same window.

'Excuse me. I'm intrigued by that thing there (pointing at some weird appliance fitted with wires and straps), do you have any idea what it's for?', is probably as good a way of getting off the ground as any other. And if you strike lucky and she does know what it's for then you'll probably get on like a house on fire.

There are times of course when the interest can be mutual. I remember a friend of mine pulling into a petrol station to buy some fuel in the days before self-service pumps. It was during a heat-wave and the staff at the garage were wearing bathing costumes and very little else. He's a pretty average sort of a bloke, but almost every woman I speak to talks about his 'smouldering looks' or his 'burning eyes', or something like that. Anyway, whatever he had did something to the girl filling his tank, and when he went up to the counter to pay she leaned across at him threateningly and said, 'How would you like to fill my tank – tiger.' If he hadn't already been late for a vital golf-match, I dread to think what might have happened. Which simply proves my point that love, infatuation, call it what you will, can creep up on us all at the least expected opportunity.

Sensing the emotion is one thing of course. Actually making the right words come out of your mouth is quite another matter, as all of us who have stammered our way through interminable adolescent formulae know to our cost.

The real point about saying 'I love you' to a total stranger is its suddenness. Play on this for all its worth. Although most people haven't any time for love at first sight, there's always the exception that proves the rule, and that exception is usually the chap who can do the whole thing convincingly and with sufficient romantic flair so that he just succeeds in sounding sincere instead of sounding like a waiter on the Costa del Sol.

Fictional characters always have it so easy, which probably explains why actors have become pastmasters at the art, after rubbing shoulders, so to speak, with all the great lovers of literature.

Lovers in plays and books start off with two big advantages over we lesser mortals. Their conversation is always pre-planned and it always comes from better-than-average brains. How many of us could cross our hearts and honestly admit that we could go up to a girl in a disco, always assuming that we could make ourselves heard, and say:

> *If I profane with my unworthiest hand*
> *This holy shrine, the gentle sin is this.*
> *My lips two blushing pilgrims stand*
> *To smooth the rough touch with a loving kiss.*

Mind you, how many girls could come up with an answer like:

> *Good pilgrim, you do wrong your hand too much*
> *Which mannerly devotion shows in this.*
> *For saints have hands that pilgrims' hands do touch*
> *And palm to palm is holy palmers' kiss.*

Having said this, though, it's only fair to point out that I am an incurable optimist when it comes to affairs of the heart. I honestly believe that if we accept our limitations, which isn't always easy or palatable, there is no reason why we shouldn't display the same reverence as Romeo, or the same encouragement as Juliet. If you try to say 'I love you' to a total stranger you're always going to run the risk of sounding corny whatever you say. But if you can say it with enough conviction and let the force of your feelings shine through the words, then anyone remotely interested will see that you are sincere and will overlook the clichés that might accidentally slip in in the heat of the moment.

The trouble is that so few of us willingly admit to having any limitations when it comes to our prowess as Don Juans. Even if we make some faltering attempts at self-analysis, we usually get it hopelessly wrong.

I've seen middle-aged, balding accountants holding hands with their secretaries in dimly-lit, grossly-overpriced restaurants whispering things like:

'I never realized I could be so happy. I know you won't believe me when I tell you this, but the moment I saw you walk into the office I felt myself slipping, and now there's no stopping me. I'm terribly afraid that I've fallen head over heels in love with you.'

That sort of stuff brings a blush to my cheeks and quite puts me off my sweetbreads, never mind what it does to the sweet young thing who is only on the look-out for a sugar-daddy. The poor old chap, who's probably been rehearsing those lines for a week on the 8.15 from Dorking, would have been far better off offering her an allowance of £3,000 a year and a discreet flat for two in Maida Vale. But then he probably couldn't have afforded it. Love and romance are full of pitfalls for the unwary.

Criticism

Critics are to actors what the last remaining tufts of hair are to a bald man. They point up our inadequacies and shortcomings on a superficial level, mocking us in the eyes of the world at large, without offering any constructive help for improving things. But once they lose interest in us and disappear, our fortunes wane and we look even less appealing to the general public.

Critics have to be suffered and endured, like journalists and reporters. But I find it's best to be philosophical about what they have to say. If you get a notice that you think is unjustified, always try and forget it. After all nothing is deader than yesterday's news and many critics criticize not the play as it is presented, but the play as they would like to present it themselves.

This is a terrible annoyance of course, though, even so, we've usually been able to pinch a few quotes from them in the past which look good outside the theatre. And that's often the only way that actors can get their own back, by quoting the critics out of context. It's really quite immoral, but all's fair in love and war – mostly war – I suppose.

The trouble with criticism in show business is that it usually appears in print. Actors seldom get a chance to have a go at the critics in the flesh. This has its compensations, though, because the things one would like to say sometimes wouldn't do one any good in the popularity stakes by the time the paper comes out.

For this reason there is really no way of going one up on a reporter. You really have to go one down to go one up, as Stephen Potter so rightly said. If you meet a reporter, and some of them are pretty disastrous personalities by the nature of their extraordinary work, you can't remonstrate or be too arrogant with them, for the simple reason that they can always get back at you in print, especially if they work for a popular paper with a very large audience which like nothing better than to see you put down.

So my policy is always to try to be nice to them and to try not to hang about with them for too long either. The only tiresome thing which I find with some reporters is that at the end of a rather long interview they reach for their battered briefcases and bring out scripts for pilot comedy series, which they hope I'm going to star in. Most of them, bless their hearts, seem to be playwrights *manqués*, searching for a producer.

Criticism from other quarters can be dealt with more positively, though this isn't always the case, especially when it comes from fans. I remember being in *The Wild Duck* at the Lyric, Hammersmith in which I was called upon to knock myself out in five exhausting acts. One night after the play I arrived in the bar, still panting and sweating from my efforts, merely to be told by one of the three or four faithful fans who get to know one rather too well, 'that was very nice'. I had another drink and remembered *Whose Life Is It Anyway?* Just then I thought I wouldn't mind spending the whole of *The Wild Duck* sitting propped up in bed. With fans like that, who needs enemies?

What can be even more galling is the criticism from directors or fellow-actors which you know is wrong, or quite irrelevant. I love the story of the wonderful old ham cast in a rep production of *Macbeth*. The director had seen Macbeth as a man suffering an inferiority complex and had blocked out his movements as those of a nervous, frightened maniac – a sort of cross between Mole in *The Wind in the Willows* and Adolf Hitler. However, the lead had very different ideas and throughout rehearsals he and the director were constantly contradicting each other about the interpretation of the part. When the first night came they had established a sort of uneasy truce. But the sight of a full house sent the blood to the old boy's head and when it came to 'Is this a dagger etc.' the blocking went to pieces along with the cowering nervousness of the first act. He started to charge about the stage, declaiming like one of the three weird sisters, and finally backed off-stage through the castle gate through which Macduff was about to enter, leaving himself on the wrong side for his next entry.

The director had been watching from the wings and was apoplectic with rage. He tore into Macbeth in scarcely muffled curses and abuse, but the only response he got was a stentorian reply, which rang around the house and silenced Lady Macbeth, who had just got to the bit about drugging the groom's possets:

'If it was good enough for Wolfit, young man, it's certainly good enough for you.'

Oh to have that confidence and that command!

One of the problems with playing the sort of characters I portray is that everyone expects me to behave like that in real life. In some ways it's quite helpful as I get into trouble by nature and the people in Marks & Sparks think it's hilarious if I get anything wrong or forget my money, so I'm usually spared any criticism, if not embarrassment.

But there are times when being Tom Good to most people backfires. I remember an incident with a taxi driver only too vividly which brought this point home to me. I was in a desperate hurry to get to my destination and like a fool I'd decided to go by car because I thought it would save time. There was something on, the Cup Final maybe, because the roads were thick with traffic. After waiting to pull into the endless stream of cars I eventually saw a taxi slowing down, to let me out, as I thought. So I pulled out smartly, just in front of him as it turned out, and gave him a cheery wave of thanks as I drove past.

But the taxi-driver had slammed on his brakes and the passenger, for whom he was stopping, had been pitched onto the floor of the cab and was kneeling on the floor looking daggers at me out of the window:

'Why don't you stick to your f***ing tractor,' the driver yelled out, 'or the goat.'

I drove on, blushing to my socks, and, watching the road intently thereafter, nearly knocked a nun off a zebra-crossing.

If I can give myself a pat on the back for anything, it's probably for being fairly punctual, so I don't often get ticked off for being late. But I know lots of people who make a habit of being late just to exercise their skill in getting out of it.

There was a chap working in a studio with me who always seemed to disappear for a couple of hours for his lunch break. At first people didn't mind too much, but when this became a regular habit, he was taken aside and told to buck up his ideas:

'Why should you take twice as long over lunch as anyone else?' he was asked.

'Probably because I eat twice as much,' he answered and swanned off. He didn't stay to enjoy many more canteen lunches, though.

Knowing how to give criticism, however, is just as much of an art as being able to take it. There are some types of criticism which border on the insult.

I've overheard some pretty choice remarks addressed to barbers while I've been waiting round the partition reading last month's *Mayfair*.

'I wanted a trim, not a nibble,' said one irate retired military man, after a pimply assistant had tried to improve upon what was already a very severe short back and sides. While at the other extreme came the anguished cry of, 'Do I get a refund if you take off all the hair,' which emanated from one shaggy youth whose father had brought him in for a hair cut before going back to school.

I've always fought shy of antagonizing barbers, though. Memories of Sweeney Todd and half-remembered ideas that barbers might once have been surgeons have usually stifled my annoyance, at least until I have been standing upright once again and able to fend for myself.

Besides I take exception to those people who imagine that because they are customers they have carte blanche to abuse the staff. 'Speak as you would be spoken to' has always seemed a perfectly reasonable maxim, that like all perfectly reasonable maxims is easy to say and jolly hard to stick to.

Criticism when it is directed at one's peers or one's family is quite a different matter and here I can be as trenchant as the next man. The mother of a friend of mine had a wonderful way of registering approval or disapproval of her daughter's friends when they telephoned. If she liked them she would come and say, 'So-and-so is on the phone for you, dear.' If she didn't like them the message would come out as either, 'Your friend, so-and-so, is on the phone', or 'That so-and-so is on the phone.' Anyone branded as, 'your friend, that Richard' was way beyond the pale in that house at least.

Criticism to an actor of course means something very different to criticism addressed, say, to a private in the army. A Sergeant-Major's criticism is seldom constructive, at least in the short term, whereas all actors cherish the secret hope that critics might even help them to improve, or might even praise their work.

I remember falling into this trap with Noel Coward – the trap about praise that is. Coward had been to see me in *Present Laughter* and he told me afterwards: 'You know, you really are one of our best farcers', and then he paused. I was waiting for the great accolade to tell my children, the praise which Noel Coward had given to my wonderful work and my remarkable talent, and he then continued, 'You never ever hang about.'

Well, it could have been a great deal worse, even if it was a bit of a let down at the time, but as Somerset Maugham wrote in *Of Human Bondage*: 'People ask you for criticism, but they only want praise.'

Awkward or Embarrassing Situations

I never believe those people who maintain that they never find themselves in awkward or embarrassing situations. Either they're lying or they're not human, or in some circumstances both.

I think there are two distinct types of awkward or embarrassing situations. You may feel just as terrible in both of them, but in one case the embarrassment is usually your own, while in the other you feel embarrassed for the other person, if you follow my meaning. The first type arises from trying to get someone else to do something for you. The second comes from trying to do something for someone else.

Bank managers seem to be prime culprits in the first case. I've come to the conclusion that all the terrible traumas that we go through in visiting the inner sanctum to look blankly at our balance sheets and have a lecture on living within our means are quite unnecessary. The simple truth is that there's really nothing to talk about. If we're in trouble the bank manager can't help us anyway, and if we've got money in the bank all he can do is bow and scrape. So going to see him is really a waste of time, especially in our present economic climate. But this does not prevent us from dutifully trudging along to ask if we can borrow enough to buy a new mowing machine, or pay the garage to change the oil in the car.

Some people, however, seem to have got it down to a fine art, like the ones who spend half their lives filling in Social Security forms and living like lords on the proceeds. They and the bank manager share a *lingua franca* which the rest of us catch snippets of from the business pages of the daily paper and *The Financial World Tonight* on the radio.

They breeze into the manager's office with an air of calm authority, sit down before being invited to and then launch into a five-minute synopsis of what they want and why they want it, sprinkling their monologue with phrases like 'critical path analysis', 'double taxation relief', and 'watered stock'.

I don't have a clue what half of it means, and I'm pretty sure that the common or garden bank manager doesn't know either. But where it doesn't matter if I show my ignorance, the manager stands to lose face if he appears anything but totally au fait with what is being said.

So after the tirade is finished, there is a respectable pause, designed to show that some deliberation is taking place, and the bank manager then mutters something like:

'Well, you must appreciate that under the present circumstances we have to be rather careful of how we dispose of our assets. But in view of what you've told me, I don't see that there should be any reason to prevent us agreeing to what you have asked for. Shall we say fifty thousand now and fifty thousand in six months? This will involve an adjustment to the rates of course. Well I think that covers everything – Do come and see me at any time.'

They shake hands, agree to have a round of golf soon and the manager goes back to doing his crossword while the client goes off to settle the hire purchase on his Rolls.

Doctors have a similar aura surrounding them. There's a line in *Hamlet* which says, 'There's such divinity doth hedge a king' which I've always thought could be applied to doctors, if you swapped 'obscurity' for 'divinity' and 'doctor' for 'king'.

Doctors can be embarrassing either because they chat airily about parts of our anatomy using menacing words which we have never heard before, or because they chat about our bodies in ways that are all too easy to understand:

'You say you want me to give you a life insurance report? I say you'd be better off paying into a funeral fund. You smoke forty a day, you drink an average of eight pints a night, you're five stone overweight and you insist on jogging every morning.'

Going to the doctor can be a wretched business, too, even if you're just going for simple treatment, and doctors aren't always the most sympathetic when it comes to helping their patients out of some dilemmas.

'Which would you prefer me to get, a tin-opener or a hacksaw,' one harrassed casualty doctor asked a man who had somehow got his thumb stuck in a six-foot length of copper piping and was sitting in the casualty department, surrounded by the Saturday night drunks and the last of the rugger injuries, with his appendage sticking up in the air like a radio mast.

'Don't worry Doc, just plug the other end into the mains, that should get me out,' said the patient with a cheerful grin, putting the doctor well and truly in his place.

People in shops can be awkward sometimes as well, though as I mentioned earlier I have a built-in excuse for making an ass of myself. I reserve the greatest sympathy for all those unfortunates who want to try to change unwanted Christmas presents, just as the shops are in the teeth of the January sales.

The classic case of this of course is Bob Newhart's episode with an unwanted toupée. Fortunately I've never been given an unwanted hat, never mind a hair-piece, but there have been times when I have had to dispose of unwanted presents, and trying to take them back to the shops has to be the final resort.

What do you do with a full-length body stocking sent by a well-meaning viewer of *The Good Life*, 'to keep out the chill when you're working in that muddy garden in the winter'? The label showed where it had come from, which was one consolation. If it had been one of the mail-order firms, taking it back to the shops would have been a non-starter. It was also clear from the colour and size of the gift that it would have been better suited for Mrs Good than for me.

The shop seemed to be full of women fitting themselves out for trips to the Antarctic. There were socks of every length and design, strange body garments with bits hanging down at the back and boasting phrases like 'double-thicknesses', 'hygienic and comfortable' and 'as worn on Everest', and my pale-green creation displayed in all its glory on a ridiculously slim dummy in the window.

'I wonder if I could exchange this?' I asked, in the hope that no one would overhear.

'I think we might be able to arrange it,' whispered the middle-aged assistant, giving me a coy wink.

'I can see why you wouldn't want to be seen in this,' she continued, opening out the entire garment across the counter in full view of the whole shop. 'They'd have to call it the *Ghoul Life!*' Helpless giggling broke out from all parts of the shop floor.

After that experience I have taken to disposing of my unwanted presents in a less conspicuous way. What I usually do at Christmas is to rewrap them very quickly, put them in a cupboard and then give them to people I don't like very much the following Christmas. This has always worked well and has never caused any problems, except for one notable exception when I inadvertently gave a present back to the person who had given it to me the year before, still in the same paper.

What really makes perfectly natural situations embarrassing is the way that other people seem to take exception to what we say. Asking people to stop doing something which is clearly unnecessary or in some cases not allowed always seems to put their backs up, no matter how tactful you try to be.

I've asked people before now not to smoke in No Smoking areas, and received some very colourful replies. Yet there are others who can make their point far more effectively and with the minimum of embarrassment to themselves. I have always admired the sangfroid of a lady passenger I read of who was travelling in a No Smoking car of *The Flying Scotsman* when she was joined by a bluff Glaswegian who sat down opposite her, took out a revolting, old pipe and started to light it up as he asked,

'Yu dunna mind ef I smook?'

'Not in the slightest,' the good lady replied, 'as long as you don't mind me being sick.'

Another perfectly reasonable complaint which seems to be more in evidence than ever is the short measure controversy. The snag I find, however, is that the barman who pulls you three-quarters of a pint and 'a good head', also happens to look like an ex-Royal Marine commando. Pleasant approaches like, 'Now then, mine host, I'll have the weights and measures chappies on to you,' or 'Sorry to be a nuisance, but I think the barrel's still a bit lively,' don't get you anywhere. The barman either turns nasty and asks you to leave, or else he asks if you want to make an issue of it, and what was intended as a quiet drink after a tiring day turns into a defence of your virility.

The sort of comment which shows that you're capable of giving as good as you get is the one which catches the barman off his guard:

'Excuse me, can you put a whisky in this?'

'Certainly sir.'

'Well, in that case would you mind filling up with beer.'

And then there is the one which I have always longed to have the nerve to use.

'How's business these days?'

'Not so good, you know. People are coming in less than they used to, especially during the week. Well there isn't the money around, what with Christmas, and the recession and everything.'

'You'd like it then if you could sell a bit more beer.'

'Too right I would.'

'Well, why not try selling less froth then.'

Experience has taught me that you've got to have very small barmen attending to you before you try anything like that.

I've given up drinking expensive wine in restaurants for similar reasons, and now we always drink the house wine. You need about £16 to get a decent bottle of wine in a restaurant these days and when you can buy it round the corner at your local liquormarket for half the price it really isn't worth spending the money in a restaurant. This is especially true if you actually notice what you're being served.

I've seen people getting into the most awful rows with waiters when they've tried to send back wine which they thought was the wrong temperature, or in one case the wrong bottle. But you've got to be jolly sure of what you're doing if you do decide to take on the head-waiter of any restaurant with pretentions to haute cuisine.

I was sitting alongside a chap who was having a blazing row with the wine waiter over a bottle of fairly costly claret which he had ordered. This chap had evidently been told that the wine should have been served at room temperature, and as far as he was concerned it wasn't. The conversation was gradually dying throughout the rest of the restaurant, as it always does when this sort of thing starts up. The head-waiter hurried over to see what all the fuss was about and when he got the wine-waiter's version he gave the customer a look of complete and utter disdain and imperiously said:

'You must excuse the misunderstanding, sir. But in view of the fact that you ordered this with the truite meunière, it was rather confusing as to which temperature you wished the wine to be served at.'

If the customer had not made himself so objectionable in the first place, the waiter might have been kinder, he might even have been embarrassed for the poor man, who had made a perfectly reasonable choice, even if it did flout the best gourmet conventions.

Feeling bad on other people's account can be just as wretched as being acutely embarrassed yourself. An actor friend of mine went along to a barber to get a Roman haircut after he had been cast in a production of *Julius Caesar*. The style interested the young man cutting his hair and they got talking about it.

'I'm an actor you see,' explained my friend, 'and the next play I'm in is set in ancient Rome so I've got to look like a Roman, you know, short at the front. At least you're using scissors. I read somewhere that originally they had their hair singed.'

'What play's that then,' the barber asked him.

'*Julius Caesar.*'

'Who wrote that then?'

'Well, Shakespeare actually,' my friend told him after a slight pause.

'Oh God ... of course,' said the barber, crestfallen.

My chum felt so awkward he ended up giving him his two complimentary tickets.

Twice I've tried to help out people I've seen walking towards me with their flies wide open, merely because of the profound debt of gratitude I owe to a huge, black guard on the underground who saw me in this state once and yelled out with a beaming smile: 'Oh dear, man, de flies is all undone!'

Here again, though, my approach was essentially far too timid and as it turned out far too misleading. I tried to attract the first man's attention silently as he was walking towards me by making furtive movements towards my crutch. But he didn't catch on straightaway and as we drew nearer I started to feel very self-conscious. In the end I broke my silence and whispered to him as he passed me:

'Did you know your flies are undone?'

'Yes,' he said, 'But what am I supposed to do about it when the zip's bust?'

The second time was really even more alarming as the unfortunate man in question was foreign and his command of English did not extend to trouser fittings.

'Your flies are undone,' I told him, giving up mime for a bad job.

'No. I come by ship to Duver,' he told me confidently.

'No. Your zipper is undone,' I persisted.

'Yes, shipper,' he said slightly bemused.

Eventually restored to making rapid up-and-down movements with my hands indicating what he should do. His trousers were fitted with buttons and I don't think he really understood what I had been telling him because he was still muttering, 'Very good shippers' as he did himself up and walked off in the opposite direction.

Come to think of it, his might have been the best policy after all. He didn't seem the least bit put out by being told that he was about to expose himself, and I certainly finished by far the more embarrassed of the two. After all, if the good Samaritan had found that the man lying by the road worked for the *Candid Camera* team, he, too, would have felt a right Charlie.

Maybe the best way to deal with awkward or embarrassing situations is just to ignore them. Certainly from my own experience the more you try to settle them by conversation the worse they become. On the other hand a more charitable approach might be to know how to kill them before they get too horribly out of control.

Climbing Napes Needle

A. A. Milne

Ken and I went to the Lakes together in August, staying at a farm-house at Seathwaite. We had decided to do a little rockclimbing. We knew nothing about it, but had brought a rope, nailed boots, and the standard book by Owen Glynne Jones. The climbs in this book were graded under such headings as Easy, Medium, Moderately Stiff, and Extremely Stiff. We decided to start with a Moderately Stiff one, and chose the Napes Needle on Great Gable, whose charm is that on a post-card it looks Extremely Stiff. Detached by the hands of a good photographer from its context, it becomes a towering pinnacle rising a thousand feet above the abyss. Roped together, since it seemed to be the etiquette, Ken and I would scale this mighty pinnacle, and send post-cards to the family.

We were a little shy about the rope when we started out, carrying it lightly over the arm at first as if we had just found it and were looking for its owner ... and then more grimly over the other arm, as one who makes for a well down which some wanderer has fallen. The important thing was not to be mistaken for what we were: two novices who had been assured that a rope made climbing less dangerous, when, in fact, they were convinced that it would make climbing very much more so. There was also the question of difficulty. To get ourselves to the top of the Needle would be Moderately Stiff; but it was (surely) Extremely Stiff to expect us to drag a rope up there too. I felt all this more keenly than Ken, because it had already been decided, anyhow by myself, that I was to 'lead'. Not only had I won the Gymnastics Competition Under 14 in 1892, but compared with Ken's my life was now of no value. Ken had just got engaged to be married. If I led, we might both be killed (as seemed likely with this rope) or I might be killed alone, but it was impossible that I should ever be breaking the news to his lady of an accident which I had callously survived. I was glad of this, of course; but I should have liked it better if it had been I who was engaged and Ken who was being glad.

We scrambled up the lower slopes of Great Gable and reached the foot of the Needle. Seen close it was a large splinter of rock about sixty feet high, shaped like an acute-angled pyramid with a small piece of the top cut off, leaving a flat summit which could just take Ken and me and (we supposed) the rope. We had practised tying ourselves on, and we now tied ourselves on. I just started up, dragging the rope behind me.

The Napes Needle has this advantage over, from what I hear, the Matterhorn: that the difficult part is not really dangerous and the dangerous part is not really difficult. The dangerous part, as one would expect, comes at the top. One begins by forcing oneself diagonally up a flat slab of rock, the left leg, from knee to ankle, wedged in a crack, and the rest of oneself free as a trolley-bus to follow the left leg upwards. Only the reassurance of the book, as shouted up to me by Ken that this, though difficult, was not dangerous, kept me at it. No doubt my leg *was* jambed – no doubt about it, as I found when I tried to move it; no doubt I couldn't roll down the mountain without it; but the rest of my body felt horribly defenceless, and every nerve in it was saying 'This is silly, and one should stick to Essex.' With a sudden jerk which made all that the book said ridiculous, I loosened my leg and got it in a little higher up. The very slave of circumstance and impulse, like Sardanapalus, 'borne away with every breath' a little farther from Ken (which meant twice as far to fall) I puffed on ... until a moment came when I could go no farther. Knee still in crack, heart still in mouth, body still *in vacuo*, I sidled backward to Ken.

'It's no good. Sorry.'

'Were you really stuck?'

'Absolutely. There's more in this than we thought.'

'Shall I try?'

At some other time I might have said: 'My dear man, if I can't, you can't.' At some other time I might have said: 'For Maud's sake, no!' At this time I said 'Yes, do.' I wanted to lie down.

In a little while he was back with me, and we were studing the Easy group.

'All the same,' said Ken, looking up at the Needle again.

'All the same,' said I.

'Think of Bruce.'

'I think of nothing else.'

'Say "I can do it".'

'I can do it.'

We got up.

'Suppose I came up behind you and pushed a bit?'

'What's the rope doing?'

'Hanging about.'

'Is that right?'

'Well, I don't see what else it *can* do.'

'Nor do I. I don't like the look of the dangerous bit at the top, do you?'

'It may look better when we get there.'

'Yes. Well, let's get there. Dash it, we can't just carry the rope home again. Come on.'

It was a little easier this time; I felt more like a tram, and less like a 'bus; I got to the sticking-place and waited for Ken's hand to reach my foot. With its support I straightened my knee and got a handhold higher up. We went on doing this until Ken had reached the sticky place, by which time I was in sight of home. Soon we were sitting side by side on a broad shelf, puffing happily. The 'difficult' part was over.

There remained a vertical slab of rock in the shape of the lower four-fifths of an isosceles triangle. It was about fifteen feet high, and there was a ledge like a narrow mantelpiece halfway up. Owen Glynne Jones (who may have been a nuisance in the home) made a practice of pulling himself on to mantelpieces by the fingers, so as to keep in training, and no doubt it is in the repertory of every real climber. We were merely a couple of tourists. When in doubt we collaborated. Ken reached up to the ledge and grasped it firmly, and I climbed up him. When I was standing on the ledge, my fingers were a couple of feet below the top.

In making these climbs it is impossible to lose the way. Every vital handhold is registered in the books, every foothold scored by the nails of previous climbers. To get to the top I wanted one more foothold and one handhold, and I knew where they were. I shuffled to the left and looked round the corner.

On the precipitous left-hand face of the pyramid, a little out of reach, there was an excrescence of rock the size and shape of half a cricket-ball. That was the handhold. Just within reach of raised foot and bent knee a piece of the rock sloped out for a moment at an angle of 45°, before resuming the perpendicular. That was the foothold. I should imagine that the whole charm of the Napes Needle to an enthusiast rests on that forbidding foothold.

To a non-enthusiast, as I was at that moment, the whole charm of a foothold is that it holds the foot solidly, at right angles to whatever one is climbing up. This didn't. Could one's nails (and Jones) be trusted? When all one's weight was on that slippery-looking, nail-scratched slope, while one grabbed for the cricket-ball, did one simply disappear down the left-hand face, leaving Ken with a lot of rope and no bother, or did one's head appear triumphantly over the top? That was the question, and there was only one way of finding the answer. After all, there must be something in this rope business, or people wouldn't carry them about. If I fell, I could only fall thirty feet. It was absurd to suppose that I should then break in half; there was no record of anyone having broken in half; no, I should simply dangle for a little, assure Ken's anxious head that all that blood he saw everywhere was only where I had hit myself on the way down, and then climb gaily up the rope to safety. All this was just the give-and-take of the climber's life. All those scratches were just signs of where other people had slipped, disappeared, and come laughing back. Without the rope one would be a dead man, but with it the whole climb was child's play ... or just plain folly?

Oh, well ...

It was delightful to sit on the top of the Needle and dangle our legs, and think 'We've done it'. About once every ten years it comes back to me that, in addition to all the things I can't do and haven't done, I *have* climbed the Napes Needle. So have thousands of other people. But they, probably, knew something about it.

A few days later we climbed Kern Knotts Chimney. My ideal reader of this book would be somebody just sufficiently acquainted with the subject to think that by Kern Knotts Chimney I mean Kern Knotts Crack. If I had climbed the Crack, this would have been a different sort of book. The Chimney is only Moderately Stiff. Blocking the top of the actual chimney, which is the second stage of the climb, is a large rocking-stone. Somehow this has to be surmounted. Our faith in Jones was now such as to – I was going to say 'to move mountains' but that would be an unfortunate metaphor. It was this bit of the mountain which was *not* going to move, according to Jones, and we trusted him. But it wobbled alarmingly. There is a technique of chimney-climbing which we didn't seem to have mastered. We had a fireside discussion as to whether it would be bad form to throw the rope over this boulder and haul ourselves up by it.

'Good heavens, you can do what you like with the rope,' said Ken. 'That's what it's for.'

'Then if you had a lasso and lassoed the top of the Monument and climbed up, you could say you had climbed the Monument?'

'That's absurd. You might as well say -'

'What?'

'Almost anything,' said Ken, thinking hard.

'Such as?'

'Well, you'll admit that you can stand on the other man's shoulders? *That's* quite fair?'

'Of course. But a rope –'

'Then if you had a friend 475 feet high and you climbed up his braces and stood on his shoulders –'

'Oh, *shut* up. Give us the rope.'

We reached the top. It may be things like this which get you blackballed from the Alpine Club. I wouldn't know.

No Man is an Island

Basil Boothroyd

The people next door are immensely tall, towering above the hedge. Mother, father, a late teenager of each sex, none of them an inch under eight feet.

They only need one more for a basketball team.

This is our fault. We should have asked more questions before moving. We asked quite a lot. How was the neighbourhood for aircraft noises, night barking, brass band practice, egg-boxes and children's knickers flung through the front gates from passing cars. How tall are the people next door was something we just didn't think of.

It's not as if we're inexperienced. Our first house in the country, not to be confused with a country house, was full of surprises. For one, it wavered in the wind, or when heavy cats jumped in at upper windows, though luckily it was shored up by its adjoining properties in the village High Street. We were so dazzled by the estate agent's claim that it was built of rare Flemish bricks, we didn't even notice that some of them, under the front bedroom's outer sill, bore the announcement Boot Repairs: well faded, but springing sharply out in certain angles of the sun.

There was also a right of way through our back garden, from one twitten, as they say in Sussex, to another. This wasn't really brought home until the first hot day, when I strung a hammock between the two stronger fruit trees and the ladies of the village filed past me with their shopping baskets and rechargeable radio batteries, the date being well before transistors. 'Lovely, now,' they would say. Or, swinging me with a light push, 'All right for some.'

I felt like Lenin's tomb.

Though indirectly, the house itself ruined a dream of rustic Saturdays. We arrived on a Saturday. In mid-afternoon. With rolls of carpet still sticking out of the car, and the bare necessities of soap and kettles exhumed from the packing cases, I made for the village cricket ground. Feet newly free of London dust soon itch for country pleasures.

All was up to standard. Cows in the outfield. The vicar umpiring. Flannels of all shades, some frankly grey, and the peculiar flat acoustic of the rustic bat.

Then an old fool joined me on my bench and said, 'You've taken number four High Street,' which was flattering. One day's residence, and the word was round? 'You know that's been condemned,' he continued. He moved closer, with details about rotten joists. He could have had the place for £200 before the war, but it was only held up by leaning against number six.

'Good afternoon,' I said, leaving. He shouted something after me about the drains, and I never went back to that cricket ground again. It had associations of doom.

Two hundred pounds, though. Imagine. Even adding a bit for new joists and general stabilisation. We never did that, and it's still standing, or was this morning when I drove past, accelerating a little as usual. You never know when falling-down day could come.

All we ever did to it was paint the front door red. Five years later, when we were trying to sell, a bridging loan hanging over us like thunder, this paid an unexpected dividend. Earlier negotiations had fallen through at a late hour. The purchaser's ballpoint was practically poised over the clinching document when he suddenly thought about drains and joists. I don't know why. He was from Ipswich, and unlikely to have watched any local cricket.

But he sent men to look at the drains. In spite of digging up the small front garden, which they left mounded with neat earth like a fresh grave, they couldn't find the drains. Then he sent wood men, and they pursued us from room to room displaying, with professional excitement, handfuls of newly plucked timber rot. He himself made no further visits, but stayed, for all we know, in Ipswich, his pen in his pocket.

We were thus in a moral dilemma not of our seeking. *Caveat emptor* is all right for some. But could we, now knowing the full range of dreadful secrets, honestly conceal it from the trickle of succeeding prospects? No. We dismissed them on the step, before they even got their orders to view unfolded. They would be buying trouble, we told them, comprising no drains and all recorded varieties of worm, rot and beetle.

Stuck with the house, but our conscience clear, we gave up all hope, staring ruin in the face. We were talking of begging in the streets and putting our son down for Barnardo's, when a middle-aged lady drove up in a good car, wanting a wedding present for a neice. She was imperious, stubborn. She forced her way in, brushing aside all bogeys. Damp? Drains? Death-watch? In an old house, she said, you expect these things.

Desperate, we took her into the basement and showed her the mushrooms sprouting from the walls. They amused her. We dragged her up again, to enjoy the view from the front window, which was a row of backsides, sitting on our wall waiting for the bus. She praised the convenience of a bus stop so handy.

In the end, conventional weapons failing, I resorted to the ultimate deterrent, or Lenin's tomb round the back. It was my highest card. She trumped it with her cheque for the asking price, no haggling. Her niece, she said, had always wanted a house with a red front door.

So you can never tell, with property.

We moved out into the real country after that. Still not to a country house in any true sense. We never, for example, threw it open to the public. But it was a little grander, more spacious both inside and out, and at least you could have got some of the public in, which is more than you can say about this one.

It was not, of course, as grand and spacious as it now seems, having left it. On moving house, the first candidates for the dustbin are your rose-coloured glasses with special hindsight attachment. Otherwise, transferred to a built-up area, even though residentially desirable, you can soon kid yourselves that you've come down from forty rooms and twelve acres. My recurring dream along those lines is getting more intermittent now, and should eventually fade for good. It has me revisiting the old place, and finding that our successors are sprawled out on broad terraces, overlooking a vista of lime walks and water gardens. Fountains plash. A vassal, nicely blending Jeeves and that old retainer from the barley-water ads, moves softfootedly among them with exotic foods. Nightingales sing. Kingfishers dart brilliantly by.

I have to remind myself, determinedly waking, that we would often call it 'this bloody house' when we were actually there, and that we seriously expected, at times, to be driven mad by the scream of the power-saw from the timber-yard down the lane. I remember, or try to, how the radiators cracked and moaned, and the wind rose through the floorboards like knives. Awful, it must have been. I tell myself.

This house, the new one, new to us, that is, though placed in the early thirties by the surveyor's report with a bill attached which we first took to be a joke, had an asking price of rather special interest. Having paid it, no haggling, I mentioned this to my wife. I was fresh from an accidental stumble in BRA-DAP of the encyclopedia. My eye, bent on the principles of Buddhism, for purposes of no interest here, had slipped back a column.

'Did you know that we're giving more for this place than George III gave for Buckingham Palace?'

This was true. Inflation, though threadbare by now as a topic, still has its dramatic surprises.

She replied that she still couldn't open the larder window and we should have to get a man in.

'Of course,' I went on, wishing to be fair, 'that was in 1762. It wasn't Buckingham Palace then.'

'It isn't Buckingham Palace now,' she said, executing a backward dog-leg from the washing-up position, owing to cramped conditions.

This was also true, as you will, I hope, read on and learn.

The X's, as we call them, as distinct from the Y's on our other flank, who build boats, and BF's, or bonfire fanatics, beyond our bottom hedge, are not to be blamed for being an eight-foot family. Besides, they're nice, and respecters of privacy as far as their dimensions will permit. A nasty family, visibly stalking around from the waist up, could be peering down the back of our pants all the time as we stoop to the trowelling. Luckily, they try not to do this, and we in turn try not to stare at their passing chests.

But there's a propinquity. Exchange the country for the town, and you get that. We shall live with it if we can, remembering our solemn oath, jointly sworn on a solicitor's bill for £316, never to move again, to stick it out here till the end of the line, even if the staircase does have twists in it like barley-sugar and is probably notorious among local undertakers. Your end up a bit, Charlie, or we're into the hat-stand.

They are an outdoor crowd, the X's, with a lot of small cars round the front that they don't use. Instead they stay home, round the back, and play together with musical laughter, being what the Americans call close. As indeed they are. This is refreshing in times of the estranged family and broken home.

Moreover, they show a proper diffidence over recovering, from our side, such errant recreational items as shuttlecocks, frisbees, suction-tipped arrows and almost every kind of ball, from tennis, foot and all-purpose large multicoloured, to small red rubber trailing wisps of failed elastic and, in still weather, ping-pong.

Cricket, no. Lawns are small here. That was chiefly what drew us. Batting at the toolshed end, they would have a leg boundary of some five yards, making the game ridiculous.

They could easily reach over and scoop up the lost property, but instead go to the pains of calling formally at our front door. Please can we have our ball back. We honour them for that, and in return try to keep our TV at low volume during shoot-outs.

We have also noticed, now that all members of the team have called, presumably on a rota basis, that they are of perfectly ordinary height on these occasions. It's only on the ground that they tower, and we couldn't at first think how they did it.

We then found that our garden level inexplicably turns out to be about two feet below theirs, and we worried about this. Had the address subsided? Was it subsiding still? We kept waking in the night with a sinking feeling. At yet it has shown no signs, no fresh course of bricks pushing up round the bottom of the house, exposing angry slugs, no disquietingly deeper step one morning on to the back flagstones.

We remain alert. Again, we should have questioned the agent, but even if we had we should simply, in our diffident way, have taken his word.

'Is the house subsiding?'

'No.'

Next question.

Anyway, a man who failed to mention that none of the interior doors will shut without a kung-fu kick at latch level would hardly admit that we are built over abandoned iron-workings.

And if we are, the descent will be slow. Years of it probably won't reveal more than an extra inch of the X's. And besides, as far as they're concerned, neighbourliness is all, now that we're townies. What needs to be established, with neighbours, is no chatting over the hedge but a readiness to lend milk in emergencies.

Mr Y builds his boats behind a higher, denser hedge, invisible, but pin-pointed by sawing, hammering, the rasp of giant sandpaper, grunts of achievement as he boxes a compass or sheets home a binnacle. Not seeing him is both pleasing and maddening. Is he a midget? He may surface later, being at present on his haunches all the time, fitting rudders. Or his property may be subsiding.

Boat number one, the flagship, which we can glimpse accidently from an upper window by leaning well out, looks ready for sea. This is only twelve miles away, and we can't understand why he doesn't take it down and drop it in, He could be a bad sailor, or lack confidence in the caulking. Is there a purely academic satisfaction in building boats, boredom setting in at the idea of actual contact with water?

Time may tell. Meanwhile, two things are sure: he can't go on indefinitely, gardens this size can only support a limited fleet of finished craft; and we must stop all this speculation about the neighbours, tempting though it is to the newly moved.

Besides, we ourselves may present aspects of puzzlement. Was there a twitch of curtains across the road the other morning, when I traversed our crescent of gravel with a dustbin over my head? Those new people walk about wearing dustbins. But it was just that our predecessors here had their bins sited unacceptably under the kitchen window, and I was shifting them round the other side, held conveniently aloft, when one of them slipped down, owing to arm failure after being up all night sawing a cat-flap.

So now you know, you lot over there. Give up the curtain twitching and tell us about that perplexing PO Telephones van that seems to live up your drive. Are you paid a little something to give it a home, as with telegraph poles in front gardens? Is your lodger, the one in the front attic room who has his light on at funny hours, an engineer with fringe transport benefits? Mysterious. We ask ourselves what sort of job even the post office could work a 24-hour day on all this time, whether installing, repairing or tracing heavy breathing.

None of our business.

But newcomers are perversely teased by such trifles. It's like being in foreign parts, where you read, with sharpened attention, the cutlery, matchboxes, no spitting notices, or tea-bag labels that yield only the exotic message 'Brooke Bond'.

Three houses down, on our side, a cardboard notice has been lashed to the gatepost for months, saying TORTIOSE LOST. It bugs us. Passing on the way to the pillar box, and happening to glance in, we see neither children nor traces of any, no telltale pointers (house-hunters beware) in the form of strewn plastic firearms or capsized doll's perambulators; just a pair of old ladies, possibly twins but we shall have to get closer, whom one might suppose to (a) keep no tortoises, (b) know how to spell them, and (c) stop putting, so to speak, a candle in the window by now. A tortoise gone as long as this is a gone tortoise.

Still, three houses off might as well be Albania, and its secrets as impenetrable. Immediate relations are OK, and we like the X's increasingly, if only for not objecting to the arrival of our dustbins more or less under their kitchen window.

We have decided to show our appreciation by returning shuttlecocks (and recently a badminton racket) unasked.

Butch Minds the Baby

Damon Runyon

One evening along about seven o'clock I am sitting in Mindy's restaurant putting on the gefillte fish, which is a dish I am very fond of, when in come three parties from Brooklyn wearing caps as follows: Harry the Horse, Little Isadore, and Spanish John.

Now these parties are not such parties as I will care to have much truck with, because I often hear rumours about them that are very discreditable, even if the rumours are not true. In fact, I hear that many citizens of Brooklyn will be very glad indeed to see Harry the Horse, Little Isadore and Spanish John move away from there, as they are always doing something that is considered a knock to the community, such as robbing people, or maybe shooting or stabbing them, and throwing pineapples, and carrying on generally.

I am really much surprised to see these parties on Broadway, as it is well known that the Broadway coppers just naturally love to shove such parties around, but there they are in Mindy's, and there I am, so of course I give them a very large hello, as I never wish to seem inhospitable, even to Brooklyn parties. Right away they come over to my table and sit down, and Little Isadore reaches out and spears himself a big hunk of my gefillte fish with his fingers, but I overlook this, as I am using the only knife on the table.

Then they all sit there looking at me without saying anything, and the way they look at me makes me very nervous indeed. Finally I figure that maybe they are a litle embarrased being in a high-class spot such as Mindy's, with legitimate people around and about, so I say to them, very polite:

'It is a nice night.'

'What is nice about it?' asks Harry the Horse, who is a thin man with a sharp face and sharp eyes.

Well, now that it is put up to me in this way, I can see there is nothing so nice about the night, at that, so I try to think of something else jolly to say, while Little Isadore keeps spearing at my gefillte fish with his fingers, and Spanish John nabs one of my potatoes.

'Where does Big Butch live?' Harry the Horse asks.

'Big Butch?' I say, as if I never hear the name before in my life, because in this man's town it is never a good idea to answer any question without thinking it over, as some time you may give the right answer to the wrong guy, or the wrong answer to the right guy. 'Where does Big Butch live?' I ask them again.

'Yes, where does he live?' Harry the Horse says, very impatient. 'We wish you to take us to him.'

'Now wait a minute, Harry,' I say, and I am now more nervous than somewhat, 'I am not sure I remember the exact house Big Butch lives in, and furthermore I am not sure Big Butch will care to have me bringing people to see him, especially three at a time, and especially from Brooklyn. You know Big Butch has a very bad disposition, and there is no telling what he may say to me if he does not like the idea of me taking you to him.'

'Everything is very kosher,' Harry the Horse says. 'You need not be afraid of anything whatever. We have a business proposition for Big Butch. It means a nice score for him, so you take us to him at once, or the chances are I will have to put the arm on somebody around here.'

Well, as the only one around here for him to put the arm on at this time seems to be me, I can see where it will be good policy for me to take these parties to Big Butch especially as the last of my gefillte fish is just going down Little Isadore's gullet, and Spanish John is finishing up my potatoes, and is donking a piece of ryebread in my coffee, so there is nothing more for me to eat.

So I lead them over into West Forty-ninth Street, near Tenth Avenue, where Big Butch lives on the ground floor of an old brownstone-front house, and who is sitting out on the stoop but Big Butch himself. In fact, everybody in the neighbourhood is sitting out on the front stoops over there, including women and children, because sitting out on the front stoops is quite a custom in this section.

Big Butch is peeled down to his undershirt and pants, and he has no shoes on his feet, as Big Butch is a guy who loves his comfort. Furthermore, he is smoking a cigar, and laid out on the stoop beside him on a blanket is a little baby with not much clothes on. This baby seems to be asleep, and every now and then Big Butch fans it with a folded newspaper to shoo away the mosquitoes that wish to nibble on the baby. These mosquitoes come across

the river from the Jersey side on hot nights and they seem to be very fond
of babies.

'Hello Butch,' I say, as we stop in front of the stoop.

'Sh-h-h-h!' Butch says, pointing at the baby, and making more noise with
his shush than an engine blowing off steam. Then he gets up and tiptoes
down to the sidewalk where we are standing, and I am hoping that Butch
feels all right, because when Butch does not feel so good he is apt to be very
short with one and all. He is a guy of maybe six foot two and a couple of
feet wide, and he has big hairy hands and a mean look.

In fact, Big Butch is known all over this man's town as a guy you must
not monkey with in any respect, so it takes plenty of weight off me when I
see that he seems to know the parties from Brooklyn, and nods at them very
friendly, especially at Harry the Horse. And right away Harry states a most
surprising proposition to Big Butch.

It seems that there is a big coal company which has an office in an old
building down in West Eighteenth Street, and in this office is a safe, and in
this safe is the company pay roll of twenty thousand dollars cash money.
Harry the Horse knows the money is there because a personal friend of his
who is the paymaster for the company puts it there late this very afternoon.

It seems that the paymaster enters into a dicker with Harry the Horse and
Little Isadore and Spanish John for them to slug him while he is carrying
the pay roll from the bank to the office in the afternoon, but something
happens that they miss connections on the exact spot, so the paymaster has
to carry the sugar on to the office without being slugged, and there it is now
in two fat bundles.

Personally it seems to me as I listen to Harry's story that the paymaster
must be a very dishonest character to be making deals to hold still while he
is being slugged and the company's sugar taken away from him, but of course
it is none of my business, so I take no part in the conversation.

Well, it seems that Harry the Horse and Little Isadore and Spanish John
wish to get the money out of the safe, but none of them knows anything
about opening safes, and while they are standing around in Brooklyn talking
over what is to be done in this emergency Harry suddenly remembers that
Big Butch is once in the business of opening safes for a living.

In fact, I hear afterwards that Big Butch is considered the best safe-opener
east of the Mississippi River in his day, but the law finally takes to sending
him to Sing Sing for opening these safes, and after he is in and out of Sing
Sing three different times for opening safes Butch gets sick and tired of the

place, especially as they pass what is called the Baumes Law in New York, which is a law that says if a guy is sent to Sing Sing four times hand running, he must stay there the rest of his life, without any argument about it.

So Big Butch gives up opening safes for a living, and goes into business in a small way, such as running beer, and handling a little Scotch now and then, and becomes an honest citizen. Furthermore, he marries one of the neighbour's children over on the West Side by the name of Mary Murphy, and I judge the baby on this stoop comes of this marriage between Big Butch and Mary because I can see that it is a very homely baby, indeed. Still, I never see many babies that I consider rose geraniums for looks, anyway.

Well, it finally comes out that the idea of Harry the Horse and Little Isadore and Spanish John is to get Big Butch to open the coal company's safe and take the pay-roll money out, and they are willing to give him fifty per cent of the money for his bother, taking fifty per cent for themselves for finding the plant, and paying all the overhead, such as the paymaster, out of their bit, which strikes me as a pretty fair sort of deal for Big Butch. But Butch only shakes his head.

'It is old-fashioned stuff,' Butch says. 'Nobody opens pete boxes for a living any more. They make the boxes too good, and they are all wired up with alarms and are a lot of trouble generally. I am in a legitimate business now and going along. You boys know I cannot stand another fall, what with being away three times already, and in addition to this I must mind the baby. My old lady goes to Mrs Clancy's wake tonight up in the Bronx, and the chances are she will be there all night, as she is very fond of wakes, so I must mind little John Ignatius Junior.'

'Listen, Butch,' Harry the Horse says, 'this is a very soft pete. It is old-fashioned, and you can open it with a toothpick. There are no wires on it, because they never put more than a dime in it before in years. It just happens they have to put the twenty G's in it tonight because my pal the paymaster makes it a point not to get back from the jug with the scratch in time to pay off today, especially after he sees we miss out on him. It is the softest touch you will ever know, and where can a guy pick up ten G's like this?'

I can see that Big Butch is thinking the ten G's over very seriously, at that, because in these times nobody can afford to pass up ten G's, especially a guy in the beer business which is very, very tough just now. But finally he shakes his head again and says like this:

'No,' he says, 'I must let it go, because I must mind the baby. My old lady is very, very particular about this, and I dast not leave little John

Ignatius Junior for a minute. If Mary comes home and finds I am not
minding the baby she will put the blast on me plenty. I like to turn a few
honest bobs now and then as well as anybody, but,' Butch says, 'John Ignatius
Junior comes first with me.'

Then he turns away and goes back to the stoop as much as to say he is
through arguing, and sits down beside John Ignatius Junior again just in
time to keep a mosquito from carrying off one of John's legs. Anybody can
see that Big Butch is very fond of this baby, although pesonally I will not
give you a dime for a dozen babies, male and female.

Well, Harry the Horse and Little Isadore and are very much disappointed,
and stand around talking among themselves, and paying no attention to me,
when all of a sudden Spanish John, who never has much to say up to this
time, seems to have a bright idea. He talks to Harry and Isadore, and they
get all pleasured up over what he has to say, and finally Harry goes to Big
Butch.

'Sh-h-h-h!' Big Butch says, pointing to the baby as Harry opens his mouth.

'Listen, Butch,' Harry says in a whisper, 'we can take the baby with us,
and you can mind it and work, too.'

'Why,' Big Butch whispers back, 'this is quite an idea indeed. Let us go
into the house and talk things over.'

So he picks up the baby and leads us into his joint, and gets out some
pretty fair beer, though it is needled a little, at that, and we sit around the
kitchen chewing the fat in whispers. There is a crib in the kitchen, and Butch
puts the baby in this crib, and it keeps on snoozing away first rate while we
are talking. In fact, it is sleeping so sound that I am commencing to figure
that Butch must give it some of the needled beer he is feeding us, because I
am feeling a little dopey myself.

Finally Butch says that as long as he can take John Ignatius Junior with
him he sees no reason why he shall not go and open the safe for them, only
he says he must have five per cent more to put in the baby's bank when he
gets back, so as to round himself up with his ever-loving wife in case of a
beef from her over keeping the baby out in the night air. Harry the Horse
says he considers this extra five per cent a little strong, but Spanish John,
who seems to be a very square guy, says that after all it is only fair to cut
the baby in if it is to be with them when making the score, and Little Isadore
seems to think this is all right, too. So Harry the Horse gives in, and says
five per cent it is.

Well, as they do not wish to start out until after midnight, and as there is plenty of time, Big Butch gets out some more needled beer, and then he goes looking for the tools with which he opens safes, and which he says he does not see since the day John Ignatius Junior is born and he gets them out to build the crib.

Now this is a good time for me to bid one and all farewell, and what keeps me there is something I cannot tell you to this day, because personally I never before have any idea of taking part in a safe opening, especially with a baby, as I consider such actions very dishonourable. When I come to think over things afterwards, the only thing I can figure is the needled beer, but I wish to say I am really very much surprised at myself when I find myself in a taxicab along about one o'clock in the morning with these Brooklyn parties and Big Butch and the baby.

Butch has John Ignatius Junior rolled up in a blanket, and John is still pounding his ear. Butch has a satchel of tools, and what looks to me like a big flat book, and just before we leave the house Butch hands me a package and tells me to be very careful with it. He gives Little Isadore a smaller package, which Isadore shoves into his pistol pocket, and when Isadore sits down in the taxi something goes wa-wa, like a sheep, and Big Butch becomes very indignant because it seems Isadore is sitting on John Ignatius Junior's doll, which says 'Mamma' when you squeeze it.

It seems Big Butch figures that John Ignatius Junior may wish something to play with in case he wakes up, and it is a good thing for Little Isadore that the mamma doll is not squashed so it cannot say 'Mamma' any more, or the chances are Little Isadore will get a good bust in the snoot.

We let the taxicab go a block away from the spot we are headed for in West Eighteenth Street, between Seventh and Eighth Avenues, and walk the rest of the way two by two. I walk with Big Butch carrying my package, and Butch is lugging the baby and his satchel and the flat thing that looks like a book. It is so quiet down in West Eighteenth Street at such an hour that you can hear yourself think, and in fact I hear myself thinking very plain that I am a big sap to be on a job like this, especially with a baby, but I keep going just the same which shows you what a very big sap I am, indeed.

There are very few people in West Eighteenth Street when we get there, and one of them is a fat guy who is leaning against a building almost in the centre of the block, and who takes a walk for himself as soon as he sees us. It seems that this fat guy is the watchman at the coal company's office and is also a personal friend of Harry the Horse, which is why he takes the walk when he sees us coming.

It is agreed before we leave Big Butch's house that Harry the Horse and Spanish John are to stay outside the place as lookouts, while Big Butch is inside opening the safe, and that Little Isadore is to go with Butch. Nothing whatever is said by anybody about where I am to be at any time, and I can see that, no matter where I am, I will still be an outsider, but, as Butch gives me the package to carry, I figure he wishes me to remain with him.

It is no bother at all getting into the office of the coal company, which is on the ground floor, because it seems the watchman leaves the front door open, this watchman being a most obliging guy, indeed. In fact, he is so obliging that by and by he comes back and lets Harry the Horse and Spanish John tie him up good and tight, and stick a handkerchief in his mouth and chuck him in an areaway next to the office, so nobody will think he has anything to do with opening the safe in case anybody comes around asking.

The office looks out on the street, and the safe that Harry the Horse and Little Isadore and Spanish John wish Big Butch to open is standing up against the rear wall of the office facing the street windows. There is one little electric light burning very dim over the safe so that when anybody walks past the place outside, such as a watchman, they can look in through the window and see the safe at all times, unless they are blind. It is not a tall safe, and it is not a big safe, and I can see Big Butch grin when he sees it, so I figure this safe is not much of a safe, just as Harry the Horse claims.

Well, as soon as Big Butch and the baby and Little Isadore and me get into the office, Big Butch steps over to the safe and unfolds what I think is the big flat book, and what is it but a sort of screen painted on one side to look exactly like the front of a safe. Big Butch stands this screen up on the floor in front of the real safe, leaving plenty of space in between, the idea being that the screen will keep anyone passing in the street outside from seeing Butch while he is opening the safe, because when a man is opening a safe he needs all the privacy he can get.

Big Butch lays John Ignatius Junior down on the floor on the blanket behind the phony safe front and takes his tools out of the satchel and starts to work opening the safe, while Little Isadore and me get back in a corner where it is dark, because there is not room for all of us back of the screen. However, we can see what Big Butch is doing, and I wish to say while I never before see a professional safe-opener at work, and never wish to see another, this Butch handles himself like a real artist.

He starts drilling into the safe around the combination lock, working very fast and very quiet, when all of a sudden what happens but John Ignatius Junior sits up on the blanket and lets out a squall. Naturally this is most disquieting to me, and personally I am in favour of beaning John Ignatius Junior with something to make him keep still, because I am nervous enough as it is. But the squalling does not seem to bother Big Butch. He lays down his tools and picks up John Ignatius Junior and starts whispering, 'There, there, there, my itty oddleums. Da-dad is here.'

Well, this sounds very nonsensical to me in such a situation, and it makes no impression whatever on John Ignatius Junior. He keeps on squalling, and I judge he is squalling pretty loud because I see Harry the Horse and Spanish John both walk past the window and look in very anxious. Big Butch jiggles John Ignatius Junior up and down and keeps whispering baby talk to him, which sounds very undignified coming from a high-class safe-opener, and finally Butch whispers to me to hand him the package I am carrying.

He opens the package, and what is in it but a baby's nursing bottle full of milk. Moreover, there is a little tin stew pan, and Butch hands the pan to me and whispers to me to find a water tap somewhere in the joint and fill the pan with water. So I go stumbling around in the dark in a room behind the office and bark my shins several times before I find a tap and fill the pan. I take it back to Big Butch, and he squats there with the baby on one arm, and gets a tin of what is called canned heat out of the package, and lights this canned heat with his cigar lighter, and starts heating the pan of water with the nursing bottle in it.

Big Butch keeps sticking his finger in the pan of water while it is heating, and by and by he puts the rubber nipple of the nursing bottle in his mouth and takes a pull at it to see if the milk is warm enough, just like I see dolls who have babies do. Apparently the milk is okay, as Butch hands the bottle to John Ignatius Junior, who grabs hold of it with both hands, and starts sucking on the business end. Naturally he has to stop squalling, and Big Butch goes to work on the safe again, with John Ignatius Junior sitting on the blanket, pulling on the bottle and looking wiser than a treeful of owls.

It seems the safe is either a tougher job than anybody figures, or Big Butch's tools are not so good, what with being old and rusty and used for building baby cribs, because he breaks a couple of drills and works himself up into quite a sweat without getting anywhere. Butch afterwards explains to me that he is one of the first guys in this country to open safes without explosives, but he says to do this work properly you have to know the safes so as to drill to the tumblers of the lock just right, and it seems that this particular safe is a new type to him, even if it is old, and he is out of practice.

Well, in the meantime, John Ignatius Junior finishes his bottle and starts mumbling again, and Big Butch gives him a tool to play with, and finally Butch needs this tool and tries to take it away from John Ignatius Junior, and the baby lets out such a squawk that Butch has to let him keep it until he can sneak it away from him, and this causes more delay.

Finally Big Butch gives up trying to drill the safe open, and he whispers to us that he will have to put a little shot in it to loosen up the lock, which is all right with us, because we are getting tired of hanging around and listening to John Ignatius Junior's glug-glugging. As far as I am personally concerned, I am wishing I am home in bed.

Well, Butch starts pawing through his satchel looking for something and it seems that what he is looking for is a little bottle of some kind of explosive with which to shake the lock on the safe up some, and at first he cannot find this bottle, but finally he discovers that John Ignatius Junior has it and is gnawing at the cork, and Butch has quite a battle making John Ignatius Junior give it up.

Anyway, he fixes the explosive in one of the holes he drills near the combination lock on the safe, and then puts in a fuse, and just before he touches off the fuse Butch picks up John Ignatius Junior and hands him to Little Isadore, and tells us to go into the room behind the office. John Ignatius Junior does not seem to care for Little Isadore, and I do not blame him, at that, because he starts to squirm around quite some in Isadore's arms and lets out a squall, but all of a sudden he becomes very quiet indeed, and, while I am not able to prove it, something tells me that Little Isadore has his hand over John Ignatius Junior's mouth.

Well, Big Butch joins us right away in the back room, and sound comes out of John Ignatius Junior again as Butch takes him from Little Isadore, and I am thinking that it is a good thing for Isadore that the baby cannot tell Big Butch what Isadore does to him.

'I put in just a little bit of a shot,' Big Butch says, 'and it will not make any more noise than snapping your fingers.'

But a second later there is a big whoom from the office, and the whole joint shakes, and John Ignatius laughs right out loud. The chances are he thinks it is the Fourth of July.

'I guess maybe I put in too big a charge,' Big Butch says, and then he rushes into the office with Little Isadore and me after him, and John Ignatius

Junior still laughing very heartily for a small baby. The door of the safe is swinging loose, and the whole joint looks somewhat wrecked, but Big Butch loses no time in getting his dukes into the safe and grabbing out two big bundles of cash money, which he sticks inside his shirt.

As we go into the street Harry the Horse and Spanish John come running up much excited, and Harry says to Big Butch like this:

'What are you trying to do,' he says, 'wake up the whole town?'

'Well,' Butch says, 'I guess maybe the charge is too strong, at that, but nobody seems to be coming, so you and Spanish John walk over to Eighth Avenue, and the rest of us will walk to Seventh, and if you go along quiet, like people minding their own business, it will be all right.'

But I judge Little Isadore is tired of John Ignatius Junior's company by this time, because he says he will go with Harry the Horse and Spanish John, and this leaves Big Butch and John Ignatius Junior and me to go the other way. So we start moving, and all of a sudden two cops come tearing around the corner towards which Harry and Isadore and Spanish John are going. The chances are the cops hear the earthquake Big Butch lets off and are coming to investigate.

But the chances are, too, that if Harry the Horse and the other two keep on walking along very quietly like Butch tells them to, the coppers will pass them up entirely, because it is not likely that coppers will figure anybody to be opening safes with explosives in this neighbourhood. But the minute Harry the Horse sees the coppers he loses his nut, and he outs with the old equalizer and starts blasting away, and what does Spanish John do but get his out, too and open up.

The next thing anybody knows, the two coppers are down on the ground with slugs in them, but other coppers are coming from every which direction, blowing whistles and doing a little blasting themselves, and there is plenty of excitement, especially when the coppers who are not chasing Harry the Horse and Little Isadore and Spanish John start poling around the neighbourhood and find Harry's pal, the watchman, all tied up nice and tight where Harry leaves him, and the watchman explains that some scoundrels blow open the safe he is watching.

All this time Big Butch and me are walking in the other direction toward Seventh Avenue, and Big Butch has John Ignatius in his arms, and John Ignatius is now squalling very loud indeed. The chances are he is still thinking of the big whoom back there which tickles him so and is wishing to hear some more whooms. Anyway, he is beating his own best record for squalling, and as we go walking along Big Butch says to me like this:

'I dast not run,' he says, 'because if any coppers see me running they will start popping at me and maybe hit John Ignatius Junior, and besides running will joggle the milk up in him and make him sick. My old lady always warns me never to joggle John Ignatius Junior when he is full of milk.'

'Well, Butch,' I say, 'there is no milk in me, and I do not care if I am joggled up, so if you do not mind, I will start doing a piece of running at the next corner.'

But just then around the corner of Seventh Avenue towards which we are headed comes two or three coppers with a big fat sergeant with them, and one of the coppers, who is half-out of breath as if he has been doing plenty of sprinting, is explaining to the sergeant that somebody blows a safe down the street and shoots a couple of coppers in the getaway.

And there is Big Butch, with John Ignatius Junior in his arms and twenty G's in his shirt front and a tough record behind him, walking right up to them.

I am feeling very sorry, indeed, for Big Butch, and very sorry for myself, too, and I am saying to myself that if I get out of this I will never associate with anyone but ministers of the gospel as long as I live. I can remember thinking that I am getting a better break than Butch, at that, because I will not have to go to Sing Sing for the rest of my life, like him, and I also remember wondering what they will give John Ignatius Junior, who is still tearing off these squalls, with Big Butch saying, 'There, there, there, Daddy's itty woogleums.' Then I hear one of the coppers say to the fat sergeant:

'We better nail these guys. They may be in on this.'

Well, I can see it is goodbye to Butch and John Ignatius Junior and me, as the fat sergeant steps up to Big Butch, but instead of putting the arm on Butch, the fat sergeant only points at John Ignatius Junior and asks very sympathetic:

'Teeth?'

'No,' Big Butch says. 'Not teeth. Colic. I just got the doctor here out of bed to do something for him, and we are going to a drug store to get some medicine.'

Well, naturally I am very much surprised at this statement, because of course I am not a doctor, and if John Ignatius Junior has colic it serves him right, but I am only hoping they do not ask for my degree, when the fat sergeant says:

'Too bad. I know what it is. I got three of them at home. But,' he says, 'it acts more like it is teeth than colic.'

Then as Big Butch and John Ignatius Junior and me go on about our business I hear the fat sergeant say to the copper, very sarcastic:

'Yea, of course a guy is out blowing safes with a baby in his arms! You will make a great detective, you will!'

I do not see Big Butch for several days after I learn that Harry the Horse and Little Isadore and Spanish John get back to Brooklyn all right, except they are a little nicked up here and there from the slugs the coppers toss at them, while the coppers they clip are not damaged so very much. Furthermore, the chances are I will not see Big Butch for several years, if it is left to me, but he comes looking for me one night, and he seems to be all pleasured up about something.

'Say,' Big Butch says to me, 'you know I never give a copper credit for knowing any too much about anything, but I wish to say this fat sergeant we run into the other night is a very, very smart duck. He is right about it being teeth that is ailing John Ignatius Junior, for what happens yesterday but John cuts his first tooth.'

Men in Fiction

E. M. Delafield

Professional Men

Novelists, although they do not much like one to say so, are terribly conventional, especially when they write about men. Take professional men in fiction, for instance. They may be all kinds of things, but there are also all kinds of things that they mayn't be. Who, for instance, ever made his or her hero a dentist? The present writer does not want to be harsh about this. Beyond a doubt, it is difficult to visualize the scene in which a young man comes to the knowledge that his true vocation lies in fumbling about inside the open mouths of his fellow-creatures – but there must be ways of getting round this, and of making this very important and necessary calling sound as interesting as it really is. Writers, however, have as yet made no attempt to find out these ways.

Doctors, on the contrary, are numerous in fiction. Mostly, they come out well, but not in detective fiction. In detective fiction, the doctor is only put in because it is absolutely necessary that, after one glance at the corpse, he should look up and say with quiet certainty:

'The squire has been shot through the left lung, and his head battered in by a short, blunt instrument, almost certainly a poker like the one lying on the floor in a pool of blood beside him. The bruise on his left side was caused by a hobnailed boot. Death must have occurred exactly six hours and fifteen minutes ago, which fixes the time of the murder at precisely quarter past eight this morning. There is nothing to be done for him now.'

After this, the doctor leaves the police in charge, and it isn't till hours afterwards that someone or other finds out that the old square's injuries were all inflicted after death, which was really due to drowning.

It is never said, in the detective story, whether the doctor's practice suffers heavily from this professional carelessness in failing to notice that the old squire's lungs were full of water all the time.

When the story is not a detective story, but a long novel about a doctor's whole life, he is a very different type of person. He is never called in to a murder case at all, and indeed, the only cases of which much notice is taken in the book are confinement cases. These take place usually in distant and obscure farm-houses, in the middle of the night, and to the accompaniment of a fearful gale, or a flood, or a snowstorm, or any other convulsion of Nature which will make it additionally inconvenient for the doctor to attend the scene.

Authors like obstetrical details, but the present writer does not, and knows, besides, that in real life doctors are quite often called out in the night on account of croup, or pleurisy, or even a bilious attack if sufficiently violent, as on account of child-birth.

The doctor in this kind of book always has a frightful financial struggle. He never attains to Harley Street, or anywhere in the least like it. His wife is almost always a perfectly lovely young creature with extravagant tastes that help to ruin him, or else she dies young, leaving him to a housekeeper who never puts flowers in the sitting-room. In the latter case the doctor thinks about his wife when he comes in, from one of his perpetual baby-cases, at three in the morning, with the prospect of the surgery before him at seven. (Doctors in books never get more than four hours' sleep on any night of the year, and often none at all. But they always persist in opening the surgery at this unreasonable hour.)

One could go on for a long while about doctors in fiction, but theirs, of course, is not the only profession dear to authors, although certainly one of the most popular.

Business men are much written about, and curiously enough are treated in an almost exactly opposite way to doctors, since they nearly always have helpful and endearing wives, who would never dream of dying and leaving them to housekeepers, and they end up highly successful, and immensely rich, although starting from a degree of poverty and illiteracy that would seem to make this practically impossible.

The early parts of the book are almost entirely given up to the most terrifically sordid and realistic description of their early surroundings, the language – one word and two initials – that their fathers and neighbours used when intoxicated, the way in which their elder sisters went wrong, and the diseases that ravaged their mothers. But by degrees, this is worked through. The situation lightens, and the business – which started as a stall in the Warwick Road, or something like that – begins to prosper. Its owner turns his attention to social advancement, and in the course of it marries a pretty, innocent, but extremely practical young thing with quite a short name, like Anne, or Sally, or Jane. They rise in the world together. Then another woman, with a much longer name – more like Madeleine, or Rosalind – and of more exalted social standing, interferes.

The length to which the affair subsequently proceeds depends entirely upon what the author feels about his public: whether that's the sort of thing they want from him or whether it isn't. (Publishers are usually helpful about this, although biased on the side of propriety, as a rule, because of the circulating libraries.) Anyway, Anne, or Sally, or Jane takes him back in the long run, absolutely always.

Unlike real life, affairs of this kind, in books, never lead to the complete wreck of the homestead, or of the business. On the contrary. So that novels about business men have at least the advantage of a happy ending – a thing which some readers like, though others would go miles to avoid it.

Lovers

The well-known saying that All the world loves a lover, is, like so many other well-known sayings, quite inaccurate. There are numbers of people who find lovers more annoying than almost anything, and these include employers, doctors, many parents and grandparents, and others too numerous to mention. Authors of fiction, although such income as they achieve is largely derived from the exploitation of lovers and their various reactions, do not really care much about them in real life, for authors, unfortunately, are usually more than a little egotistical by nature.

In fiction, however, there is no doubt that lovers are popular. In fact it almost seems, sometimes – judging by the way editors and publishers go on about what they call the love-interest – as if, but for that, fiction wouldn't ever be read at all, in which case there would be little point in writing it. We will not, however, dwell upon this improbable and melancholy contingency. Instead, we will get started about the men in faction who are lovers – which, of course, most of them are. And we are bound to say that the first thing that strikes us about nearly all of them is that they attach much more importance to love than do the ordinary men of everyday life.

Take the agricultural lover – since authors are extraordinarily fond of writing about the passions of farm labourers, although comparatively indifferent to those of navvies, engine-drivers, or stokers.

The agricultural lover is seldom less than six feet tall, and he wears his shirt open at the neck whatever the weather, although there are many months in the year when a woollen muffler would be a sign of greater common sense; and if the novel is at all a modern one, he takes about with him a smell of soil and sweat wherever he goes. (In our experience, brilliantine is much more noticeable, at any rate on Sundays, but of this nothing is said.)

Well, this son of the soil is invariably fated to fall in love with somebody too utterly unsuitable for words, either because she lives in London, which constitutes – for reasons unstated – an immense social gulf between her and the farm labourer, or else because she is so frail and frivolous by nature that anyone, except a lover in a book, would have seen through her at the first glance.

In the first case, the outlook is bad, but not hopeless. The girl from London either writes, paints, dances, or does all three. She is probably engaged or semi-engaged, to a talented youth of her own social standing, and they exchange immense letters, full of quotations and similes and things, which are very often given in full. She has, to all appearances, never been in the country in her life before, because she always does something amazingly unpractical, like falling down an old mine-shaft – with which authors seem to think that the countryside is freely peppered – or setting out alone to cross the moors just when a snowstorm is coming up. Then, when she has got herself into serious difficulties, the agricultural lover pulls on his boots – boots play an enormous part in these idylls of the soil – and takes one look at the sky and says with great confidence: 'Reckon the moon should be up over the quarry by the time the cock crows from Hangman's Hill,' and goes off, finding his way unerringly through pitch darkness, and floods of rain, and drifts of snow, and anything else the author can think of to show how well he understands Nature. And by the time he has found the girl and carried her into the farm as though she were a child, the whole thing is settled.

Though, personally, we have never thought, and never shall think, that that sort of girl is in the least likely to make a suitable wife for any farm labourer.

The other kind is quite different. She is a village girl, and is referred to by those who are taken in by her artifices as a 'lil' maid', and by those who aren't as 'a light o' love' or 'a wanton lass'. Her chief, sometimes her only, characteristics are vanity and sex-appeal. In the end, after the agricultural lover has fought somebody in a pub for using a Word about her, and has thrown various other fits, she usually goes off and marries his stepbrother from the Colonies, or a rich widower forty years older than herself; and the lover, instead of realizing that this is all for the best, walks out into the night. Common sense tells one that sooner or later he will be obliged to walk out of it again, but before this inevitable, though unromantic, point is reached, the author usually brings the book to an end.

Lovers in books that are not agricultural are, of course, numerous, but there is not enough space to deal with them all in one article.

Husbands

Authors, beyond a doubt, go very wrong indeed when it comes to husbands in fiction. They only seem to know about two kinds. The first and most popular of these is quite young, and most deadly serious. He has a simple and yet manly sort of name, like John or Richard or Christopher. He marries, and his wife is lovely, and he adores her. Instead of getting accustomed to her charms with the rapidity so noticeable in real life, and taking her comfortably for granted by the end of the second year, he adores her more and more, although on every page she is growing colder, more heartless, and more extravagant. She lives, in fact, for nothing except cocktails, night-clubs, clothes, and the admiration of other men.

(The present writer, who has been married for years and years, often wonders very much what makes authors think that any man ever looks at a married woman when there are unmarried girls anywhere within miles. The present writer is not complaining – only just wondering.)

To return to John:

He puts up with things that no husband outside the pages of a book would either tolerate, or be asked to tolerate, by even the most optimistic wife. He sits up at night over the bills that his Claire has run up. He always does his accounts at night, and they always take hours and hours. He never seems to have any bills of his own, although in real life it is usually six of one and half a dozen of the other.

One might suppose, after two or three of these nocturnal bouts, that John would either put a notice in the papers disclaiming responsibility for his wife's debts, or have the sense to separate from her. But neither of these courses so much as presents itself to him. He tells her that he is overdrawn at the bank, and so on (and makes as much fuss about it as though no one had ever before been in this painful, but thoroughly familiar, quandary), and explains that he is already working as hard as it is possible for anybody to work. And then he goes and spoils the effect of all of it by suddenly telling her how much he adores her.

In real life, very few English husbands ever say at all that they adore their wives – and absolutely none at the very moment when they have been scrutinizing bills that they cannot pay.

Sometimes John and Claire have a child, and Claire is not at all pleased about it. As she makes no secret of this, it is not reasonable of John to be filled with incredulous dismay and disappointment when she neglects it – but all the same, he is. After this, things run a rapid down-hill course, and Claire goes off with somebody else, and John is plunged into an abyss of despair, although it is perfectly impossible that there shouldn't be times when it must occur to him that he is thoroughly well rid of her.

But if so, we are never told about them.

And the child grows up, and adores her father, and they are perfectly happy together; and after about fifteen years Claire wants to come back again, and John has the incredible idiocy to let her do so, and she turns out to be dying, and he forgives her.

And if that is the author's idea of being a successful husband, it does not coincide with ours.

The other type of husband in fiction has really only one noticeable characteristic, and that is a most phenomenal and cast-iron stupidity. He is, in fact, rather out of place in this article, because in the books where husbands are of this kind, it is naturally the wife upon whom the author has concentrated. A good many pages are given up to her struggles between Love and Honour, and in the end she decides that the brave, straightforward, and modern thing to do is to go to the man she loves. (This is not the husband, needless to say.) And authors, strangely enough, very seldom tell one what the husband feels about it, or what happened to him afterwards. Though after all, he has to go on living ordinary everyday life, just like anybody else.

On the whole, husbands are not particularly well viewed by authors. It is not, perhaps, for us to judge, but the thought does occur to one that possibly this may be because authors themselves very, very seldom make good husbands.

Fathers

In books, fathers are almost always called 'Daddy', because this is somehow
more touching than just 'Father'. And fathers in books are nothing if not
touching. Unless they are absolute monsters of cruelty or stupidity. We will,
however, deal with the touching ones first.

Their chief characteristic is a kind of whimsical playfulness, that would be
quite bad enough taken on its own merits, but is made much worse by
masking a broken heart, or an embittered spirit, or an intolerable loneliness.
Fathers of this sort, conversationally, are terribly fond of metaphors, and talk
like this:

'Life, sonny, is a wild beast. Something that lies in wait for you, and then
springs out and tears you to pieces.'

Or:

'Grown-ups have their own games, dear, just like you kiddies. Sometimes
they pretend to be heroes, and princes, and wear glittering armour and go
about looking for dragons, and lovely princesses. But the armour has a way
of falling to pieces, and when they find the princess, somebody else has got
there first and carried her off, and there is only the dragon left.'

'And is the dragon real, Daddy, or does he fall to pieces, too?' asks the
obliging child, who never misses its cues.

'Yes, little one, the dragon is real enough,' says Daddy, with a strange,
far-away expression. 'You'll learn that some day. The dragon is always real.
It's only the prince and princess who are not real.'

Also – this is our own addition – the entire conversation, which is not real.
Because a flesh-and-blood father who went on like that would find his children
quite unresponsive.

'Now,' they would say, 'tell us something sensible, about an aeroplane, or
a cat-burglar.'

But in books, the relation between the father and his child, or children, is
a good deal idealized so that the kind of conversation given above may take
place frequently. Also, the children ask questions. Not the sort of question
that one hears so frequently in daily life:

'Father, why can't we get a nicer car, like the one the Robinsons have?'
or 'Do you have to brush your *head* now, instead of hair?' or even '*Why* aren't
we allowed to stay in the bathroom more than ten minutes and you have it
for nearly an hour?'

But questions that give openings for every possible note to be struck in the entire gamut of whimsical pathos of humour:

'Has *your* heart ever been broken, Daddy?' and 'Why do your eyes look so sad, even when you're smiling, Daddy?'

The answer to the first one is: 'Hearts don't break very easily, girlie. Sometimes we think they're broken, but Time has a magic wand and mends the pieces, and we go on – not quite the same as before, ever, but able to work a little and dream a little, and even – laugh a little.'

The answer to the second one is – but there are many alternatives, for it really is an admirable question, in the amount of scope that it gives. Daddy can talk about the lady called Memory, who looks out of his eyes, and about the Help that a smile is, and all that kind of thing; or he may be of a more virile type – a clean-limbed, straight-gazing Englishman – and then he just says something brief but pregnant, about White Men who Play the Game and Keep Straight Upper Lips and Put their Backs into It. And, in any case, whatever he says sinks deeply into the consciousness of his child, and returns again and again to its assistance on strange and critical occasions, as when it violently wants to cheat at an examination, or – later in life – is in danger of sexual indiscretion.

Fathers in books are almost always either widowers, or else unfortunately married. This leaves them free to concentrate on their offspring, from the page when, with clumsy, unaccustomed fingers, they deal with unfamiliar buttons and tapes – (why unfamiliar? their own shirts and pyjamas have buttons, anyway) – till the end, when either the daughter marries, or the son is killed in India, and the father left alone. They are, indeed, a lesson against putting all one's eggs into a single basket.

The other type of father is generally either a professor, a country clergyman, or an unspecified bookworm – and always very, very absent-minded. His children are usually daughters, and he calls them 'my dear', and everything he says, he says 'mildly' or 'absently'.

The daughters of real-life professors, country clergymen, and bookworms must wish to goodness that their fathers were more like this, instead of – as they probably are – the usual quite kind, but interfering, domestically tyrannical and fault-finding, heads-of-the-household.

Finally, and fortunately not very often, we get the absolutely brutal father. He is usually lower-middle class, and his daughters have illegitimate babies – since this is the one thing of all others that infuriates such fathers – and his sons run into debt and then hang or shoot themselves sooner than face the parental wrath; and his wife dies, or goes mad, or deserts him. Books about this kind of father are compact of gloom, and are described by the reviewers as being Powerful.

On the whole, fathers in fiction are a poor lot, and bring us, by a natural transition, to the subject of the next article, which will be Criminals in Fiction.

Criminals

When it comes to criminals, authors of fiction completely let themselves go. They endow their heroes with qualities that they simply wouldn't dare, for one moment, to bestow upon any respectable, law-abiding citizen – qualities like chivalry, and tender-heartedness, and idealism. You feel that they absolutely adore them, and admire their crimes far more than they would anybody else's virtues. And we will at once forestall the remark that shallow-minded readers may feel inclined to make, by saying definitely that it is *not* women writers who usually indulge in this kind of hero. On the contrary.

Well, the things that jump to the eye about the criminal of fiction are several. To begin with, he has no Christian name, but is just known as Jaggles, or Ginger Mac, or Flash Ferdinand. And he is always frightfully, frightfully quiet. Not so much when he is actually on the job – because then, after all, quietness would naturally be taken for granted – but in his manner, and appearance, and behaviour, and voice. And this quietness merely denotes his immense reserves of fire and fury, all of which come out later when the blackmailer is threatening the helpless girl, or the heavily armed householder is getting ready to shoot. But, even in his gravest straits, or most heated moments, the criminal hero never shouts. He just says, very, very quietly, things like: 'The game's up, I think', or 'Check-mate – Colonel'. And he always remembers to smile a little, with the utmost nonchalance, whilst covering his man, or, if necessary, men, with a six-shooter, or heavy automatic, or machine-gun, or whatever it is that he carries about with him.

Curiously enough, the criminal of fiction is rather good at love-making. Hee takes an interest in it. This is probably because, as a rule, he seldom has any contacts at all, except with devoted but intellectually inferior male followers, detectives and victims. One is never told that he has parents or brothers and sisters, or ordinary social acquaintances. So, naturally, he can concentrate on the one woman he ever seems to have anything to do with.

And either she loves him and says that she will wait (meaning until he has finished his sentence at Wormwood Scrubbs) – or else she throws herself between him and the detective's gun, and dies of it.

Either *dénouement* is rather unsatisfactory.

In real life, people who serve sentences in prison very seldom come out quite the same as they went in, and it isn't every woman, unfortunately, who improves by waiting.

As for throwing oneself about in front of bullets, this is not really as easy as it sounds, and might quite well end in a mere flesh wound, and would anyhow almost certainly bring down the most frightful curses on the person who got in the way, for men like to settle things for themselves, unhampered by feminine interference.

A delicate question to those who have the interests of morality at heart is: Do these criminals of fiction ever repent? The answer is – as so often in life – both Yes and No.

If the book is to have a happy ending, Ginger Mac, just before embarking on a final enterprise, says: This is the last time – the very last! and then kills off somebody so unspeakably bad that it is almost a good deed to have rid the world of him, and then goes to find the woman he is in love with, and says that he is utterly unworthy of her, which is probably very true. And the book ends with some rather ambiguous phrase, as it wouldn't quite do for criminality to triumph openly. So the author just says something like:

'But as she turned away, he saw that there were tears in her beautiful eyes.'

Or:

'In a year's time,' she echoed. 'In a year's time, *who knows?*'

Well – the author knows, and so does Flash Ferdinand, and so does the least experienced reader. So that's all right.

When the criminal does not repent, he dies. This rule is never violated. To the mind of the fiction-writer, there seems to be nothing whatever between reformation and death. The possibility of persistence in wrong-doing does not apparently occur to him. So Jaggles, gentleman-buccaneer or burglar-sportsman, or whatever he may be called, either jumps off the highest sky-scraper in New York to avoid capture, or is shot at the very last minute, and dies saying that it was a Great Game after all.

There are, of course, other types of criminals than the ones we have indicated. There is the criminal in the detective-novel proper, for instance – but the writing of detective-novels proper has now been brought to such a fine art that nobody can possibly tell who the criminal is, till the last paragraph but one. And then it turns out to be the idiot grandmother, or the fine old white-haired magistrate, or the faithful servant.

Lastly, there is the criminal in those short, powerful, gloomy, sociological novels that have pages and pages without any conversation at all, and that are so full of little dots.... In these cases, there is never any doubt as to guilt. The criminal committed the murder all right, but the guilt lies with almost everybody else in the world – the rich, Society, the Church, politicians, the older generation, the younger generation, the men who administer the law, and so on.

It is all very painful and realistic, and ends up with the execution, and more dots, and then some utterly irrelevant statement like: 'Outside, a small, orange-hued dog was nosing in the gutter –' and then a final crop of dots....

All You Need To Know About Europe

Alan Coren

Germany

The People

Germans are split into two broad categories: those with tall spikes on their hats, and those with briefcases. Up until 1945, the country's history was made by those with spikes. After 1945, it was made by those with briefcases. In common with the rest of Europe, its history is therefore now known as economics. Ethnically, the Germans are Teutonic, but prefer not to talk about it any more. This ethnos was originally triform, being made up of Vandals, Gepidae, and Goths, all of whom emigrated – south from Sweden in about 500 BC; why they emigrated is not exactly clear, but many scholars believe it was because they saw the way Sweden was going, i.e. neutral. Physically, Germans are tall and blond, though not as tall and blond as they sometimes think, especially when they are short, dark Austrians with a sense of destiny. When they sing, the Germans link arms and rock sideways; it is best described as horizontal marching.

The Land

The country, or *Lebenstraum*, is extremely beautiful and situated in the very centre of Europe, thus lending itself to expansion in any direction, a temptation first succumbed to in the fifth century AD (the *Volkerwanderung*) when Germany embraced most of Spain, and regularly indulged in since. It is interesting to note that this summer there will be three million Germans in Spain, thus outnumbering the first excursion by almost a hundred to one.

The History

For almost two thousand years, Germany was split into separate states that fought one another. In the nineteenth century, they combined and began fighting everyone else. They are currently split up again and once more fighting one another. If they combine, the result is anybody's guess. Having lost the last war, they are currently enjoying a *Wirtschaftswunder*, which can be briefly translated as 'The best way to own a Mercedes is to build one.' That is about all there is to German history, since no one has ever known what was going on, and if this is the case, then the Truth cannot be said to exist. Germany has, as you can see, provided many of the world's greatest philosophers.

Belgium

The People
Belgium is the most densely populated country in Europe, and is at the same time fiercely divided on the subjects of language and religion. This means that it is impossible to move anywhere in the country, which is packed with mobs standing chin to chin and screaming incomprehensible things at one another in the certain knowledge that God is on their side, whoever He is. That there has not been more bloodshed is entirely due to the fact that there isn't room to swing a fist. Consequently, what the Belgian authorities most fear is contraception: if it ever catches on, and the population thins to the point where rifles may be comfortably unslung from shoulders, the entire nation might disappear overnight.

The Land
The land is entirely invisible, except in the small hours of the morning, being for the rest of the time completely underfoot. It is therefore no surprise to learn that Belgium's largest industries are coal and mineral mining, as underground is the only place where there is room to work. Plans have been suggested for reclaiming land from the sea, on the Dutch pattern, but were always shelved as soon as it was realised that there was neither room for the water that would have to be removed from the sea, nor, alternatively, any spare land to spread to extend the coastline outwards.

The History
Belgium has always suffered horribly at the hands of occupying forces, which, given the overcrowding, is only to be expected. The bayoneting of babies by Prussians, for example, was never intentional; it was simply that it was

impossible to walk about with fixed bayonets in such confined spaces without finding something struck on the end of them. For the same reason, the sprout was developed by Brussels agronomists, this being the largest cabbage a housewife could possibly carry through the teeming streets.

France

The People

The French are our closest neighbours, and we are therefore bound to them by bonds of jealousy, suspicion, competition, and envy. They haven't brought the shears back, either. They are short, blue-vested people who carry their own onions when cycling abroad, and have a yard which is 3.37 inches longer than other people's. Their vanity does not stop there: they believe themselves to be great lovers, an easy trap to fall into when you're permanently drunk, and the natural heirs to Europe. It has been explained to them that there is a difference between natural heirs and legitimate heirs, but they cannot appreciate subtle distinctions, probably because French has the smallest vocabulary of any language in Europe.

The Land

France is the largest country in Europe, a great boon for drunks, who need room to fall, and consists of an enormous number of bars linked by an intricate system of serpentine cobbles. Exactly why France is so cobbled has never been fully explained, though most authorities favour the view that the French like to be constantly reminded of the feel of grapes underfoot. The houses are all shuttered to exclude light, as a precaution against hangovers, and filled with large lumpy beds in which the French spend 83.7 per cent of their time recovering from sex or booze or both. The lumpiness is due, of course, to the presence of undeclared income under the mattresses.

The History

French history, or 'gloire' starts with Charlemagne, and ends with Charlemagne. Anything subsequent was in the hands of bizarre paranoiacs who thought they were God (Louis XIV) or thought they were Charlemagne (Napoleon) or thought they were God and Louis XIV and Charlemagne and Napoleon (de Gaulle). Like most other European nations, the French have fought everyone, but unlike the rest have always claimed that both victories and defeats came after opposition to overwhelming odds. This is probably because they always saw two of everything.

Luxembourg

The People

There are nine people in Luxembourg, and they are kept pretty busy making stamps. It is not the smallest country in Europe: there are only eight people in Monaco, five in Andorra, and Herr J. F. Klausner in Liechtenstein, so as the fourth non-smallest country in Europe, it enjoys a rather unique position. The people are of middle height, with the small, deft fingers of master-perforators, and all look rather alike, except for their Uncle Maurice who lost an ear on the Somme. They are a rather arrogant people (they refer to World War I as the Battle of Maurice's Ear) but not unartistic: *My Day At The Zoo*, by the country's infant prodigy, ran into nine copies and won the Prix Maurice for 1969.

The Land

On a clear day, from the terrace of the Salon de Philatelie, you can't see Luxembourg at all. This is because a tree is in the way. Beyond the tree lies Belgium. The centre of the country is, however, very high, mainly because of the chimney on it, and slopes down to a great expanse of water, as they haven't got around to having the bathroom overflow pipe fixed. The climate is temperate (remember that ninety per cent of Luxembourg is indoors) and the local Flora is varied and interesting, especially on her favourite topic, the 1908 five-cent blue triangular.

The History

Old Luxembourg (now the coal-cellar of the modern country), was founded in the twelfth century by King John of Bohemia, who wanted somewhere to keep the lawn-mower. It escaped most of the wars and pestilences that swept Europe in the subsequent eight centuries, often because the people were out when they called, and is therefore one of the most stable political and economic elements in the EEC: its trade-balance is always favourable (imports come in at the back gate and leave by the front door as exports). Luxembourg is also the oldest ally of Stanley Gibbons Ltd, although it is probably most famous as the birthplace of Horace Batchelor.

Netherlands

The People
Like the Germans, the Dutch fall into quite distinct physical types: the small, corpulent, red-faced Edams, and the thinner, paler, larger Goudas. As one might expect of a race that evolved underwater and subsisted entirely upon cheese, the Dutch are somewhat single-minded, conservative, resilient, and thoughtful. Indeed, the sea informs their entire culture: the bicycle, that ubiquitous Dutch vehicle, was designed to facilitate underwater travel, offering least resistance to waves and weed, the clog was introduced to weigh down the feet and prevent drifting, and the meerschaum pipe, with its characteristic lid, was designed expressly to exclude fish and the larger plankton. And those who would accuse the Dutch of overeating would do well to reflect on the notorious frangibility of dykes: it's no joke being isolated atop a flooded windmill with nothing to eat but passing tulips. You have to get it while you can.

The Land
Strictly speaking, the land does not exist: it is merely dehydrated sea, and concern was originally expressed when the EEC was first mooted that the Six might suddenly turn into the Five after a bad night. Many informed observers believe that this fear is all that lies behind the acceptance of Britain's membership, i.e. we are a sort of First Reserve in case Rain Stops Holland. Nevertheless, it is interesting country, sweeping up from the coastal plain into the central massif, a two-foot high ridge of attractive silt with fabulous views of the sky, and down again to the valleys, inches below. Apart from cheese and tulips, the main product of the country is advocaat, a drink made from lawyers.

The History
Incensed by poor jokes about the Low Countries, the Dutch, having emerged from the sea, became an extremely belligerent people, taking on Spain, France, England, and Austria in quick succession, a characteristic that has almost entirely disappeared from the modern Dutch temperament. It is now found only among expatriate Dutchmen, like Orangemen and Afrikaaners.

*

Italy

The People

The median Italian, according to the latest figures of the Coren Intelligence Unit, is a cowardly baritone who consumes 78.3 kilometres of carbohydrates a month and drives about in a car slightly smaller than he is, looking for a divorce. He is governed by a stable conservative government, called the Mafia, who operate an efficient police force, called the Mafia, which is the official arm of the judiciary, called the Mafia. The Italians are an extremely cultivated folk, and will often walk miles to sell a tourist a copy of the Sistine Chapel ceiling made entirely from sea-shells. They invented the mandoline, a kind of boudoir banjo shaped like a woman's bottom, not surprisingly.

The Land

Italy is boot-shaped, for reasons lost in the mists of geology. The South is essentially agricultural, and administered by local land authorities, called the Mafia; the North is industrial, and run by tightly interlocked corporations, called the Mafia. The largest Italian city is New York, and is linked to the mainland by a highly specialised and efficient communications system, called the Mafia.

The History

Italy was originally called Rome, which came to hold power over Europe by moving into new areas every week or so and threatening to lean on them if they did not fork out tithe (L. *protectio*). It was run by a series of Caesars (Eduardus Gaius Robinsonius, Georgius Raftus, Paulus Munius, etc.) who held sway until the Renaissance, when Leonardo invented the tank and the aeroplane, and thus ushered in modern Italy (in World War II, the Italians, ever brilliant, possessed the only tank with a reverse gear). In the 1920s, the Caesars reasserted themselves in their two main linear branches, the Caponi and the Mussolini, whose symbol was the fasces, which signified 'United We Stand,' but they didn't.

On Being Idle

Jerome K. Jerome

Now this is a subject on which I flatter myself I really am *au fait*. The gentleman who, when I was young, bathed me at wisdom's font for nine guineas a term – no extras – used to say he never knew a boy who could do less work in more time; and I remember my poor grandmother once incidentally observing, in the course of an instruction upon the use of the prayerbook, that it was highly improbable that I should ever do much that I ought to do, but, that she felt convinced beyond a doubt that I should leave undone pretty well everything that I ought to do.

I am afraid I have somewhat belied half the dear old lady's prophecy. Heaven help me! I have done a good many things that I ought not to have done, in spite of my laziness. But I have fully confirmed the accuracy of her judgment so far as neglecting much that I ought not to have neglected is concerned. Idling always has been my strong point. I take no credit to myself in the matter – it is a gift. Few possess it. There are plenty of lazy people and plenty of slowcoaches, but a genuine idler is a rarity. He is not a man who slouches about with his hands in his pockets. On the contrary, his most startling characteristic is that he is always intensely busy.

It is impossible to enjoy idling thoroughly unless one has plenty of work to do. There is no fun in doing nothing when you have nothing to do. Wasting time is merely an occupation then, and a most exhausting one. Idleness, like kisses, to be sweet must be stolen.

Many years ago, when I was a young man, I was taken very ill – I never could see myself that much was the matter with me, except that I had a beastly cold. But I suppose it was something very serious, for the doctor said that I ought to have come to him a month before, and that if it (whatever it was) had gone on for another week he would not have answered for the consequences. It is an extraordinary thing, but I never knew a doctor called into any case yet, but what it transpired that another day's delay would have rendered cure hopeless. Our medical guide, philosopher, and friend is like the hero in a melodrama, he always comes upon the scene just, and only just, in the nick of time. It is Providence, that is what it is.

Well, as I was saying, I was very ill, and was ordered to Buxton for a month, with strict injunctions to do nothing whatever all the while that I was there. 'Rest is what you require,' said the doctor, 'perfect rest.'

It seemed a delightful prospect. 'This man evidently understands my complaint,' said I, and I pictured to myself a glorious time – a four weeks' *dolce far niente* with a dash of illness in it. Not too much illness, but just illness enough – just sufficient to give it the flavour of suffering, and make it poetical. I should get up late, sip chocolate, and have my breakfast in slippers and a dressing gown. I should lie out in the garden in a hammock, and read sentimental novels with a melancholy ending, until the book would fall from my listless hand, and I should recline there, dreamily gazing into the deep blue of the firmament, watching the fleecy clouds, floating like white-sailed ships, across its depths, and listening to the joyous song of the birds, and the low rustling of the trees. Or, when I became too weak to go out of doors, I should sit, propped up with pillows, at the open window of the ground floor front, and look wasted and interesting, so that all the pretty girls would sigh as they passed by.

And, twice a day, I should go down in a Bath chair to the Colonnade, to drink the waters. Oh, those waters! I knew nothing about them then, and was rather taken with the idea. 'Drinking the waters' sounded fashionable and Queen Anneified, and I thought I should like them. But, ugh! after the first three or four mornings! Sam Weller's description of them, as 'having a taste of warm flat-irons,' conveys only a faint idea of their hideous nauseousness. If anything could make a sick man get well quickly, it would be the knowledge that he must drink a glassful of them every day until he was recovered. I drank them neat for six consecutive days, and they nearly killed me; but, after then, I adopted the plan of taking a stiff glass of brandy and water immediately on the top of them, and found much relief thereby. I have been informed since, by various eminent medical gentlemen, that the alcohol must have entirely counteracted the effects of the chalybeate properties contained in the water. I am glad I was lucky enough to hit upon the right thing.

But 'drinking the waters' was only a small portion of the torture I experienced during that memorable month, a month which was, without exception, the most miserable I have ever spent. During the best part of it,

I religiously followed the doctor's mandate, and did nothing whatever, except moon about the house and garden, and go out for two hours a day in a Bath chair. That did break the monotony to a certain extent. There is more excitement about Bath-chairing – especially if you are not used to the exhilarating exercise – than might appear to the casual observer. A sense of danger, such as a mere outsider might not understand, is ever present to the mind of the occupant. He feels convinced every minute that the whole concern is going over, a conviction which becomes especially lively whenever a ditch or a stretch of newly macadamized road comes in sight. Every vehicle that passes he expects is going to run into him; and he never finds himself ascending or descending a hill, without immediately beginning to speculate upon his chances, supposing – as seems extremely probable – that the weak-kneed controller of his destiny should let go.

But even this diversion failed to enliven after a while, and the *ennui* became perfectly unbearable. I felt my mind giving way under it. It is not a strong mind, and I thought it would be unwise to tax it too far. So somewhere about the twentieth morning, I got up early, had a good breakfast, and walked straight to Hayfield at the foot of the Kinder Scout – a pleasant, busy, little town, reached through a lovely valley, and with two sweetly pretty women in it. At least they were sweetly pretty then; one passed me on the bridge, and, I think, smiled; and the other was standing at an open door, making an unremunerative investment of kisses upon a red-faced baby. But it is years ago, and I daresay they have both grown stout and snappish since that time. Coming back, I saw an old man breaking stones, and it roused such strong longing in me to use my arms, that I offered him a drink to let me take his place. He was a kindly old man, and he humoured me. I went for those stones with the accumulated energy of three weeks, and did more work in half-an-hour than he had done all day. But it did not make him jealous.

Having taken the plunge, I went further and further into dissipation, going out for a long walk every morning, and listening to the band in the Pavilion every evening. But the days still passed slowly notwithstanding, and I was heartily glad when the last one came, and I was being whirled away from gouty, consumptive Buxton to London, with its stern work and life. I looked out of the carriage as we rushed through Hendon in the evening. The lurid glare overhanging the mighty city seemed to warm my heart, and, when later on, my cab rattled out of St Pancras' station, the old familiar roar that came swelling up around me sounded the sweetest music I had heard for many a long day.

I certainly did not enjoy that month's idling. I like idling when I ought not to be idling; not when it is the only thing I have to do. That is my pig-headed nature. The time when I like best to stand with my back to the fire, calculating how much I owe, is when my desk is heaped highest with letters that must be answered by the next post. When I like to dawdle longest over my dinner, is when I have a heavy evening's work before me. And if, for some urgent reason, I ought to be up particularly early in the morning, it is then, more than at any other time, that I love to lie an extra half-hour in bed.

Ah! how delicious it is to turn over and go to sleep again: 'just for five minutes.' Is there any human being, I wonder, besides the hero of a Sunday-school 'tale for boys,' who ever gets up willingly? There are some men to whom getting up at the proper time is an utter impossibility. If eight o'clock happens to be the time that they should turn out, then they lie till half-past. If circumstances change and half-past eight becomes early enough for them, then it is nine before they can rise; they are like the statesman of whom it was said that he was always punctually half an hour late. They try all manner of schemes. They buy alarum clocks (artful contrivances that go off at the wrong time, and alarm the wrong people). They tell Sarah Jane to knock at the door and call them, and Sarah Jane does knock at the door, and does call them, and they grunt back 'awri,' and then go comfortably to sleep again. I knew one man who would actually get out, and have a cold bath; and even that was of no use, for, afterwards, he would jump into bed again to warm himself.

I think myself that I could keep out of bed all right, if I once got out. It is the wrenching away of the head from the pillow that I find so hard, and no amount of over-night determination makes it easier. I say to myself, after having wasted the whole evening, 'Well, I won't do any more work tonight; I'll get up early tomorrow morning;' and I am thoroughly resolved to do so – then. In the morning, however, I feel less enthusiastic about the idea, and reflect that it would have been much better if I had stopped up last night. And then there is the trouble of dressing, and the more one thinks about that, the more one wants to put it off.

It is a strange thing this bed, this mimic grave, where we stretch our tired limbs, and sink away so quietly into the silence and rest. 'Oh bed, oh bed, delicious bed, that heaven on earth to the weary head,' as sang poor Hood, you are a kind old nurse to us fretful boys and girls. Clever and foolish, naughty and good, you take us all in your motherly lap, and hush our wayward crying. The strong man full of care – the sick man full of pain – the little maiden, sobbing for her faithless lover – like children, we lay our aching heads on your white bosom, and you gently soothe us off to by-by.

Our trouble is sore indeed, when you turn away, and will not comfort us. How long the dawn seems coming, when we cannot sleep! Oh! those hideous nights, when we toss and turn in fever and pain, when we lie, like living men among the dead, staring out into the dark hours that drift so slowly between us and the light. And oh! those still more hideous nights, when we sit by another in pain, when the low fire startles us every now and then with a falling cinder, and the tick of the clock seems a hammer, beating out the life that we are watching.

But enough of beds and bedrooms. I have kept to them too long, even for an idle fellow. Let us come out, and have a smoke. That wastes time just as well, and does not look so bad. Tobacco has been a blessing to us idlers. What the civil service clerks before Sir Walter's time found to occupy their minds with, it is hard to imagine. I attribute the quarrelsome nature of the Middle Ages young men entirely to the want of the soothing weed. They had no work to do, and could not smoke, and the consequence was they were for ever fighting and rowing. If, by any extraordinary chance, there was no war going, then they got up a deadly family feud with the next-door neighbour, and if, in spite of this, they still had a few spare moments on their hands, they occupied them with discussions as to whose sweetheart was the best looking, the arguments employed on both sides being battle-axes, clubs, etc. Questions of taste were soon decided in those days. When a twelfth-century youth fell in love, he did not take three paces backwards, gaze into her eyes, and tell her she was too beautiful to live. He said he would stop outside and see about it. And if, when he got out, he met a man and broke his head – the other man's head, I mean – then that proved that his – the first fellow's girl – was a pretty girl. But if the other fellow broke *his* head – not his own, you know, but the other fellow's – the other fellow to the second fellow, that is, because of course the other fellow would only be the other fellow to him, not the first fellow, who – well, if he broke his head, then *his* girl – not the other fellow's, but the fellow who *was* the – Look her, if A broke B's head, then A's girl was a pretty girl; but if B broke A's head, then A's girl wasn't a pretty girl, but B's girl was. That was their method of conducting art criticism.

Nowadays we light a pipe, and let the girls fight it out amongst themselves. They do it very well. They are getting to do all our work. They are doctors, and barristers, and artists. They manage theatres, and promote swindles, and edit newspapers. I am looking forward to the time when we men shall have nothing to do but lie in bed till twelve, read two novels a day, have nice little five o'clock teas all to ourselves, and tax our brains with nothing more trying than discussions upon the latest patterns in trousers, and arguments as to what Mr Jones's coat was made of and whether it fitted him. It is a glorious prospect for idle fellows.

The Groundsman's Horse

Peter Tinniswood

During the course of a long and happy life one emotion has remained in my heart unfailingly and unflinchingly in the face of all the dangers and horrors that Mother Nature could throw at me – hurricane, typhoon, earthquake, war, famine, the cricket reports of Mr Tony Lewis.

The emotion is this:

An undying love for all our 'dumb friends'.

Thus it is that over the years I have cast my vote loyally and consistently for the Conservative and Unionist Party.

Thus it is that I send anonymously a bag of carrots each week to the BBC for the personal consumption of Mr Raymond Brooks-Ward.

Thus it is, too, that I have steadfastly maintained my membership of The Tiger Appreciation Society and been unstinting in my admiration for that great and noble statesman, philosopher, Olympic athlete and England opening bat, wicket-keeper and fast bowler, Lord Mountbatman of Burma.

It is the mention of Burma which reminds me of an episode in my life pertaining to our 'dumb friends', which even now many, many years later brings a glow of pride and feelings of the deepest satisfaction.

I was in Burma in the company of my father, who at the time was acting as adviser to the colonial administration during a particularly tricky outbreak of sightscreen desecration among the hill tribes of the Shan Plateau.

They were worrying times.

The Shans were seeking to impose their own version of the lbw rule on the loyal population of the towns and villages, and there were dark reports of the harassment of umpires and baggage masters in inaccessible valleys, over which MCC had only the most tenuous of influence.

My father, however, was a sanguine man.

Years of service in the farthest outposts of the British Empire had taught him that only the basest of savages, the most primitive of barbarians would fail to respond to the blandishments of a peace party of I Zingari mercenaries, who would play a ceremonial limited-over match with the dissidents and distribute to the masses free supplies of bakelite statuettes of Mr E. R. Dexter.

The efficacy of his philosophy had been proved time and time again in the harsh experience of 'action in the field'.

Indeed at that time the only remaining pocket of resistance to MCC rule in the whole of the British Empire existed in remote islands of the Cocos group and certain recalcitrant city states in the West Riding of Yorkshire.

So it was that as we strolled through that Burmese town basking in the full and gentle bloom of a simpering spring afternoon there was a confident lilt to my father's tread and the faintest whisper of a smile upon his face.

He was happily recounting to me stories of early days spent on active service with The Royal Burma Frontier Scouts ('Plum' Warner's Own) when of a sudden he stopped dead in his tracks.

His eyes widened.

His lower lip sagged.

And he exclaimed:

'Good God, laddie, look at that.'

I followed the direction of the pointing forearm.

And there a most singular sight struck my youthful eyes.

A broken-backed nag, head bowed, ribs protruding through scabrous flesh, matted fetlocks slouching through tropic dust, was plodding wearily down the centre of the pockmarked highway.

At its head was an emaciated figure in scarecrow rags, his bare feet blistered and scarred, his unkempt beard straggling over a hollow, naked chest and his sunken cheeks engrimed by the dust and dirt of years of neglect.

My father forthwith grasped my hand firmly and, striding purposefully across the street, placed himself forcefully in front of the horse and man.

'Whoa!' he bellowed.

Horse and man stopped, although neither raised its head.

'It isn't? It can't be,' said my father, and slowly and carefully he encircled the two wretched figures, his eyes narrowed, his brow furrowed.

Then he exclaimed:

'By jingo, it is. It's the groundsman's horse from Swanton St George.'

The effect of my father's words on the horse's attendant was remarkable to behold.

A choked gurgle came to his throat.

His bloodshot eyes rolled in their deep black sockets.

His knees began to tremble and suddenly he collapsed to the ground in a dead swoon.

I moved forward, but my father drew me back.

'Leave him be,' he shouted.

I froze in my tracks.

Silence.

My father clicked his tongue and swatted his thigh with the quarter-sized, bullet-scarred Strutt and Parker cricket bat he carried with him everywhere as Protection against mosquitoes and my beloved mother's bad temper.

He was motionless for what seemed to me an eternity (almost as long as an innings by Mr Trevor Bailey, I was to think much later).

Then, wrinkling his nose, he extended his right leg and with the toe of his boot turned over the poor wretch who was still lying on the ground in the deepest of faints.

I gasped.

It was a white man.

My father grunted to himself with evident satisfaction.

Then he turned his attention to the pitiful nag which stood by his side, swatting its emaciated rump with a threadbare tail, vainly trying to keep at bay the attentions of the legations of flies which swarmed about its various orifices in a cloying, buzzing black mass like a clutch of animated eccles cakes.

My father nodded.

'Yes, by thunderation, it is the groundsman's horse,' he said, 'And I shall prove it to you forthwith.'

And with that he threw back his head and roared in a stentorian voice:

'Heavy roller!'

The effect was instantaneous.

The horse laid its ears flat against its skull, drew back its lips to reveal a set of yellowing and splintered teeth, and quite without warning lowered its head, lashed out with its back feet and set off at a canter down the dusty road, bucking and whinnying for all the world like Mr Ian Chappell appealing for lbw against Miss Rachel Heyhoe-Flint.

My father nodded again.

'That proves it conclusively,' he said. 'It always was shy of hard work with the roller.'

The horse did not travel far.

Such was the parlous nature of its condition that after twenty yards it ceased its mad flight and stood in the shade of a Robertson-Glasgow tree, wheezing and panting, its flanks shaking uncontrollably.

My father arranged for both horse and attendant to be transported to our bungalow.

There in the stables in the shade of the giant Johnstonian oaks and the brooding Fingleton palms they were fed and watered and bedded down for the night in warm, clean hay.

It took a week for both to recover, and then my father was to learn from the groundsman (for thus was the identity of the poor wretch who had collapsed before his feet) the true story of their banishment to a land so different from the lush greensward and billowing beeches of their native Swanton St George.

Apparently the groundsman's horse had long been a feared institution at the village cricket team.

A fierce, uncontrollable brute, it obeyed only the commands of the groundsman, Festering, a sly and sullen lout of a man with a nose like a wicket-keeper's thumb.

It was allowed to graze unhindered on the village cricket pitch.

Such was its ill temper and ferocity that its presence was not removed even during the progress of matches.

No one dared approach it save for the groundsman, and thus a local rule was established: if the ball hit the horse, wheresoever it was standing, a four was awarded.

Most visiting teams were prepared to accept this condition, and all went well until the arrival of an Australian touring team, the Marsupials.

The Antipodean wanderers were skippered by Warren Croaker, who was later to achieve cricketing immortality by beating to death an umpire, with whose decision he disagreed (a practice much favoured by later generations of Australian Test cricketers).

Croaker was tried, convicted and sentenced to be executed by firing squad.

Dressed in flannels, pads and typical 'baggy' cap he was bound to the sight-screen at the Adelaid Oval and shot by a detachment of The Third Battalion Sam Loxton Dragoons.

His last words as he lay dying were reported to have been:

'Thank God, I was wearing my box.'

However, I digress.

Back to the match, Swanton St George versus The Marsupials.

The visitors from 'Down Under' took first knock and quickly amassed the staggering total of 239.

Swanton St George commenced their innings and were soon in 'the deepest trouble' at thirty-four for eight.

Certain defeat stared them in the face (to use the immortal and memorable words of that undisputed doyen of cricket writers, Mr.E. R. Dexter).

It was at this moment that the groundsman, Festering, appeared at the wicket.

At once the wheels of the score-box began to whirr as, to use the expression of our Antipodean cousins from across the seas, the 'curator' struck four after four after four off his opponents' bowling.

But one thing was strikingly obvious – each of his fours was gained by the ball's bitting the grazing horse.

Slowly but surely the Swanton St George total approached the forbidding total set by their guests, the descendants of convicts, murderers and defrocked members of MCC.

The 200 was reached when a ball smitten by Festering struck the horse a sickening blow on the left off paston.

The 220 was reached by the ball's hitting the heedless nag a resounding smack on a rump, the size of which was only exceeded many years later by the posterior portions of Mr M. C. Cowdrey.

It was then that (to borrow once more the sublime prose of Mr E. R. Dexter) 'excitement reached fever pitch'.

One over to go. Fifteen runs required.

Partnering Festering was the padre of the village, the Rev. Marchling-Thumper, who was later to become private chaplain to *The Sporting Chronicle*.

He was facing the bowling of the Australian skipper, Croaker.

The first delivery he received struck him a blistering blow in the ribcage.

'Run, you sod,' bellowed Festering.

The clerical gent scampered breathlessly to the bowler's end, glowering darkly at Festering, whose ill-chosen words had so offended his frail and delicate spirit.

One run gained. Fourteen to go.

It was then that spectators noticed a most singular occurrence – the groundsman's horse was approaching nearer and nearer to the wicket.

More singular still, it was actually beginning to move in the direction of each ball struck by Festering.

One four.

Two fours.

A wild swipe that did not connect.

A two, when a 'Chinese drive' flashed over first slip.

One ball to go. Four runs needed for victory.

Croaker polished the ball on his gin-stained flannels, glowering the while out of the corner of his eyes at the groundsman's horse.

He bowled.

Festering struck out.

The ball travelled no more than five feet on the off side.

The Australians cried out jubilantly.

Surely no more than a single could be obtained from the stroke?

But no.

The groundsman's horse threw back its head, whinnied and galloping like a dervish through the crowded off-side field, butted the Australian backward point just as he was about to pounce on the ball.

The Antipodean fell to the ground, shattering his hip flask beyond redemption.

The horse with a wicked grin of triumph bent down and gently nuzzled the ball towards the umpire.

'Four,' yelled Festering. 'The ball touched the horse. We've won.'

There are no words to do justice to the uproar that followed.

Not even the combined efforts of the pens of Mr Tony Lewis, Mr E. R. Dexter and 'the Proust of cricket literature', Mr Robin Marlar, could bring it to life on the printed page.

Accusation was followed by counter-accusation.

Wild imprecations filled the gentle English country air.

Such was the vileness of the Australian oaths, that the bells in the church belfry were shattered to smithereens, and the treasured statue of the Blessed St Tony Greig of the Sorrows was split from cravat to money belt.

Peace was only restored when the Rev. Marchling-Thumper, who had taken refuge in the communal cricket bag, emerged from his hiding place white and trembling and, in a sacerdotal voice reminiscent of the dulcet tones of Mr Bill Alley at his most pious, shouted:

'Stop. Stop, I beg you.'

The clerical gent pointed a wavering forefinger at the groundsman, Festering, who was placidly feeding to his horse liberal quantities of Grannie Sinfield's Home-Made Gloucester Fudge.

'There is your culprit,' said the cricketing prelate.

Instantly Festering was surrounded by players from both sides.

His arms were twisted, his ribs were pummelled and he was forced to confess.

His plot was simple, effective and fiendish – he had trained his horse to run after balls hit by him and allow them to strike its body.

Shame. Disgrace.

The skipper of the village team apologized profusely to Croaker.

The provision of eight firkins of prime Rae and Stollmeyer dark English ale and seventeen local virgins was sufficient to assuage him.

The apologies were accepted.

And thus it was that Festering and his horse were banished in ignominy to far-off Burma.

And as they plodded up the gangplank to the steamer which was to take them from Southampton to Rangoon, a voice addressed to Festering piped up from the back of the crowd.

'Run, you sod,' it said.

The voice belonged to the Rev. Marchling-Thumper.

My father listened to the story with tears in his eyes.

'You have suffered enough,' he said to Festering. 'Now I shall give you peace. Now I shall lead you to a land where everything you desire will be granted to you.'

Within the week he had taken the groundsman and his horse to the rebellious regions of the Shan plateau.

The effect was amazing.

The Shan tribesmen, primitive and innocent as they were, had never in the whole of their lives seen such a creature.

They threw down their arms, abandoned their lbw mutiny, and within weeks had settled down to a life of peace and obedience.

Indeed such was their amazement at this strange creature which had come to their midst from lands thousands of miles across the oceans that they deified it immediately.

And to this day the creature is to be seen stuffed and standing in a place of honour in the chief township of the Shan plateau.

Although what happened to the groundsman's horse is still unknown.

Equal Opportunies

Jonathan Lynn and Antony Jay

The dramas in the political life of the Rt Hon. James Hacker MP made fascinating viewing in the popular TV series, *Yes, Minister*. Here is an extract from his personal diaries – augmented by his invaluable if not always supportive aide Sir Humphrey.

June 7th

Today was a fairly quiet Saturday afternoon in the constituency. The end of our first complete Parliamentary session is approaching and I was feeling that I've done pretty well, one way or another: no great cock-ups after my first ever year in office (or at least, none which we haven't survived somehow) and I have a sense that I am beginning to understand the administrative machine at last.

You may think that a year is rather too long a period in which to achieve an understanding of the one department of which I am the titular head. In political terms, of course, that's true. Nonetheless if, had I become Chairman of ICI after a lifetime as a journalist and polytechnic lecturer and with no previous experience of running a major industry, I had a thorough understanding of how it all worked after only one year, I would be considered a great success.

We politicians blunder into Whitehall like babies in the wood. So few of us have ever run *anything* before, other than a medical practice, a law firm, or a political journal – and suddenly we find ourselves the head of a ministry with between twenty thousand and a hundred thousand employees.

All in all, I think we do pretty well! [*It was in this bullish mood that Hacker had agreed that day to give an interview to Cathy Webb, a fourth former in one of the comprehensive schools in Hacker's constituency.*]

However my enthusiastic feelings about my first year in office were, I must admit, a little shaken after I was interviewed at teatime by a precocious schoolgirl for the school magazine.

She began by asking me how I had reached my present eminent position. I summarized my political career so far, culminating, I said, with carefully calculated modesty, 'with the moment when the Prime Minister saw fit, for whatever reason, to invite one to join the Cabinet and, well, here one is.' I didn't want to seem conceited. In my experience the young have a nose for that sort of thing.

She asked me if it isn't a terrific responsibility. I explained to her that if one chooses, as I have chosen: to dedicate one's life to public service, the service of others, then responsibility is one of those things one has to accept.

Cathy was full of admiration, I could see it in her eyes. 'But all that power ... ' she murmured.

'I know, I know,' I replied, attempting the casual air of a man who is used to it. 'Frightening, in a way. But actually, Cathy ... (I was careful to use her name, of course, because it showed I did not consider myself above my constituents, even schoolchildren – future voters, after all) ... this power actually makes one rather humble!'

Annie[1] hurried in and interrupted me. The phone had been ringing elsewhere in the house.

'Bernard just rang, oh Humble One,' she said. I *wish* she wouldn't send me up like that in front of other people, I mean, I've got a pretty good sense of humour, but there is a limit.

She went on to tell me that Central House[2] wanted me to see some programme on television. On BBC2.

I had already remembered the wretched programme, and made a note *not* to watch.

'Oh Lord,' I said. 'Maureen Watkins MP. One of our backbenchers – not my favourite lady, a rampaging feminist, I don't think I'll bother.'

In the nick of time I noticed Cathy making a note. I had to explain that my remark was 'off the record', a concept that she seemed to have some difficulty with. It reminded me how lucky we are to have those well-trained lobby correspondents to deal with most of the time.

[1] Mrs Hacker.
[2] Hacker's Party HQ.

Anyway, she crossed it out. But to my surprise she spoke up in defence of Maureen Watkins.

'I like her,' she said. 'Don't you think that women are still exploited? All of my friends in 4B think that they are exploited at work and at home and that it's still a world designed by men and run by men for the convenience of men.'

I was slightly surprised by this little speech. It didn't sound entirely ... home-grown, if you know what I mean. Cathy must have realized, because she had the grace to add: 'You know – like she says.'

I must say, I'm getting a bit fed up with all this feminist crap. Nowadays, if you so much as compliment a woman on her appearance, you're told you're a sexist. This dreadful lesbian lobby is getting everywhere.

So I decided to argue the point with young Cathy. 'Surely it's not like that any longer,' I said with a warm smile. 'Anyway, she doesn't carry any weight in the House, thank goodness.'

'Not in the House, perhaps,' interjected Annie. 'It's full of men.'

I thanked my dear wife for her helpful comment, renewed my smile in Cathy's direction, and asked her if there was anything else she wanted to know.

'Just one last question,' she said. 'As a Cabinet Minister with all this power, what have you actually achieved?'

I was pleased to answer that question. It seemed an easy one. 'Achieved?' I repeated reflectively. 'Well, all sorts of things. Membership of the Privy Council, membership of the party policy committee ...'

She interrupted. It seemed that she wanted to make the question more specific. What, she wanted to know, had I actually done that makes life better for other people.

Well, of course, I was completely non-plussed. Children ask the oddest questions. Right out of left field, as our American allies would say. Certainly no one had ever asked me such a question before.

'Makes life *better*?' I repeated.

'Yes,' she said.

'For *other people*?' I thought hard, but absolutely nothing sprang to mind. I tried to think as I spoke. 'There must be a number of things. I mean, that's what one's whole job is about, eighteen hours a day, seven days a week ...'

Cathy interrupted me as I made the mistake of momentarily drawing breath. She has a future with the BBC, that kid! 'Could you just give me one or two examples, though? Otherwise my article might be a bit boring.'

'Examples. Yes, of course I can,' I said, and found that I couldn't.

Her pencil was poised expectantly above her lined exercise book. I realized that some explanation was called for.

'Well,' I began, 'you see, it's difficult to know where to start. So much of government is collective decisions, all of us together, the best minds in the country hammering it out.'

She seemed dissatisfied with my explanation.

'Yes,' she said doubtfully, 'but what is it you'll look back on afterwards and say "I did that"? You know, like a writer can look at his books.'

Persistent little blighter.

I started to explain the facts of political life. 'Yes, well, politics is a complex business, Cathy.' I was careful to use her name again. 'Lots of people have to have their say. Things take time. Rome wasn't built in a day.'

As I looked at her face, I could see an air of disappointment written across it. [*In view of the insight that Hacker's frequently mixed metaphors give us into the clouded state of his mind, we have retained them unless clarity is threatened. – Ed.*] I began to feel slightly disappointed with myself. I realized that I could not give a proper answer to her question. I also began to feel more than a little irritated that this wretched child should have produced these feelings of inadequacy in me. Enough was enough. It was time to bring the interview to an end.

I pointed out that time was flying, and that I still had to do my boxes.[3] I hustled her out, emphasizing how much I'd enjoyed our little talk, and reminding her that she had agreed to let me approve the article before it was printed.

I returned and sat down heavily in my favourite fireside armchair. I was feeling very brought down.

'Bright kid,' commented Annie.

'That's the last time I ever give an interview to a school magazine,' I responded. 'She asked me some very difficult questions.'

'They weren't difficult,' said Annie firmly. 'Just innocent. She was assuming that there is some moral basis to your activities.'

I was puzzled. 'But there is,' I replied.

Annie laughed.

But she didn't just laugh. She laughed till the tears ran down her face, she

---

[3] The red ministerial dispatch boxes, which contained everything that he had to read, comment on and approve while out of the office.

laughed hopelessly and helplessly. I sat and watched her, becoming more and more confused, trying to laugh with her but unable to share the joke. And every time she looked at me she went into another uncontrollable gust of hysteria.

Finally she calmed down, caught her breath, wiped her eyes, and wheezed 'Oh Jim, don't be silly.'

I wasn't amused. I gazed gloomily into the carefully arranged embers of the artificial gas log fire.

'What are you sighing for?' Annie asked.

I tried to explain.

'What *have* I achieved?' I asked. 'Cathy was right.'

Annie suggested that, since Cathy and I had agreed I had all that power, I should go and achieve something forthwith. She *will* persist in making these silly suggestions.

'You know I'm only a Cabinet Minister,' I snapped.

Annie smiled. 'It really does make you humble.'

My humility is not in question, and never has been. The point is that I can't change anything in the foreseeable future. Changing things means getting bills through Parliament, and all the time's been taken up for the next two years.

Annie was unimpressed.

'Why don't you reform the Civil Service?' she suggested.

She makes it sound like one simple task instead of a lifetime of dedicated carnage. Which reforms in particular did she have in mind, I wondered? Anyway, any real reform of the Civil Service is impossible, as I explained to her.

'Suppose I thought up fifty terrific reforms. Who will have to implement them?'

She saw the point at once. 'The Civil Service,' we said in unison, and she nodded sympathetically. But Annie doesn't give up easily.

'All right,' she suggested, 'not fifty reforms. Just one.'

'One?'

'If you achieve *one* important reform of the Civil Service – that would be something.'

Something? It would get into the *Guinness Book of Records*. I asked her what she was proposing.

'Make them put more women in top civil servants' jobs. Women are half the population. Why shouldn't they be half the Permanent Secretaries? How many women are there at the top?'

I tried to think. Certainly not many. I'd hardly come across any.

'Equal opportunities,' I said. I liked the sound it made. It has a good ring to it, that phrase. 'I'll have a go,' I said. 'Why not? There's a principle at stake.'

Annie was delighted. 'You mean you're going to do something out of pure principle?'

I nodded.

'Oh Jim,' she said, with real love and admiration in her voice.

'Principles,' I added, 'are excellent vote-winners.'

Shortly afterwards, Annie developed a headache and went to bed unusually early. I wanted to pursue the conversation with her but she seemed to have lost interest. Odd, that!

June 9th

Today I learned a thing about equal opportunities, or the lack of them, in the Civil Service.

Quite coincidentally I had a meeting with Sarah Harrison, who is the only woman Under-Secretary in the DAA.[4]

Sarah really is a splendid person. Very attractive, intelligent, and about thirty-nine or forty-years-old, which is pretty young for an Under-Sec. She has a brisk and – I suppose – slightly masculine approach to meetings and so forth, but seems to be jolly attractive and feminine in spite of all that.

She has brought me a very difficult letter of complaint from one of the opposition front bench on a constituency matter; something to do with special powers for local authorities for land development in special development areas. I had no idea what it all meant or what I was supposed to do about it.

It turned out that I didn't have to do *anything* about it. She explained that some of the facts were wrong, and other points were covered by statutory requirements so that I didn't have any alternatives anyway.

This is the kind of Civil Service advice that makes a Minister's life easy. No decision needed, not even an apology required. Nothing to do at all, in fact. Great.

I asked her to draft a reply, and she'd already done it. She handed it

[4] Department of Administrative Affairs.

across my desk for me to sign. It was impeccable. I found myself wondering why they don't make more Under-Secretaries like her – and realized that this was the moment to actually *find out*. So I asked her how many women are there at the top of the Civil Service.

She had an immediate answer to that question. 'None of the Permanent Secretaries. Four out of one hundred and fifty odd Deputy Secretaries.'

I wondered silently if there are any that aren't odd. Presumably not, not by the time they become Deputy Secretaries.

I asked her about her grade – Under-Secretary. As I expected, she knew the precise figure.

'Oh, there's twenty-seven of us.'

That seemed not so bad. 'Out of how many?' I asked.

'Five hundred and seventy-eight.'

I was shocked. Appalled. I wonder why *she* wasn't. At least, she didn't seem to be, she was answering these questions in her usual bright, cheerful, matter-of-fact sort of way.

'Doesn't this appal you?' I asked.

'Not really,' she smiled. 'I think it's comic. But then I think the whole Civil Service is comic. It's run by men, after all.'

As a man who was about to devote himself to the cause of women's rights, I felt able to rise above that one. I was on her side.

'What can you do about it?' I asked. She looked blank. I rephrased it. 'What can *I* do about it?' I said.

She looked me straight in the eye, with a cool clear gaze. Her eyes were a beautiful deep blue. And she wears an awfully nice perfume.

'Are you serious, Minister?'

I nodded.

'It's easy,' she said. 'Bring top women from the professions and commerce and industry, straight into the top grades. The pay is quite good for women. There's long holidays, index-linked pensions. You'd get a lot of very high-quality applicants.'

'And they could do this job?' I asked.

'Of course.' She seemed surprised at the question. 'I mean, with all due respect,[5] if you can make a journalist MP into an instant Minister, why can't you make a senior partner of a top legal firm into an Under-Secretary?'

[*Hacker, before he became a Minister, had been a journalist, editing the journal*

---

[5] Always an ominous phrase from a civil servant.

Reform – *Ed.*] 'Most of the work here only needs about two O-Levels anyway,' she added.

Bernard came in to remind me of my next appointment. He escorted Sarah out. 'Bernard,' I said.

'Yes Minister?' he replied as always. I've been trying to establish a closer personal relationship with him for nearly a year now, why does he persist in such formality?

'I wish you'd call me Jim,' I complained. 'At least when we're alone.'

He nodded earnestly. 'I'll try to remember that,' he replied. Hopeless!

I waved the papers from my meeting with Sarah. 'Sarah says this complaint is complete nonsense,' I informed him. 'And she's done a reply.'

Bernard was pleased. 'Fine, we can CGSM it.'

'CGSM?' I asked.

'Civil Service code,' he explained. 'It stands for Consignment of Geriatric Shoe Manufacturers.' I waited for the explanation. 'A load of old cobblers,' he added helpfully.

I took the paper from him.

'I am not a civil servant,' I remarked loftily.' I shall write my own code on it.'

I wrote 'Round Objects' in the margin.

June 11th

Today I had a meeting with Sir Humphrey about equal opportunities. But I had taken care not to let on in advance – in his diary Bernard had written 'Staffing'.

He came in, smiling, confident, benign, patrician, apparently without a care in the world. So I decided to shake him up a bit, then and there.

'Humphrey,' I began, 'I have made a policy decision.'

He froze, half-way down into his chair, in a sort of Groucho Marx position, eyeing me warily with pursed lips.

[*Presumably Hacker intended to say that Sir Humphrey eyed him warily, and that simultaneously he had pursed his lips. – Ed.*]

'A policy decision, Minister?' He recovered himself rapidly and pretended to be pleased with this piece of news.

'Yes,' I replied cheerfully, 'I am going to do something about the number of women in the Civil Service.'

'Surely there aren't all that many?' He looked puzzled.

He was missing the point. Bernard hastened to explain.

'The Minister thinks we need *more*.'

'Many more,' I added firmly.

Now Sir Humphrey really *was* taken aback. His mind was racing. He just couldn't see what I was driving at. 'But we're actually quite well up to Establishment on typists, cleaners, tea-ladies . . .' He petered out, then sought advice. 'Any ideas, Bernard?'

'Well,' said Bernard helpfully, 'we are a bit short of temporary secretaries.'

Clearly Bernard had not got the point either.

'I'm talking about Permanent Secretaries.' I said.

Sir Humphrey was stunned. He seemed unable to formulate a sentence in reply. So I went on.

'We need some female mandarins.' Sir Humphrey was still mentally pole-axed. He didn't respond at all. Bernard also seemed completely baffled. He sought clarification.

'Sort of . . . satsumas, Minister?' he inquired desperately.

I'm never quite sure if Bernard has a highly-intelligent deadpan wit, or is faintly moronic. So I told him to sit down.

'How many Permanent Secretaries,' I asked Sir Humphrey, 'are there at the moment?'

'Forty-one, I believe.'

A precise answer.

'Forty-one,' I agreed pleasantly. 'And how many are women?'

Suddenly Sir Humphrey's memory seemed to fail him. 'Well, broadly speaking, not having the exact figures to hand, I'm not exactly sure.'

'Well, approximately?' I encouraged him to reply.

'Well,' he said cautiously, '*approximately* none.'

Close but no cigar, as our American allies would say. *Precisely* none was the correct answer. And Sir Humphrey knew that only too well. [*Hacker was right. The Permanent Secretaries form an exclusive little club in all but name, so exclusive that a newly-nominated Permanent Secretary could, in effect, be blackballed. This would be an 'informal' process not fully clear to their political 'Lords and Masters', but nonetheless effective for all that. – Ed.*]

I was beginning to enjoy myself. 'And I believe there are one hundred and fifty Deputy Secretaries,' I continued gleefully. 'Do you know how many of them are women?'

Sir Humphrey hedged. Either he genuinely didn't know the answer to this one, or wasn't going to say if he did. 'It's difficult to say,' was the best reply he could manage.

This surprised me. 'Why is it difficult?' I wanted to know.

Bernard tried to be helpful again . 'Well, there's a lot of old women among the men.'

I ignored him. 'Four,' I said to Humphrey, 'Four women Dep. Secs. out of one hundred and fifty-three, to be precise.'

Sir Humphrey seemed impressed that there were so many. 'Are there indeed,' he said, slightly wide-eyed.

I had enjoyed my little bit of fun. Now I came bluntly to the point. I had a proposal to make. I've been thinking about it since my first conversation with Sarah.

'I am going to announce,' a quota of twenty-five per cent women Deputy Secretaries and Permanent Secretaries to be achieved within the next four years.'

I think Sir Humphrey was rattled, but it was hard to tell because he's such a smooth operator.

'Minister, I am obviously in total sympathy with your objectives,' he said. This remark naturally increased my suspicions.

'Good,' I said.

'Of course there should be more women at the top. Of *course*. And all of us are deeply concerned by the apparent imbalance.' I noted the skilful use of the word 'apparent'. 'But these things take time.'

I was ready for that one. 'I want to make a start right away.' I replied.

'I agree wholeheartedly,' responded Sir Humphrey enthusiastically. 'And I propose that we make an immediate start by setting up an inter-departmental committee . . .'

This was not what I meant, and he knew it. I told him firmly that I didn't want the usual delaying tactics.

'This needs a sledgehammer,' I declared. 'We must cut through the red tape.'

Bloody Bernard piped up again. 'You can't cut tape with a sledgehammer, it would just . . .' and then he made a sort of squashing gesture. I squashed *him* with a look.

Humphrey seemed upset that I'd accused him of delaying tactics. 'Minister, you do me an injustice,' he complained. 'I was not about to suggest delaying tactics.'

Perhaps I had done him an injustice. I apologized, and waited to see what he *was* about to suggest.

'I was merely going to suggest,' he murmured in a slightly hurt tone, 'that if we are to have a twenty-five per cent quota of women we must have a much larger intake at the recruitment stage. So that eventually we'll have twenty-five per cent in the top jobs.'

'When?' I asked.

I knew the answer before he said it. 'In twenty-five years.'

'No, Humphrey,' I said, still smiling and patient. 'I don't think you've quite got my drift, I'm talking about *now*.'

At last Sir Humphrey got the point. 'Oh,' he said, staggered. 'You mean – *now*!'

'Got it in one, Humphrey,' I replied with my most patronizing smile.

'But Minister,' he smiled smoothly, 'it takes time to do things now.' And he smiled patronizingly back at me. It's amazing how quickly he recovers his poise.

I've been hearing that kind of stuff for nearly a year now. It no longer cuts any ice with me. 'Ah yes,' I said, 'the three articles of Civil Service faith: it takes longer to do things quickly, it's more expensive to do things cheaply, and it's more democratic to do things secretly. No Humphrey, I've suggested four years. That's masses of time.'

He shook his head sadly. 'Dear me no, Minister, I don't mean political time, I mean *real* time.' He sat comfortably back in his chair, gazed at the ceiling, and then continued in a leisurely sort of way. 'Civil servants are grown like oak trees, not mustard and cress. They bloom and ripen with the seasons.' I'd never heard such pretentious crap. But he was in full flow. 'They mature like . . .'

'Like you?' I interrupted facetiously.

'I was going to say,' he replied tartly, 'that they mature like an old port.'

'Grimsby, perhaps?'

He smiled a tiny humourless smile. 'I *am* being serious, Minister.'

He certainly was. Apart from being entirely serious about his own importance, he was seriously trying to use all this flim-flam to get me to lose track of my new proposal – or, as I think of it, my new policy decision. I decided to go straight for the jugular.

'I foresaw this problem,' I said firmly. 'So I propose that we solve it by bringing in top women from outside the Service to fill vacancies in the top grades.'

Humphrey's face was a picture. He was absolutely aghast. The colour drained out of his face.

'Minister ... I don't think I quite ...' His voice petered out as he reached the word 'understood'.

I was enjoying myself hugely.

'Watch my lips more,' I said helpfully, and pointed to my mouth with my forefinger. 'We ... will ... bring ... women ... in ... from ... out- ... side!' I said it very slowly and carefully, like a deranged speech therapist. He just sat there and stared at me, transfixed, a rabbit with a snake.

Finally he pulled himself together.

'But,' he began, 'the whole strength of our system is that it is incorruptible, pure, unsullied by outside influences.'

'I just can't see the sense in that old chestnut and I said so. 'People move from one job to another throughout industry. Humphrey – why should the Civil Service be different?'

'It *is* different. The Civil Service demands subtlety ...'

'Discretion,' said Bernard.

'Devotion to duty,' said Humphrey.

'Soundness!' said Bernard.

'*Soundness!*' repeated Sir Humphrey emphatically. 'Well said Bernard. *Soundness.*' Bernard had clearly hit upon one of the key compliments in the Civil Service vocabulary.

[*Bernard Woolley of course, had an important vested interest in this conversation. If Hacker's policy of bringing women in from outside were implemented, this might well have an adverse effect on the promotion prospects of more junior civil servants such as Woolley. And if women could be brought in to fill top jobs from outside, so could men. What, then, would Bernard Woolley's prospects have been? – Ed.*]

Sir Humphrey went on to explain that civil servants require endless patience and boundless understanding, they need to be able to change horses midstream, constantly, as the politicians change their minds. Perhaps it was my imagination, but it seemed to me that he was putting the word 'minds' in quotes – as if to imply, 'as politicians change what they are pleased to call their minds'.

I asked him if he had all these talents. With a modest shrug he replied: 'Well, it's just that one has been properly ...'

'Matured,' I interjected. 'Like Grimsby.'

'Trained.' He corrected me with a tight-lipped smile.

'Humphrey,' I said, 'ask yourself honestly if the system is not at fault. *Why* are there so few women Deputy Secretaries?'

'They keep leaving,' he explained, with an air of sweet reason, 'to have babies. And things.'

This struck me as a particularly preposterous explanation, 'Leaving to have babies? At the age of nearly fifty? Surely not!'

But Sir Humphrey appeared to believe it. Desperately he absolved himself of all responsibility or knowledge. 'Really Minister, I don't know. Really I don't. I'm on your side. We do indeed need more women at the top.'

'Good,' I replied decisively, 'because I'm not waiting twenty-five years. We've got a vacancy for a Deputy Secretary here, haven't we?'

He was instantly on his guard. He even thought cautiously for a moment before replying.

'Yes.'

'Very well. We shall appoint a woman. Sarah Harrison.'

Again he was astounded, or aghast, or appalled. Something like that. Definitely not pleased, anyway. But he contented himself with merely repeating her name, in a quiet controlled voice.

'Sarah Harrison?'

'Yes,' I said. 'I think she's very able, don't you?'

'Very able, for a woman. For a person.' He had corrected himself with scarcely a hesitation.

'And,' I added, 'she has ideas. She's an original thinker.'

'I'm afraid that's true,' agreed Sir Humphrey, 'but she doesn't let it interfere with her work.'

So I asked him what he had against her. He insisted that he had *nothing* against her, that he was totally *pro* her. He confirmed that she is an excellent worker, and he pointed out that he is a great supporter of hers and had in fact advocated her promotion to Under-Secretary only last year at a very early age.

'Would you say she is an outstanding Under-Secretary?' I asked him.

'Yes,' he replied, without equivocation.

'So,' I said, 'on balance it's a good idea, isn't it?'

'On balance? Yes ... and no.'

I told him that that was not a clear answer. He said it was a balanced answer. Touché. Then he went on to explain that the point is, in his opinion, that she's too young and it's not her turn yet.

I leaped upon that argument. I'd been expecting it. 'That is precisely what's *wrong* with the Civil Service – Buggins' Turn! Whereas the best people should be promoted, as soon as possible.'

'Exactly,' agreed Sir Humphrey, 'as soon as it's their turn.'

'Rubbish. Napoleon ruled Europe in his thirties. Alexander the Great conquered the world in his twenties.'

'They would have made *very* poor Deputy Secretaries,' remarked Sir Humphrey contemptuously.

'At least they didn't wait their turn,' I pointed out.

'And look what happened to them.' Sir Humphrey clearly thought he'd won our little debate. So I decided to make the argument rather more personal.

'Look what's happened to *us*,' I said calmly. 'Instead of this country being run by bright energetic youthful brains it is being run by tired routine-bound fifty-five-year-olds who just want a quiet life.'

Humphrey stared at me coldly. 'Had you anyone specific in mind, Minister?'

I smiled. 'Yes . . . and no, Humphrey.' Game, set and match to yours truly, I felt.

Sir Humphrey decided to move the debate back to the specific problem. He informed me, in his most matter-of-fact fashion, that Sarah Harrison is an excellent civil servant and a bright hope for the future. But he also reiterated that she is our most junior Under-Secretary and that he cannot and will not recommend her for promotion.

There was a clear implication in that final comment that it was ultimately up to him, and that I should mind my own business.

I told him he was a sexist.

I'm surprised he didn't laugh at me. Surprisingly, this trendy insult seemed to cut him to the quick. He was outraged.

'Minister,' he complained bitterly, 'how can you say such a thing? I'm very pro-women. Wonderful people, women. And Sarah Harrison is a dear lady. I'm one of her most ardent admirers. But the fact is that if the cause of women is to be advanced it must be done with tact and care and discretion. She is our only woman contender for a top job. We mustn't push her too fast. Women find top jobs very difficult, you know.'

He *is* a sexist.

'Can you hear yourself?' I asked incredulously.

Unabashed, he continued in the same vein. 'If women were able to be good Permanent Secretaries, there would be more of them, wouldn't there? Stands to reason.'

I've never before heard a reply that so totally begs the question.

'No Humphrey!' I began, wondering where to begin.

But on he went. 'I'm no anti-feminist. I love women. Some of my best friends are women. My wife, indeed.' Methinks Sir Humphrey doth protest too much. And on and on he went. 'Sarah Harrison is not very experienced, Minister, and her two children are still of school age, they might get mumps.'

Another daft argument. Anybody can be temporarily off work through their own ill-health, not just their children's. 'You might get shingles, Humphrey, if it comes to that,' I said.

He missed my point. 'I might indeed Minister, if you continue in this vein,' he muttered balefully. 'But what if her children caused her to miss work all the time?'

I asked him frankly if this were likely. I asked if she were likely to have reached the rank of Under-Secretary if her children kept having mumps. I pointed out that she was the best person for the job.

He didn't disagree about that. But he gave me an indignant warning: 'Minister, if you go around promoting women just because they're the best person for the job, you could create a lot of resentment throughout the whole Civil Service.'

'But not from the women in it,' I pointed out.

'Ah,' said Sir Humphrey complacently, 'but there are so few of them that it wouldn't matter so much.'

A completely circular argument. Perhaps this is what is meant by moving in Civil Service circles.

[*Later in the week Sir Humphrey Appleby had lunch with Sir Arnold Robinson, the Cabinet Secretary, at the Athenaeum Club. Sir Humphrey, as always, made a note on one of his long thin pieces of memo paper simulating a margin. – Ed.*]

Arnold's feelings are the same as mine when it comes to women. We both like them well enough, in their way. But like me – and unlike the Minister – he sees quite clearly that they are different from us. In the following ways:–

1. *Bad for teamwork:* They put strains on a team, by reacting differently from us.
2. *Too emotional:* They are not rational like us.
3. *Can't be Reprimanded:* They either get into a frightful bate or start blubbing.
4. *Can be Reprimanded:* Some of them can be, but are frightfully hard and butch and not in the least bit attractive.
5. *Prejudices:* They are full of them.

6. *Silly Generalizations:* They make them.

7. *Stereotypes:* They think in them.

I asked Arnold for his advice. Arnold suggested that I lecture the Minister at such lengths on the matter that he becomes bored and loses interest in the whole idea.

There is a remote chance of success for such a plan. But Hacker does not get bored easily. He even finds *himself* interesting. They all do in fact. All the ones who listen to what they're saying of course. On second thoughts, that is by no means all of them.

But the fact remains that Hacker's boredom threshold is high. He even reads most of the stuff that we put into his red boxes, with apparent interest!

Arnold also suggested that standard second ploy: to tell the Minister that the Unions won't wear it. [*'It'* being the importation of women into the Service to fill some top jobs. – *Ed.*] We agreed that this was a line of action worth pursuing.

We also discussed the feminine angle. His wife is in favour of promoting the Harrison female, and may well – from what I know of Mrs H. – be behind all this. However, she may not know that Harrison is extremely attractive. I'm sure Mrs H. and Mrs H. have never met. This could well be fruitful.

I pointed out that the Cabinet will be in favour of Hacker's proposal. But we agreed that we could doubtless get the Cabinet to change their minds. They change their minds fairly easily. Just like a lot of women. Thank God they don't blub.

[*Appleby Papers 37/6PJ/457*].

[*It is interesting to compare Sir Humphrey's self-confident account of this luncheon with the notes made by Sir Arnold Robinson on Sir Humphrey's report, which were found among the Civil Service files at Walthamstow. – Ed.*]

Told Appleby that I wasn't impressed with his Minister's plan to bring in women from outside, novel though the idea may be.

[*'Wasn't impressed'* would be an example of Civil Service understatement. Readers may imagine the depth of feeling behind such a phrase. The use of the Civil Service killer word *'novel'* is a further indication of Sir Arnold's hostility. – *Ed.*]

Suggested that he bore the Minister out of the idea. Appleby claimed that this would not work. Probably correct.

So I made various other suggestions. For instance, the Trade Union ploy: suggesting to the Minister that the Unions won't wear it. Appleby missed the point completely. He told me that the Unions would like it. He's probably right, but it was completely beside the point!

I also suggested pointing the Minister's wife in the right direction. And suggested that we try to ensure that the Cabinet throws it out. Appleby agreed to try all these plans. But I am disturbed that he had thought of none of them himself.

Must keep a careful eye on H.A. Is early retirement a possibility to be discussed with the PM?

A.R.

[*Naturally, Sir Humphrey never saw these notes, because no civil servant is ever shown his report except in wholly exceptional circumstances.*

And equally naturally, Hacker never knew of the conversation between Sir Arnold and Sir Humphrey over luncheon at the Athenaeum.

It was in this climate of secrecy that our democracy used to operate. Civil servants' word for secrecy was 'discretion'. They argued that discretion was the better part of valour. – Ed.]

[*Hacker's diary continues. – Ed.*]
June 16th
Sir Humphrey walked into my office today, sat down and made the most startling remark that I have yet heard from him.

'Minister,' he said, 'I have come to the conclusion that you were right.'

Finally, after nearly a year, it seemed that he was beginning to take me seriously.

However, I was immediately suspicious, and I asked him to amplify his remark. I had not the least idea to which matter he was referring. Of course, asking Humphrey to amplify his remarks is often a big mistake.

'I am fully-seized of your ideas and have taken them on board and I am now positively against discrimination against women and positively in favour of positive discrimination in their favour – discriminating discrimination of course.'

I think it was something like that. I got the gist of it anyway.

Then he went on, to my surprise: 'I understand a view is forming at the very highest level that this should happen.' I think he must have been referring to the PM. Good news.

Then, to my surprise he asked why the matter of equal opportunities for women should not apply to politics as well as the Civil Service. I was momentarily confused. But he explained that there are only twenty-three women MPs out of a total of six hundred and fifty. I agreed that this too is deplorable, but, alas, there is nothing at all that we can do about that.

He remarked that these figures were an indication of discrimination against women by the political parties. Clearly, he argued, the way they select candidates is fundamentally discriminatory.

I found myself arguing in defence of the parties. It was a sort of reflex action. 'Yes and no.' I agreed. 'You know, it's awfully difficult for women to be MPs – long hours, debates late at night, being away from home a lot. Most women have a problem with that and with homes, and husbands.'

'And mumps,' he added helpfully.

I realized that he was sending me up. And simultaneously trying to suggest that I too am a sexist. An absurd idea, of course, and I told him so in no uncertain terms.

I steered the discussion towards specific goals and targets, I asked what we would do to start implementing our plan.

Humphrey said that the first problem would be that the unions won't agree to this quota.

I was surprised to hear this, and immediately suggested that we get them in to talk about it.

This suggestion made him very anxious. 'No, no, no,' he said. 'No. That would stir up a hornet's nest.'

I couldn't see why. Either Humphrey was paranoid about the unions – or it was just a ploy to frighten me. I suspect the latter.

[*Hacker was now learning fast. – Ed.*]

The reason I suspect a trick is that he offered no explanation as to why he shouldn't talk to the union leaders. Instead he went off on an entirely different tack.

'If I might suggest we be realistic about this . . .' he began.

I interrupted. 'By realistic, do you mean drop the whole scheme?'

'No!' he replied vehemently. 'Certainly not! But perhaps a pause to regroup, a lull in which we reassess the position and discuss alternative strategies, a space of time for mature reflection and deliberation . . .'

I interrupted again. 'Yes, you mean drop the whole scheme.' This time I wasn't asking a question. And I dealt with the matter with what I consider to be exemplary firmness. I told him that I had set my hand to the plough and made my decision. 'We shall have a twenty-five per cent quota of women in the open structure in four years from now. And to start with I shall promote Sarah Harrison to Dep. Sec.'

He was frightfully upset. 'No Minister!' he cried in vain. 'I'm sure that's the wrong decision.'

This was quite a remarkable reaction from the man who had begun the meeting by telling me that I was absolutely right.

I emphasized that I could not be moved on this matter because it is a matter of principle. I added that I shall have a word with my cabinet colleagues, who are bound to support me as there are a lot of votes in women's rights.

'I thought you said it was a matter of principle, Minister, not of votes.'

He was being to clever by half. I was able to explain, loftily, that I was referring to my cabinet colleagues. For me it *is* a matter of principle.

A very satisfactory meeting. I don't think he can frustrate me on this one.

June 17th

Had a strange evening out with Annie. She collected me from the office at five-thirty, because we had to go to a Party drinks 'do' at Central House.[6]

I had to keep her waiting a while because my last meeting of the day ran late, and I had a lot of letters to sign.

Signing letters, by the way, is an extraordinary business because there are so many of them. Bernard lays them out in three or four long rows, all running the full length of my conference table which seats twelve a side. Then I whizz along the table, signing the letters as I go. It's quicker to move me than them. As I go Bernard collects the signed letters up behind me, and moves a letter from the second row to replace the signed and collected one in the first row. Then I whizz back along the table, signing the next row.

I don't actually read them all that carefully. It shows the extent of my trust for Bernard. Sometimes I think that I might sign absolutely anything if I were in a big enough hurry.

Bernard had an amusing bit of news for me today.

'You remember that letter you wrote "Round objects" on?' he asked.

'Yes.'

[6] Hacker's Party HQ.

'Well,' he said with a slight smile, 'it's come back from Sir Humphrey's office. He commented on it.'

And he showed me the letter. In the margin Humphrey had written: 'Who is Round and to what does he object?'

Anyway, I digress. While all this signing was going on, Annie was given a sherry by Humphrey in his office. I thought it was jolly nice of him to take the trouble to be sociable when he could have been on the 5.59 for Haslemere. Mind you, I think he likes Annie and anyway perhaps he thinks it's polite to chat up the Minister's wife.

But, as I say, Annie and I had a strange evening. She seemed rather cool and remote. I asked her if anything was wrong, but she wouldn't say what. Perhaps she resented my keeping her waiting so long, because I know she finds Humphrey incredibly boring. Still, that's the penalty you have to pay if you're married to a successful man.

[*A note in Sir Humphrey's diary reveals the true cause of Mrs Hacker's disquiet. – Ed.*]

Had a sherry with Mrs Hacker this evening. The Minister was delayed signing letters, which was not entirely coincidental. Naturally I had taken care to ensure that his previous meeting overran somewhat.

I brought the conversation around to the matter of changing and reforming the Civil Service. As expected, she was pretty keen on the whole idea.

Immediately she asked me about the promotion of the Harrison female. 'What about promoting this woman that Jim was talking about?'

I talked about it all with great enthusiasm. I said that the Minister certainly has an eye for talent. I said that Sarah was undoubtedly very talented. And thoroughly delightful. A real charmer.

I continued for many minutes in the same vein. I said how much I admired this new generation of women civil servants compared with the old battle-axes of yesteryear. I said that naturally most of the new generation aren't as beautiful as Sarah, but they all are thoroughly feminine.

Mrs Hacker was becoming visibly less enthusiastic about Sarah Harrison's promotion, minute by minute. She remarked that Hacker had never discussed what Sarah looked like.

I laughed knowingly. I said that perhaps he hadn't noticed, though that would be pretty hard to believe. I laid it on pretty thick – made her sound like a sort of administrative Elizabeth Taylor. I said that no man could fail to notice how attractive she was, *especially* the Minister, as he spends such a considerable amount of time with her. And will spend even more if she's promoted.

My feeling is that the Minister will get no further encouragement from home on this matter.

[*Appleby Papers 36/RJC/471*]

[*Sir Arnold Robinson and Sir Humphrey Appleby were plainly quite confident, as we have already seen, that they could sway a sufficient number of Hacker's cabinet colleagues to vote against this proposal when it came before them.*

The source of their confidence was the practice, current in the 1970s and 1980s, of holding an informal meeting of Permanent Secretaries on Wednesday mornings. This meeting took place in the office of the Cabinet Secretary, had no agenda and was – almost uniquely among Civil Service meetings – unminuted.

Permanent Secretaries would 'drop in' and raise any question of mutual interest. This enabled them all to be fully-briefed about any matters that were liable to confront their Ministers in Cabinet, which took place every Thursday morning i.e. the next day. And it gave them time to give their Ministers encouragement or discouragement as they saw fit on particular issues.

Fortunately Sir Humphrey's diary reveals what occurred at the Permanent Secretaries' meeting that fateful Wednesday morning. – Ed.]

I informed my colleages that my Minister is intent on creating a quota of twenty-five per cent women in the open structure, leading to an eventual fifty per cent. Parity, in other words.

Initially, my colloeagues' response was that it was an interesting suggestion.

[*'Interesting' was another Civil Service form of abuse, like 'Novel' or, worse still, 'Imaginative'. – Ed.*]

Arnold set the tone for the proper response. His view was that it is right and proper that men and women be treated fairly and equally. In principle we should all agree, he said, that such targets should be set and goals achieved.

Everyone agreed immediately that we should agree in principle to such an excellent idea, that it was right and proper to set such targets and achieve such goals.

Arnold then canvassed several of my colleagues in turn, to see if they could implement this excellent proposal in their departments.

Bill [*Sir William Carter, Permanent Secretary at the Foreign and Commonwealth Office. – Ed.*] said that he was in full agreement, naturally. He believes that the Civil Service must institute some positive discrimination in favour of women. But regretfully he felt obliged to point out that it cannot happen in the FCO for obvious reasons. Clearly we cannot post women ambassadors to Iran, or any of the Muslim countries, for instance. Generally speaking most of the Third World countries are not as advanced as we are in connection with women's rights – and as we have to send our diplomats to new postings every three years, and entertain many Islamic VIPs in this country, the proposal would definitely not work for the FCO. Nonetheless he wished to make it clear that he applauded the principle.

Ian [*Sir Ian Simpson. Permanent Secretary of the Home Office. – Ed.*] said that he was enthusiastically in favour of the principle. He believes we all could benefit from the feminine touch. Furthermore, women are actually *better* at handling some problems than men. He had no doubt about this. Regretfully, however, an exception would have to be made in the case of the Home Office: women are not the right people to run prisons, or the police. And quite probably, they wouldn't want to do it anyway.

We all agreed that this was probably so.

Peter [*Sir Peter Wainwright, Permanent Secretary of the Department of Defence. – Ed.*] said that, alas! the same applies to Defence. Women are hardly the people to control all those admirals and generals. Nor is it a practical possibility to place a woman at the Head of Security.

I observed that M. would have to become F. This provoked a gratifying degree of merriment around the table.

Arnold, speaking for us all, agreed that Defence must clearly be a man's world. Like Industry. And Employment, with all those trade union barons to cope with.

John [*Sir John McKendrick, Permanent Secretary of the Department of Health and Social Security. – Ed.*] took an even more positive line. He was happy to inform us that women are already well represented near the top of the DHSS, which has two of the four women Dep. Secs. currently in Whitehall. Neither of them is in line for Permanent Secretary, obviously, as they are Deputy Chief Medical Officers, (and in any case they may not be suitable for other reasons). Furthermore, women constitute eighty per cent of the typing grades, so he was delighted to be able to tell us that his Department is not doing too badly by them. He added that, in principle, he was in favour of them going to the very top.

Arnold summed up all the views expressed: the feeling of the meeting was – unquestionably – that in principle we were all thoroughly in favour of equal rights for the ladies. It is just that there are special problems in individual departments.

I raised again the question of the quota and stated that I was against it.

Everyone immediately supported me. There was a feeling that it was not on and a bad idea – in fact a typical politician's idea.

I gave my view: namely, that we must always have the right to promote the best man for the job, regardless of sex.

Furthermore – and I made it clear that I was speaking as an ardent feminist myself – I pointed out that the problem lay in recruiting the right sort of women. Married women with families tend to drop out because, in all honesty, they cannot give their work their full single-minded attention. And unmarried women with no children are not fully-rounded people with a thorough understanding of life.

There was general agreement that family life was essential and that it was hard for spinsters to be fully-rounded individuals.

I summed up my remarks by saying that, in practice, it is rarely possible to find a fully-rounded married woman with a happy home and three children who is prepared to devote virtually her whole life, day and night, to a Government Department. It's Catch 22 – or, rather, Catch 22, subparagraph (a).

Arnold had allowed considerable time for this discussion, which indicates the importance that he attached to the problem. He concluded the matter by asking everyone present to ensure that all of their respective Ministers oppose the quota idea in Cabinet by seeing that each Minister's attention is drawn to each Department's own special circumstances. But he also asked all present to be sure to recommend the *principle* of equal opportunities at every level.

Through the chair, I made one final point. My Minister sees the promotion of women as one means of achieving greater diversity at the top of the Service. I asked all my colleagues to stress, when briefing their

Ministers, that quite frankly one could not find a more diverse collection of people than us.

It was unanimously agreed that we constitute a real cross-section of the nation.

[*Appleby Papers* – *41/AAG/583*].

[*Hacker's diary continues* – *Ed.*]
June 19th
Cabinet today. And with a very odd outcome. I put forward my proposal for a quota with women for top Civil Service jobs.

All my Cabinet colleagues agreed *in principle* but then they all went on to say that it wouldn't work in their particular Departments. So in the end they didn't really support me at all.

Curiously enough, I'm no longer getting the support from Annie that I was. Not about the quota, specifically, but about promoting Sarah. I had expected her to be *at least* one hundred per cent behind it. But she goes all distant when I talk about it. In fact, she seems to be dead against it now. Extraordinary.

However, as the quota policy is now in ruins it seems that Sarah's promotion is the only thing left that I can immediately achieve in this area. I have arranged that Humphrey and I speak to her tomorrow. I am determined to push it through.

June 20th
My whole equal opportunities policy is destroyed, and quite frankly I feel pretty bitter about the whole thing in general and women in particular. Or at least one particular woman in particular.

Before I saw Sarah today I told Humphrey that we at least could make one tiny positive step today. Lighting a spark.

'Carrying a torch, even,' he replied. What was that supposed to mean?

Anyway, Sarah came in. I explained the background to her: that we have a vacancy for a Deputy Secretary in a Department and that, in spite of her being the most junior of our Under-Secs but because she is the outstanding person in her grade, we were happy to be able to tell her that Humphrey and I were recommending her for promotion to the rank of Deputy Secretary.

Her reaction was a little surprising.

'Oh,' she said. 'I don't know what to say.' And then she laughed.

I couldn't imagine what she was laughing at.

'You don't have to say anything,' I said.

'A single thank you should suffice,' said Humphrey.

She was still smiling. Then she dropped the bombshell. 'No – I mean – oh gosh! Look, this is awfully embarrassing – I mean, well, I was going to tell you this week – the fact is I'm resigning from the Civil Service.'

You could have knocked me down with a feather. And Humphrey too, by the look of him.

I said something brilliantly witty and apposite, like 'What?', and Humphrey gasped 'resigning?'

'Yes,' she said. 'So thank you, but no thank you.'

Humphrey asked her if there was some problem with her children at home. Bernard suggested mumps.

I suggested that Bernard shut up.

Sarah said she was joining a merchant bank. As a Director.

She'll earn more than me. Perhaps even more than Humphrey!

I tried to explain to her that this news was a frightful blow. 'You see, Sarah, the reason that I'm telling you of your promotion – or rather, Humphrey and I together – is that I have been fighting a losing battle to improve the promotion prospects of women at the top of the Service. And, well, you were to be my Trojan Horse.'

She then explained the reason for her move. 'Quite honestly Minister, I want a job where I don't spend endless hours circulating information that isn't relevant about subjects that don't matter to people who aren't interested. I want a job where there is achievement rather than merely activity. I'm tired of pushing paper. I would like to be able to point at something and say "I did that."'

The irony of what she was saying was extraordinary. I understand her feeling only too well.

Sir Humphrey didn't. He looked blank. 'I don't understand,' he said.

She smiled. 'I know. That's why I'm leaving.'

I explained that I *did* understand. But I asked her if she was saying that governing Britain is unimportant.

'No,' she said, 'it's very important. It's just that I haven't met anyone who's doing it.'

She added that she'd had enough of the pointless intrigue. I asked what she had in mind. 'Your using me as a Trojan Horse, for instance. And they probably told you that the unions wouldn't wear it if you promoted me.'

I was staggered. Had there been a leak? I asked her how she knew.

She was delighted. She grinned from ear to ear. 'Oh *I didn't* know. I just know how things are done here.'

We both stared at Humphrey, who had the grace to look slightly embarrassed.

I made one last effort to persuade her to change her mind. 'Look here Sarah,' I said sternly, 'you don't seem to appreciate that I've fought quite a battle for you.'

Suddenly her eyes blazed. For the first time I recognized the toughness that had brought her to near the top. And the sense of style and dignity. I realized that I'd said something awfully wrong.

'Oh, have you?' she asked. 'Well. I didn't ask you to fight a battle for me. I'm not pleased at the idea of being part of a twenty-five per cent quota. Women are not inferior beings, and I don't enjoy being patronized. I'm afraid you're as paternalist and chauvinist as the rest of them. I'm going somewhere where I shall be accepted as an equal, on my own merits, as a person.'

I was speechless. Clearly I'd offended her. And I suddenly realized that you can't win.

'May I go now?'

There was, of course, no reason to keep her sitting there. I apologized for offending her, though I couldn't see how I'd done it.

'No,' she said, in a kindly way. 'And thank you – I know you both *mean* well.' And off she went, leaving two very puzzled and deflated chaps.

'Women!' I said.

'Yes Minister,' murmured Humphrey, nodding sadly as if to say 'I told you so!'

[*This was not quite the end of the matter. Recently published papers revealed that Hacker fought on for his twenty-five per cent quota for some considerable time – some weeks, anyway. And, as Sir Harold Wilson once said, a week is a long time in politics.*

Sir Humphrey's ingenuity rose to the occasion. He warned Hacker that the Race Relations Board had heard on the grapevine of his proposed quota for women. He told Hacker that if there was to be any affirmative action within the Civil Service, there must also be a quota of blacks within the Civil Service. Humphrey explained that there was a principle at stake.

Hacker was less than enthusiastic about this new principle. He was certainly not a racist, but he could see clearly that whereas a quota for women was a vote-winner, a quota for blacks was in all probability a vote-loser.

Some days later Hacker raised what he called 'this whole business of minority groups – women, blacks, trade unionists and so forth.'

Sir Humphrey explained to Hacker that women and trade unionists were not minority groups, even though they share the same paranoia which is the hallmark of any minority group.

So finally Hacker proposed what Appleby had always proposed: namely, that they start by creating equal opportunities for both women and blacks. In the recruitment grades.

And they drew up terms of reference for an inter-departmental committee to report on methods of choosing the right individuals to be civil servants, to report four years hence. By which time Hacker would certainly no longer be the Minister. – Ed.]

Why Herbert Killed His Mother

Winifred Holtby

Once upon a time there was a Model Mother who had a Prize Baby. Nobody had ever had such a Baby before. He was a Son, of course. All prize babies are masculine, for should there be a flaw in their gender this might deprive them of at least twenty-five per cent of the marks merited by their prize-worthiness.

The Mother's name was Mrs Wilkins, and she had a husband called Mr Wilkins; but he did not count much. It is true that he was the Baby's father, and on the night after the child was born he stood Drinks All Round at the Club; though he was careful to see that there were only two other members in the Bar at the time he suggested it, because although one must be a Good Father and celebrate properly, family responsibilities make a man remember his bank balance. Mr Wilkins remembered his very often, particularly when Mrs Wilkins bought a copy of *Vogue*, or remarked that the Simpsons, who lived next door but one, had changed their Austin Seven for a Bentley. The Wilkinses had not even an old Ford; but then the buses passed the end of their road, and before the Prize Baby arrived, Mrs Wilkins went to the Stores and ordered a very fine pram.

Mrs Wilkins had determined to be a Real Old-Fashioned Mother. She had no use for these Modern Women who Drink Cocktails, Smoke Cigarettes, and dash about in cars at all hours with men who are not their husbands. She believed in the true ideal of Real Womanliness, Feminine Charm, and the Maternal Instinct. She won a ten-shilling prize once from a daily paper, with a circulation of nearly two million, for saying so, very prettily, on a postcard.

Before the Baby came she sat with her feet up every afternoon sewing little garments. She made long clothes with twenty tucks round the hem of each robe, and embroidered flannels, fifty inches from hem to shoulder tape, and fluffy bonnets, and teeny-weeny little net veils; she draped a bassinet with white muslin and blue ribbons, and she thought a great deal about violets, forget-me-nots and summer seas in order that her baby might have blue eyes. When Mrs. Burton from 'The Acacias' told her that long clothes were unhygienic, and that drapery on the bassinet held the dust, and that heredity had far more to do with blue eyes than thoughts about forget-me-nots, she shook her head charmingly, and said: 'Ah, well. You *clever* women know so much. I can only go by what my darling mother told me.' Mrs Burton said: 'On the contrary. You have a lot of other authorities to go by nowadays,' and she produced three pamphlets, a book on Infant Psychology, and a programme of lectures on 'Health, Happiness and Hygiene in the Nursery'. But Mrs Wilkins sighed, and said: 'My poor little brain won't take in all that stuff. I have only my Mother Love to guide me.' And she dropped a pearly tear on to a flannel binder.

Mrs Burton went home and told Mr Burton that Mrs Wilkins was hopeless, and that her baby would undoubtedly suffer from adenoids, curvature of the spine, flat feet, halitosis, bow legs, indigestion and the Œdipus Complex. Mr Burton said 'Quite, quite.' And everyone was pleased.

The only dissentient was the Wilkins baby, who was born without any defect whatsoever. He was a splendid boy, and his more-than-proud parents had him christened Herbert James Rodney Stephen Christopher, which names they both agreed went very well with Wilkins. He wore for the ceremony two binders, four flannels, an embroidered robe with seventeen handmade tucks, a woolly coat, two shawls, and all other necessary and unnecessary garments, and when he stared into the Rector's face, and screamed lustily, his aunts said: 'That means he'll be musical, bless him.' But his mother thought: 'What a strong will he has! And what sympathy there is between us! Perhaps he knows already what I think about the Rector.'

As long as the monthly nurse was there, Mrs Wilkins and Herbert got along very nicely on Mother Love; but directly she left trouble began.

'My baby,' Mrs Wilkins had said, 'shall never be allowed to lie awake and cry like Mrs Burton's poor little wretch. Babies need cuddling.' So whenever Herbert cried at first she cuddled him. She cuddled him in the early morning when he woke up Mr Wilkins and wanted his six o'clock bottle at four. She cuddled him half-hourly for three days and then she smacked him. It was a terrible thing to do, but she did it. She fed him when he seemed hungry, and showed him to all the neighbours who called, and kept him indoors when it rained, which it did every day, and nursed him while she had her own meals, and when she didn't gave him Nestlé's. And he still flourished.

But what with the crying and the washing that hung in the garden, the neighbours began to complain, and Mrs Burton said: 'Of course, you're killing that child.'

Mrs Wilkins knew that the Maternal Instinct was the safest guide in the world; but when her husband showed her an advertisement in the evening paper which began: 'Mother, does your child cry?' she read it. She learned there that babies cry because their food does not agree with them. 'What-not's Natural Digestive Infants' Milk solves the Mother's problem.' Mrs Wilkins thought that no stone should be left unturned and bought a specimen tin of What-not's Natural Digestive Infants' Milk, and gave it to Herbert. Herbert flourished. He grew larger and rounder and pinker, and more dimpled than ever. But still he cried.

So Mrs Wilkins read another advertisement in the evening paper. And there she learned that when babies cry it is because they are not warm enough, and that all good mothers should buy Flopsy's Fleecy Pram Covers. So, being a good mother, she bought a Flopsy's Fleecy Pram Cover and wrapped Herbert in it. And still Herbert flourished. And still he cried.

So she continued to read the evening papers, for by this time both she and Mr Wilkins were nearly distracted, and one of the neighbours threatened to complain to the landlord, and Mrs Simpson kept her loud speaker going all night and day to drown the noise, she said. And now Mrs Wilkins learned that the reason her baby cried was because his elimination was inadequate so she bought him a bottle of Hebe's Nectar for the Difficult Child, and gave him a teaspoonful every morning. But still he cried.

Then the spring came, and the sun shone, and the bulbs in the garden of Number Seven were finer than they had ever been before, and Mrs Wilkins put Herbert out in the garden in his pram, and he stopped crying.

She was such a nice woman and such a proud mother that she wrote at once to the proprietors of What-not's Natural Digestive Infants' Milk, and Flopsy's Fleecy Pram Covers, and Hebe's Nectar for the Difficult Child, and told them that she had bought their things for Herbert and that he had stopped crying.

Two days later a sweet young woman came to the Wilkins' house, and said that What-not's Limited had sent her to see Herbert, and what a fine Baby he was, and how healthy, and could she take a photograph? And Mrs Wilkins was very pleased, and thought: 'Well, Herbert is the most beautiful Baby in the world, and won't this be a sell for Mrs Burton,' and was only too delighted. So the young woman photographed Herbert in his best embroidered robe drinking Natural Digestive Infants' Milk from a bottle, and went away.

The next day a kind old man came from Flopsy's Fleecy Pram Covers Limited, and photographed Herbert lying under a Fleecy Pram Cover. It was a hot afternoon and a butterfly came and settled on the pram; but the kind old man said that this was charming.

The next day a scientific-looking young man with horn-rimmed spectacles came from Hebe's Nectar Limited and photographed Herbert lying on a fur rug wearing nothing at all. And when Mr Wilkins read his Sunday paper, there he saw his very own baby, with large black capitals printed above him, saying: 'My Child is now no longer Difficult, declares Mrs Wilkins, of Number 9, The Grove, SW10.'

Mrs Burton saw it too, and said to Mr Burton: 'No wonder, when at last they've taken a few stones of wool off the poor little wretch.'

But Mr and Mrs Wilkins saw it differently. They took Herbert to a Court Photographer and had him taken dressed and undressed, with one parent, with both parents, standing up and sitting down; and always he was the most beautiful baby that the Wilkinses had ever seen.

One day they saw an announcement in a great Sunday paper of a £10,000 prize for the loveliest baby in the world. 'Well, dear, this will be nice,' said Mrs Wilkins. 'We shall be able to buy a saloon car now.' Because, of course, she knew that Herbert would win the prize.

And so he did. He was photographed in eighteen different poses for the first heat; then he was taken for a personal inspection in private for the second heat; then he was publicly exhibited at the Crystal Palace for the semi-finals, and for the Final Judgment he was set in a pale blue bassinet and examined by three doctors, two nurses, a Child Psychologist, a film star, and Mr Cecil Beaton. After that he was declared the Most Beautiful Baby in Britain.

That was only the beginning. Baby Britain had still to face Baby France, Baby Spain, Baby Italy, and Baby America. Signor Mussolini sent a special message to Baby Italy, which the other national competitors thought unfair. The Free State insisted upon sending twins, which were disqualified. The French President cabled inviting the entire contest to be removed to Paris, and the Germans declared that the girl known as Baby Poland, having been born in the Polish Corridor, was really an East Prussian and should be registered as such.

But it did not matter. These international complications made no difference to Herbert. Triumphantly he overcame all his competitors, and was crowned as World Baby on the eve of his first birthday.

Then, indeed, began a spectacular period for Mr and Mrs Wilkins. Mrs Wilkins gave interviews to the Press on 'The Power of Mother Love', 'The Sweetest Thing in the World', and 'How I Run My Nursery'. Mr Wilkins wrote some fine manly articles on 'Fatherhood Faces Facts', and 'A Man's Son' – or, rather, they were written for him by a bright young woman until Mrs Wilkins decided that she should be present at the collaborations.

Then a firm of publishers suggested to Mr Wilkins that he should write a Christmas book called *Herbert's Father*, all about what tender feelings fathers had, and what white, pure thoughts ran through their heads when they looked upon the sleeping faces of their sons, and about how strange and wonderful it was to watch little images of themselves growing daily in beauty, and how gloriously unspotted and magical were the fairy-like actions of little children. Mr Wilkins thought that this was a good idea if someone would write the book for him, and if the advance royalties were not less than £3,000 on the date of publication; but he would have to ask Mrs Wilkins. Mrs Wilkins was a trifle hurt. Why *Herbert's Father*? What right had Paternity to override Maternity? The publisher pointed out the success of Mr A. A. Milne's *Christopher Robin*, and Mr Lewis Hind's *Julius Caesar*, and of Mr A. S. M. Hutchinson's *Son Simon*, to say nothing of Sir James Barrie's *Little White Bird*. 'But none of these children was my Herbert,' declared Mrs Wilkins – which, indeed, was undeniable. So the contract was finally signed for *The Book of Herbert*, by His Parents.

It was a success. Success? It was a Triumph, a Wow, a Scream, an Explosion. There was nothing like it. It was The Christmas Gift. It went into the third hundredth thousand before December 3rd. It was serialized simultaneously in the *Evening Standard*, *Home Chat*, and *The Nursery World*. Mr Baldwin referred to it at a Guildhall Banquet. The Prince used a joke from it in a Broadcast Speech on England and the Empire. The Book Society failed to recommend it, but every bookstall in the United Kingdom organized a display stand in its honour, with photographs of Herbert and copies signed with a blot 'Herbert, His Mark' exquisitely arranged.

The Herbert Boom continued. Small soap Herberts (undressed for the bath) were manufactured and sold for use in delighted nurseries. Royalty graciously accepted an ivory Herbert, designed as a paper-weight, from the loyal sculptor. A Herbert Day was instituted in order to raise money for the

Children's Hospitals of England, and thirty-seven different types of Herbert Calendars, Christmas Cards, and Penwipers were offered for sale – and sold.

Mrs Wilkins felt herself justified in her faith. This, she said, was what mother love could do. Mr Wilkins demanded 10 per cent royalties on every Herbert article sold. And they all bought a country house near Brighton, a Bentley car, six new frocks for Mrs Wilkins, and an electric refrigerator, and lived happily ever after until Herbert grew up.

But Herbert grew up.

When he was four he wore curls and a Lord Fauntelroy suit and posed for photographers. When he was fourteen he wore jerseys and black finger-nails and collected beetles. When he left one of England's Great Public Schools he wore plus-fours and pimples and rode a motor-cycle and changed his tie three times in half an hour before he called on the young lady at the tobacconist's round the corner. He knew what a Fella does, by Jove, and he knew what a Fella doesn't. His main interests in life were etiquette, Edgar Wallace, and the desire to live down his past. For on going to a preparatory school he had carefully insisted that his name was James. His father, who knew that boys will be boys, supported him, and as he grew to maturity, few guessed that young James Wilkins, whose beauty was certainly not discernible to the naked eye, was Herbert, the Loveliest Baby in the World. Only Mrs Wilkins, in a locked spare bedroom, cherished a museum of the Herbert photographs, trophies, first editions, soap images, ivory statuettes, silver cups, and Christmas cards. The Herbert vogue had faded, as almost all vogues do, until not even a gag about Herbert on the music hall stage raised a feeble smile.

But Mrs Wilkins found the position hard to bear. It is true that the fortunes of the family were soundly laid, that Mr Wilkins had invested the profits of his son's juvenile triumphs in Trustee Stock, and that no household in South Kensington was more respected. But Mrs Wilkins had tasted the sweet nectar of publicity and she thirsted for another drink.

It happened that one day, when (Herbert) James was twenty-three, he brought home the exciting news that he had become engaged to Selena Courtney, the daughter of Old Man Courtney, whose office in the city Herbert adorned for about six hours daily.

Nothing could have been more fortunate. Mr Wilkins was delighted, for Courtney, of Courtney, Gilbert and Co., was worth nearly half a million. Herbert was delighted, for he was enjoying the full flavour of Young Love and Satisfied Snobbery combined, which is, as everyone knows, the perfect fulfilment of a True Man's dreams. The Courtneys were delighted, because they thought young Wilkins a very decent young man, with none of this damned nonsense about him. And Mrs Wilkins – well, her feelings were mixed. It was she, after all, who had produced this marvel, and nobody seemed to remember her part in the production, nor to consider the product specially marvellous. Besides, she was a little jealous, as model mothers are allowed to be, of her prospective daughter-in-law.

The engagement was announced in *The Times* – the reporters came, rather bored, to the Kensington home of Mrs Wilkins. She was asked to supply any details about her son's career. 'Any adventures? Any accidents? Has he ever won any prizes?' asked a reporter.

This was too much. 'Come here!' said Mrs Wilkins; and she led the reporters up to the locked spare bedroom.

What happened there was soon known to the public. When (Herbert) James, two evenings later, left the office on his way to his future father-in-law's house in Belgrave Square, hoping to take his fiancée after dinner to a dance given by Lady Soxlet, he was confronted by placards announcing 'The Perfect Baby to Wed'. Taking no notice he went on to the Tube Station; but there he saw yet further placards. 'The World's Loveliest Baby now a Man', and 'Little Herbert Engaged'.

Still hardly conscious of the doom awaiting him, he bought an evening paper, and there he saw in black letters across the front page: 'Herbert's Identity at last Discovered', and underneath the fatal words: 'The young City man, Mr James Wilkins, whose engagement to Miss Selena Courtney, of 299 Belgrave Square, was announced two days ago, has been revealed by his mother, Mrs Wilkins, to be Herbert, the Wonder Baby.' There followed descriptions of the Perfect Childhood, stories taken from the Herbert Legend; rapid advertisements rushed out by What-Not's Natural Digestive Infants' Milk, Flopsy's Fleecy Pram Covers, and Hebe's Nectar for the Difficult Child, illustrated by photographs of the Infant Herbert. The publishers of the *Book of Herbert* announced a new edition, and a famous Daily Paper, whose circulation was guaranteed to be over 2,000,000, declared its intention of publishing a series of articles called 'My Herbert is a Man, by Herbert's Mother'.

Herbert did not proceed to Belgrave Square. He went to Kensington. With his own latchkey he opened the door and went up to his mother's boudoir. He found her laughing and crying with joy over the evening paper. She looked up and saw her son.

'Oh, darling,' she said. 'I thought you were taking Selena to a dance.'

'There is no Selena,' declared Herbert grimly. 'There is no dance. There is only you and me.'

He should, doubtless, have said: 'You and I,' but among the things a Fella does, correct grammar is not necessarily included.

'Oh, Herbert,' cried Mrs Wilkins, with ecstatic joy. 'My mother instinct was right. Mother always knows, darling. You have come back to me.'

'I have,' said Herbert.

And he strangled her with a rope of twisted newspapers.

The judge declared it justifiable homicide, and Herbert changed his name to William Brown and went to plant tea or rubber or something in the Malay States, where Selena joined him two years later – and Mr Wilkins lived to a ripe old age at the Brighton house and looked after his dividends, and everyone was really very happy after all.

The Schartz-Metterklume Method

Saki (H. H. Munro)

Lady Carlotta stepped out on to the platform of the small wayside station and took a turn or two up and down its uninteresting length, to kill time till the train should be pleased to proceed on its way. Then, in the roadway beyond, she saw a horse struggling with a more than ample load, and a carter of the sort that seems to bear a sullen hatred against the animal that helps him to earn a living. Lady Carlotta promptly betook her to the roadway, and put rather a different complexion on the struggle. Certain of her acquaintances were wont to give her plentiful admonition as to the undesirability of interfering on behalf of a distressed animal, such interference being 'none of her business'. Only once had she put the doctrine of non-interference into practice, when one of its most eloquent exponents had been besieged for nearly three hours in a small and extremely uncomfortable may-tree by an angry boar-pig, while Lady Carlotta, on the other side of the fence, had proceeded with the water-colour sketch she was engaged on, and refused to interfere between the boar and his prisoner. It is to be feared that she lost the friendship of the ultimately rescued lady. On this occasion she merely lost the train, which gave way to the first sign of impatience it had shown throughout the journey, and steamed off without her. She bore the desertion with philosophical indifference; her friends and relations were thoroughly well used to the fact of her luggage arriving without her. She wired a vague non-committal message to her destination to say that she was coming on 'by another train'. Before she had time to think what her next move might be she was confronted by an imposingly attired lady, who seemed to be taking a prolonged mental inventory of her clothes and looks.

'You must be Miss Hope, the governess I've come to meet,' said the apparition, in a tone that admitted of very little argument.

'Very well, if I must I must, said Lady Carlotta to herself with dangerous meekness.

'I am Mrs Quabarl,' continued the lady; 'and where, pray, is your luggage?'

'It's gone astray,' said the alleged governess, falling in with the excellent rule of life that the absent are always to blame; the luggage had, in point of fact, behaved with perfect correctitude. 'I've just telegraphed about it, she added, with a nearer approach to truth.

'How provoking,' said Mrs Quabarl; 'these railway companies are so careless. However, my maid can lend you things for the night,' and she led the way to her car.

During the drive to the Quabarl mansion Lady Carlotta was impressively introduced to the nature of the charge that had been thrust upon her; she learned that Claude and Wilfrid were delicate, sensitive young people, that Irene had the artistic temperament highly developed, and that Viola was something or other else of a mould equally commonplace among children of that class and type in the twentieth century.

'I wish them not only to be *taught*,' said Mrs Quabarl, 'but *interested* in what they learn. In their history lessons, for instance, you must try to make them feel that they are being introduced to the life-stories of men and women who really lived, not merely committing a mass of names and dates to memory. French, of course, I shall expect you to talk at mealtimes several days in the week.'

'I shall talk French four days of the week and Russian in the remaining three.'

'Russian? My dear Miss Hope, no one in the house speaks or understands Russian.'

'That will not embarrass me in the least,' said Lady Carlotta coldly.

Mrs Quarbarl, to use a colloquial expression, was knocked off her perch. She was one of those imperfectly self-assured individuals who are magnificent and autocratic as long as they are not seriously opposed. The least show of unexpected resistance goes a long way towards rendering them cowed and apologetic. When the new governess failed to express wondering admiration of the large newly purchased and expensive car, and lightly alluded to the superior advantages of one or two makes which had just been put on the market, the discomfiture of her patroness became almost abject. Her feelings were those which might have animated a general of ancient warfaring days, on beholding his heaviest battle-elephant ignominiously driven off the field by slingers and javelin throwers.

At dinner that evening, although reinforced by her husband, who usually duplicated her opinions and lent her moral support generally, Mrs Quabarl regained none of her lost ground. The governess not only helped herself well and truly to wine, but held forth with considerable show of critical knowledge on various vintage matters, concerning which the Quabarls were in no wise able to pose as authorities. Previous governesses had limited their conversation on the wine topic to a respectful and doubtless sincere expression of a preference for water. When this one went as far as to recommend a wine firm in whose hands you could not go very far wrong Mrs Quabarl thought it time to turn the conversation into more usual channels.

'We got very satisfactory references about you from Canon Teep,' she observed; 'a very estimable man, I should think.'

'Drinks like a fish and beats his wife, otherwise a very lovable character,' said the governess imperturbably.

'My *dear* Miss Hope! I trust you are exaggerating,' exclaimed the Quabarls in unison.

'One must in justice admit that there is some provocation,' continued the romancer. 'Mrs Teep is quite the most irritating bridge-player that I have ever sat down with; her leads and declarations would condone a certain amount of brutality in her partner, but to souse her with the contents of the only soda-water syphon in the house on a Sunday afternoon, when one couldn't get another, argues an indifference to the comfort of others which I cannot altogether overlook. You may think me hasty in my judgements, but it was practically on account of the syphon incident that I left.'

'We will talk of this some other time, said Mrs Quabarl hastily.

'I shall never allude to it again,' said the governess with decision.

Mr Quabarl made a welcome diversion by asking what studies the new instructress proposed to inaugurate on the morrow.

'History to begin with,' she informed him.

'Ah, history,' he observed sagely; 'now in teaching them history you must take care to interest them in what they learn. You must make them feel that they are being introduced to the life-stories of men and women who really lived –'

'I've told her all that,' interposed Mrs Quabarl.

'I teach history on the Schartz-Metterklume method,' said the governess loftily.

'Ah, yes,' said her listeners, thinking it expedient to assume an acquaintance at least with the name.

'What are you children doing out here?' demanded Mrs Quabarl the next morning, on finding Irene sitting rather glumly at the head of the stairs, while her sister was perched in an attitude of depressed discomfort on the window-seat behind her, with a wolf-skin rug almost covering her.

'We are having a history lesson, came the unexpected reply. 'I am supposed to be Rome, and Viola up there is the she-wolf; not a real wolf, but the figure of one that the Romans used to set store by – I forget why. Claude and Wilfrid have gone to fetch the shabby women.'

'The shabby women?'

'Yes, they've got to carry them off. They didn't want to, but Miss Hope got one of father's fives-bats and said she'd give them a number nine spanking if they didn't, so they've gone to do it.'

A loud, angry screaming from the direction of the lawn drew Mrs Quabarl thither in hot haste, fearful lest the threatened castigation might even now be in process of infliction. The outcry, however, came principally from the two small daughters of the lodgekeeper, who were being hauled and pushed towards the house by the panting and dishevelled Claude and Wilfrid, whose task was rendered even more arduous by the incessant, if not very effectual, attacks of the captured maidens' small brother. The governess, fives-bat in hand, sat negligently on the stone balustrade, presiding over the scene with the cold impartiality of a Goddess of Battles. A furious and repeated chorus of 'I'll tell muvver' rose from the lodge children, but the lodge-mother, who was hard of hearing, was for the moment immersed in the preoccupation of her washtub. After an apprehensive glance in the direction of the lodge (the good woman was gifted with the highly militant temper which is sometimes the privilege of deafness) Mrs Quabarl flew indignantly to the rescue of the struggling captives.

'Wilfrid! Claude! Let those children go at once. Miss Hope, what on earth is the meaning of this scene?'

'Early Roman history; the Sabine women, don't you know? It's the Schartz-Metterklume method to make children understand history by acting it themselves; fixes it in their memory, you know. Of course, if, thanks to your interference, your boys go through life thinking that the Sabine women ultimately escaped, I really cannot be held responsible.'

'You may be very clever and modern, Miss Hope,' said Mrs Quabarl firmly, 'but I should like you to leave here by the next train. Your luggage will be sent after you as soon as it arrives.'

'I'm not certain exactly where I shall be for the next few days,' said the dismissed instructress of youth; 'you might keep my luggage till I wire my address. There are only a couple of trunks and some golf-clubs and a leopard cub.'

'A leopard cub!' gaped Mrs Quabarl. Even in her departure this extraordinary person seemed destined to leave a trail of embarrassment behind her.

'Well, its rather left off being a cub; it's more than half-grown, you know. A fowl every day and a rabbit on Sundays is what it usually gets. Raw beef makes it too excitable. Don't trouble about getting the car for me, I'm rather inclined for a walk.'

And Lady Carlotta strode out of the Quabarl horizon.

The advent of the genuine Miss Hope, who had made a mistake as to the day on which she was due to arrive, caused a turmoil which that good lady was quite unused to inspiring. Obviously the Quabarl family had been woefully befooled, but a certain amount of relief came with the knowledge.

'How tiresome for you, dear Carlotta, said her hostess, when the overdue guest ultimately arrived; 'how very tiresome losing your train and having to stop overnight in a strange place.'

'Oh, dear, no,' said Mrs Quabarl; 'not at all tiresome – for me.'

Lucia and the Garden Fête

E. F. Benson

Lucia, one of the great comic snobs and intriguers of English fiction, has taken a house in the village of Tilling for the summer. Setting out to become Tilling's social leader, she faces strong competition in resident rival Elizabeth Mapp. But Lucia is dauntless and her strategies, matchless ...

Lucia was writing letters in the window of the garden-room next morning. One, already finished, was to Adele Brixton asking her to send to Mallards the Queen Elizabeth costume for the tableaux: a second, also finished, was to the Padre, saying that she found she would not have time to attend committees for the hospital fête, and begging him to co-opt Miss Mapp. She would however, do all in her power to help the scheme, and make any little suggestions that occurred to her. She added that the chance of getting fruit gratis for the refreshment department would be far brighter if the owner of it was on the board.

The third letter, firmly beginning 'Dearest Liblib' (and to be signed very large, LUCIA), asking her to dine in two days' time, was not quite done when she saw dearest Liblib, with a fixed and awful smile, coming swifly up the street. Lucia, sitting sideways to the window, could easily appear absorbed in her letter and unconscious of Elizabeth's approach, but from beneath half-lowered eyelids she watched her with the intensest interest. She was slanting across the street now, making a bee-line for the door of Mallards ('and if she tries to get in without ringing the bell, she'll find the chain on the door,' thought Lucia).

The abandoned woman, disdaining the bell, turned the handle and pushed. It did not yield to her intrusion, and she pushed more strongly. There was the sound of jingling metal, audible even in the garden-room, as the hasp that held the end of the chain gave way; the door flew open wide, and with a few swift and nimble steps she just saved herself from falling flat on the floor of the hall.

Lucia, pale with fury, laid down her pen and waited for the situation to develop. She hoped she would behave like a lady, but was quite sure it would be a firm sort of lady. Presently up the steps to the garden-room came that fairy tread, the door was opened an inch, and that odious voice said:

'May I come in, dear?'

'Certainly,' said Lucia brightly.

'Lulu dear,' said Elizabeth, tripping across the room with little brisk steps. 'First I must apologize: so humbly. Such a stupid accident. I tried to open your front door, and gave it a teeny little push and your servants had forgotten to take the chain down. I am afraid I broke something. The hasp must have been rusty.'

Lucia looked puzzled.

'But didn't Grosvenor come to open the door when you rang?' she asked.

'That was just what I forgot to do, dear,' said Elizabeth. 'I thought I would pop in to see you without troubling Grosvenor. You and I such friends, and so difficult to remember that my dear little Mallards – Several things to talk about!'

Lucia got up.

'Let us first see what damage you have done,' she said with an icy calmness, and marched straight out of the room, followed by Elizabeth. The sound of the explosion had brought Grosvenor out of the dining-room, and Lucia picked up the dangling hasp and examined it.

'No, no sign of rust,' she said. 'Grosvenor, you must go down to the ironmonger and get them to come up and repair this at once. The chain must be made safer and you must remember always to put it on, day and night. If I am out, I will ring.'

'So awfully sorry, dear Lulu,' said Elizabeth, slightly cowed by this firm treatment. 'I had no idea the chain would be up. We all keep our doors on the latch in Tilling. Quite a habit.'

'I always used to in Riseholme,' said Lucia. 'Let us go back to the garden-room, and you will tell me what you came to talk about.'

'Several things,' said Elizabeth when they had settled themselves. 'First, I am starting a little jumble-sale for the hospital, and I wanted to look out some old curtains and rugs, laid away in cupboards, to give to it. May I just go upstairs and downstairs and poke about to find them?'

'By all means,' said Lucia. 'Grosvenor shall go round with you as soon as he has come back fromt he ironmonger's.'

'Thank you, dear,' said Elizabeth, 'though there's no need to trouble Grosvenor. Then another thing. I persuaded Mr Georgie to send me a sketch for our picky exhibition. Promise me that you'll send me one too. Wouldn't be complete without something by you. How you get all you do into the day is beyond me; your sweet music, your sketching, and your dinner-parties every evening.'

Lucia readily promised, and Elizabeth then appeared to lose herself in reverie.

'There *is* one more thing,' she said at last. 'I have heard a little gossip in the town both today and yesterday about a fête which it is proposed to give in my garden. I feel sure it is mere tittle-tattle, but I thought it would be better to come up here to know from you that there is no foundation for it.'

'But I hope there is a great deal,' said Lucia. 'Some tableaux, some singing, in order to raise funds for the hospital. It would be so kind of you if you would supply the fruit for the refreshment booth from your garden. Apropos I should be so pleased to buy some of it every day myself. It would be fresher than if, as at present, it is taken down to the greengrocer and brought up again.'

'Anything to oblige you, dear Lulu,' said Elizabeth. 'But that would be difficult to arrange. I have contracted to send all my garden-produce to Twistevant's – such a quaint name, is it not? – for these months, and for the same reason I should be unable to supply this fête which I have heard spoken of. The fruit is no longer mine.'

Lucia had already made up her mind that, after this affair of the chain, nothing would induce her to propose that Elizabeth should take her place on the committee. She would cling to it through storm and tempest.

'I see,' she said. 'Perhaps then you could let us have some fruit from Diva's garden, unless you have sold that also.'

Elizabeth came to the point, disregarding so futile a suggestion.

'The fête itself, dear one,' she said, 'is what I must speak about. I cannot possibly permit it to take place in my garden. The rag-tag and bob-tail of Tilling passing through my hall and my sweet little sitting-room and spending the afternoon in my garden! All my carpets soiled and my flower-beds trampled on! And how do I know that they will not steal upstairs and filch what they can find?'

Lucia's blood had begun to boil: nobody could say that she was preserving a benevolent neutrality. In consequence she presented an icy demeanour, and if her voice trembled at all, it was from excessive cold.

'There will be no admission to the rooms in the house,' she said. 'I will lock all the doors, and I am sure that nobody in Tilling will be so ill bred as to attempt to force them open.'

That was a nasty one. Elizabeth recoiled for a moment from the shock, but rallied. She opened her mouth very wide to begin again, but Lucia got in first.

'They will pass straight from the front door into the garden,' she said, 'where we undertake to entertain them, presenting their tickets of admission or paying at the door. As for the carpet in your sweet little sitting-room, there isn't one. And I have too high an opinion of the manners of Tilling in general to suppose that they will trample on your flower-beds.'

'Perhaps you would like to hire a menagerie,' said Elizabeth, completely losing her self-control, 'and have an exhibition of tigers and sharks in the garden-room.'

'No: I should particularly dislike it,' said Lucia earnestly. 'Half of the garden-room would have to be turned into a sea-water tank for the sharks and my piano would be flooded. And the rest would have to be full of horse-flesh for the tigers. A most ridiculous proposal, and I cannot entertain it.'

Elizabeth gave a dreadful gasp as if she was one of the sharks and the water had been forgotten. She adroitly changed the subject.

'Then again, there's the rumour – of course it's only rumour – that there is some idea of entertaining such inmates of the workhouse as are not bedridden. Impossible.'

'I fancy the Padre is arranging that,' said Lucia. 'For my part, I'm delighted to give them a little treat.'

'And for my part,' said Miss Mapp, rising (she had become Miss Mapp again in Lucia's mind), 'I will not have my little home-sanctuary invaded by the rag-tag –'

'The tickets will be half a crown,' interposed Lucia.

'– and bob-tail of Tilling,' continued Miss Mapp.

'As long as I am tenant here,' said Lucia, 'I shall ask here whom I please, and when I please, and – and how I please. Or do you wish me to send you a list of the friends I ask to dinner for your sanction?'

Miss Mapp, trembling very much, forced her lips to form the syllables: 'But, dear Lulu –'

'Dear Elizabeth, I must beg you not to call me Lulu,' she said. 'Such a detestable abbreviation –'

Grosvenor had appeared at the door of the garden-room.

'Yes, Grosvenor, what is it?' asked Lucia in precisely the same voice.

'The ironmonger is here, ma'am,' she said, 'and he says that he'll have to put in some rather large screws, as they're pulled out –'

'Whatever is necessary to make the door safe,' said Lucia. 'And Miss Mapp wants to look into cupboards and take some things of her own away. Go with her, please, and give her every facility.

Lucia, quite in the grand style, turned to look out of the window in the direction of Mallards Cottage, in order to give Miss Mapp the opportunity of a discreet exit. She threw the window open.

'Georgino! Georgino!' she called, and Georgie's face appeared above the paling.

'Come round and have 'ickle talk, Georgie,' she said. 'Sumfin I want to tell you. Presto!'

She kissed her hand to Georgie and turned back into the room. Miss Mapp was still there, but now invisible to Lucia's eye. She hummed a gay bar of Mozartino, and went back to her table in the bow-window where she tore up the letter of resignation and recommendation she had written to the Padre, and the half-finished note to Miss Mapp, which so cordially asked her to dinner, saying that it was so long since they had met, for they had met again now. When she looked up she was alone, and there was Georgie tripping up the steps by the front door. Though it was standing open (for the ironmonger was already engaged on the firm restoration of the chain) he very properly rang the bell and was admitted.

'There you are,' said Lucia brightly as he came in. 'Another lovely day.'

'Perfect. What has happened to your front door?'

Lucia laughed.

'Elizabeth came to see me,' she said gaily. 'The chain was on the door, as I have ordered it always shall be .But she gave the door such a biff that the hasp pulled out. It's being repaired.'

'No!' said Georgie, 'and did you give her what for?'

'She had several things she wanted to see me about,' said Lucia, keeping an intermittent eye on the front door. 'She wanted to get out of her cupboards some stuff for the jumble-sale she is getting up in aid of the hospital, and she is at it now under Grosvenor's superintendence. Then she wanted me to send a sketch for the picture exhibition, I said I would be delighted. Then she

said she could not manage to send any fruit for our fête here. She did not
approve of the fête at all, Georgie. In fact she forbade me to give it. We had
a little chat about that.'

'But what's to be done then?' asked Georgie.

'Nothing that I know of, except to give the fête,' said Lucia. 'But it would
be no use asking her to be on the committee for an object of which she
disapproved, so I tore up the letter I had written to the Padre about it.'

Lucia suddenly focused her eyes and her attention on the front door, and
a tone of warm human interest melted the deadly chill of her voice.

'Georgie, there she goes,' she said. 'What a quantity of things! There's an
old kettle and a boot-jack, and a rug with a hole in it, and one stair-rod.
And there's a shaving from the front door where they are putting in bigger
screws, stuck to her skirt.... And she's dropped the stair-rod.... Major
Benjy's picking it up for her.'

Georgie hurried to the window to see these exciting happenings, but Miss
Mapp, having recovered the stair-rod, was already disappearing.

'I wish I hadn't given her my picture of the Land-gate,' said he. 'It was
one of my best. But aren't you going to tell me all about your interview?
Properly, I mean: everything.'

'Not worth speaking of,' said Lucia. 'She asked me if I would like to have
a menagerie and keep tigers and sharks in the garden-room. That sort of
thing. Mere raving. Come out, Georgie. I want to do a little shopping.
Coplen told me there were some excellent greengages from the garden which
he was taking down to Twistevant's.'

It was the hour when the collective social life of Tilling was at its briskest.
The events of the evening before, tea-parties, and games of bridge had become
known and were under discussion, as the ladies of the place with their baskets
on their arms collided with each other as they popped in and out of shops
and obstructed the pavements. Many parcels were being left at Wasters
which Miss Mapp now occupied, for jumble-sales on behalf of deserving
objects were justly popular, since everybody had a lot of junk in their houses,
which they could not bear to throw away, but for which they had no earthly
use. Diva had already been back from Taormina to her own house (as
Elizabeth to hers) and had disinterred from a cupboard of rubbish a pair of
tongs, the claws of which twisted round if you tried to pick up a lump of
coal and dropped it on the carpet, but which were otherwise perfect. Then
there was a scuttle which had a hole in the bottom, through which coal dust
softly dribbled, and a candlestick which had lost one of its feet, and a glass

inkstand once handsome, but now cracked. These treasures, handsome donations to a jumble-sale, but otherwise of no particular value, she carried to her own hall, where donors were requested to leave their offerings, and she learned from Withers, Miss Mapp's parlour-maid, the disagreeable news that the jumble-sale was to be held here. The thought revolted her; all the rag-tag and bob-tail of Tilling would come wandering about her house, soiling her carpets and smudging her walls. At this moment Miss Mapp herself came in carrying the tea-kettle and the boot-jack and the other things. She had already thought of half a dozen withering retorts she might have made to Lucia.

'Elizabeth, this will never do,' said Diva. 'I can't have the jumble-sale held here. They'll make a dreadful mess of the place.'

'Oh no, dear,' said Miss Mapp, with searing memories of a recent interview in her mind. 'The people will only come into your hall where you see there's no carpet, and make their purchases. What a beautiful pair of tongs! For my sale? Fancy! Thank you, dear Diva.'

'But I forbid the jumble-sale to be held here,' said Diva. 'You'll be wanting to have a menagerie here next.'

This was amazing luck.

'No, dear, I couldn't dream of it,' said Miss Mapp. 'I should hate to have tigers and sharks all over the place. Ridiculous!'

'I shall put up a merry-go-round in quaint Irene's studio at Taormina,' said Diva.

'I doubt if there's room, dear,' said Miss Mapp, scoring heavily again, 'but you might measure. Perfectly legitimate, of course, for if my house may be given over to parties for paupers, you can surely have a merry-go-round in quaint Irene's and I a jumble-sale in yours.'

'It's not the same thing,' said Diva. 'Providing beautiful tableaux in your garden is quite different from using my panelled hall to sell kettles and coal-scuttles with holes in them.'

'I dare say I could find a good many holes in the tableaux,' said Miss Mapp.

Diva could think of no adequate verbal retort to such coruscations, so for answer she merely picked up the tongs, the coal-scuttle, the candlestick and the inkstand, and put them back in the cupboard from which she had just taken them, and left her tenant to sparkle by herself.

Most of the damaged objects for the jumble-sale must have arrived by now, and after arranging them in tasteful groups Miss Mapp sat down in a rickety basket-chair presented by the Padre for fell meditation. Certainly it was not pretty of Diva (no one could say that Diva was pretty) to have withdrawn her treasures, but that was not worth thinking about. What did demand her highest mental activities was Lucia's conduct. How grievously different she had turned out to be from that sweet woman for whom she had originally felt so warm an affection, whom she had planned to take so cosily under her wing, and administer in small doses as treats to Tilling society! Lucia had turned upon her and positively bitten the caressing hand. By means of showy little dinners and odious flatteries, she had quite certainly made Major Benjy and the Padre and the Wyses and poor Diva think that she was a very remarkable and delightful person and in these manoeuvres Miss Mapp saw a shocking and sinister attempt to set herself up as the Queen of Tilling society. Lucia had given dinner-parties on three consecutive nights since her return, she had put herself on the committee for this fête, which (however much Miss Mapp might say she could not possibly permit it) she had not the slightest idea how to stop, and though Lucia was only a temporary resident here, these weeks would be quite intolerable if she continued to inflate herself in this presumptuous manner. It was certainly time for Miss Mapp to reassert herself before this rebel made more progress, and though dinner-giving was unusual in Tilling, she determined to give one or two most amusing ones herself, to none of which, of course, she would invite Lucia. But that was not nearly enough: she must administer some frightful snub (or snubs) to the woman. Georgie was in the same boat and must suffer too, for Lucia would not like that. So she sat in this web of crippled fire-irons and napless rugs like a spider, meditating reprisals. Perhaps it was a pity, when she needed allies, to have quarrelled with Diva, but a dinner would set that right. Before long she got up with a pleased expression. 'That will do to begin with: he won't like that at all,' she said to herself and went out to do her belated marketing.

She passed Lucia and Georgie, but decided not to see them, and, energetically waving her hand to Mrs Bartlett, she popped into Twistevant's, from the door of which they had just come out. At that moment quaint Irene, after a few words with the Padre, caught sight of Lucia, and hurried across the street to her. She was hatless, as usual, and wore a collarless shirt and knickerbockers unlike any other lady of Tilling, but as she approached Lucia her face assumed an acid and awful smile, just like somebody else's, and then she spoke in a cooing velvety voice that was quite unmistakable.

'The boy stood on the burning deck, Lulu,' she said. 'Whence all but he had fled, dear. The flames that lit the battle-wreck, sweet one, shone round him –'

Quaint Irene broke off suddenly, for within a yard of her at the door of Twistevant's appeared Miss Mapp. She looked clean over all their heads, and darted across the street to Wasters, carrying a small straw basket of her own delicious greengages.

'Or, lor!' said Irene. 'The Mapp's in the fire, so that's done. Yes. I'll recite for you at your fête. Georgie, what a saucy hat! I was just going to Taormina to rout out some old sketches of mine for the Art Show, and then this happens. I wouldn't have had it not happen for a hundred pounds.'

'Come and dine tonight,' said Lucia warmly, breaking all records in the way of hospitality.

'Yes, if I needn't dress, and you'll send me home afterwards. I'm half a mile out of the town and I may be tipsy, for Major Benjy says you've got jolly good booze, quai hai, the King, God bless him! Goodbye.'

'Most original!' said Lucia. 'To go on with what I was telling you, Georgie, Liblib said she would not have her little home-sanctuary – Good morning, Padre. Miss Mapp shoved her way into Mallards this morning without ringing, and broke the chain which was on the door, such a hurry was she in to tell me that she will not have her little home-sanctuary, as I was just saying to Georgie, invaded by the rag-tag and bob-tail of Tilling.'

'Hoots awa!' said the Padre. 'What in the world has Mistress Mapp got to do with it? An' who's holding a jumble-sale in Mistress Plaistow's? I keeked in just now wi' my bit o' rubbish and never did I see such a mess. Na, na! Fair play's a jool, an' we'll go richt ahead. Excuse me, there's wee wifie wanting me.'

'It's war,' said Georgie as the Padre darted across to the Mouse, who was on the other side of the street, to tell her what had happened.

'No, I'm just defending myself,' said Lucia. 'It's right that people should know she burst my door-chain.'

'Well, I feel like the fourth of August, 1914,' said Georgie. 'What do you suppose she'll do next?'

'You may depend upon it, Georgie, that I shall be ready for her whatever it is,' said Lucia. 'I shan't raise a finger against her, if she behaves. But she *shall* ring the bell and I *won't* be dictated to and I *won't* be called Lulu. However, there's no immediate danger of that. Come, Georgie, let us go home and finish our sketches. Then we'll have them framed and send them Liblib for the picture exhibition. Perhaps that will convince her of my general good will, which I assure you is quite sincere.'

The jumble-sale opened next day, and Georgie, having taken his picture of Lucia's house and her picture of his to be framed in a very handsome manner, went on to Wasters with the idea of buying anything that could be of the smallest use for any purpose, and thus showing more good will towards the patroness. Miss Mapp was darting to and fro with lures for purchasers, holding the kettle away from the light so that the hole in its bottom should not be noticed, and she gave him a smile that looked rather like a snarl, but after all very like the smile she had for others. Georgie selected a hearth-brush, some curtain rings and a kettle-holder.

Then in a dark corner he came across a large cardboard tray, holding miscellaneous objects with the label 'All 6d. Each.' There were thimbles, there were photographs with slightly damaged frames, there were chipped china ornaments and cork-screws, and there was the picture of the Land-gate which he had painted himself and given Miss Mapp. Withers, Miss Mapp's parlour-maid, was at a desk for the exchange of custom by the door, and he exhibited his purchases for her inspection.

'Ninepence for the hearth-brush and threepence for the curtain rings,' said Georgie in a trembling voice, 'and sixpence for the kettle-holder. Then there's this little picture out of the sixpenny tray, which makes just two shillings.'

Laden with these miscellaneous purchases he went swiftly up the street to Mallards. Lucia was at the window of the garden-room, and her gimlet-eye saw that something had happened. She threw the sash up.

'I'm afraid the chain is on the door, Georgie,' she called out. 'You'll have to ring. What is it?'

'I'll show you,' said Georgie.

He deposited the hearth-brush, the curtain rings and the kettle-holder in the hall, and hurried out to the garden-room with the picture.

'The sketch I gave her,' he said. 'In the sixpenny tray. Why, the frame cost a shilling.'

Lucia's face became a flint.

'I never heard of such a thing, Georgie,' said she. 'The monstrous woman!'

'It may have got there by mistake,' said Georgie, frightened at this Medusa countenance.

'Rubbish, Georgie,' said Lucia.

Pictures from the annual exhibition of the Art Society of which Miss Mapp was President had been arriving in considerable numbers at Wasters, and stood stacked round the walls of the hall where the jumble-sale had been held a few days before, awaiting the judgment of the hanging committee which consisted of the President, the Treasurer and the Secretary: the two latter were Mr and Mrs Wyse. Miss Mapp had sent in half a dozen water-colours, the Treasurer a study in still life of a tea-cup, an orange and a wallflower, the Secretary a pastel portrait of the King of Italy, whom she had seen at a distance in Rome last spring. She had reinforced the vivid impression he had made on her by photographs. All these, following the precedent of the pictures of Royal Academicians at Burlington House, would be hung on the line without dispute, and there could not be any friction concerning them. But quaint Irene had sent some at which Miss Mapp felt lines must be drawn. They were, as usual, very strange and modern: there was one, harmless but insane, that purported to be Tilling Church by moonlight: a bright green pinnacle all crooked (she supposed it was a pinnacle) rose up against a strip of purple sky and the whole of the rest of the canvas was black. There was the back of somebody with no clothes on lying on an emerald-green sofa: and, worst of all, there was a picture called 'Women wrestlers,' from which Miss Mapp hurriedly averted her eyes. A proper regard for decency alone, even if Irene had not mimicked her reciting 'The Boy stood on the burning deck,' would have made her resolve to oppose, tooth and nail, the exhibition of these shameless athletes. Unfortunately Mr Wyse had the most unbounded admiration for quaint Irene's work, and if she had sent in a picture of mixed wrestlers he would probably have said, 'Dear me, very powerful!' He was a hard man to resist, for if he and Miss Mapp had a very strong difference of opinion concerning any particular canvas he broke off and fell into fresh transports of admiration at her own pictures and this rather disarmed opposition.

The meeting of the hanging committee was to take place this morning at noon. Half an hour before that time, an errand boy arrived at Wasters from the frame-maker's bringing, according to the order he had received, two parcels which contained Georgie's picture of Mallards and Lucia's picture of Mallards Cottage: they had the cards of their perpetrators attached. 'Rubbishy little daubs,' thought Miss Mapp to herself, 'but I suppose those two Wyses will insist.' Then an imprudent demon of revenge suddenly took complete possession of her, and she called back the boy, and said she had a further errand for him.

At a quarter before twelve the boy arrived at Mallards and rang the bell. Grosvenor took down the chain and received from him a thin square parcel labelled 'With care'. One minute afterwards he delivered a similar parcel to Foljambe at Mallards Cottage, and had discharged Miss Mapp's further errand. The two maids conveyed these to their employers, and Georgie and Lucia, tearing off the wrappers, found themselves simultaneously confronted with their own pictures. A typewritten slip accompanied each, conveying to them the cordial thanks of the hanging committee and its regrets that the limited wall space at its disposal would not permit of these works of art being exhibited.

Georgie ran out into his little yard and looked over the paling of Lucia's garden. At the same moment Lucia threw open the window of the garden-room which faced towards the paling.

'Georgie, have you received —' she called.

'Yes,' said Georgie.

'So have I.'

'What are you going to do?' he asked.

Lucia's face assumed an expression eager and pensive, the far-away look with which she listened to Beethoven. She thought intently for a moment.

'I shall take a season ticket for the exhibition,' she said, 'and con-stantly —'

'I can't quite hear you,' said Georgie.

Lucia raised her voice.

'I shall buy a season ticket for the exhibition,' she shouted, 'and go there every day. Believe me, that's the only way to take it. They don't want our pictures, but we mustn't be small about it. Dignity, Georgie.'

There was nothing to add to so sublime a declaration, and Lucia went across to the bow-window, looking down the street. At that moment the Wyses' Royce lurched out of Porpoise Street, and turned down towards the High Street. Lucia knew they were both on the hanging committee which had just rejected one of her own most successful sketches (for the crooked chimney had turned out beautifully), but she felt not the smallest resentment towards them. No doubt they had acted quite conscientiously and she waved her hand in answer to a flutter of sables from the interior of the car. Presently she went down herself to the High Street to hear the news of the morning, and there was the Wyses' car drawn up in front of Wasters. She remembered then that the hanging committee met this morning, and a suspicion, too awful to be credible, flashed through her mind. But she thrust it out, as being unworthy of entertainment by a clean mind. She did her shopping and on her return took down a pale straw-coloured sketch by Miss Mapp that hung in the garden-room, and put in its place her picture of Mallards Cottage and the crooked chimney. Then she called to mind that powerful platitude, and said to herself that time would show....

Miss Mapp had not intended to be present at the desecration of her garden by paupers from the workhouse and such low haunts. She had consulted her solicitor, about her power to stop the entertainment, but he assured her that there was no known statute in English law, which enabled her to prevent her tenant giving a party. So she determined, in the manner of Lucia and the Elizabethan fête at Riseholme, to be unaware of it, not to know that any fête was contemplated, and never afterwards to ask a single question about it. But as the day approached she suspected that the hot tide of curiosity, rapidly rising in her, would probably end by swamping and submerging her principles. She had seen the Padre dressed in a long black cloak, and carrying an axe of enormous size, entering Mallards; she had seen Diva come out in a white plain gown and scuttle down the street to Taormina, and those two prodigies taken together suggested that the execution of Mary Queen of Scots was in hand. (Diva as the Queen!) She had been boards and post carried in by the garden-door and quantities of red cloth, so there was perhaps to be a stage for these tableaux. More intriguing yet was the apparition of Major Benjy carrying a cardboard crown glittering with gold paper. What on earth did that portend? Then there was her fruit to give an eye to: those choir-boys, scampering all over the garden in the intervals between their glees would probably pick every pear from the tree. She starved to know what was going on, but since she avoided all mention of the fête herself, others were most amazingly respectful to her reticence. She knew nothing, she could only make these delirious guesses, and there was *that* Lucia, being the centre of executioners and queens and choir-boys, instead of in her proper place, made much of by kind Miss Mapp, and enjoying such glimpses of Tilling society as she chose to give her. 'A fortnight ago,' thought kind Miss Mapp, 'I was popping in and out of the house, and she was Lulu. Anyhow, that was a nasty one she got over her picture, and I must bear her no grudge. I shall go to the fête because I can't help it, and I shall be very cordial to her and admire her tableaux. We're all Christians together, and I despise smallness.'

It was distressing to be asked to pay half a crown for admittance to her own Mallards, but there seemed positively no other way to get past Grosvenor. Very distressing, too, it was to see Lucia in full fig as Queen Elizabeth, graciously receiving new-comers on the edge of the lawn, precisely as if this was her party and these people who had paid half a crown to come in, her invited guests. It was a bitter thought that it ought to be herself who (though not dressed in all that flummery, so unconvincing by daylight) welcomed the crowd; for to whom, pray, did Mallards belong, and who had allowed it (since she could not stop it) to be thrown open? At the bottom of the steps into the garden-room was a large placard 'Private', but of course that would not apply to her. Through the half-opened door, as she passed, she caught a glimpse of a familiar figure, though sadly travestied, sitting in a robe and a golden crown and pouring something into a glass: no doubt then the garden-room was the green-room of performers in the tableaux, who, less greedy of publicity than Lulu, hid themselves here till the time of their exposure brought them out. She would go in there presently, but her immediate duty, bitter but necessary, was to greet her hostess. With a very happy inspiration she tripped up to Lucia and dropped a low curtsey.

'Your Majesty's most obedient humble servant,' she said, and then trusting that Lucia had seen that this obeisance was made in a mocking spirit, abounded in geniality.

'My dear, what a love of a costume!' she said. 'And what a lovely day for your fête! And what a crowd! How the half-crowns have been pouring in! All Tilling seems to be here, and I'm sure I don't wonder.'

Lucia rivalled these cordialities with equal fervour and about as much sincerity.

'Elizabeth! How nice of you to look in!' she said. 'Ecco, le due Elizabethe! And you like my frock? Sweet of you! Yes. Tilling has indeed come to the aid of the Hospital! And your jumble-sale too was a wonderful success, was it not? Nothing left, I am told.'

Miss Mapp had a moment's hesitation as to whether she should not continue to stand by Lucia and shake hands with new arrivals and give them a word of welcome, but she decided she could do more effective work if she made herself independent and played hostess by herself. Also this mention of the jumble sale made her slightly uneasy. Withers had told her that Georgie had bought his own picture of the Land-gate from the sixpenny tray, and Lucia (for all her cordiality) might be about to spring some horrid trap on her about it.

'Yes, indeed,' she said. 'My little sale-room was soon as bare as Mother

Hubbard's cupboard. But I mustn't monopolize you, dear, or I shall be lynched. There's a whole *queue* of people waiting to get a word with you. How I shall enjoy the tableaux! Looking forward to them so!'

She sidled off into the crowd. There were those dreadful old wretches from the workhouse, snuffy old things, some of them smoking pipes on her lawn and scattering matches, and being served with tea by Irene and the Padre's curate.

'So pleased to see you all here,' she said, 'sitting in my garden and enjoying your tea. I must pick a nice nosegay for you to take back home. How de do, Mr Sturgis. Delighted you could come and help to entertain the old folks for us. Good afternoon, Mr Wyse; yes, my little garden is looking nice, isn't it? Susan, dear! Have you noticed my bed of delphiniums? I must give you some seed. Oh, there is the town-crier ringing his bell! I suppose that means we must take our places for the tableaux. What a good stage! I hope the posts will not have made very big holes in my lawn. Oh, one of those naughty choir-boys is hovering about my figtree. I cannot allow that.

She hurried off to stop any possibility of such depredation, and had made some telling allusions to the eighth commandment when on a second peal of the town-crier's bell, the procession of mummers came down the steps of the garden-room and advancing across the lawn disappeared behind the stage. Poor Major Benjy (so weak of him to allow himself to be dragged into this sort of thing) looked a perfect guy in his crown (who could he be meant for?) and as for Diva – Then there was Georgie (Drake indeed!), and last of all Queen Elizabeth with her train held up by two choir-boys. Poor Lucia! Not content with a week of mumming at Riseholme she had to go on with her processions and dressings-up here. Some people lived on limelight.

Miss Mapp could not bring herself to take a seat close to the stage, and be seen applauding – there seemed to be some hitch with the curtain: no, it righted itself, what a pity! – and she hung about on the outskirts of the audience. Glees were interposed between the tableaux; how thin were the voices of these little boys out of doors! Then Irene, dressed like a sailor, recited that ludicrous parody. Roars of laughter. Then major Benjy was King Cophetua: that was why he had a crown. Oh dear, oh dear! It was sad to reflect that an elderly, sensible man (for when at his best, he was that) could be got hold of by a pushing woman. The final tableau, of course (anyone might have guessed that), was the knighting of Drake by Queen Elizabeth. Then amid sycophantic applause the procession of guys returned and went back into the garden-room. Mr and Mrs Wyse followed them, and it seemed pretty clear that they were going to have a private tea in there. Doubtless she would be soon sought for among the crowd with a message from Lucia to hope that she would join them in her own garden-room, but as nothing of the sort came, she presently thought that it would be only kind to Lucia to do so, and add her voice to the general chorus of congratulation that was no doubt going on. So with a brisk little tap on the door, and the inquiry 'May I come in?' she entered.

There they all were, as pleased as children with dressing-up. King Cophetua still wore his crown, tilted slightly to one side like a forage cap, and he and Queen Elizabeth and Queen Mary were seated round the tea-table and calling each other your Majesty. King Cophetua had a large whisky and soda in front of him and Miss Mapp felt quite certain it was not his first. But though sick in soul at these puerilities she pulled herself together and made a beautiful curtsey to the silly creatures. And the worst of it was that there was no one left of her own intimate circle to whom she could in private express her disdain, for they were all in it, either actively or, like the Wyses, truckling to Lucia.

Lucia for the moment seemed rather surprised to see her, but she welcomed her and poured her out a cup of rather tepid tea, nasty to the taste. She must truckle, too, to the whole lot of them, though that tasted nastier than the tea.

'How I congratulate you all,' she cried. 'Padre, you looked too cruel as executioner, your mouth so fixed and stern. It was quite a relief when the curtain came down. Irene, quaint one, how you made them laugh! Diva, Mr Georgie, and above all our wonderful Queen Lucia. What a treat it has all been! The choir! Those beautiful glees. A thousand pities, Mr Wyse, that the Contessa was not here.'

There was still Susan to whom she ought to say something pleasant, but positively she could not go on, until she had eaten something solid. But Lucia chimed in.

'And your garden, Elizabeth,' she said. 'How they are enjoying it. I believe if the truth was known they are all glad that our little tableaux are over, so that they can wander about and admire the flowers. I must give a little party some night soon with Chinese lanterns and fairy-lights in the beds.'

'Upon my word, your Majesty is spoiling us all,' said Major Benjy. 'Tilling's never had a month with so much pleasure provided for it. Glorious.'

Miss Mapp had resolved to stop here if it was anyhow possible, till these sycophants had dispersed, and then have one private word with Lucia to indicate how ready she was to overlook all the little frictions that had undoubtedly arisen. She fully meant, without eating a morsel of humble pie herself, to allow Lucia to eat proud pie, for she saw that just for the present she herself was nowhere and Lucia everywhere. So Lucia should glut herself into a sense of complete manoeuvres. Major Benjy and Diva soon took themselves off: she saw them from the garden-window going very slowly down the street, ever so pleased to have people staring at them, and Irene, at the Padre's request, went out to dance a hornpipe on the lawn in her sailor clothes. But the two Wyses (always famous for sticking) remained and Georgie.

Mr Wyse got up from the tea-table and passed round behind Miss Mapp's chair. Out of the corner of her eye she could see he was looking at the wall where a straw-coloured picture of her own hung. He always used to admire it, and it was pleasant to feel that he was giving it so careful and so respectful a scrutiny. Then he spoke to Lucia.

'How well I remember seeing you painting that,' he said, 'and how long I took to forgive myself for having disturbed you in my blundering car. A perfect little masterpiece, Mallards Cottage and the crooked chimney. To the life.'

Susan heaved herself up from the sofa and joined in the admiration.

'Perfectly delightful,' she said. 'The lights, the shadows. Beautiful! What a touch!'

Miss Mapp turned her head slowly as if she had a stiff neck, and verified her awful conjecture that it was no longer a picture of her own that hung there, but the very picture of Lucia's which had been rejected for the Art Exhibition. She felt as if no picture but a bomb hung there, which might explode at some chance word, and blow her into a thousand fragments. It was best to hurry from this perilous neighbourhood.

'Dear Lucia,' she said, 'I must be off. Just one little stroll, if I may, round my garden, before I go home. My roses will never forgive me, if I go away without noticing them.'

She was too late.

'How I wish I had known it was finished!' said Mr Wyse. 'I should have begged you to allow us to have it for our Art Exhibition. It would have been the gem of it. Cruel of you, Mrs Lucas!'

'But I sent it in to the hanging committee,' said Lucia. 'Georgie sent his, too, of Mallards. They were both sent back to us.'

Mr Wyse turned from the picture to Lucia with an expression of incredulous horror, and Miss Mapp quietly turned to stone.

'But impossible,' he said. 'I am on the hanging committee myself, and I hope you cannot think I should have been such an imbecile. Susan is on the committee too: so is Miss Mapp. In fact, we are the hanging committee. Susan, that gem, that little masterpiece never came before us.'

'Never,' said Susan. 'Never. Never, never.'

Mr Wyse's eye transferred itself to Miss Mapp. She was still stone and her face was as white as the wall of Mallards Cottage in the masterpiece. Then for the first time in the collective memory of Tilling Mr Wyse allowed himself to use slang.

'There has been some hanky-panky,' he said. 'That picture never came before the hanging committee.'

The stone image could just move its eyes and they looked, in a glassy manner, at Lucia. Lucia's met them with one short gimlet thrust, and she whisked round to Georgie. Her face was turned away from the others, and she gave him a prodigious wink, as he sat there palpitating with excitement.

'Georgino mio,' she said. 'Let us recall exactly what happened. The morning, I mean, when the hanging committee met. Let me see: let me see. Don't interrupt me: I will get it all clear.'

Lucia pressed her hands to her forehead.

'I have it,' she said. 'It is perfectly vivid to me now. You had taken our little pictures down to the framer's, Georgie, and told him to send them in to Elizabeth's house direct. That was it. The errand boy from the framer's came up here that very morning, and delivered mine to Grosvenor, and yours to Foljambe. Let me think exactly when that was. What time was it, Mr Wyse, that the hanging committee met?'

'At twelve, precisely,' said Mr Wyse.

'That fits in perfectly,' said Lucia. 'I called to Georgie out of the window here, and we told each other that our pictures had been rejected. A moment later, I saw your car go down to the High Street and when I went down there soon afterwards, it was standing in front of Miss – I mean Elizabeth's house. Clearly what happened was that the framer misunderstood Georgie's instructions, and returned the pictures to us before the hanging committee sat at all. So you never saw them, and we imagined all the time – did we not, Georgie? – that you had simply sent them back.'

'But what must you have thought of us?' said Mr Wyse, with a gesture of despair.

'Why, that you did not conscientiously think very much of our art,' said Lucia. 'We were perfectly satisfied with your decision. I felt sure that my little picture had a hundred faults and feeblenesses.'

Miss Mapp had become unpetrified. Could it be that by some miraculous oversight she had not put into those parcels the formal, typewritten rejection of the committee? It did not seem likely, for she had a very vivid remembrance of the gratification it gave her to do so, but the only alternative theory was to suppose a magnanimity on Lucia's part which seemed even more miraculous. She burst into speech.

'How we all congratulate ourselves,' she cried, 'that it has all been cleared up! Such a stupid errand-boy! What are we to do next, Mr Wyse? Our exhibition must secure Lucia's sweet picture, and of course Mr Pillson's too. But how are we to find room for them? Everything is hung.'

'Nothing easier,' said Mr Wyse. 'I shall instantly withdraw my paltry little piece of still life, and I am sure that Susan –'

'No, that would never do,' said Miss Mapp, currying favour all round. 'That beautiful wallflower, I could almost smell it: that King of Italy. Mine shall go: two or three of mine. I insist on it.'

Mr Wyse bowed to Lucia and then to Georgie.

'I have a plan better yet,' he said. 'Let us put – if we may have the privilege of securing what was so nearly lost to our exhibition – let us put these two pictures on easels as showing how deeply we appreciate our good fortune in getting them.'

He bowed to his wife, he bowed – was it quite a bow? – to Miss Mapp, and had there been a mirror, he would no doubt have bowed to himself.

'Besides,' he said, 'our little sketches will not thus suffer so much from their proximity to –' and he bowed to Lucia. 'And if Mr Pillson will similarly allow us –' he bowed to Georgie.

Georgie, following Lucia's lead, graciously offered to go round to the Cottage and bring back his picture of Mallards, but Mr Wyse would not hear of such a thing. He and Susan would go off in the Royce now, with Lucia's masterpiece, and fetch Georgie's from Mallards Cottage, and the sun should not set before they both stood on their distinguished easels in the enriched exhibition. So off they went in a great hurry to procure the easels before the sun went down and Miss Mapp, unable alone to face the reinstated victims of her fraud, scurried after them in a tumult of mixed emotions. Outside in the garden Irene, dancing hornpipes, was surrounded by both sexes of the enraptured youth of Tilling, for the boys knew she was a girl, and the girls thought she looked so like a boy. She shouted out 'Come and dance, Mapp,' and Elizabeth fled from her own sweet garden as if it had been a plague-stricken area, and never spoke to her roses at all.

The Queen and Drake were left alone in the garden-room.

'Well, I never!' said Georgie. 'Did you? She sent them back all by herself.'

'I'm not the least surprised,' said Lucia. 'It's like her.'

'But why did you let her off?' he asked. 'You ought to have exposed her and have done with her.'

Lucia showed a momentary exultation, and executed a few steps from a Morris-dance.

'No, Georgie, that would have been a mistake,' she said. 'She knows that we know, and I can't wish her worse than that. And I rather think, though he makes me giddy with so much bowing, that Mr Wyse has guessed. He certainly suspects something of the sort.'

'Yes, he said there had been some hanky-panky,' said Georgie. 'That was a strong thing for him to say. All the same –'

Lucia shook her head.

'No, I'm right,' she said. 'Don't you see I've taken the moral stuffing out of that woman far more completely than if I had exposed her?'

'But she's a cheat,' cried Georgie. 'She's a liar, for she sent back our pictures with a formal notice that the committee had rejected them. She hasn't got any moral stuffing to take out.'

Lucia pondered this.

'That's true, there doesn't seem to be much,' she said. 'But even then, think of the moral stuffing that I've put into myself. A far greater score, Georgie, than to have exposed her, and it must be quite agonizing for her to have that hanging over her head. Besides, she can't help being deeply grateful to me if there are any depths in that poor shallow nature. There may be: we must try to discover them. Take a broader view of it all, Georgie.... Oh, and I've thought of something fresh! Send round to Mr Wyse for the exhibition your picture of the Land-gate, which poor Elizabeth sold. He will certainly hang it and she will see it there. That will round everything off nicely.'

Lucia moved across to the piano and sat down on the treble music-stool.

'Let us forget all about these *piccoli disturbi*, Georgie,' she said, 'and have some music to put us in tune with beauty again. No, you needn't shut the door: it is so hot, and I am sure that no one else will dream of passing that notice of 'Private,' or come in here unasked. Ickle bit of divine Mozartino?'

Lucio found the duet at which she had worked quietly at odd moments. 'Let us try this,' she said, 'though it looks rather diffy. Oh, one thing more, Georgie. I think you and I had better keep those formal notices of rejection from the hanging committee just in case. We might need them some day, though I'm sure I hope we shan't. But one must be careful in dealing with that sort of woman. That's all I think. Now let us breathe harmony and loveliness again. Uno, due ... pom.'

Village School

Laurie Lee

The village to which our family had come was a scattering of some twenty to thirty houses down the south-east slope of a valley. The valley was narrow, steep, and almost entirely cut off; it was also a funnel for winds, a channel for the floods and a jungly, bird-crammed, insect-hopping sun-trap whenever there happened to be any sun. It was not high and open like the Windrush country, but had secret origins, having been gouged from the Escarpment by the melting ice-caps some time before we got there. The old flood-terraces still showed on the slopes, along which the cows walked sideways. Like an island, it was possessed of curious survivals – rare orchids and Roman snails; and there were chemical qualities in the limestone-springs which gave the women pre-Raphaelite goitres. The sides of the valley were rich in pasture and the crests heavily covered in beechwoods.

Living down there was like living in a bean-pod; one could see nothing but the bed one lay in. Our horizon of woods was the limit of our world. For weeks on end the trees moved in the wind with a dry roaring that seemed a natural utterance of the landscape. In winter they ringed us with frozen spikes, and in summer they oozed over the lips of the hills like layers of thick green lava. Mornings, they steamed with mist or sunshine, and almost every evening threw streamers above us, reflecting sunsets we were too hidden to see.

Water was the most active thing in the valley, arriving in the long rains from Wales. It would drip all day from clouds and trees, from roofs and eaves and noses. It broke open roads, carved its way through gardens, and filled the ditches with sucking noises. Men and horses walked about in wet sacking, birds shook rainbows from sodden branches, and streams ran from holes, and back into holes, like noisy underground trains.

I remember, too, the light on the slopes, long shadows in tufts and hollows, with cattle, brilliant as painted china, treading their echoing shapes. Bees blew like cake-crumbs through the golden air, white butterflies like sugared wafers, and when it wasn't raining a diamond dust took over which veiled and yet magnified all things.

Most of the cottages were built of Cotswold stone and were roofed by split-stone tiles. The tiles grew a kind of golden moss which sparkled like crystallized honey. Behind the cottages were long steep gardens full of cabbages, fruit-bushes, roses, rabbit-hutches, earth-closets, bicycles, and pigeon-lofts. In the very sump of the valley wallowed the Squire's Big House – once a fine, though modest sixteenth-century manor, to which a Georgian façade had been added.

The villagers themselves had three ways of living: working for the Squire, or on the farms, or down in the cloth-mills at Stroud. Apart from the Manor, and the ample cottage gardens – which were an insurance against hard times – all other needs were supplied by a church, a chapel, a vicarage, a manse, a wooden hut, a pub – and the village school.

The village school at that time provided all the instruction we were likely to ask for. It was a small stone barn divided by a wooden partition into two rooms – The Infants and The Big Ones. There was one dame teacher, and perhaps a young girl assistant. Every child in the valley crowding there, remained till he was fourteen years old, then was presented to the working field or factory with nothing in his head more burdensome than a few mnemonics, a jumbled list of wars, and a dreamy image of the world's geography. It seemed enough to get by with, in any case; and was one up on our poor old grandparents.

This school, when I came to it, was at its peak. Universal education and unusual fertility had packed it to the walls with pupils. Wild boys and girls from miles around – from the outlying farms and half-hidden hovels way up at the ends of the valley – swept down each day to add to our numbers, bringing with them strange oaths and odours, quaint garments and curious pies. They were my first amazed vision of any world outside the womanly warmth of my family; I didn't expect to survive it for long, and I was confronted with it at the age of four.

The morning came, without any warning, when my sisters surrounded me, wrapped me in scarves, tied up my bootlaces, thrust a cap on my head, and stuffed a baked potato in my pocket.

'What's this?' I said.

'You're starting school today.'

'I ain't. I'm stopping 'ome.'

'Now, come on, Loll. You're a big boy now.'

'I ain't.'

'You are.'

'Boo-hoo.'

They picked me up bodily, kicking and bawling, and carried me up to the road.

'Boys who don't go to school get put into boxes, and turn into rabbits, and get chopped up Sundays.'

I felt this was overdoing it rather, but I said no more after that. I arrived at the school just three feet tall and fatly wrapped in my scarves. The playground roared like a rodeo, and the potato burned through my thigh. Old boots, ragged stockings, torn trousers and skirts, went skating and skidding around me. The rabble closed in; I was encircled; grit flew in my face like shrapnel. Tall girls with frizzled hair, and huge boys with sharp elbows, began to prod me with hideous interest. They plucked at my scarves, spun me round like a top, screwed my nose, and stole my potato.

I was rescued at last by a gracious lady – the sixteen-year-old junior-teacher – who boxed a few ears and dried my face and led me off to The Infants. I spent that first day picking holes in paper, then went home in a smouldering temper.

'What's the matter, Loll? Didn't he like it at school, then?'

'They never gave me the present!'

'Present? What present?'

'They said they'd give me a present.'

'Well, now, I'm sure they didn't.'

'They did! They said: "You're Laurie Lee, ain't you? Well, just you sit there for the present." I sat there all day but I never got it. I ain't going back there again!'

But after a week I felt like a veteran and grew as ruthless as anyone else. Somebody had stolen my baked potato, so I swiped somebody else's apple. The Infant Room was packed with toys such as I'd never seen before – coloured shapes and rolls of clay, stuffed birds and men to paint. Also a frame of counting beads which our young teacher played like a harp, leaning her bosom against our faces and guiding our wandering fingers ...

The beautiful assistant left us at last, and was replaced by an opulent widow. She was tall, and smelt like a cart-load of lavender; and wore a hair net, which I thought was a wig. I remember going close up and having a good look – it was clearly too square to be hair.

'What are you staring at?' the widow inquired.

I was much to soft-hearted to answer.

'Go on. Do tell. You needn't be shy.'

'You're wearing a wig,' I said.

'I can assure you I'm not!' She went very red.

'You are. I seen it,' I said.

The new teacher grew flustered and curiously cross. She took me upon her knee.

'Now look very close. Is that really a wig?'

I looked hard, saw the net, and said, 'Yes.'

'Well, really!' she said, while the Infants gaped. 'I can assure you it's *not* a wig! And if you only could watch me getting dressed in the morning you'd know it wasn't one either.'

She shook me from her knee like a sodden cat, but she'd stirred my imagination. To suggest I might watch her getting dressed in the morning seemed to me both outrageous and wonderful.

This tiny, white-washed Infants' room was a brief but cosy anarchy. In that short time allowed us we played and wept, broke things, fell asleep, cheeked the teacher, discovered the things we could do to each other, and exhaled our last guiltless days.

My desk companions were those two blonde girls, already puppyishly pretty, whose names and bodies were to distract and haunt me for the next fifteen years of my life. Poppy and Jo were limpet chums; they sat holding hands all day; and there was a female self-possession about their pink sticky faces that made me shout angrily at them.

Vera was another I studied and liked; she was lonely, fuzzy, and short. I felt a curious compassion for stumpy Vera; and it was through her, and no beauty, that I got into trouble and received the first public shock of my life. How it happened was simple, and I was innocent, so it seemed. She came up to me in the playground one morning and held her face close to mine. I had a stick in my hand, so I hit her on the head with it. Her hair was springy, so I hit her again and watched her mouth open with a yell.

To my surprise a commotion broke out around me, cries of scandal from the older girls, exclamations of horror and heavy censure mixed with Vera's sobbing wails. I was intrigued, not alarmed, that by wielding a beech stick

I was able to cause such a stir. So I hit her again, without spite or passion, then walked off to something else.

The experiment might have ended there, and having ended would have been forgotten. But no; angry faces surrounded me, very red, all spitting and scolding.

'Horrid boy! Poor Vera! Little monster! Urgh! We're going to tell teacher about you!'

Something was wrong, the world seemed upset, I began to feel vaguely uneasy. I had only hit Vera on her wiry black hair, and now everybody was shouting at me. I ran and hid, feeling sure it would pass, but they hunted me down in the end. Two big righteous girls hauled me out by my ears.

'You're wanted in the Big Room for 'itting Vera. You're 'alf going to cop it!' they said.

So I was dragged to that Room, where I'd never been before, and under the savage eyes of the elder children teacher gave me a scalding lecture. I was confused by now and shaking with guilt. At last I smirked and ran out of the room. I had learnt my first lesson, that I could not hit Vera, no matter how fuzzy her hair. And something else too; that the summons to the Big Room, the policeman's hand on the shoulder, comes almost always as a complete surprise, and for the crime that one has forgotten.

My brother Jack, who was with me in the Infants, was too clever to stay there long. Indeed he was so bright he made us uncomfortable, and we were all of us glad to get rid of him. Sitting pale in his pinafore, gravely studying, commanding the teacher to bring him fresh books, or to sharpen his pencils, or to make less noise, he was an Infant Freak from the start. So he was promoted to the Big Room with unprecedented promptness, given a desk and a dozen atlases to sit on, from which he continued to bully the teachers in that cold clear voice of his.

But I, myself, was a natural Infant, content to serve out my time, to slop around and whine and idle: and no one suggested I shouldn't. So I remained long after bright Jack had moved on, the fat lord of my nursery life, skilled at cutting out men from paper, chalking suns on the walls, making snakes from clay, idling voluptuously through the milky days with a new young teacher to feed on. But my time was slowly running out; my Big Room bumps were growing. Suddenly, almost to my dismay, I found that I could count up to a hundred, could write my name in both large and small letters, and subtract certain numbers from each other. I had even just succeeded in subtracting Poppy from Jo, when the call came down from on high. Infant no longer, I was being moved up – the Big Room was ready for me.

I found there a world both adult and tough, with long desks and inkwells, strange maps on the walls, huge boys, heavy boots, scratching pens, groans of labour, and sharp and sudden persecutions. Gone for ever were the infant excuses, the sanctuary of lisping charms. Now I was alone and unprotected, faced by a struggle which required new techniques, where one made pacts and split them, made friends and betrayed them, and fought for one's place near the stove.

The stove was a symbol of caste among us, the tub of warmth to which we cleaved during the long seven months of winter. It was made of cast-iron and had a noisy mouth which rattled coke and breathed out fumes. It was decorated by a tortoise labelled 'Slow But Sure', and in winter it turned red hot. If you pressed a pencil against it, the wood burst into flames; and if you spat on the top, the spit hopped and gambolled like tiny ping-pong balls.

My first days in the Big Room were spent in regret for the young teacher I'd left in the Infants, for her braided breasts and unbuttoning hands and her voice of sleepy love. Quite clearly the Big Room boasted no such comforts; Miss B, the Head Teacher, to whom I was now delivered, being about as physically soothing as a rake.

She was a bunched and punitive little body and the school had christened her Crabby; she had a sour yellow look, lank hair coiled in earphones, and the skin and voice of a turkey. We were all afraid of the gobbling Miss B; she spied, she pried, she crouched, she crept, she pounced – she was a terror.

Each morning was war without declaration; no one knew who would catch it next. We stood to attention, half-crippled in our desks, till Miss B walked in, whacked the walls with a ruler, and fixed us with her squinting eye. 'Good a-morning, children!' 'Good morning, Teacher!' The greeting was like a rattling of swords. Then she would scowl at the floor and begin to growl 'Ar Farther ...'; at which we said the Lord's Prayer, praised all good things, and thanked God for the health of our King. But scarcely had we bellowed the last Amen than Crabby coiled, uncoiled, and sprang, and knocked some poor boy sideways.

One seldom knew why; one was always off guard, for the punishment preceded the charge. The charge, however, followed hard upon it, to a light shower of angry spitting.

'Shuffling your feet! Playing with the desk! A-smirking at that miserable Betty! I will not have it. I'll not, I say. I repeat – I will not have it!'

Many a punch-drunk boy in a playground battle, out-numbered and beaten to his knees, would be heard to cry: 'I will not have it! I'll not, I say! I repeats I will not have it!' It was an appeal to the code of our common suffering, and called for immediate mercy.

So we did not much approve of Crabby – though she was responsible for our excellent reflexes. Apart from this, her teaching was not memorable. She appears in my recollection as merely a militant figure, a hunched-up little creature all spring-coils and slaps – not a monster by any means, but a natural manifestation of what we expected of school.

For school in my day, that day, Crabby's day, seemed to be designed simply to keep us out of the air and from following the normal pursuits of the fields. Crabby's science of dates and sums and writing seemed a typical invention of her own, a sour form of fiddling or prison-labour like picking oakum or sewing sacks.

So while the bright times passed, we sat locked in our stocks, our bent backs turned on the valley. The June air infected us with primitive hungers, grass-seed and thistle-down idled through the windows, we smelt the fields and were tormented by cuckoos, while every out-of-door sound that came drifting in was a sharp nudge in the solar plexus. The creaking of wagons going past the school, harness-jingle, and the cries of the carters, the calling of cows from the 17-Acre, Fletcher's chattering mower, gunshot from the warrens – all tugged and pulled at our active wishes till we could have done Miss B a murder.

And indeed there came the inevitable day when rebellion raised its standard, when the tension was broken and a hero emerged whom we would willingly have named streets after. At least, from that day his name was honoured, though we gave him little support at the time . . .

Spadge Hopkins it was, and I must say we were surprised. He was one of those heavy, full-grown boys, thick-legged, red-fisted, bursting with flesh, designed for the great outdoors. He was nearly fourteen by then, and physically out of scale – at least so far as our school was concerned. The sight of him squeezed into his tiny desk was worse than a bullock in ballet-shoes. He wasn't much of a scholar; he groaned as he worked, or hacked at his desk with a jack-knife. Miss B took her pleasure in goading him, in forcing him to read out loud; or asking him sudden unintelligible questions which made him flush and stumble.

The great day came; a day of shimmering summer, with the valley outside in a state of leafy levitation. Crabby B was at her sourest, and Spadge

Hopkins had had enough. He began to writhe in his desk, and roll his eyes, and kick with his boots, and mutter; 'She'd better look out. 'Er, – Crabby B. She'd better, that's all. I can tell you …'

We didn't quite know what the matter was, in spite of his meaning looks. Then he threw down his pen, said; 'Sod it all,' got up, and walked to the door.

'And where are you going, young man, may I ask?' said Crabby with her awful leer.

Spadge paused and looked her straight in the eye.

'If it's any business of yourn.'

We shivered with pleasure at this defiance, Spadge leisurely made for the door.

'Sit down this instant!' Crabby suddenly screamed. 'I won't have it!'

'Ta-ta,' said Spadge.

Then Crabby sprang like a yellow cat, spitting and clawing with rage. She caught Spadge in the doorway and fell upon him. There was a shameful moment of heavy breathing and scuffling, while the teacher tore at his clothes. Spadge caught her hands in his great red fists and held her at arm's length, struggling.

'Come and help me, someone!' wailed Crabby, demented. But nobody moved; we just watched. We saw Spadge lift her up and place her on the top of the cupboard, then walk out of the door and away. There was a moment of silence, then we all laid down our pens and began to stamp on the floor in unison. Crabby stayed where she was, on top of the cupboard, drumming her heels and weeping.

We expected some terrible retribution to follow, but nothing happened at all. Not even the trouble-spark, Spadge, was called to account – he was simply left alone. From that day Crabby never spoke to him, or crossed his path, or denied him anything at all. He perched idly in his desk, his knees up to his chin, whistling in a world of his own. Sometimes Miss B would consider him narrowly and if he caught her glance he just winked. Otherwise he was free to come and go, and to take time off as he pleased.

But we never rebelled again; things changed. Crabby B was replaced by a new Head Teacher – a certain Miss Wardley from Birmingham. This lady was something quite new in our lives. She wore sharp glass jewellery which winked as she walked, and she sounded her 'gees' like gongs. But she was fond of singing and she was fond of birds, and she encouraged us in the study of both. She was more sober than Crabby, her reins looser but stronger; and after the first hilarity of her arrival and strangeness, we accepted her proper authority.

Not that she approved very much of me. 'Fat-and-Lazy' was the name she called me. After my midday dinner of baked cabbage and bread I would often nod off in my desk. 'Wake up!' she would cry, cracking my head with a ruler, 'you and your litle red eyes!' She also took exception to my steady sniff, which to me came as natural as breathing. 'Go out into the road and have a good blow, and don't come back till you're clear.' But I wouldn't blow, not for anyone on earth, especially if ordered to do so: so I'd sit out on the wall, indignant and thunderous, and sniff away louder than ever. I wouldn't budge either, or come back in, till a boy was sent to fetch me. Miss Wardley would greet me with freezing brightness. 'A little less beastly now? How about bringing a hanky tomorrow? I'm sure we'd all be grateful.' I'd sit and scowl, then forget to scowl, and would soon be asleep again ...

My brothers, by this time, were all with me at school. Jack, already the accepted genius, was long past our scope or help. It was agreed that his brains were of such distinction that they absolved him from mortal contacts. So he was left in a corner where his flashes of brilliance kept him twinkling away like a pin-table. Young Tony came last, but he again was different, being impervious either to learning or authority, importing moreover a kind of outrageous cheekiness so inspired that it remained unanswerable. He would sit all day picking holes in blotting paper, his large eyes deep and knowing, his quick tongue scandalous, his wit defiant, his will set against all instruction. There was nothing anyone could do about him, except to yelp at the things he said.

I alone, the drowsy middleman of these two, found it hard to win Miss Wardley's approval. I achieved this in the end by writing long faked essays on the lives and habits of otters. I'd never seen an otter, or even gone to look for one, but the essays took her in. They were read out aloud, and even earned me medals, but that's nothing to boast about.

Our village school was poor and crowded, but in the end I relished it. It had a lively reek of steaming life: boys' boots, girls' hair, stoves and sweat, blue ink, white chalk, and shavings. We learnt nothing abstract or tenuous there – just simple patterns of facts and letters, portable tricks of calculation, no more than was needed to measure a shed, write out a bill, read a swine-disease warning. Through the dead hours of the morning, through the long afternoons, we chanted away at our tables. Passers-by could hear our rising voices in our bottled-up room on the bank; 'Twelve-inches-one-foot. Three-feet-make-a-yard. Fourteen-pounds-make-a-stone. Eight-stone-a-hundredweight.' We absorbed these figures as primal truths declared by some ultimate power. Unhearing, unquestioning, we rocked to our chanting, hammering the gold nails home. 'Twice-two-are-four. One-God-is-Love. One-Lord-is-King. One-King-is-George. One-George-is-Fifth. ...' So it was always; had been, would be for ever; we asked no questions; we didn't hear what we said; yet neither did we ever forget it.

So do I now, through the reiterations of those days, recall that schoolroom which I scarcely noticed – Miss Wardley in glory on her high desk throne, her long throat tinkling with glass. The bubbling stove with its chink of red fire; the old world map as dark as tea; dead field-flowers in jars on the windowsills; the cupboard yawning with dog-eared books. Then the boys and the girls, the dwarfs and the cripples; the slow fat ones and the quick boney ones; giants and louts, angels and squinters – Walt Kerry, Bill Timbrell, Spadge Hopkins, Clergy Green, the Ballingers and Browns, Betty Gleed, Clarry Hogg, Sam and Sixpence, Poppy and Jo – we were ugly and beautiful, scrofulous, warted, ring-wormed, and scabbed at the knees, we were noisy, crude, intolerant, cruel, stupid, and superstitious. But we moved together out of the clutch of the Fates, inhabitors of a world without doom; with a scratching, licking and chewing of pens, a whisper and passing of jokes, a titter of tickling, a grumble of labour, a vague stare at the wall in a dream ...

'Oh, miss, please miss, can I go round the back?'

An unwilling nod permits me. I stamp out noisily into a swoop of fresh air and a musical surge of birds. All round me now is the free green world, with Mrs Birt hanging out her washing. I take stock of myself for a moment, alone. I hear the schoolroom's beehive hum. Of course I don't really belong to that lot at all; I know I'm something special, a young king perhaps placed secretly here in order to mix with the commoners. There is clearly a mystery about my birth, I feel so unique and majestic. One day, I know, the secret will be told. A coach with footmen will appear suddenly at our cottage, and Mother (my mother?) will weep. The family will stand very solemn and respectful, and I shall drive off to take up my throne. I'll be generous, of course, not proud at all; for my brothers there shall be no dungeons. Rather will I feed then on cakes and jellies, and I'll provide all my sisters with princes. Sovereign mercy shall be their portion, little though they deserve it. . . .

I return to the school room and Miss Wardley scowls (she shall curtsy when I am king). But all this is forgotten when Walt Kerry leans over and demands the results of my sums. 'Yes, Walt. Of course, Walt. Here, copy them out. They ain't hard – I done 'em all.' He takes them, the bully, as his tributary right, and I'm proud enough to give them. The little Jim Fern, sitting beside me, looks up from his ruined pages. 'Ain't you a good scholar! You and your Jack. I wish I was a good scholar like thee.' He gives me a sad, adoring look, and I begin to feel much better.

Playtime comes and we charge outdoors, releasing our steamed-up cries. Somebody punches a head. Somebody bloodies their knees. Boys cluster together like bees. 'Let's go round the back then, shall us, eh?' To the dark narrow alley, rich with our mysteries, we make our clattering way. Over the wall is the girl's own place, quite close, and we shout then greetings.

'I 'eard you, Bill Timbrell! I 'eard what you said! You be careful, I'll tell our teacher!'

Flushed and refreshed, we stream back to our playground, whistling, indivisibly male.

'D'you 'ear what I said then? Did you then, eh? I told 'em! They 'alf didn't squeal!'

We all double up; we can't speak for laughing, we can't laugh without hitting each other.

Miss Wardley was patient, but we weren't very bright. Our books showed a squalor of blots and scratches as though monkeys were being taught to write. We sang in sweet choirs, and drew like cavemen, but most other faculties escaped us. Apart from poetry, of course, which gave no trouble at all. I can remember Miss Wardley, with her squeaking chalk, scrawling the blackboard like a shopping list:

'Write a poem – which must scan – on one or more of the following; A Kitten. Fairies. My Holidays. An Old Tinker. Charity. Sea Wrack ...' ('What's that, miss?')

But it was easy in those days, one wrote a dozen an hour, one simply didn't hesitate, just began at the beginning and worked steadily through the subjects, ticking them off with indefatigable rhymes.

Sometimes there was a beating, which nobody minded – except an occasional red-faced mother. Sometimes a man came and took out our teeth. ('My mum says you ain't to take out any double-'uns ...' '... Fourteen, fifteen, sixteen, seventeen ...' 'Is they all double-'uns?' 'Shut up, you little horror.') Sometimes the Squire would pay us a visit, hand out prizes, and make a misty-eyed speech. Sometimes an Inspector arrived on a bicycle and counted our heads and departed. Meanwhile Miss Wardley moved jingling amongst us, instructing, appealing, despairing:

'You're a grub, Walter Kerry. You have the wits of a hen. You're a great hulking lout of an oaf. You can just stay behind and do it over again. You can all stay behind, the lot of you.'

When lessons grew too tiresome, or too insoluble, we had our traditional ways of avoiding them.

'Please, miss, I got to stay 'ome tomorrow, to 'elp with the washing – the pigs – me dad's sick.'

'I dunno, miss; you never learned us that.'

'I 'ad me book stole, miss. Carry Burdock pinched it.'

'Please, miss, I got a gurt 'eadache.'

Sometimes these worked, sometimes they didn't. But once, when some tests hung over our heads, a group of us boys evaded them entirely by stinging our hands with horse-flies. The task took all day, but the results were spectacular – our hands swelled like elephants' trunks. ''Twas a swarm, please, miss. They set on us. We run, but they stung us awful.' I remember how we groaned, and that we couldn't hold our pens, but I don't remember the pain.

At other times, of course, we forged notes from our mothers, or made ourselves sick with berries, or claimed to be relations of the corpse at funerals (the churchyard lay only next door). It was easy to start wailing when the hearse passed by, 'It's my auntie, miss – it's my cousin Wilf – can I go miss, please miss, can I?' Many a lone coffin was followed to its grave by a straggle of long-faced children, pinched, solemn, raggedly dressed, all strangers to the astonished bereaved.

So our school work was done – or where would we be today? We would be as we are; watching a loom or driving a tractor, and counting in images of fives and tens. This was as much as we seemed to need, and Miss Wardley did not add to the burden. What we learned in her care were the less formal truths – the names of flowers, the habits of birds, the intimacy of objects in being set to draw them, the treacherous innocence of boys, the sly charm of girls, the idiot's soaring fancies, and the tongue-tied dunce's informed

authority when it came to talking about stoats. We were as merciless and
cruel as most primitives are. But we learnt at that school the private nature
of cruelty; and our inborn hatred for freaks and outcasts was tempered by
meeting them daily.

There was Nick and Edna from up near the Cross, the children of that
brother and sister – the boy was strong and the girl was beautiful, and it
was not at school that we learned to condemn them. And there was the gipsy
boy Rosso, who lived up the quarry where his tribe had encamped for the
summer. He had a chocolate-smooth face and crisp black curls, and at first
we cold-shouldered him. He was a real outsider (they ate snails, it was said)
and his slant Indian eyes repelled us. Then one day, out of hunger, he stole
some sandwiches and was given the cane by Miss Wardley. Whatever the
rights and wrongs of the case, that made him one of us.

We saw him run out of school, grizzling from the beating, and kneel down
to tie up his boots. The shopkeeper's wife, passing by at that moment, stopped
to preach to him a little sermon. 'You didn't have to steal, even if you was
hungry. Why didn't you come to me?' The boy gave her a look, picked
himself up, and ran off without a word. He knew, as we did, the answer to
that one: we set our dogs on the gipsies here. As we walked back home to
our cabbage dinners we were all of us filled with compassion. We pictured
poor Rosso climbing back to his quarry, hungry to his miserable tents, with
nothing but mud and puddles to sit in and the sour banks to scavenge for
food. Gipsies no longer seemed either sinister or strange. No wonder they eat
snails, we thought.

The narrow school was just a conveyor belt along which the short years drew
us. We entered the door marked 'Infants', moved gradually to the other, and
were then handed back to the world. Lucky, lucky point of time; our eyes
were on it always. Meanwhile we had moved to grander desks, saw our
juniors multiplying in number, Miss Wardley suddenly began to ask our
advice and to spoil us as though we were dying. There was no more to be
done, no more to be learned. We began to look round the schoolroom with
nostalgia and impatience. During playtime in the road we walked about
gravely, patronizing the younger creatures. No longer the trembling,
whitefaced battles, the flights, the buttering-up of bullies; just a punch
here and there to show our authority, then a sober stroll with our
peers.

At last Miss Wardley was wringing our hands, tender and deferential.

'Good-bye, old chaps, and jolly good luck! Don't forget to come back and see me.'

She gave each one of us a coy sad glance. She knew that we never would.

Oh I Say Thanks Awfully

Arthur Marshall

Like many another loyal subject, I have kept by me the official list of the wedding gifts displayed to the public at St James's Palace on the occasion of the marriage of HRH The Princess Elizabeth to Lieutenant Philip Mountbatten, RN, in November 1947, and now, on this happy Jubilee occasion, I have taken to wondering how they (the gifts) have been getting on. What, for example, of the 'dagger in beaded sheath', the 17 sets of doilies, the 'magic gem of the Orient' and the 'hand-made model of a cat', not to speak of the happy snap of the Dionne Quintuplets, kindly sent along by the Dionne Quintuplets? Presumably the 10 lbs of icing sugar, the turkey, the 4 dozen tins of salmon and the 500 cases of tinned pineapple have long since gone down the royal red lanes.

I had previously understood that it was not permissible to send presents to royalty and that they were always politely returned but I was evidently wrong. The more the merrier seems to have been the motto (there were 2,583 in all) and if I had sent in half a dozen egg cosies and three boxes of Turkish Delight, they would clearly have been acceptable. The skies opened and presents simply showered down. There is really only one way to describe the actual listing of the gifts. Higgledy-piggledy. Perhaps the descriptions of the offerings and the names of the donors were noted down just as they happened to turn up.

The gifts from the King and Queen and fellow royalties certainly appear first on the list and contain some surprises. We find that 45 'members of the royal family', including the Princess Royal and the King of Norway, clubbed together, if you please, and came through with nothing but a mahogany breakfront bookcase. A handsome one, I don't doubt, but surely not quite enough from such a large and rich team. Queen Mary, then pretty long in the tooth, provided 20 assorted gifts off her own bat. Was she, as people of her age often do, off-loading? 'A Chinese screen and a miniature bookcase' sound like things that have been cluttering up the place and collecting dust for years and can now be got rid of. One of the Queen's presents to her daughter was toast-racks (just like you and me, you see), and though the King's present of 'a pair of guns' might cause anxious looks and raised eyebrows in lower strata of society, they are of course perfectly OK in a world where people like going bang-bang on the moors and need to have something to boom off with.

From the general public there were, naturally, duplications, it not having been possible to issue, as many ordinary families do, a list of acceptable presents to intending donors. There were also frequent multiplications, for example 14 prayer books, 22 bibles, 11 car rugs, 13 wedding cakes, 105 embroidered cloths (table, tea or tray), 156 handkerchiefs, and silk nightdresses galore. Strangest of all were the numbers of people, 74 of them, who felt called upon to send pairs of nylon stockings, one individual donor coughing up as many as 18. They provided between them 159 pairs. Whatever would Freud have to say to that?

Some items might be listed as 'Gifts, the usefulness of which is not immediately apparent'. 'Two collapsible umbrellas' are all right, provided collapsible means folding, but where to find in one's house the absolutely right spot for 'an aboriginal letter in carved wood', a wading stick, a pair of baby clogs, a Basuto bride's charm, 'an inscribed glass shrine on a marble base', and, most difficult to place, 'a paraphrase of the 23rd Psalm, mounted under glass', of all psalms the one that would least benefit from paraphrasing. And how on earth would a lady-in-waiting write to express grateful thanks for 'a reversible doll', a hurricane pipe, a gold bicycle mascot and 'a miniature harp in bog oak'? ('Her Royal Highness has asked me to thank you for the miniature harp in, if we mistake not, bog oak.')

There ought really to have been a prize for the most bizarre gift. High in the ratings would have been 'a hide mounted barometer, slung to hang in stirrup'. Stirrups to me mean horses and so what could be handier? The Princess, out riding and worried about the weather, has merely to dismount and take a swift dekko at the forecast. There was also 'a leather mounted calendar', similarly stirrup hung, so she could ascertain the date as well. Then there were 'two harmstrings from Uganda'. Whatever can harmstrings be? They don't sound like good news to me. I misread them first as 'hamstrings', items which must nowadays, sadly, be in all too full supply. Treasured and unique possessions came flooding in and all animal lovers will rejoice to find 'collar of the dog "Patty"', the only British survivor of the

Kabul massacre in 1879'. Quaint but interesting are 'a truncheon made from laburnum grown in Northern Ireland' and 'writing table accessories made from coal and decorated with nails from the shoes of the Princess's ponies'. And for an appetising, late post-theatre snack, how about raiding the larder for that 'piece of condensed soup' part of the stores in HMS Victory of the Battle of Trafalgar'? Just heat through in a saucepan, toss in a few croûtons, and bring to table.

Things of the mind and books were by no means neglected and, anyway, they had to fill up that mahogany breakfront bookcase of which we spoke (and which still seems pretty mingy). The Aberdovey Women's Institute, whose anxious discussions one likes to imagine, sent along a copy of Berta Ruck's 'Tomboy in Lace', while Mrs St Aubyn Ratcliffe provided her very own 'Furry Folk and Fairies', and two editions of it, what's more. Indeed, the number of writers who decided to conquer their diffidence and bravely send in their own works is really very startling. There were as many as 56 of them, their donations and subjects covering a very wide field: 'Elephants Never Forget', 'The Medical Discoveries of Edward Bach', 'Ballet Education', 'Wedding Etiquette Complete', 'You and the Jury', 'The Finding of the Third Eye' and other treats that one rather doubts ever get very deeply dipped into.

Now, what would one have welcomed most oneself? Well, there were 12 bottles of sloe gin, six of ordinary, a bottle of rum and about a roomful of champagne. There were boxes of chocs and superb silver, glass, furniture and carpets. There was, touchingly, a bunch of violets. But the list is chiefly remarkable for the enormous number of objects which I really feel that I can rub along without: a plastic cushion, 43 lengths of tweed, 'a match holder in the form of a toadstool mounted with a silver frog' (a gift dreamt up by a very close descendant of the last Czar of all the Russias), five copies of a book called 'Daily Light', 'a shaped plastic table' (whatever can an unshaped table look like?), an oil painting of Leeds (a daunting subject until we discover that Leeds is a horse), a 'red velvet vestette', which I take to be a tiny waistcoat, a handmade figure of a coolie, one of Queen Victoria's slippers, a pair of 'Watajoy' travelling bags, a Tibetan incense burner, a bottle of Australian claret, a stinkwood chest, a pink satin suspender belt, 39 Loyal Addresses, a 'yellow hand-painted umbrella' and an ostrich egg.

Cleaning

Victoria Wood

A large, messy, stripped-pine kitchen. Ursula, a large messy lady novelist in a smock sits drinking tea with Kent, a disdainful Northern man.

Ursula You know, it's amazing: you're the only person who's answered the advert. I just cannot get a cleaner. I'm afraid it's all rather neglected in here.

Kent Well, yes, I was just admiring that blue mink hat, but I see now it's a mouldy pizza.

Ursula I'm a novelist, and it's so hard to do everything. Is the tea all right?

Kent Not really.

Ursula Oh sorry, is it too strong?

Kent I'm just a bit perturbed by the way it's taken the tarnish off this teaspoon.

Ursula Biscuit?

Kent Have they got chemicals in?

Ursula Preservatives?

Kent I was hoping for disinfectant.

Ursula No, I baked them myself.

Kent I bet Mr Kipling's worried.

Ursula Aren't you going to finish it?

Kent I'll keep it by me – you never I know, I may need to force a lock.

Pause.

Anyone ever told you you've got a look of Molly Weir?

Ursula No.

Kent I'm not surprised.

Ursula Have you been a cleaner for long?

Kent Well, I was abroad for some years.

Ursula Really?

Kent Lived with Picasso, actually.

Ursula The painter?

Kent Yes. I had a put-u-up in the back bedroom. I had to come away. It was nice, but, you know, everything tasted of turps. Henry Moore was the same – a stranger to Harpic.

Ursula You obviously know a lot about cleaning.

Kent I was approached by 'Mastermind' to set the questions for the specialised subject 'The history of the J-cloth from 1963 to the present time'.

Ursula Goodness, so you're a sort of academic are you?

Kent Oh yes. I was all set to be an Oxford don a few months back – it was all a question of me scraping up the bus-fare – but I couldn't see eye to eye with them over the gown. I said Joan Crawford had it right – a padded shoulder demands a platform shoe.

Ursula I don't really notice clothes – I've had this for years.

Kent My mother had something similar.

Ursula Really?

Kent She used to throw it over her bubble car in the cold weather.

Ursula This is a lovely old farm table, isn't it? Do you like stripped pine?

Kent   No, I don't. I was brought up in a dresser drawer, so all this brings back the stench of unbearable poverty.

Ursula   Oh goodness! Will you be able to clean it, then, do you think?

Kent   Oh yes. In fact I shall probably get a better finish if I'm shuddering.

Ursula   You see, being a novelist, I get rather engrossed, rather tend to let the housework go . . .

Kent   Mm, it's the first time I've seen windows so dirty they were soundproof.

Ursula   I've been working so hard, I must sort myself out, change this dress . . .

Kent   You know that soup down your front?

Ursula   Whoops.

Kent   Well, they don't make it any more. And I wouldn't go swimming till you've washed your hair; it could be another Torrey Canyon.

Ursula   It's just my deadline – my novel . . .

Kent   There's only one woman novelist struck home with me: Shirley Conran, *Superwoman* – I could not put it down.

Ursula   The new one, *Lace*, have you read that?

Kent   How they could call it explicit! I read right through and I was still no wiser over getting felt-tip off formica.

Ursula   Do you think you'll be able to take this little job?

Kent   Not really, no. I couldn't clean for a woman, I find them a very unnecessary sex.

Ursula   But my name was on the card, it was a woman's name.

Kent   That's no real indication of gender; it could have been an auxiliary fireman dropping a heavy hint.

Ursula   So I can't twist your arm?

Kent   I'd rather you didn't touch anything of mine. I'm very squeamish, skin-wise. In fact my social life took a real upturn when I found they did Marigold gloves in large sizes.

Ursula   You're a novelist's dream, I could listen to you all afternoon – do stay.

Kent   No, I can't settle. I keep fretting about dysentery.

Ursula   Oh, just a few secs. I mean, where are you from, for instance?

Kent   Well, I was born under a pile of anthracite on the East Lancs Road. My father was a steeple-jack; he got drunk one day and never came down. I left home at fifteen when my mother caught me in bed with a Bleachmatic. I toured the working-men's clubs with a magic act; I used to close with a song. When I got better at it I used to saw myself in half and finish with a duet. Then I went to Monte, modelling ...

Ursula   I'd forgotten all about him.

Kent   Who?

Ursula   Monty Modlyn.

Kent   Monte Carlo, as a model. Got into drugs, marijuana, then cocaine, then Shake 'n' Vac. Then I became a monk, but we had words over my safari jacket.

Ursula   Do you have a close relationship with anyone?

Kent   Well, I've hung round a few lavatories, but I usually only stay long enough to buff up the taps. I'm a loner. There'll never be more than one slice in my toaster.

Ursula   Do you still see your mother?

Kent   Oh yes, I go round once a week, take her some Duraglit or a packet of firelighters. I do have four brothers.

Ursula   What do they do?

Kent   They're a string quartet.

Ursula   So is cleaning your main source of income?

Kent   Well, I won quite a bit of Northumberland in a raffle, so I don't go short.

Ursula   So, you don't really need this job?

Kent No.

Ursula What a pity! You know, I'd love to put you in a novel.

Kent Oh, you can put me in a novel.

Ursula Really?

Kent Piece of pastry – two pounds an hour, four hours a week, I can squeeze you in between Beryl Bainbridge's seventh, and Melvyn Bragg's twenty-fourth. Just change my name and call me broad-shouldered, all right?

The £1,000,0000 Bank-Note

Mark Twain

When I was twenty-seven years old, I was a mining broker's clerk in San Francisco, and an expert in all the details of stock traffic. I was alone in the world, and had nothing to depend upon but my wits and a clean reputation; but these were setting my feet in the road to eventual fortune, and I was content with the prospect.

My time was my own after the afternoon board, Saturdays, and I was accustomed to put it in on a little sailboat on the bay. One day I ventured too far, and was carried out to sea. Just at nightfall, when hope was about gone, I was picked up by a small brig which was bound for London. It was a long and stormy voyage, and they made me work my passage without pay, as a common sailor. When I stepped ashore in London my clothes were ragged and shabby, and I had only a dollar in my pocket. This money fed and sheltered me twenty-four hours. During, the next twenty-four I went without food and shelter.

About ten o'clock on the following morning, seedy and hungry, I was dragging myself along Portland Place, when a child that was passing, towed by a nursemaid, tossed a luscious big pear – minus one bite – into the gutter. I stopped, of course, and fastened my desiring eye on the muddy treasure. My mouth watered for it, my stomach craved it, my whole being begged for it. But every time I made a move to get it some passing eye detected my purpose, and of course I straightened up, then, and looked indifferent, and pretended that I hadn't been thinking about the pear at all. This same thing kept happening and happening, and I couldn't get the pear. I was just getting desperate enough to brave all the shame, and to seize it, when a window behind me was raised, and a gentleman spoke out of it, saying:

'Step in here, please.'

I was admitted by a gorgeous flunky, and shown into a sumptuous room where a couple of elderly gentlemen were sitting. They sent away the servant, and made me sit down. They had just finished their breakfast, and the sight of the remains of it almost overpowdered me. I could hardly keep my wits together in the presence of that food, but as I was not asked to sample it, I had to bear my trouble as best I could.

Now, something had been happening there a little before, which I did not know anything about until a good many days afterward, but I will tell you about it now. Those two old brothers had been having a pretty hot argument a couple of days before, and had ended by agreeing to decide it by a bet, which is the English way of settling everything.

You will remember that the Bank of England once issued two notes of a million pounds each, to be used for a special purpose connected with some public transaction with a foreign country. For some reason or other only one of these had been used and canceled; the other still lay in the vaults of the Bank. Well, the brothers, chatting along, happened to get to wondering what might be the fate of a perfectly honest and intelligent stranger who should be turned adrift in London without a friend, and with no money but that million-pound bank-note, and no way to account for his being in possession of it. Brother A said he would starve to death; Brother B said he wouldn't. Brother A said he couldn't offer it at a bank or anywhere else, because he would be arrested on the spot. So they went on disputing till Brother B said he would bet twenty thousand pounds that the man would live thirty days, *anyway*, on that million, and keep out of jail, too. Brother A took him up. Brother B went down to the Bank and bought that note. Just like an Englishman, you see; pluck to the backbone. Then he dictated a letter, which one of his clerks wrote out in a beautiful round hand, and then the two brothers sat at the window a whole day watching for the right man to give it to.

They saw many honest faces go by that were not intelligent enough; many that were intelligent, but not honest enough; many that were both, but the possessors were not poor enough, or, if poor enough, were not strangers. There was always a defect, until I came along; but they agreed that I filled the bill all around; so they elected me unanimously, and there I was, now, waiting to know why I was called in. They began to ask me questions about myself, and pretty soon they had my story. Finally they told me I would answer their purpose. I said I was sincerely glad, and asked what it was. Then one of them handed me an envelope, and said I would find the explanation inside. I was going to open it, but he said no; take it to my lodgings, and look it over carefully, and not be hasty or rash. I was puzzled, and wanted to discuss the matter a little further, but they didn't; so I took my leave, feeling hurt and insulted to be made the butt of what was apparently some kind of a practical joke, and yet obliged to put up with it, not being in circumstances to resent affronts from rich and strong folk.

I would have picked up the pear, now, and eaten it before all the world, but it was gone; so I had lost that by this unlucky business, and the thought of it did not soften my feeling toward those men. As soon as I was out of sight of that house I opened my envelope, and saw that it contained money! My opinion of those people changed, I can tell you! I lost not a moment, but shoved note and money into my vest-pocket, and broke for the nearest cheap eating house. Well, How I did eat! When at last I couldn't hold any more, I took out my money and unfolded it, took one glimpse and nearly fainted. Five millions of dollars! Why, it made my head swim.

I must have sat there stunned and blinking at the note as much as a minute before I came rightly to myself again. The first thing I noticed, then, was the landlord. His eye was on the note, and he was petrified. He was worshipping, with all his body and soul, but he looked as if he couldn't stir hand or foot. I took my cue in a moment, and did the only rational thing there was to do. I reached the note toward him, and said carelessly:

'Give me the change, please.'

Then he was restored to his normal condition, and made a thousand apologies for not being able to break the bill, and I couldn't get him to touch it. He wanted to look at it, and keep on looking at it; he couldn't seem to get enough of it to quench the thirst of his eye, but he shrank from touching it as if it had been something too sacred for poor common clay to handle. I said:

'I am sorry if it is an inconvenience, but I must insist. Please change it; I haven't anything else.'

But he said that wasn't any matter; He was quite willing to let the trifle stand over till another time. I said I might not be in his neighborhood again for a good while; but he said it was of no consequence, he could wait, and, moreover, I could have anything I wanted, any time I chose, and let the account run as long as I pleased. He said he hoped he wasn't afraid to trust as rich a gentleman as I was, merely because I was of a merry disposition, and chose to play larks on the public in the matter of dress. By this time another customer was entering, and the landlord hinted to me to put the monster out of sight; then he bowed me all the way to the door, and I started straight for that house and those brothers, to correct the mistake which had been made before the police should hunt me up, and help me do it. I was pretty nervous, in fact pretty badly frightened, though, of course, I was no way in fault; but I knew men well enough to know that when they find they've given a tramp a million-pound bill when they thought it was a one-pounder, they are in a frantic rage against *Him* instead of quarrelling with their own nearsightedness, as they ought. As I approached the house my excitement began to abate, for all was quiet there, which made me feel pretty sure the blunder was not discovered yet. I rang. The same servant appeared. I asked for those gentlemen.

'They are gone.' This in the lofty, cold way of that fellow's tribe.

'Gone? Gone where?'

'On a journey.'

'But whereabouts?'

'To the Continent, I think.'

'The Continent?'

'Yes, sir.'

'Which way – by what route?'

'I can't say, sir.'

'When will they be back?'

'In a month, they said.'

'A month! Oh, this is awful! Give me *some* sort of idea of how to get a word to them. It's of the last importance.'

'I can't, indeed. I've no idea where they've gone, sir.'

'Then I must see some member of the family.'

'Family's away too; been abroad months – in Egypt and India, I think.'

'Man, there's been an immense mistake made. They'll be back before night. Will you tell them I've been here, and that I will keep coming till it's all made right, and they needn't be afraid?'

'I'll tell them, if they come back, but I am not expecting them. They said you would be here in an hour to make inquiries, but I must tell you it's all right, they'll be here on time and expect you.'

So I had to give it up and go away. What a riddle it all was! I was like to lose my mind. They would be here 'on time'. What could that mean? Oh, the letter would explain, maybe. I had forgotten the letter; I got it out and read it. This is what it said:

You are an intelligent and honest man, as one may see by your face. We conceive you to be poor and a stranger. Enclosed you will find a sum of

money. It is lent to you for thirty days, without interest. Report at this
house at the end of that time. I have a bet on you. If I win it you shall
have any situation that is in my gift – any, that is, that you shall be able
to prove yourself familiar with and competent to fill.

No signature, no address, no date.

Well, here was a coil to be in! You are posted on what had preceded all
this, but I was not. It was just a deep, dark puzzle to me. I hadn't the least
idea what the game was, nor whether harm was meant me or a kindness. I
went into a park, and sat down to try to think it out, and to consider what
I had best do.

At the end of an hour, my reasonings had crystallized into this verdict.

Maybe those men mean me well, maybe they mean me ill; no way to
decide that – let it go. They've got a game, or a scheme, or an experiment,
of some kind on hand; no way to determine what it is – let it go. There's a
bet on me; no way to find out what it is – let it go. That disposes of the
indeterminable quantities; the remainder of the matter is tangible, solid, and
may be classed and labeled with certainty. If I ask the Bank of England to
plae this bill to the credit of the man it belongs to, they'll do it, for they
know him, although I don't; but they will ask me how I came in possession
of it, and if I tell the truth, they'll put me in the asylum, naturally, and a
lie will land me in jail. The same result would follow if I tried to bank the
bill anywhere or to borrow money on it. I have got to carry this immense
burden around until those men come back, whether I want to or not. It is
useless to me, as useless as a handful of ashes, and Yet I must take care of
it, and watch over it, while I beg my living. I couldn't *give* it away, if I
should try, for neither honest citizen nor highwayman would accept it or
meddle with it for anything. Those brothers are safe. Even if I lose their bill,
or burn it, they are still safe, because they can stop payment, and the Bank
will make them whole; but meantime, I've got to do a month's suffering
without wages or profit – unless I help win that bet, whatever it may be,
and get that situation that I am promised. I *should* like to get that; men of
their sort have situations in their gift that are worth having.

I got to thinking a good deal about that situation. My hopes began to rise
high. Without doubt the salary would be large. It would begin in a month;
after that I should be all right. Pretty soon I was feeling first rate. By this
time I was tramping the streets again. The sight of a tailor shop gave me a
sharp longing to shed my rags, and to clothe myself decently once more.

Could I afford it? No; I had nothing in the world but a million pounds. So I forced myself to go on by. But soon I was drifting back again. The temptation persecuted me cruelly. I must have passed that shop back and forth six times during that manful struggle. At last I gave in; I had to. I asked if they had a misfit suit that had been thrown on their hands. The fellow I spoke to nodded his head toward another fellow, and gave me no answer. I went to the indicated fellow, and he indicated another fellow with *his* head, and no words. I went to him, and he said:

'Tend to you presently.'

I waited till he was done with what he was at, then he took me into a back room, and overhauled a pile of rejected suits, and selected the rattiest one for me. I put it on. It didn't fit, and wasn't in any way attractive, but it was new, and I was anxious to have it; so I didn't find any fault, but said with some diffidence:

'It would be an accommodation to me if you could wait some days for the money. I haven't any small change about me.'

The fellow worked up a most sarcastic expression of countenance, and said:

'Oh, you haven't? Well, of course, I didn't expect it. I'd only expect gentlemen like you to carry large change.'

I was nettled, and said:

'My friend, you shouldn't judge a stranger always by the clothes he wears. I am quite able to pay for this suit; I simply didn't wish to put you to the trouble of changing a large note.'

He modified his style a little at that, and said, though still with something of an air:

'I didn't mean any particular harm, but as long as rebukes are going, I might say it wasn't quite your affair to jump to the conclusion that we couldn't change any note that you might happen to be carrying around. On the contrary, we *can*.'

I handed the note to him, and said:

'Oh, very well; I apologize.'

He received it with a smile, one of those large smiles which goes all around over, and has folds in it, and wrinkles, and spirals, and looks like the place where you have thrown a brick in a pond; and then in the act of his taking a glimpse of the bill this smile froze solid, and turned yellow, and looked like those wavy, wormy spreads of lava which you find hardened on little levels on the side of Vesuvius. I never before saw a smile caught like that, and perpetuated. The man stood there holding the bill, and looking like that, and the proprietor hustled up to see what was the matter, and said briskly:

'Well, what's up? what's the trouble? what's wanting?'

I said: 'There isn't any trouble. I'm waiting for my change.'

'Come, come; get him his change, Tod; get him his change.'

Tod retorted: 'Get him his change! It's easy to say, sir; but look at the bill yourself.'

The proprietor took a look, gave a low, eloquent whistle, then made a dive for the pile of rejected clothing, and began to snatch it this way and that, talking all the time excitedly, and as if to himself:

'Sell an eccentric millionaire such an unspeakable suit as that – Tod's a fool – a born fool. Always doing something like this. Drives every millionaire away from this place, because he can't tell a millionaire from a tramp, and never could. Ah, here's the thing I'm after. Please get those things off, sir, and throw them in the fire. Do me the favor to put on this shirt and this suit; it's just the thing, the very thing – plain, rich, modest, and just ducally nobby; made to order for a foreign prince – you may know him, sir, his Serene highness the Hospodar of Halifax; had to leave it with us and take a mourning suit because his mother was going to die – which she didn't. But that's all right; we can't always have the things the way we – that is, the way they – there! trousers all right, they fit you to a charm, sir; now the waistcoat; aha, right again! now the coat – Lord! look at that, now Perfect – the whole thing! I never saw such a triumph in all my experience.'

I expressed my satisfaction.

'Quite right, sir, quite right; it'll do for a makeshift, I'm bound to say. But wait till you see what we'll get up for you on your own measure. Come, Tod, book and pen; get at it. Length of leg, 32" – and so on. Before I could get in a word he had measured me, and was giving orders for dress suits, morning suits, shirts, and all sorts of things. When I got a chance I said:

'But, my dear sir, I *can't* give these orders, unless you can wait indefinitely, or change the bill.'

'Indefinitely! It's a weak word, sir, a weak word. Eternally – *that's* the word, sir. Tod, rush these things through, and send them to the gentleman's address without any waste of time. Let the minor customers wait. Set down the gentleman's address and –'

'I'm changing my quarters. I will drop in and leave the new address.'

'Quite right, sir, quite right. One moment – let me show you out, sir. There – good day, sir, good day.'

Well, don't you see what was bound to happen? I drifted naturally into buying whatever I wanted, and asking for change. Within a week I was sumptuously equipped with all needful comforts and luxuries, and was housed in an expensive private hotel in Hanover Square. I took my dinners there, but for breakfast I stuck by Harris's humble feeding house, where I had got my first meal on my million-pound bill. I was the making of Harris. The fact had gone all abroad that the foreign crank who carried million-pound bills in his vest-pocket was the patron saint of the place. That was enough. From being a poor, struggling, little hand-to-mouth enterprise, it had become celebrated, and overcrowded with customers. Harris was so grateful that he forced loans upon me, and would not be denied; and so, pauper as I was, I had money to spend, and was living like the rich and the great. I judged that there was going to be a crash by and by, but I was in, now, and must swim across or drown. You see there was just that element of impending disaster to give a serious side, a sober side, to a state of things which would otherwise have been purely ridiculous. In the night, in the dark, the tragedy part was always to the front, and always warning, always threatening; and so I moaned and tossed, and sleep was hard to find. But in the cheerful daylight the tragedy element faded out and disappeared, and I walked on air, and was happy to giddiness, to intoxication, you may say.

And it was natural; for I had become one of the notorieties of the metropolis of the world, and it turned my head, not just a little, but a good deal. You could not take up a newspaper, English, Scotch, or Irish, without finding in it one or more references to the 'vest-pocket million-pounder' and his latest doings and sayings. At first, in these mentions, I was at the bottom of the personal gossip column; next, I was listed above the knights; next, above the baronets; next, above the barons, and so on; and so on, climbing steadily as my notoriety augmented, until I reached the highest altitude possible, and there I remained, taking precedence of all dukes not royal, and of all ecclesiastics except the primate of all England. But mind, this was not fame; as Yet I had achieved only notoriety. Then came the climaxing stroke – the accolade, so to speak – which in a single instant transmuted the perishable dross of notoriety into the enduring gold of fame: *Punch* caricatured me! Yes, I was a made man, now; my place was established. I might be joked about still, but reverently, not hilariously, not rudely; I could be smiled at, but not laughed at. The time for that had gone by. *Punch* pictured me all a-flutter with rags, dickering with a beefeater for the Tower of London. Well, you can imagine how it was with a young fellow who had never been taken notice of before, and now all of a sudden couldn't say a thing that wasn't taken up and repeated everywhere; couldn't stir abroad without constantly overhearing the remark flying from lip to lip, 'There he goes; that's him!' couldn't take his breakfast without a crowd to look on; couldn't appear in an opera box without concentrating there the fire of a thousand lorgnettes. Why, I just swam in glory all day long – that is the amount of it.

You know, I even kept my old suit of rags, and every now and then appeared in them, so as to have the old pleasure of buying trifles, and being insulted, and then shooting the scoffer dead with the million-pound bill. But I couldn't keep that up. The illustrated papers made the outfit so familiar that when I went out in it I was at once recognized and followed by a crowd, and if I attempted to purchase the man would offer me his whole shop on credit before I could pull my note to him.

About the tenth day of my fame I went to fulfil my duty to my flag by paying my respects to the American minister. He received me with the enthusiasm proper in my case, upbraided me for being so tardy in my duty, and said that there was only one way to get his forgiveness, and that was to take the seat at his dinner party that night made vacant by the illness of one of his guests. I said I would, and we got to talking. It turned out that he and my father had been schoolmates in boyhood, Yale students together later, and always warm friends up to my father's death. So then he required me to put in at his house all the odd time I might have to spare, and I was very willing, of course.

In fact I was more than willing; I was glad. When the crash should come, he might somehow be able to save me from total destruction; I didn't know how, but he might think of a way, maybe. I couldn't venture to unbosom myself to him at this late date, a thing which I would have been quick to do in the beginning of this awful career of mine in London. No, I couldn't venture it now; I was in too deep; that is, too deep for me to be risking revelations to so new a friend, though not yet clear beyond my depth, as *I* looked at it. Because, you see, with all my borrowing, I was carefully keeping within my means – I mean within my salary. Of course I couldn't *know* what my salary was going to be, but I had a good enough basis for an estimate in the fact that, if I won the bet, I was to have *choice* of any situation in that rich old gentleman's gift provided I was competent – and I should certainly prove competent; I hadn't any doubt about that. And as to the bet, I wasn't worrying about that; I had always been lucky. Now my estimate of the salary was six hundred to a thousand a year; say, six hundred for the first year, and so on up year by year, till I struck the upper figure by proved merit. At present I was only in debt for my first year's salary. Everybody had been trying to lend me money, but I had fought off the most of them on one pretext or another; so this indebtedness represented only £300 borrowed money, the other £300 represented my keep and my purchases. I believed my second year's salary would carry me through the rest of the month if I went on being cautious and economical, and I intended to look sharply out for that. My month ended, my employer back from his journey, I should be all right once more, For I should at once divide the two years' salary among my creditors by assignment, and get right down to my work.

It was a lovely dinner party of fourteen. The Duke and Duchess of Shoreditch, and their daughter the Lady Anne-Grace-Eleanor-Celeste-and-so-forth-and-so-forth-de-Bohun, the Earl and Countess of Newgate, Viscount Cheapside, Lord and Lady Blatherskite, some untitled people of both sexes, the minister and his wife and daughter, and this daughter's visiting friend, an English girl of twenty-two, named Portia Langham, whom I fell in love with in two minutes, and she with me – I could see it without glasses. There was still another guest, an American – but I am a little ahead of my story. While the people were still in the drawing room, whetting up for dinner, and coldly inspecting the late-comers, the servant announced:

'Mr Lloyd Hastings.'

The moment the usual civilities were over, Hastings caught sight of me, and came straight with cordially outstretched hand; then stopped short when about to shake; and said with an embarrassed look:

'I beg your pardon , sir, I thought I knew you.'

'Why, you do know me, old fellow.'

'No! Are *you* the – the –'

'Vest-pocket monster? I am, indeed. Don't be afraid to call me by my nickname; I'm used to it.'

'Well, well, well, this is a surprise. Once or twice I've seen your own name coupled with the nickname, but it never occurred to me that *you* could be the Henry Adams referred to. Why, it isn't six months since you were clerking for Blake Hopkins in Frisco on a salary, and sitting up nights on an extra allowance, helping me arrange and verify the Gould and Curry Extension papers and statistics. The idea of your being in London, and a vast millionaire, and a colossal celebrity! Why, it's the Arabian Nights come again. Man, I can't take it in at all; can't realize it; give me time to settle the whirl in my head.'

'The fact is, Lloyd, you are no worse off than I am. I can't realize it myself.'

'Dear me, it *is* stunning, now isn't it? Why, it's just three months today since we went to the Miners' restaurant –'

'No; the What Cheer.'

'Right, it *was* the What Cheer; went there at two in the morning, and had a chop and coffee after a hard six hours' grind over those Extension papers, and I tried to persuade you to come to London with me, and offered to get leave of absence for you and pay all your expenses, and give you something over if I succeeded in making the sale; and you would not listen to me, said I wouldn't succeed, and you couldn't afford to lose the run of business and be no end of time getting the hang of things again when you got back home. And yet here you are. How odd it all is! How did you happen to come, and whatever *did* give you this incredible start?'

'Oh, just an accident. It's a long story – a romance, a body may say. I'll tell you all about it, but not now.'

'When?'

'The end of this month.'

'That's more than a fortnight yet. It's too much of a strain on a person's curiosity. Make it a week.'

'I can't. You'll know why, by and by. But how's the trade getting along?'

His cheerfulness vanished like a breath, and he said with a sigh:

'You were a true prophet, Hal, a true prophet. I wish I hadn't come. I don't want to talk about it.'

'But you must. You must come and stop with me tonight, when we leave here, and tell me all about it.'

'Oh, may I? Are you in earnest?' and the water showed in his eyes.

'Yes; I want to hear the whole story, every word.'

'I'm so grateful! Just to find a human interest once more, in some voice and in some eye, in me and affairs of mine, after what I've been through here – Lord! I could go down on my knees for it!'

'He gripped my hand hard, and braced up, and was all right and lively after that for the dinner – which didn't come off. No; the usual thing happened, the thing that is always happening under that vicious and aggravating English system – the matter of precedence couldn't be settled, and so there was no dinner. Englishmen always eat dinner before they go out to dinner, because *they* know the risks they are running; but nobody ever warns the stranger, and so he walks placidly into the trap. Of course nobody was hurt this time, because we had all been to dinner, none of us being novices except Hastings, and he having been informed by the minister at the time that he invited him that in deference to the English custom he had not provided any dinner. Everybody took a lady and processioned down to the dining room, because it is usual to go through the motions; but there the dispute began. The Duke of Shoreditch wanted to take precedence, and sit at the head of the table, holding that he outranked a minister who represented merely a nation and not a monarch; but I stood for my rights, and refused to yield. In the gossip column I ranked all dukes not royal, and said so, and claimed precedence of this one. It couldn't be settled, of course, struggle as we might and did, he finally (and injudiciously) trying to play birth and antiquity, and I 'seeing' his Conqueror and 'raising' him with Adam, whose direct posterity I was, as shown by my name, while *he* was of a collateral branch, as shown by *his*, and by his recent Norman origin; so we all processioned back to the drawing room again and had a perpendicular lunch – plate of sardines and a strawberry, and you group yourself and stand up and eat it. Here the religion of precedence is not so strenuous; the two persons of highest rank chuck up a shilling, the one the wins has first go at his strawberry, and the loser gets the shilling. The next two chuck up, then the next two, and so on. After refreshment, tables were brought, and we all played cribbage, sixpence a game. The English never play any game for amusement. If they can't make something or lose something – they don't care which – they won't play.

We had a lovely time; certainly two of us had, Miss Langham and I. I was so bewitched with her that I couldn't count my hands if they went above a double sequence; and when I struck home I never discovered it, and started up the outside row again, and would have lost the game every time, only the girl did the same, she being in just my condition, you see; and consequently neither of us ever got out, or cared to wonder why we didn't; we only just knew we were happy, and didn't wish to know anything else, and didn't want to be interrupted. And I *told* her – I did indeed – told her I loved her; and she – well, she blushed till her hair turned red, but she liked it; she *said* she did. Oh, there was never such an evening! Every time I pegged I put on a postscript; every time she pegged she acknowledged receipt of it, counting the hands the same. Why, I couldn't even say 'Two for his heels' without adding, 'My, how sweet you do look!' and she would say, 'Fifteen two, fifteen four, fifteen six, and a pair are eight, and eight are sixteen – *do* you think so?' – peeping out aslant from under her lashes, you know, so sweet and cunning. Oh, it was just *too*-too!

Well, I was perfectly honest and square with her; told her I hadn't a cent in the world but just the million-pound note she'd heard so much talk about, and *it* didn't belong to me; and that started her curiosity, and then I talked low, and told her the whole history right from the start, and it nearly killed her, laughing. What in the nation she could find to laugh about, I couldn't see, but there it was; every half minute some new detail would fetch her, and I would have to stop as much as a minute and a half to give her a chance to settle down again. Why, she laughed herself lame, she did indeed; I never saw anything like it. I mean I never saw a painful story – a story of a person's troubles and worries and fears – produce just *that* kind of effect before. So I loved her all the more, seeing she could be so cheerful when there wasn't anything to be cheerful about; for I might soon need that kind of wife, you know, the way things looked. Of course I told her we should have to wait a couple of years, till I could catch up on my salary; but she didn't mind that, only she hoped I would be as careful as possible in the matter of expenses, and not let them run the least risk of trenching on our third year's pay. Then she began to get a little worried, and wondered if we were making any mistake, and starting the salary on a higher figure for the first year than I would get. This was good sense, and it made me feel a little less confident than I had been feeling before; but it gave me a good business idea, and I brought it frankly out.

'Portia, dear, would you mind going with me that day, when I confront those old gentlemen?'

She shrank a little, but said:

'N-o; if my being with you would help hearten you. But – would it be quite proper, do you think?'

'No, I don't know that it would; in fact I'm afraid it wouldn't; but you see, there's so *much* dependent upon it that –'

'Then I'll go anyway, proper or improper,' she said, with a beautiful and generous enthusiasm. 'Oh, I shall be so happy to think I'm helping.'

'Helping, dear? Why, you'll be doing it all. You're so beautiful and so lovely and so winning, that with you there I can pile our salary up till I break those good old fellows, and they'll never have the heart to struggle.'

Sho! you should have seen the rich blood mount, and her happy eyes shine!

'You wicked flatterer! There isn't a word of truth in what you say, but still I'll go with you. Maybe it will teach you not to expect other people to look with your eyes.'

Were my doubts dissipated? Was my confidence restored? You may judge by this fact: privately I raised my salary to twelve hundred the first year on the spot. But I didn't tell her; I saved it for a surprise.

All the way home I was in the clouds, Hastings talking, I not hearing a word. When he and I entered my parlor, he brought me to myself with his fervent appreciations of my manifold comforts and luxuries.

'Let me just stand here a little and look my fill! Dear me, it's a palace; it's just a palace! And in it everything a body *could* desire, including cozy coal fire and supper standing ready. Henry, it doesn't merely make me realize how rich you are; it makes me realize, to the bone, to the marrow, how poor I am – how poor I am, and how miserable, how defeated, routed, annihilated!'

Plague take it! this language gave me the cold shudders. It scared me broad awake, and made me comprehend that I was standing on a half-inch crust, with a crater underneath. *I* didn't know I had been dreaming – that is, I hadn't been allowing myself to know it for a while back; but *now* – oh, dear! Deep in debt, not a cent in the world, a lovely girl's happiness or woe in my hands, and nothing in front of me but a salary which might never – oh, *would* never – materialize! Oh, oh, oh, I am ruined past hope; nothing can save me!

'Henry, the mere unconsidered drippings of your daily income would –'

'Oh, my daily income! Here, down with this hot Scotch, and cheer up your soul. Here's with you! Or, no – you're hungry; sit down and –'

'Not a bite for me; I'm past it. I can't eat, these days; but I'll drink with you till I drop. Come!'

'Barrel for barrel, I'm with you! Ready? Here we go! Now, then, Lloyd, unreel your story while I brew.'

'Unreel it? What, again?'

'Again? What do you mean by that?'

'Why, I mean do you want to hear it *over* again?'

'Do I want to hear it *over* again? This *is* a puzzler. Wait; don't take any more of that liquid. You don't need it.'

'Look here, Henry, you alarm me. Didn't I tell you the whole story on the way here?'

'You?'

'Yes, I.'

'I'll be hanged if I heard a word of it.'

'Henry, this is a serious thing. It troubles me. What did you take up yonder at the minister's?'

Then it all flashed on me, and I owned up, like a man.

'I took the dearest girl in this world – prisoner!'

So then he came with a rush, and we shook, and shook, and shook till our hands ached; and he didn't blame me for not having heard a word of a story which had lasted while we walked three miles. He just sat down then, like the patient, good fellow he was, and told it all over again. Synopsized, it amounted to this: He had come to England with what he thought was a grand opportunity; he had an 'option' to sell the Gould and Curry Extension for the 'locators' of it, and keep all he could get over a million dollars. He had worked hard, had pulled every wire he knew of, had left no honest expedient untried, had spent nearly all the money he had in the world, had not been able to get a solitary capitalist to listen to him, and his option would run out at the end of the month. In a word, he was ruined. Then he jumped up and cried out:

'Henry, you can save me! You can save me, and you're the only man in the universe that can. Will you do it? *Won't* you do it?'

'Tell me how. Speak out, my boy.'

'Give me a million and my passage home for my "option"! Don't, *don't* refuse!'

I was in a kind of agony. I was right on the point of coming out with the words, 'Lloyd, I'm a pauper myself – absolutely penniless, and in *debt!*' But a white-hot idea came flaming through my head, and I gripped my jaws together, and calmed myself down till I was as cold as capitalist. Then I said, in a commercial and self-possessed way:

'I will save you, Lloyd –'

'Then I'm already saved! God be merciful to you forever! If ever I –'

'Let me finish, Lloyd. I will save you, but not in that way; for that would not be fair to you, after your hard work, and the risks you've run. I don't need to buy mines; I can keep my capital moving, in a commercial center like London without that; it's what I'm at, all the time; but here is what I'll do. I know all about that mine, of course; I know its immense value, and can swear to it if anybody wishes it. You shall sell out inside of the fortnight for three millions cash, using my name freely, and we'll divide, share and share alike.'

Do you know, he would have danced the furniture to kindling wood in his insane joy, and broken everything on the place, if I hadn't tripped him up and tied him.

Then he lay there, perfectly happy, saying:

'I may use your name! Your name – think of it! Man, they'll flock in droves, these rich Londoners; they'll *fight* for that stock! I'm a made man, I'm a made man forever, and I'll never forget you as long as I live!'

In less than twenty-four hours London was abuzz! I hadn't anything to do, day after day, but sit at home, and say to all comers:

'Yes, I told him to refer to me. I know the man, and I know the mine. His character is above reproach, and the mine is worth far more than he asks for it.'

Meantime I spent all my evenings at the minister's with Portia. I didn't say a word to her about the mine; I saved it for a surprise. We talked salary, sometimes love and salary together. And my! the interest the minister's wife and daughter took in our little affair, and the endless ingenuities they invented to save us from interruption, and to keep the minister in the dark and unsuspicious – well, it was just lovely of them!

When my month was up, at last, I had a million dollars to my credit in the London and County Bank, and Hastings was fixed in the same way. Dressed at my level best, I drove by the house in Portland Place, judged by the look of things that my birds were home again, went on toward the minister's and got my precious, and we started back, talking salary with all our might. She was so excited and anxious that it made her just intolerably beautiful. I said:

'Dearie, the way you're looking it's a crime to strike for a salary a single penny under three thousand a year.'

'Henry, Henry, you'll ruin us!'

'Don't you be afraid. Just keep up those looks, and trust to me. It'll come out right.'

So as it turned out, I had to keep bolstering up *her* courage all the way. She kept pleading with me, and saying:

'Oh, please remember that if we ask for too much we may get no salary at all; and then what will become of us, with no way in the world to earn our living?'

We were ushered in by that same servant, and there they were, the two old gentlemen. Of course they were surprised to see that wonderful creature with me, but I said:

'It's all right, gentlemen; she is my future stay and helpmate.'

And I introduced them to her, and called them by name. It didn't surprise them; they knew I would know enough to consult the directory. They seated us, and were very polite to me, and very solicitous to relieve her from embarrassment, and put her as much at her ease as they could. Then I said:

'Gentlemen, I am ready to report.'

'We are glad to hear it,' said *my* man, 'for now we can decide the bet which my brother Abel and I made. If you have won for me, you shall have any situation in my gift. Have you the million-pound note?'

'Here it is, sir,' and I handed it to him.

'I've won!' he shouted, and slapped Abel on the back. '*Now* what do you say, brother?'

'I say he *did* survive, and I've lost twenty thousand pounds. I never would have believed it.'

'I've a further report to make,' I said, 'and a pretty long one. I want you to let me come soon, and detail my whole month's history; and I promise you it's worth hearing. Meantime, take a look at that.'

'What, man! Certificate of deposit for £200,000? Is it yours?'

'Mine. I earned it by thirty days' judicious use of that little loan you let me have. And the only use I made of it was to buy trifles and offer the bill in change.'

'Come, this is astonishing! It's incredible, man!'

'Never mind, I'll prove it. Don't take my word unsupported.'

But now Portia's turn was come to be surprised. Her eyes were spread wide, and she said:

'Henry, is that really your money? Have you been fibbing to me?'

'I have indeed, dearie. But you'll forgive me, *I* know.'

She put up an arch pout, and said:

'Don't you be so sure. You are a naughty thing to deceive me so!'

'Oh, you'll get over it, sweetheart, you'll get over it; it was only fun, you know. Come, let's be going.'

'But wait, wait! The situation, you know. I want to give you the situation, said one man.

'Well,' I said, 'I'm just as grateful as I can be, but really I don't want one.'

'But you can have the very choicest one in my gift.'

'Thanks again, with all my heart; but I don't even want *that* one.'

'Henry, I'm ashamed of you. You don't half thank the good gentleman. May I do it for you?'

'Indeed you shall, dear, If you can improve it. Let us see you try.'

She walked to my man, got up in his lap, put her arm round his neck, and kissed him right on the mouth. Then the two old gentlemen shouted with laughter, but I was dumfounded, just petrified, as you may say. Portia said:

'Papa, he has said you haven't a situation in your gift that he'd take; and I feel just as hurt as —'

'My darling! — Is that your papa?'

'Yes; he's my step-papa, and the dearest one that ever was. You understand now, don't you, why I was able to laugh when you told me at the minister's, not knowing my relationships, what trouble and worry papa's and Uncle Abel's scheme was giving you?'

Of course I spoke right up, now, without any fooling, and went straight to the point.

'Oh, my dearest dear sir, I want to take back what I said. You *have* got a situation open that I want.'

'Name it.'

'Son-in-law.'

'Well, well, well! But you know, if you haven't ever served in that capacity, you of course can't furnish recommendations of a sort to satisfy the conditions of the contract, and so —'

'Try me — oh, do, I beg of you! Only just try me thirty or forty years, and if —'

'Oh, well, all right; it's but a little thing to ask. Take her along.'

Happy, we two? There're not words enough in the unabridged to describe it. And when London got the whole history, a day or two later, of my month's adventures with that bank-note, and how they ended, did London talk, and have a good time? Yes.

My Portia's papa took that friendly and hospitable bill back to the Bank of England and cashed it; then the Bank canceled it and made him a present of it, and he gave it to us at our wedding, and it has always hung in its frame in the sacredest place in our home, ever since. For it gave me my Portia. But for it I could not have remained in London, would not have appeared at the minister's, never should have met her. And so I always say, 'Yes, it's a million-pounder, as you see; but it never made but one purchase in its life, and *then* got the article for only about a tenth part of its value.'

Doctor in Clover

Richard Gordon

Dr Gaston Grimsdyke, graduate of St Swithin's Medical School and pupil of Sir Lancelot Spratt, has moved to the country in search of rural bliss. He finds, however, that intrigue and deception abound even in a pastoral paradise ...

I arrived in the country on one of those April days when all the flowers look freshly painted and all the girls look beautiful. The English spring had arrived, as described in the poems and travel advertisements instead of the grey slushy thing we usually get.

I'd already spent a few week-ends at Long Wotton, and found it a friendly place where the inhabitants are all acquainted, if not, as I later suspected from the general feeblemindedness, all actually related. Although I'm not much of a one for country pursuits – guns make such a frightful noise, fishing gives me a bad cold for weeks, and I regard horses as highly unroadworthy vehicles – it was pleasant to find myself respected locally as a learned chap, and not just the fellow who dishes out the chits for false teeth. Also, there was a very amiable young sub-postmistress, and I was looking forward to a few months quietly letting life go by and Avril Atkinson and Porterhampton fade into my subconscious.

After a week or so I was even becoming a little bored, with existence presenting no problems more complicated than keeping the uncle's house-keeper happy, and she seemed very satisfied with the story of the bishop and the parrot. Then I returned one evening from repairing the effects of a pitchfork on some bumpkin's left foot – a very pleasant consultation, with everyone touching their forelocks and asking if I could use a side of bacon – and found the old dear herself standing at the garden gate, looking distraught.

'Doctor, Doctor!' she called. 'Something terrible's happened.'

I was a bit alarmed the cream might have gone off. I was looking forward to my evening meal of fresh salmon followed by early strawberries, particularly as the old uncle had overlooked handing over the cellar keys in his hurry to be off, and I'd just found them – buried under the coal in the outhouse, of all places.

'Doctor, you're to go at once,' she went on. 'It's very urgent. To Nutbeam Hall,' she explained, when I asked where. 'It's his Lordship, there's been a terrible accident.'

A bit of a tragedy, I felt. Fancy missing a dinner like that. But the Grimsdykes never shirk their professional duty, and pausing only to load the Bentley with sufficient splints and morphine to tackle a train crash, I sped up the road to Nutbeam Hall.

Everyone in Long Wotton knew Lord Nutbeam, of course, though I don't mean they played darts with him every night in the local. In fact, most of the inhabitants had never seen him. The old boy was a bachelor, who lived in a rambling house apparently designed by Charles Addams, his younger brother's missus doing such things as ordering the coal and paying the milkman. He appeared only occasionally when they gave him an airing in an old Daimler like a mechanized glasshouse, always with brother or wife as bodyguard.

This was the pair who received me in the hall, a long, dim place crammed with furniture and as stuffy as the inside of the family vault.

'I'm the doctor,' I announced.

'But Dr Grimsdyke – ?'

'Dr Rudolph Grimsdyke is enjoying a little well-earned holiday. I'm his locum and nephew, Dr Gaston Grimsdyke.'

I saw them exchange glances. The Hon. Percy Nutbeam was a fat chap with a complexion like an old whisky-vat, which I suppose he'd acquired at his brother's expense. His wife was one of those sharp-faced little women with incisors like fangs, to whom I took an instant dislike.

'Of course, I'm perfectly well qualified,' I added, sensing they might not take kindly to anyone but the accredited family practitioner.

'Naturally, naturally,' agreed Percy Nutbeam, very sociably. 'We don't question that for a moment.'

'I am sure you've had very extensive experience, Doctor,' put in the wife.

'Well, very varied, anyway. Look here,' I told them, feeling rather awkward, 'unless it's a matter of saving life on the spot, if you'd rather call another practitioner –'

'Not at all,' said Mrs Nutbeam briskly. 'My husband and I have the utmost confidence in your handling his Lordship's case. Haven't we, Percy?'

'Of course, Amanda.'

I must admit this made me feel pretty pleased. The old uncle's full of homely advice about wool next to the skin and so on, but after all those years among the hookworm and beriberi he's as out of date in medical practice as a Gladstone bag. I could see they were delighted at an up-to-date chap like myself with all the latest from hospital.

'Then what's the trouble?' I asked.

'We fear a broken hip, Doctor,' announced Amanda Nutbeam. 'That's serious, I believe?'

'Could be. Very.'

'Our aunt died after a broken hip,' murmured Percy.

'It all depends on the constitution of the patient,' I told them, remembering my orthopaedic lectures.

'Please let me impress upon you, Doctor,' said Amanda, 'that his Lordship is very delicate.'

'Very delicate indeed,' added her husband. 'This way, Doctor, if you please.'

I went upstairs feeling pretty curious. I'd already decided it was the old story – poor old Lord Nutbeam was potty, and the family were making themselves thoroughly miserable keeping it quiet, instead of getting him decently certified and sending him baskets of fruit every Friday. I was therefore a bit startled when my clinical examination provided a couple of eye-openers.

In the first place, far from being dotty, Lord Nutbeam had an IQ in the professorial class.

'I fell from the library ladder, Doctor,' he explained from his bed. 'Appropriately enough, as I was reaching for my first edition of *Religio Medici*. You are familiar with the work? Perhaps you have also read Dr William Harvey's *De Motu Cordis* in the original Latin? I should much like to discuss it with a medical man.'

Not wishing to chat about all those books I'm going to read whenever I get a spare moment, I put my stethoscope in my ears. Then I got my second surprise. From the conversation downstairs I'd gathered Lord Nutbeam's

grip on life was as secure as on a wet conger eel, but I quickly discovered –
fractures apart – he was as hale and hearty as I was.

'I am very delicate, Doctor,' he kept on insisting, though he looked a spry
old boy with his little white moustache. 'I neither smoke nor drink and live
on soft foods. Ever since I had the fever at the age of twenty-one my dear
brother and his wife have been devoted to my welfare.'

'Don't worry,' I told him. 'We'll soon have this little matter cleared up,
and you'll be able to go on reading just where you left off.'

A few minutes later I again faced the ambulant members of the Nutbeam
family in the hall, and announced in suitably sepulchral tones that his
Lordship had indeed fractured the neck of the right femur.

'Ha!' muttered Percy Nutbeam. 'Auntie!'

'Then is *is* serious, Doctor?'

'But please let me reassure you,' I possibly gripped my lapels. 'Once we
get anyone as chirpy as Lord Nutbeam into hospital and the hands of a
decent orthopaedic surgeon we'll have him on his feet again in no time.
Meanwhile, I have administered a sedative and the fracture isn't very painful.
I guarantee he'll stand up to everything wonderfully.'

I was then rather jolted to hear Amanda Nutbeam ask, 'Doctor, don't you
think it would be far, far kinder just to do nothing?'

'A very eminent specialist left our aunt to pass peacefully away,' added
Percy.

'But dash it!' I exclaimed. 'How old was your aunt?'

'Ninety-two.'

Lord Nutbeam was fifty, the age when most men are telling their secretaries
they're in the prime of life.

'Look here, this is quite a different case –'

'His Lordship is so delicate, life is merely a burden to him,' persisted
Amanda.

'Been delicate for years, Doctor. Even in the nursery he was always being
sick.'

'Surely, Doctor, it would be a happy release?'

'He will have no more troubles among the angels,' ended Percy Nutbeam,
looking at the chandelier.

Now, I may not be the most erudite of medical practitioners, but many
years' patronage of the sport of kings has left me pretty sharp at spotting
something fishy. So I eyed this couple pretty sternly and said, 'If I don't get

Lord Nutbeam into hospital this very night, it'll be – why, gross professional misconduct, to say the least.'

'You can hardly get him there without his consent,' replied Amanda sharply.

She gave me a smile as unfriendly as one of Sir Lancelot Spratt's laparotomy incisions.

'And Lord Nutbeam would never consent to anything whatever without consulting us first,' said Percy.'

'Now just a minute –'

'You are very young, Doctor,' Amanda continued. 'I can assure you his Lordship would be much happier passing away peacefully in his own home, rather than being mutilated among strangers.'

'Our aunt,' added Percy, 'was very contented right to the end.'

'Here, I say –'

'I think your consultation is over, Doctor. The butler will show you to the door.'

I was so furious I couldn't enjoy my salmon. But I managed to cram down the strawberries and a bottle of the uncle's *Liebfraumilch*, then I paced the room and smoked a couple of cigars. I looked up Watson-Jones' *Fractures and Joint Injuries*, and I found a copy of Hadfield's *Law and Ethics for Doctors*, but though this is pretty hot on such things as Relations with the Clergy and Opening a Vein after Death, it's a bit short on handling murderous relatives. I wondered what the devil to do. I thought of telephoning another doctor, but felt this would produce only an action for slander. Finally I decided (*a*) if old Nutbeam continued to lie flat on his back he would undoubtedly perish; (*b*) you can't press-gang people into hospital; and (*c*) some pretty nasty questions were going to be asked at the inquest.

Apart from medical ethics, the thought of the beastly brother and wife itching to get their fingers on Lord Nutbeam's cash and title fairly made my blood boil. Particularly as I now realized my welcome to Nutbeam Hall didn't come from heartfelt appreciation of my clinical abilities, but because they thought I had more chance of knocking his Lordship off than my uncle had. After sitting down with a drop of the uncle's special liqueur brandy, I made my decision. My only course, as a doctor and gentleman, was to return to Nutbeam Hall forthwith and give all concerned a jolly good piece of my mind.

Five minutes later I arrived again at the front gates, turning a few choice phrases over in my thoughts, when I noticed a ruddy great Rolls parked outside. I was wondering if the Nutbeams had simply preferred to by-pass me and summon a specialist off their own bat, when the front door opened to admit a severe-looking bird of consultoid aspect, wearing striped trousers and carrying a brief-case.

'Good evening, sir,' I said.

'Good evening,' he replied, got into his Rolls, and drove off.

I'd hardly time to sort this out when the door flew open again and Mrs Nutbeam fell on me like her long-lost baby.

'Doctor, Doctor! Thank God you've come back! You must get his Lordship into hospital at once.'

'This very instant,' cried Percy, panting up behind.

'With the very best specialist available.'

'Regardless of expense.'

'Everything humanly possible must be done for him.'

'The telephone is just inside the hall, Doctor.'

'Now just a minute.' I found this rather confusing. 'A couple of hours ago you told me –'

'Please disregard whatever I said a couple of hours ago,' returned Amanda Nutbeam, 'I was too upset by my dear brother-in-law's accident to think properly.'

'We both were, Doctor. We were quite beside ourselves.'

Deciding there was no point in asking a lot of silly questions, I telephoned an eminent bone-basher in Gloucester who'd done a neat job on a patient who went through a threshing machine. Shortly afterwards I was gratified to see Lord Nutbeam departing tucked-up in an ambulance, particularly as the original Grimsdyke diagnosis had been confirmed.

Like any GP pushing his patient into hospital these days, I didn't see his Lordship again for a fortnight. I was meanwhile kept agreeably busy remedying the rustics, and though the uncle didn't even send a postcard, Miles telephoned a couple of times, but he was too concerned over Sir Lancelot's car park to ask how I was getting on. Then one Saturday I decided to drive over to Gloucester to watch an afternoon's cricket, and looked into the Jenner Memorial Hospital to see Lord Nutbeam during the tea interval.

I found his Lordship very perky in a private room with a Smith-Petersen pin holding his hip together, though we hadn't much time for a quiet chat – modern orthopaedic wards are pretty active places, with all those nice girls

from the physiotherapy department laying cool hands on fevered joints and
making you kick your legs in the air as though you were about to turn out
for the Arsenal. But the old boy seemed to be enjoying it all, and while a
little red-headed staff nurse brushed his hair he started asking my views on
the original works of Hippocrates.

'You'll soon be back among your books again,' I said, not wishing to
pursue the subject.

'Indeed, Doctor, I believe my library is the only pleasure in my life. Except
on Saturday nights, when I sometimes play the piano.'

I was reflecting that this sort of existence would have me stone dead in a
fortnight when we were interrupted by the surgeon himself, a big, red-faced,
jolly Irishman. Most orthopods are, when you come to think of it, just as
ophthalmologists look like dyspeptic watchmakers and bladder surgeons
resemble prosperous commercial travellers.

'He's all yours now, m'boy,' said the surgeon, as we left the room together
after examining the patient. 'His rehabilitation will go much smoother at
home, and this sister-in-law seems agreeable enough to nurse him. Anyway,
I'm off on Monday for a month's fishing in County Mayo. How is he for
cash, by the bye?'

'According to village gossip, crammed with it.'

'Is he now?' The orthopod seemed to brighten at the prospect of having
his fishing on Lord Nutbeam's hip. 'Odd sort of feller, don't you think? I
couldn't see him saying "Boo" to a newly hatched gosling. I'll be sending
you the usual letter about treatment. Meanwhile, tell him to confine his
reading to the bottom shelf.'

When a few mornings later they unloaded his Lordship at Nutbeam Hall
and I pushed his new wheel-chair into the library, I felt pretty contented
with myself. The whole episode had already increased my professional
standing in Long Wotton no end. I'm far from saying the natives were hostile,
but in the country they regard anyone who hasn't lived among them for
thirty years as a day tripper, and now there was plenty of glowing gossip to
warm the ears of the old uncle on his return. If I could present him with a
Lord Nutbeam skipping about the front lawn, he'd not only give fewer of
those old-fashioned looks whenever I suggested enterprising lines of treatment,
but painlessly disgorge my cash on the spot.

'I am certainly glad my brother-in-law is back in his own home, Doctor,'
remarked Amanda Nutbeam. 'It is only here, I think, that we really
understand his best interests.'

'So I've noticed,' I told her. 'And now for a few weeks of rest and quiet and nourishing food,' I added confidently, 'and his Lordship will be dancing the Highland Fling if he wants to.'

But I should have learned long ago that in the turf and therapeutics it's disastrous to back a dead certainty.

For some reason, Lord Nutbeam didn't want to get better. I'd imagined that once he was home he'd settle down to a nice long read, but instead he sat staring out of the window with cups of beef-tea getting cold at his elbow. Sometimes he picked up *The Anatomy of Melancholy*, but it didn't seem to hold him. Sometimes he pushed himself to the piano, but he could manage only a few bars of *Valse Triste*. To cheer him up, I wheeled him round the garden telling funny stories, but he never seemed to see the point. 'Alas, poor Yorick!' was the most I could get out of him.

His Lordship grew steadily feebler and feebler, while everything else in sight was burgeoning wildly in the sunshine. It wasn't long before I began to grow alarmed about his condition. Modern medicine's all very well, with antibiotics and heart-lung machines and so on, but once a chap's decided he doesn't want to live any more we're not much better off than the witch-doctors in Central Africa. And my professional problems weren't made easier by the other Nutbeams, who now the excitement had died down treated me like the man come to mend the drains. Far from his Lordship, they were terrible snobs – particularly the missus, whom everyone knew in the village was only a road-house remnant from Percy Nutbeam's youth, anyway.

'It would be much more convenient if you could make your daily visit earlier,' she said, as I limped into Nutbeam Hall one evening after a heavy day's practice among the pigsties. 'We are expecting Lord and Lady Farnborough for dinner any minute, and I should naturally prefer my guests not to be greeted in the hall by the doctor. Perhaps you would also have the goodness to change your shoes before coming to us, Dr Grimsdyke. I realize that you cannot avoid walking through the farmyards during the day, but –'

I must say, her attitude made me pretty annoyed. Particularly as I felt she wouldn't have tried it with the old uncle, not with those old-fashioned looks of his. Then, a couple of days later, Lord Nutbeam went off his food and started looking like Socrates eyeing the hemlock.

'We're all bursting to see you back to normal again,' I told him, hopefully writing a prescription for another tonic. 'Here's something which will have you chirping with the birds in no time.'

'Thank you, Doctor. You are very kind. Indeed, everyone is very, very kind. Especially, of course, my dear brother and his wife.' He listlessly turned a few pages of Gibbon's *Decline and Fall*. 'But I fear my accident had more effect than I imagined. I've hardly been out of Nutbeam Hall for many years, you know, on account of my delicate health. Meeting so many people in the hospital was something of a disturbance. You are doubtless familiar with the lines in Gray's *Elegy in a Country Churchyard –*'

Feeling that churchyards were definitely out, I interrupted with the story about the parrot. But I don't think he got that one either.

I left him in the library, wondering whether to assemble the family again and confess the old boy wasn't living up to my prognosis. But I was stopped by Percy Nutbeam himself in the hall.

'Could you spare time for a whisky and soda, Doctor?'

My professional duties being over for the day, I accepted.

'I'm very worried about my brother's condition,' he declared, after a bit of chat about the weather and the crops.

'And so am I,' I told him.

'I remember the case of our aunt so well. The collapse seemed to set in all at once. Like a pricked balloon. I suppose there's not any danger of – er, is there?'

I nodded. 'I'm afraid I've got to say there is.'

The poor chap looked so concerned I felt I must have misjudged him all along.

'Then how long, Doctor, would you give him – ?'

'Might be a matter of only a week or two,' I said gloomily.

'Good God! Not before May the twenty-eighth?'

I looked puzzled, wondering if they'd arranged a picnic or something.

'This is a very delicate business, Doctor.' He poured himself another whisky. 'But I must be frank with you. You remember Sir Kenneth Cowberry?'

'I don't think I've had the pleasure –'

'He was leaving as you returned, the night of the accident. He's the head of Hoskins, Harrison, Cowberry, and Blackthorn. My brother's accountants, you know. I thought we'd better send for him at once, in case there were any arrangements my brother might have wished –'

'Quite,' I said.

'Lord Nutbeam naturally desires to leave my wife and myself his entire fortune. After all, we have devoted our lives to his welfare.'

'Quite, quite.'

'But it was only that evening we learned – my brother is oddly secretive about money matters – that he had in fact already made over his estate to me. In order to – er, escape death duties. You may have heard of other cases, Doctor? But under the rules of the Inland Revenue Department my brother must stay alive for five years after signing the document, or it doesn't hold water. And those five years are up at midnight, May the twenty-eighth. So, Doctor, if you can keep him alive till then – I mean, I hope and trust he will have many happy years among us yet – you understand the position...?'

I didn't think highly before of this pint-sized Lord and Lady Macbeth. Now I felt it would serve them damn well right if the Government carted off the lot, to pay, among other things, my National Health salary.

'I understand the position very well,' I replied, wishing I could produce one of the uncle's looks.

I'd very much taken to old Nutbeam, and I was determined to keep him alive for the full three score and ten. But the situation was getting beyond a chap of my modest experience, and out in the country I hadn't any of my chums to ask for advice. I wished the uncle would get fed up sitting on the beach at Montego Bay and come home. I even wished Miles would turn up for the week-end. I was wondering what to say next when I had another of those profitable inspirations of mine.

'I think it would be wise,' I announced, 'to have another opinion. There might be some other condition I've overlooked. After all, doctors can make mistakes. Just like accountants.'

'As many opinions as you wish, Dr Grimsdyke.'

'There's a man in Harley Street just right for this type of case. Though his private fees are rather high.'

'That's of no concern at all, I assure you.'

'And, of course, he'll charge a guinea a mile for the visit.'

Percy Nutbeam looked a bit concerned doing the mental arithmetic, but he agreed, 'Nothing is too expensive with my brother's life at stake.'

'Plus his first-class fare and meals, naturally. He's a general surgeon, but I guarantee he's got the sharpest diagnostic nose in London. His name's Sir Lancelot Pratt.'

'Delightful air,' declared Sir Lancelot.

I'd driven over to Greater Wotton Junction to meet him, and pretty nervous I felt about it, too. In my days as a student at St Swithin's,

Sir Lancelot and myself disagreed about everything from the way I tried to treat appendicitis to the way I tried to treat the nurses, and his last remark the day I proudly told him I'd qualified was that the Archbishop of Canterbury would presumably now have to make an addition to the Litany.

I bowed him from his carriage like royalty come to open the local fat stock show.

'I hope you've no objection to travelling all this way, sir?' I began, feeling that I'd sent for Rembrandt to paint the attic.

'Objections? Why, boy? It is the duty of consultant surgeons and the fire brigade to give their services whenever and wherever they are needed. It is, moreover, extremely pleasant to escape from London on a summer morning, and I'm being handsomely paid for it. Don't be so damned humble, Grimsdyke!' He poked me in the epigastrium with his walking-stick. 'A doctor must feel humble only towards his own abilities. Excellent roses, these. Apricot Queens, I believe? What sort of mulch d'you use?'

This remark was directed to the stationmaster, Greater Wotton being one of those junctions regarded as an exercise in landscape gardening interrupted by the occasional arrival of trains. Sir Lancelot then ignored me for ten minutes' erudite discussion on the merits of horse and cow manure. Come to think of it, that sort of ability represents his genius. Most surgeons can talk only about the inside of their patients or the inside of their cars, but Sir Lancelot has informed views on everything from nuclear physics to newts.

'I am presumably obliged to travel in that,' he said, indicating my car. 'Am I permitted a bite to eat before seeing the patient?'

'I've arranged a modest meal, sir.'

Remembering that a high blood-sugar is conducive to mental tranquillity, I'd decided to give the old boy a jolly good lunch before getting down to business.

'I rarely take wine at midday,' Sir Lancelot observed later, mellowing over the roast lamb and a glass of the uncle's Château Lafite, 'but I must say Dr Rudolph Grimsdyke has excellent taste in it.'

I agreed, though I'd been a bit alarmed to notice the cellar had somehow got down to only a couple of bottles.

'The only locums I did were in the East End of London, where in those days the doctors were as half-starved as the patients.' Sir Lancelot gazed through the window, where the cuckoos were tuning up among the blossoms. 'He seems to have found himself a very agreeable spot – botanically, ornithologically, and even meteorologically.'

'But not anthropologically, sir,' I said brightly, feeling it time to mention the Nutbeams.

'According to the essayist Hazlitt,' Sir Lancelot observed with a nod, 'all country people hate each other. You will now kindly recapitulate the family history of your patient. You were not particularly explicit on the telephone.'

An hour later the pair of us were marching into Nutbeam Hall.

I think the Hon. Percy and his repulsive missus were staggered to find themselves faced with a chap in a frock coat and a wing collar, who glanced round as though he'd been sent to condemn the place by the local Medical Officer of Health.

'We are delighted, Sir Lancelot,' simpered Amanda Nutbeam, who of course thought doctors were all right as long as they had titles. 'I am so pleased you accepted our invitation to take over his Lordship's case?'

Sir Lancelot looked as though she were a junior probationer who'd dropped a bedpan in the middle of his weekly ward round.

'Madam, I have *not* assumed clinical responsibility for Lord Nutbeam. His medical adviser remains Dr Gaston Grimsdyke, at whose invitation I stand here now.'

'Oh! Of coure, Sir Lancelot –'

'That is normal professional procedure.'

These remarks put my morale up no end. Despite our differences in the past, Sir Lancelot wasn't so much offering the olive branch as proffering ruddy great groves. But I should have realized that a chap like him would back me to the scalpel hilt, now that I was qualified and one of the boys.

'We shall see the patient, if you please.' The Nutbeams looked rather flustered. 'And I should be glad if you would kindly provide me with a clean hand towel.'

I remembered Sir Lancelot always demanded a clean towel in uppish households, and in a tone inferring that it was a pretty stiff request.

'Dr Grimsdyke will lead the way,' he went on, as I stepped respectfully aside. 'The patient's doctor precedes the consultant into the sickroom. That is etiquette, and I should be the last to alter it.'

Our consultation was a great success. Sir Lancelot started by discussing ancient Chinese medicine for twenty minutes, then he examined the patient, had a chat about Byzantine architecture, and left his Lordship looking his brightest for weeks.

'And you discovered the original fracture solely from the physical signs, Grimsdyke?' he asked, as we left the room.

'Yes, sir.'

'Congratulations. The difficulty in making such a diagnosis is matched only by the disaster of missing it.'

'That's – that's very kind of you, sir.'

'I believe in giving credit where credit is due. In your case it happens to be remarkably easy.'

I felt jolly pleased with myself, all the same. Though I've always maintained that orthopaedic surgery is only a branch of carpentry, and now I come to think of it I was rather hot stuff in the woodwork class at school.

The other two Nutbeams were waiting expectantly in the hall, but at the foot of the stairs Sir Lancelot simply picked up his hat.

'Sir Lancelot – ?'

Percy looked as though this wasn't much of a run for their money.

'Yes, Mr Nutbeam?'

'Have you – er, anything to say about my brother?'

'I shall have a consultation with my colleage here, who will inform you later. That is the normal procedure.'

'But if you could hold out even a word of hope –' exclaimed Amanda, I fancy glancing stealthily at the calendar.

'I think my colleague will allow me to say that you will shortly see an improvement in his Lordship's condition.'

'Thank God for that,' they cried together.

'Now, if you please, Dr Grimsdyke, we shall return to your surgery.' He pulled out that great gold watch of his. 'We have really little time for discussion before the four o'clock train.'

Sir Lancelot didn't mention the patient on our way back to the uncle's cottage, being more interested in describing all the different methods of thatching. I had to wait till he was enjoying a cup of tea in the parlour, when he declared:

'Apart from an uncomplicated healing fracture, there's nothing whatever wrong with Lord Nutbeam. But there's one thing he needs desperately – an interest in life. Believe me, it's perfectly easy to be bored to death. What do you suggest?'

'More books, sir?'

Sir Lancelot seemed to find this amusing.

'From you, Grimsdyke, a remarkable answer. The advice about never judging others by yourself is one of the stupider of proverbs. If humanity didn't show an astounding sameness, the practice of medicine would come to a dead stop.'

He spread a scone with clotted cream and strawberry jam.

'I agree that after a lifetime playing the recluse, Lord Nutbeam's expedition to hospital was something of a shock. With the appalling advance of specialization, hospitals have become quite overcrowded with staff – it is, of course, completely impossible to get any rest in them. Did you notice his nurses?'

'As a matter of fact I did, sir. There was a staff nurse and –'

Sir Lancelot raised his hand. 'It is quite enough answer, Grimsdyke, that you noticed them. No doubt Lord Nutbeam finds the amateur ministrations of his sister-in-law less agreeable. I shall send down a qualified nurse from a London bureau tomorrow. You will see to it that she isn't overruled by the family.'

'That might be a bit difficult, sir.'

'Rubbish!' He helped himself to a slice of fruit cake. 'There's only one way to handle difficult patients, difficult relatives, and difficult horses, and that's by keeping on top. I hope my visit has clothed you with a little added authority. That's often the only value of the consultant appearing on the scene at all.'

'How about tonics, sir?'

'To my mind there is only one effective tonic. I shall arrange for that to be sent from London also. I think I have time for another cup of tea, if you please. By the by,' he went on, as I put down the pot. 'You knew your cousin Miles was putting up for the consultant staff at St Swithin's?'

'He did mention it to me, sir.'

'How's he fancy his chances?'

'I think he's modest by nature, sir,' I replied cagily.

'H'm. I am only betraying an open secret by saying that Cambridge is being remarkably difficult in the selection committee. Obstinacy is such an extremely unpleasing characteristic.' Sir Lancelot stroked his beard. 'How are your relations with your cousin?'

'We do rather move in different worlds, sir.'

'I don't know if you are sufficiently familiar to drop a hint that his chances at St Swithin's would be considerably bettered if he were a little more disgustingly human. Otherwise he's an exemplary candidate. His work has ability, his manner has confidence, and, what is more important, his wife has money. But whoever the committee elects, you have to live with the feller for the rest of your professional lifetime. And nothing is more trying than being yoked to a pillar of virtue, as you can find from the divorce courts any afternoon.'

'I'm sure Miles is dedicated to his profession, sir,' I remarked, taking the chance to slip in a good word for the chap.

'Nothing,' declared Sir Lancelot, 'is quite so dangerous as the dedicated man.' Shortly afterwards I drove him to the station. I no longer had any qualms about tackling the Nutbeams, even over the nurse.

'A nurse? That will be rather tedious, Doctor,' Amanda objected at once. 'We had one in the house before, the time my husband had pneumonia. It really was most difficult. They feel quite entitled to have their meals at the same table, and even attempt to sit with one in the evenings.'

This annoyed me more, because I'm a great admirer of the nursing profession, or at least of some of it. Remembering Sir Lancelot's advice, I said pretty stuffily, 'If you don't obey your doctor's orders, there really isn't much point in having one.'

'I assure you I can put up with any inconvenience for the sake of my brother-in-law's health,' she returned. 'I will instruct the housekeeper to prepare a room immediately.'

I myself wasn't much looking forward to sharing the clinical management of Lord Nutbeam with a nurse, knowing how Sir Lancelot's taste in them lay. His ward sisters at St Swithin's were a couple of women who could have kept Attila the Hun in bed for a month on bread-and-milk, and I expected someone about six feet tall with a chin like a football boot, old enough to have spanked Lord Nutbeam as a baby and tough enough to try it now. It was therefore with some astonishment that I arrived at Nutbeam Hall the next evening to discover the most beautiful girl I'd seen in my life.

'Good evening, Doctor,' she greeted me. 'I am Nurse Jones. I have given the patient his bath, and he is ready for you to see him now.'

I couldn't do anything except stare and bless my luck. She was a dainty, demure creature, with a little bow thing under her chin. She looked like Snow-White, just growing out of her dwarfs. I was hopeful that our professional relationship would quickly ripen into something more promising, the sub-postmistress being all very well for country rambles but having the annoying habit of continually explaining how you counted postal orders.

'Oh, jolly good,' I said. 'I hope you like it here in the country? Perhaps you'd care to see the local beauty spots one afternoon when you're off duty?' She gave a smile as gentle as the ripples on the village pond.

'That is really most kind of you, Doctor, but I'm afraid I shan't find much time to spare with such an important case.'

'We'll see, eh?' Nothing brings a man and woman together like treating someone else's illnesses. 'Let's go and inspect his Lordship.'

I found Lord Nutbeam sitting in bed sipping a glass of champagne.

'Where on earth did that come from?' I exclaimed.

'But the note from Fortnum and Mason's said you'd ordered it for me, Doctor.'

'Oh, did I? Yes, of course I did. Bollinger, eh? Sir Lancelot's favourite tipple. Jolly good tonic, don't you find?'

'I would never take alcohol except on doctor's orders, of course. But I must say, it does make me feel extremely well. How much do you want me to drink of it, Doctor? I believe six dozen bottles arrived downstairs.'

I murmured something about a bottle a day keeping the doctor away, and invited myself to a drop.

'How do you like your new nurse?' I asked, as she disappeared to find a glass.

Lord Nutbeam thought for some moments.

'She reminds me of a little Crabbe.'

'She doesn't walk sideways,' I said, feeling this rather uncomplimentary.

'"Courteous though coy, and gentle though retired,"' he quoted. '"The joy of youth and health her eyes display'd, And ease of heart her every look convey'd."'

I felt that the case had taken a turn for the better.

Nurse Jones was a great success all round. In a couple of days she had old Nutbeam out of his wheel-chair tottering round sniffing the flowers. The next week she'd taken to driving him about the countryside of an afternoon in the Daimler. And, calling one lunch-time, I was surprised to see he'd gone off his usual diet of poached egg on pulverized spinach and was tucking into a steak the size of a bath-mat.

Even the Percy Nutbeams didn't object to the new régime, partly because his Lordship was every day in every way getting better and better, and partly because of the way Nurse Jones handled the missus. Nurses are charming girls, though unfortunately inclined to be bossy, doubtless the effect of spending their formative years telling old men to get back into bed. But Nurse Jones was a sweet and gentle as Gee's Linctus, and always took care to address Mrs Nutbeam like an Edwardian housemaid straight out of the orphanage.

'The nurse at least knows her place,' Amanda admitted to me one afternoon. 'Which is a very welcome discovery in anyone these days. Though, of course, she could hardly expect to mix with people of our class. Not only was she trained at some extremely obscure hospital, but her father, I believe, is an engine driver.'

'You mean *in loco parentis?*' I suggested. But Amanda Nutbeam definitely had no sense of humour, either.

'All the same, I'm glad Sir Lancelot Spratt recommended her. She seems to be doing his Lordship the world of good.'

She was doing me the world of good, too. After passing the day sticking penicillin into rural posteriors, you can't imagine how you look forward to half an hour with a civilized popsie in the evening.

'Good evening, Nurse Jones,' I would greet her at the bedroom door. 'And how is his Lordship this evening?'

'Very well, thank you, Doctor. He has taken his vitaminized milk and played *Clair de Lune* twice on the piano.'

'And how are *you*, Nurse Jones?'

'Very well, thank you, Doctor.'

'Perhaps one afternoon you would like a spot of fresh air and a view of the beauty spots, Nurse Jones?'

'Perhaps one afternoon, Doctor.'

After a week or two, I felt the time had come to put our acquaintance on a rather jollier footing.

Old Nutbeam had hobbled out of the room somewhere, and Nurse Jones had been listening very respectfully while I held forth on the osteopathology of uniting fractures, so I put my arm round her waist and kissed her.

The result was rather unexpected. I'd imagined that she'd drop her eyes and dissolve into grateful sobs on my waistcoat. Instead, she caught me a neat uppercut on the left ramus of the mandible.

I don't know if many people have been clocked by nurses, but quite a lot of power they pack, after all those years shifting patients about with their bare hands. She hit me clean off my balance, right into the remains of his Lordship's dinner. But I was even more startled at the appearance of little Nurse Jones herself. She looked as though she'd been charged with a powerful current of electricity. She was all eyes and teeth and finger-nails.

'You despicable young man!' she hissed. 'Do you take me for one of your hospital pick-ups? Keep your hands to yourself, and your manners to the saloon bar.'

'I say, I'm most terribly sorry.' I brushed off the remains of a fruit salad. 'It was all meant in a perfectly friendly spirit. Like at Christmas.'

'Oh, I know you young doctors!' She looked as though she wanted to spit out something nasty. 'Do you imagine I put up with five years' hard labour in a hospital like a workhouse just for people like you to maul me about? Huh! I want more out of life than that. It's bad enough drudging away night and day, without having to defend yourself against ham-fisted Romeos as soon as you're left alone in the same room. You make me absolutely nauseated.'

Strong words, of course. But the Grimsdykes, I trust, are ever gentlemen, and sensitive to the first hint that their attentions might be unwelcome.

'A thousand apologies,' I told her, rather stiffly. 'It's all this hot weather we're having. I can assure you, Nurse Jones, that the incident will not occur again.'

'I can assure you, too,' she said.

At that moment old Nutbeam pottered back, and she became her usual demure self once more.

For the next few days I didn't know whether I was more confused than disappointed. After all, every houseman's tried a bit of slap-and-tickle in the sluice-room, and the worst response is usually a few remarks about not being that sort of girl and Sister might come back in a minute, anyway. But Nurse Jones could look as if butter wouldn't melt in her mouth while comfortably able to digest red-hot nails. It was puzzling, and rather a shame. I'd been particularly looking forward to those beauty spots.

Arriving at Nutbeam Hall a few evenings later, I thought at first that Nurse Jones was in form again. Then I recognized the voices behind the drawing-room door.

'For a man in your position behaving like that with one of the servants,' Mrs Nutbeam was declaring, 'is absolutely disgusting.'

'My dear!' bleated Percy. 'She's hardly a servant –'

'Of course she's a servant. I've had lady's maids in the past who were twice as good as she is.'

'But my dear –'

'And in our own home, with your own brother lying ill in the next room. Really, Percy!'

'My dear –'

'You've always treated me atrociously, but this is too much. Far too much. Haven't I enough on my mind at this moment?'

'But, my dear, how was I to know she'd make such a fuss? I was only trying to hold her hand.'

'And you have the effrontery to offer that as an excuse! If I had my way I'd bundle the little baggage out of the house in the next five minutes. It's only that she's kept your brother out of his grave that I tolerate her at all.'

'Let me tell you, my dear, the scene won't be repeated.'

'And let me tell you, my dear, that if it is, I'll break your neck.'

It was quite a consolation to find that Nurse Jones dished it out impartially to all comers.

Thereafter I paid fewer visits to Nutbeam Hall, his Lordship no longer needing my constant attentions, anyway. There wasn't even much excitement for the Percy Nutbeams watching LSD-day approaching, as he quietly became haler and heartier every moment. Under the mellowing influence of the coming largesse the ghastly couple grew quite friendly towards me, and even asked me to a cocktail party with a lot of their friends, who looked as though they'd been delivered in horse-boxes.

At last the twenty-eighth of May dawned, another jolly Elysian summer day. In the afternoon I drove to Nutbeam Hall for my final visit.

I found Percy and his wife standing in the hall, looking as if they'd just checked off the winning line in their penny points.

'Dr Grimsdyke,' Percy said at once, 'we both want to thank you for restoring my dear brother to us.'

'It is a great comfort, Doctor, to have him with us today. And, of course, for many more years to come.'

'If God spares him,' added Percy, looking at the chandelier again.

'To mark our appreciation,' Amanda went on, 'my husband and I would like you to accept this little gift. I hope it will remind you of one of your earliest successful cases.'

Whereupon Percy handed me a gold cigarette case, still in its box from Cartiers.

I stumbled out a few words of thanks, wondering how much it had set them back. Then I suggested I'd better make my *adieus* to the patient himself.

'My brother's out for his afternoon drive at the moment,' Percy told me, 'but of course he's due home any minute.'

'He never likes to be far from Nutbeam Hall,' said Amanda.

'Do wait, Doctor. Perhaps a cup of tea?'

At that moment we heard the Daimler in the drive, and as we opened the front door Lord Nutbeam got out with Nurse Jones. It was then I noticed something about him – possibly the look in his eye, like a chap reaching for his first pint at the end of a tough game of rugger – which made me slip the cigarette case into my pocket and prepare for trouble.

'Percy ... Amanda,' began Lord Nutbeam, 'allow me to introduce Lady Nutbeam.'

The two Honourables looked as though they'd been run through the middle by a red-hot cautery.

'That's impossible!' cried Mrs Nutbeam.

'Not impossible at all, my dear Amanda. Ethel and I were married half an hour ago in Gloucester Registry Office. Two very pleasant young men from the Waterworks Department were our witnesses.'

Percy Nutbeam gasped. 'But the money!'

'I'm afraid there isn't any, Percy. Not for you, anyway. The deed is, of course, annulled by my marrying before the five years are up. You will inherit the title when I eventually perish, unless Ethel and I happen to have children ...'

Mrs Nutbeam burst into tears.

'But I doubt whether there will be much money left, because I intend to spend it. I realize now how I have wasted my life, because you two cleverly insisted on keeping me under your noses. I'm not at all delicate. Ethel tells me I'm as vigorous as any man of twenty. I knew I'd been missing something, ever since I was among all those nice young people in hospital.'

Lord Nutbeam smiled benignly all round.

'Dear Doctor, do you recall I once mentioned Gray's *Elegy in a Country Churchyard?* I was about to quote – "Full many a flower is born to blush unseen, And waste its sweetness on the desert air." Charming poem. Well, I'm going to blush all over the place from now on. Ethel and I are off tomorrow for our honeymoon at Monte Carlo. You must come, Doctor, and visit us then when we've settled down. You probably prefer to stay here, Percy. And so you may, if you wish. Until we get back.'

'Don't forget the present, darling,' said Lady Nutbeam, looking as unruffled as when she changed his Lordship's pyjamas.

'Ah, the present. It was you, Doctor, who brought dear Ethel and I together. So perhaps you will accept this little token of our lasting gratitude and affection?'

And he handed me a gold cigarette case, still in its box from Cartiers.

The Verger

W. Somerset Maugham

There had been a christening that afternoon at St Peter's, Neville Square, and Albert Edward Foreman still wore his verger's gown. He kept his new one, its folds as full and stiff as though it were made not of alpaca but of perennial bronze, for funerals and weddings (St Peter's, Neville Square, was a church much favoured by the fashionable for these ceremonies) and now he wore only his second-best. He wore it with complacence, for it was the dignified symbol of his office, and without it (when he took it off to go home) he had the disconcerting sensation of being somewhat insufficiently clad. He took pains with it; he pressed it and ironed it himself. During the sixteen years he had been verger of this church he had had a succession of such gowns, but he had never been able to throw them away when they were worn out and the complete series, neatly wrapped up in brown paper, lay in the bottom drawers of the wardrobe in his bedroom.

The verger busied himself quietly, replacing the painted wooden cover on the marble font, taking away a chair that had been brought for an infirm old lady, and waited for the vicar to have finished in the vestry so that he could tidy up in there and go home. Presently he saw him walk across the chancel, genuflect in front of the high altar and come down the aisle; but he still wore his cassock.

'What's he 'anging about for?' the verger said to himself. 'Don't 'e know I want my tea?'

The vicar had been but recently appointed, a red-faced energetic man in the early forties, and Albert Edward still regretted his predecessor, a clergyman of the old school who preached leisurely sermons in a silvery voice and dined out a great deal with his more aristocratic parishioners. He liked things in church to be just so, but he never fused; he was not like this new man who wanted to have his finger in every pie. But Albert Edward was tolerant. St Peter's was in a very good neighbourhood and the parishioners were a very nice class of people. The new vicar had come from the East End and he couldn't be expected to fall in all at once with the discreet ways of his fashionable congregation.

'All this 'ustle,' said Albert Edward. 'But give 'im time, he'll learn.'

When the vicar had walked down the aisle so far that he could address the verger without raising his voice more than was becoming in a place of worship he stopped.

'Foreman, will you come into the vestry for a minute. I have something to say to you.'

'Very good, sir.'

The vicar waited for him to come up and they walked up the church together.

'A very nice christening, I thought, sir. Funny 'ow the baby stopped cryin' the moment you took him.'

'I've noticed they very often do,' said the vicar, with a little smile. 'After all I've had a good deal of practice with them.'

It was a source of subdued pride to him that he could nearly always quiet a whimpering infant by the manner in which he held it and he was not unconscious of the amused admiration with which mothers and nurses watched him settle the baby in the crook of his surpliced arm. The verger knew that it pleased him to be complimented on his talent.

The vicar preceded Albert Edward into the vestry. Albert Edward was a trifle surprised to find the two churchwardens there. He had not seen them come in. They gave him pleasant nods.

'Good-afternoon, my lord. Good-afternoon, sir,' he said to one after the other.

They were elderly men, both of them, and they had been churchwardens almost as long as Albert Edward had been verger. They were sitting now at a handsome refectory table that the old vicar had brought many years before from Italy and the vicar sat down in the vacant chair between them. Albert Edward faced them, the table between him and them, and wondered with slight uneasiness what was the matter. He remembered still the occasion on which the organist had got into trouble and the bother they had all had to hush things up. In a church like St Peter's, Neville Square, they couldn't afford a scandal. On the vicar's red face was a look of resolute benignity, but the others bore an expression that was slightly troubled.

'He's been naggin' them, he 'as,' said the verger to himself. 'He's jockeyed them into doin' something, but they don't 'alf like it. That's what it is, you mark my words.'

But his thoughts did not appear on Albert Edward's clean-cut and distinguished features. He stood in a respectful but not obsequious attitude. He had been in service before he was appointed to his ecclesiastical office, but only in very good houses, and his deportment was irreproachable. Starting as a page-boy in the household of a merchant-prince, he had risen by due degrees from the position of fourth to first footman, for a year he had been single-handed butler to a widowed peeress and, till the vacancy occurred at St Peter's, butler with two men under him in the house of a retired ambassador. He was tall, spare, grave and dignified. He looked, if not like a duke, at least like an actor of the old school who specialized in dukes' parts. He had tact, firmness and self-assurance. His character was unimpeachable.

The vicar began briskly.

'Foreman, we've got something rather unpleasant to say to you. You've been here a great many years and I think his lordship and the general agree with me that you've fulfilled the duties of your office to the satisfaction of everybody concerned.'

The two churchwardens nodded.

'But a most extraordinary circumstance came to my knowledge the other day and I felt it my duty to impart it to the churchwardens. I discovered to my astonishment that you could neither read nor write.'

The verger's face betrayed no sign of embarrassment.

'The last vicar knew that, sir,' he replied. 'He said it didn't make no difference. He always said there was a great deal too much education in the world for 'is taste.'

'It's the most amazing thing I ever heard,' cried the general. 'Do you mean to say that you've been verger of this church for sixteen years and never learned to read or write?'

'I went into service when I was twelve, sir. The cook in the first place tried to teach me once, but I didn't seem to 'ave the knack for it, and then what with one thing and another I never seemed to 'ave the time. I've never really found the want of it. I think a lot of these young fellows waste a rare lot of time readin' when they might be doin' something useful.'

'But don't you want to know the news?' said the other churchwarden. 'Don't you ever want to write a letter?'

'No, me lord, I seem to manage very well without. And of late years now they've all these pictures in the papers I get to know what's goin' on pretty well. Me wife's quite a scholar and if I want to write a letter she writes it for me. It's not as if I was a bettin' man.'

The two churchwardens gave the vicar a troubled glance and then looked down at the table.

'Well, Foreman, I've talked the matter over with these gentlemen and they quite agree with me that the situation is impossible. At a church like St Peter's, Neville Square, we cannot have a verger who can neither read nor write.'

Albert Edward's thin, sallow face reddened and he moved uneasily on his feet, but he made no reply.

'Understand me, Foreman, I have no complaint to make against you. You do your work quite satisfactorily; I have the highest opinion both of your character and of your capacity; but we haven't the right to take the risk of some accident that might happen owing to your lamentable ignorance. It's a matter of prudence as well as of principle.'

'But couldn't you learn, Foreman?' asked the general.

'No, sir, I'm afraid I couldn't, not now. You see, I'm not as young as I was and if I couldn't seem able to get the letters in me 'ead when I was a nipper I don't think there's much chance of it now.'

'We don't want to be harsh with you, Foreman,' said the vicar. 'But the churchwardens and I have quite made up our minds. We'll give you three months and if at the end of that time you cannot read and write I'm afraid you'll have to go.'

Albert Edward had never liked the new vicar. He'd said from the beginning that they'd made a mistake when they gave him St Peter's. He wasn't the type of man they wanted with a classy congregation like that. And now he straightened himself a little. He knew his value and he wasn't going to allow himself to be put upon.

'I'm very sorry, sir, I'm afraid it's no good. I'm too old a dog to learn new tricks. I've lived a good many years without knowin' 'ow to read and write, and without wishin' to praise myself, self-praise is no recommendation, I don't mind sayin' I've done my duty in that state of life in which it 'as pleased a merciful providence to place me, and if I *could* learn now I don't know as I'd want to.'

'In that case, Foreman, I'm afraid you must go.'

'Yes, sir, I quite understand. I shall be 'appy to 'and in my resignation as soon as you've found somebody to take my place.'

But when Albert Edward with this usual politeness had closed the church door behind the vicar and the two churchwardens he could not sustain the air of unruffled dignity with which he had borne the blow inflicted upon him and his lips quivered. He walked slowly back to the vestry and hung up on its proper peg his verger's gown. He sighed as he thought of all the grand funerals and smart weddings it had seen. He tidied everything up, put on his coat, and hat in hand walked down the aisle. He locked the church door behind him. He strolled across the square, but deep in his sad thoughts he did not take the street that led him home, where a nice strong cup of tea awaited him; he took the wrong turning. He walked slowly along. His heart was heavy. He did not know what he should do with himself. He did not fancy the notion of going back to domestic service; after being his own master for so many years, for the vicar and churchwardens could say what they liked, it was he that had run St Peter's, Neville Square, he could scarcely demean himself by accepting a situation. He had saved a tidy sum, but not enough to live on without doing something, and life seemed to cost more every year. He had never thought to be troubled with such questions. The vergers of St Peter's, like the popes of Rome, were there for life. He had often thought of the pleasant reference the vicar would make in his sermon at evensong the first Sunday after his death to the long and faithful service, and the exemplary character of their late verger, Albert Edward Foreman. He sighed deeply. Albert Edward was a non-smoker and a total abstainer, but with a certain latitude; that is to say he liked a glass of beer with his dinner and when he was tired he enjoyed a cigarette. It occurred to him now that one would comfort him and since he did not carry them he looked about him for a shop where he could buy a packet of Gold Flakes. He did not at once see one and walked on a little. It was a long street, with all sorts of shops in it, but there was not a single one where you could buy cigarettes.

'That's strange,' said Albert Edward.

To make sure he walked right up the street again. No, there was no doubt about it. He stopped and looked reflectively up and down.

'I can't be the only man as walks along this street and wants a fag,' he said. 'I shouldn't wonder but what a fellow might do very well with a little shop here. Tobacco and sweets, you know.'

He gave a sudden start.

'That's an idea,' he said. 'Strange 'ow things come to you when you least expect it.'

He turned, walked home, and had his tea.

'You're very silent this afternoon, Albert,' his wife remarked.

'I'm thinkin',' he said.

He considered the matter from every point of view and next day he went along the street and by good luck found a little shop to let that looked as though it would exactly suit him. Twenty-four hours later he had taken it and when a month after that he left St Peter's, Neville Square, for ever, Albert Edward Foreman set up in business as a tobacconist and newsagent. His wife said it was a dreadful come-down after being verger of St Peter's, but he answered that you had to move with the times, the church wasn't what it was, and 'enceforward he was going to render unto Cæsar what was Cæsar's. Albert Edward did very well. He did so well that in a year or so it struck him that he might take a second shop and put a manager in. He looked for another long street that hadn't got a tobacconist in it and when he found it, and a shop to let, took it and stocked it. This was a success too. Then it occurred to him that if he could run two he could run half a dozen, so he began walking about London, and whenever he found a long street that had no tobacconist and a shop to let he took it. In the course of ten years he had acquired no less than ten shops and he was making money hand over fist. He went round to all of them himself every Monday, collected the week's takings and took them to the bank.

One morning when he was there paying in a bundle of notes and a heavy bag of silver the cashier told him that the manager would like to see him. He was shown into an office and the manager shook hands with him.

'Mr Foreman, I wanted to have a talk to you about the money you've got on deposit with us. D'you know exactly how much it is?'

'Not within a pound or two, sir; but I've got a pretty rough idea.'

'Apart from what you paid in this morning it's a little over thirty thousand pounds. That's a very large sum to have on deposit and I should have thought you'd do better to invest it.'

'I wouldn't want to take no risk, sir. I know it's safe in the bank.'

'You needn't have the least anxiety. We'll make you out a list of absolutely gilt-edged securities. They'll bring you in a better rate of interest than we can possibly afford to give you.'

A troubled look settled on Mr Foreman's distinguished face. 'I've never 'ad anything to do with stocks and shares and I'd 'ave to leave it all in your 'ands,' he said.

The manager smiled. 'We'll do everything. All you'll have to do next time you come in is just to sign the transfers.'

'I could do that all right,' said Albert uncertainly. 'But 'ow should I know what I was signin'?'

'I suppose you can read,' said the manager a trifle sharply.

Mr Foreman gave him a disarming smile.

'Well, sir, that's just it. I can't. I know it sounds funny-like, but there it is, I can't read or write, only me name, an' I only learnt to do that when I went into business.'

The manager was so surprised that he jumped up from his chair.

'That's the most extraordinary thing I ever heard.'

'You see, it's like this, sir, I never 'ad the opportunity until it was too late and then some'ow I wouldn't. I got obstinate-like.'

The manager stared at him as though he were a prehistoric monster.

'And do you mean to say that you've built up this important business and amassed a fortune of thirty thousand pounds without being able to read or write? Good God, man, what would you be now if you had been able to?'

'I can tell you that, sir,' said Mr Foreman, a little smile on his still aristocratic features. 'I'd be verger of St Peter's, Neville Square.'

Conversation Abroad

Douglas Sutherland

The general rule that the Englishman at home would rather die than address a remark, even in a first class railway carriage, to a fellow traveller, is, by tacit agreement, abided by.

An even more firmly entrenched rule is that the closer a neighbour is in terms of geography, the less proper it is to indulge in any form of meaningful dialogue. Thus cheek-by-jowl householders who have lived next door to each other for a quarter of a century would not consider that sufficient reason to raise their hats should they chance to encounter each other in the street.

Communication between neighbours, be it on the same down train to London or next-door houses in Chelsea, is only permissible in (a) times of emergency like a rail strike or England threatened with having to follow on in the final Test at the Oval, or (b) a declaration of war. The exception to this is when abroad.

The odd thing about gentlemen abroad is not only that they lose their inhibitions about addressing their fellow countrymen despite their being complete strangers but that they almost feel it incumbent upon themselves to do so.

Certainly they do not go so far as flashing their lights or waving out of car windows when they spot another G.B. number plate, like football club supporters when they recognize their club's coloured scarf streaming from the back of another car swerving up the motorway. However, should they chance on one of their own sort in a hotel or even espy one at the next table in a restaurant, the urge to communicate is immediate and overpowering.

Nor is it a matter of merely indulging in a few pleasantries such as 'Where have you come from?' or 'Where are you going?'. They appear to be afflicted with a sudden and intense interest in their new acquaintances to whom they would not dream of giving the time of day if met with on home ground.

The symptoms are understandably more acute should one chance to fall in with a resident member of one of the many English communities which are dotted all over Europe and far beyond. These beleaguered souls, wearing the hair shirt of the exile from the homeland to which they will not (and indeed, in not a few cases, cannot) return are as avid for news of home as they are curious about whoever has been fortuitously thrust into their company.

Whether it be the *oiseau de passage* or the exile, the rules of the game are the same, though in the case of the exile rather more so.

The essence of the game is to extract every tittle of information about the other's tastes, friends and social and financial status while at the same time ensuring that you yourself are superior on all counts.

It is a game which requires the greatest subtlety and skill to play successfully. The prize is to part on an eternal oath of eternal friendship and, unless by some unhappy accident, never to meet again. It is only possible in the limited compass of this book to give the sketchiest outline of the rules.

Opening gambits

After the first introductions have been effected it is not done to discuss the weather. The weather will almost certainly be exactly the same as it was the previous day in any case. The bull question is 'Have you heard what the rate of exchange is today?'

This is intended to establish you immediately as someone of financial consequence to whom even the most fractional rise or drop in the franc, mark, peseta or what-have-you is a matter of the greatest moment and might require immediate action on the wire.

If your opponent is worth his salt he will come up with something like: 'Bank offered me 220 this morning. Didn't take it. If Thatcher gets her foot on the neck of the EEC today we'll be in for an improvement. I'd hold off if I were you.'

What you are both discussing, of course, is whether or not to cash £50 worth of travellers' cheques where a move of one point either way might make a difference of 50p, but honour will have been satisfied and you can settle down to weightier business.

In the meantime your wife should be batting strongly on her own wicket. The sort of remark you might overhear in the Ladies Gossip Stakes should go something like: 'As I was saying to my under-gardener just before we left ...'

Always, note, the *under*-gardener. How else is anyone to know that you keep two gardeners? There is no reason to disclose that you got the lad for nothing through the Youth Opportunities Scheme and that the 'head' gardener is retired on half-pay anyway. It is one of the rules of the game to tell the truth but not necessarily all the truth.

Here are some further examples of useful openings: 'It's terribly sad, but I really will have to retire old Sarah. She's getting awfully slow. Do you know, it now takes her all day just to clean the dining-room silver.'

It is not old Sarah's deficiencies which are of interest but the amount of dining-room silver there is to be cleaned.

Servants and their strengths and shortcomings are fertile ground in which to plant the seeds which will establish social status.

To have it known that nanny is getting quite impossible in her old age, seldom leaving her room, expecting to be cooked for and waited on hand and foot by the other servants is to establish one blow that one has a whole heirarchy of servants.

Similarly a passing reference to grooms, keepers or ghillies comfortably establishes ownership of many acres and opens the door to asking how many pheasants one's opponent shot on the opening day. It is to the other's discomfiture, of course, if it reveals that he has neither pheasants nor acres. In this case it is likely to be game, set and match to you. The only way he can get back into contention is by complaining of the headaches of having his house open to the public or running a Safari Park in the grounds.

These are extreme cases, since the likelihood of two established members of the landed gentry meeting up in some corner of a foreign field is remote in the extreme. They are too busy totting up the gate money at home and too mean to spend it horsing around abroad.

The rest of us must be content with establishing *bona fides* with far less impressive credentials and here the secret is never to overplay one's hand.

The chap who complains of the cost of leaving his Rolls Royce in the long-stay car park at the airport is blundering into a minefield. Few with any pretentions to social position would own anything so ostentatious as a Rolls and, if by chance he did, would tend to apologize for it rather than boast about it.

A gaucherie of this sort also lays open he who commits it to the simplest of counterpunches, which might go something like. 'I always have my man drop me off. One needs somebody to cope with the luggage anyway' and at once establishes that one keeps a manservant, leaving an ugly suspicion hanging in the air that the other fellow has not. Having a manservant carries far more points in the league table than having a Rolls and humping your own bags.

The female version of getting the foot on the neck, as the Rolls Royce owner's wife, struggling to establish that she buys her underwear at Janet Reger, under the pretext of complaining about the price, might find her wondering where she went wrong when met with a sympathetic rejoinder like: 'It must be awfully difficult for you, my dear. Personally I always wear Henry's.'

Peaceful relations can only be established with one side being declared the outright winner whereupon they all become the best of friends. All good clean fun and at least it saves having to struggle to make oneself understood by people who don't speak English.

Foreign Affairs

Tom Sharpe

Henry Wilt, Tom Sharpe's cult hero, has risen to be Head
of Liberal Studies at the Fenland College of Arts and
Technology. He has moved into a mansion on Willington
Road and is the proud father of quads, but still there are
unforeseen dangers ahead ...

It was Enrolment Week at the Tech. Henry Wilt sat at a table in Room 467
and stared into the face of the earnest woman opposite him and tried to look
interested.

'Well, there is a vacancy in Rapid Reading on Monday evenings,' he said.
'If you'll just fill in the form over there ...' He waved vaguely in the direction
of the window but the woman was not to be fobbed off.

'I would like to know a little more about it. I mean it does help, doesn't
it?'

'Help?' said Wilt refusing to be drawn into sharing her enthusiasm for self-
improvement. 'It depends what you mean by help.'

'My problem has always been that I'm such a slow reader I can't remember
what the beginning of a book was about by the time I've finished it,' said
the woman. 'My husband says I'm practically illiterate.'

She smiled forlornly and implied a breaking marriage which Wilt could
save by encouraging her to spend her Monday evenings away from home
and the rest of the week reading books rapidly. Wilt doubted the therapy
and tried to shift the burden of counselling somewhere else.

'Perhaps you would be better off taking Literary Appreciation,' he
suggested.

'I did that last year and Mr Fogerty was wonderful. He said I had
potential.'

Stifling the impulse to tell her that Mr Fogerty's notion of potential had
nothing to do with literature and was more physical in its emphasis – though
what the hell he could see in this earnest creature was a mystery – Wilt
surrendered.

'The purpose of Rapid Reading,' he said going into the patter, 'is to
improve your reading skills both in speed and retention of what you have
read. You will find that you concentrate more the faster you go and that ...'

He went on for five minutes delivering the set speech he had learnt by
heart over four years of enrolling potential Rapid Readers. In front of him
the woman changed visibly. This was what she had come to hear, the gospel
of evening-class improvement. By the time Wilt had finished and she had
filled in the form there was a new buoyancy about her.

There was less about Wilt. He sat on for the rest of the two hours listening
to other similar conversations at other tables and wondering how the devil
Bill Paschendaele managed to maintain his proselytizing fervour for An
Introduction To Fenland Sub-Culture after twenty years. The fellow positively
glowed with enthusiasm. Wilt shuddered and enrolled six more Rapid Readers
with a lack of interest that was calculated to dishearten all but the most
fanatical. In the intervals he thanked God he didn't have to teach the subject
any longer and was simply there to lead the sheep into the fold. As Head of
Liberal Studies Wilt had passed beyond Evening Classes into the realm of
timetables, committees, memoranda, wondering which of his staff was going
to have a nervous breakdown next, and the occasional lecture to Foreign
Students. He had Mayfield to thank for the latter. While the rest of the Tech.
had been badly affected by financial cuts the Foreign Students paid for
themselves and Dr Mayfield, now Head of Academic Development, had
created an empire of Arabs, Swedes, Germans, South Americans and even
several Japanese who marched from one lecture room to another pursuing
an understanding of the English language and more impossibly English
Culture and Customs, a hodge-podge of lectures which came under the
heading of Advanced English For Foreigners. Wilt's contribution was a
weekly discourse on British Family Life which afforded him the opportunity
to discuss his own family life with a freedom and frankness which would have
infuriated Eva and embarrassed Wilt himself had he not known that his
students lacked the insight to understand what he was telling them. The
discrepancy between Wilt's appearance and the facts had baffled even his
closest friends. In front of eighty foreigners he was assured of anonymity. He

was assured of anonymity, period. Sitting in Room 467 Wilt could while away the time speculating on the ironies of life.

In room after room, on floor above floor, in departments all over the Tech., lecturers sat at tables, people asked questions, received concerned answers and finally filled in the forms that ensured that lecturers would keep their jobs for at least another year. Wilt would keep his for ever. Liberal Studies couldn't fail for lack of students. The Education Act saw to that. Day Release Apprentices had to have their weekly hour of progressive opinions whether they liked it or not. Wilt was safe, and if it hadn't been for the boredom he would have been a happy man. The boredom and Eva.

Not that Eva was boring. Now that she had the quads to look after Eva Wilt's enthusiasms had widened to include every 'Alternative' under the sun. Alternative Medicine alternated with Alternative Gardening and Alternative Nutrition and even various Alternative Religions so that Wilt, coming home from each day's lack of choice at the Tech., could never be sure what was in store for him except that it was not what it had been the night before. About the only constant was the din made by the quads. Wilt's four daughters had taken after their mother. Where Eva was enthusiastic and energetic they were inexhaustible and quadrupled her multiple enthusiasms. To avoid arriving home before they were in bed Wilt had taken to walking to and from the Tech. and was resolutely unselfish about using the car. To add to his problems, Eva had inherited a legacy from an aunt and since Wilt's salary had doubled they had moved from Parkview Avenue to Willington Road and a large house in a large garden. The Wilts had moved up the social scale. It was not an improvement, in Wilt's opinion, and there were days when he hankered for the old times when Eva's enthusiasms had been slightly muted by what the neighbours might think. Now, as the mother of four and the matron of a mansion, she no longer cared. A dreadful self-confidence had been born.

And so at the end of his two hours Wilt took his register of new students to the office and wandered along the corridor of the Administration Block towards the stairs. He was going down when Peter Braintree joined him.

'I've just enrolled fifteen landlubbers for Nautical Navigation. What about that to start the year off with a bang?'

'The bang starts tomorrow with Mayfield's bloody course board meeting,' said Wilt. 'Tonight was as nothing. I tried to dissuade several insistent women and four pimply youths from taking Rapid Reading and failed. I wonder we don't run a course on how to solve *The Times* crossword puzzle in fifteen

minutes flat. It would probably boost their confidence more than beating
the track record for *Paradise Lost.*'

They went downstairs and crossed the hall where Miss Pansak was still
recruiting for Beginners' Badminton.

'Makes me feel like a beer,' said Braintree. Wilt nodded. Anything to delay
going home. Outside, stragglers were still coming in and cars were parked
densely along Post Road.

'What sort of time did you have in France?' asked Braintree.

'The sort of time you would expect with Eva and the brood in a tent. We
were asked to leave the first camp-site after Samantha had let down the guy
ropes on two tents. It wouldn't have been so bad if the woman inside one
hadn't had asthma. That was on the Loire. In La Vendée we were stuck
next to a German who had fought on the Russian front and was suffering
from shell-shock. I don't know if you've ever been woken in the night by a
man screaming about *Flammenwerfern* but I can tell you it's unnerving. That
time we moved on without being asked.'

'I thought you were going down to the Dordogne. Eva told Betty she'd
been reading a book about three rivers and it was simply enthralling.'

'The reading may have been but the rivers weren't,' said Wilt, 'not the
one we were next to. It rained and of course Eva had to have the tent in
what amounted to a tributary. It was bad enough putting the thing up dry.
Weighed a ton then, but moving it out of a flashflood up a hundred yards
of bramble banks at twelve o'clock at night when the damned thing was
sodden ...' Wilt stopped. The memory was too much for him.

'And I suppose it went on raining,' said Braintree sympathetically. 'That's
been our experience, anyway.'

'It did,' said Wilt. 'For five whole days. After that we moved into a hotel.'

'Best thing to do. You can eat decent meals and sleep in comfort.'

'You can perhaps. We couldn't. Not after Samantha shat in the bidet. I
wondered what the stench was sometime around 2 a.m. Anyway let's talk
about something civilized.'

They went into The Pig In A Poke and ordered pints.

'Of course all men are selfish,' said Mavis Mottram as she and Eva sat in
the kitchen at Willington Road. 'Patrick hardly ever gets home until after
eight and he always has an excuse about the Open University. It's nothing
of the sort, or if it is it's some divorcee student who wants extra coition. Not
that I mind any longer. I said to him the other night, "If you want to make

a fool of yourself running after other women that's your affair but don't think I'm going to take it lying down. You can go your way and I'll go mine."'

'What did he say to that?' Eva asked, testing the steam iron and starting on the quads' dresses.

'Oh just something stupid about not wanting it standing up anyway. Men are so coarse. I can't think why we bother with them.'

'I sometimes wish Henry was a bit coarser,' said Eva pensively. 'He always was lethargic but now he claims he's too tired because he walks to the Tech. every day. It's six miles so I suppose he could be.'

'I can think of another reason,' said Mavis bitterly. 'Still waters etcetera ...'

'Not Henry. I'd know. Besides, ever since the quads were born he's been very thoughtful.'

'Yes, but what's he been thoughtful about? That's what you have to ask yourself, Eva.'

'I meant he's been considerate to me. He gets up at seven and brings me tea in bed and at night he always makes me Horlicks.'

'If Patrick started acting like that I'd be very suspicious,' said Mavis. 'It doesn't sound natural.'

'It doesn't, does it, but that's Henry all over. He's really kind. The only thing is he isn't very masterful. He says it's because he's surrounded by five women and he knows when he's beaten.'

'If you go ahead with this au pair girl plan that will make six,' said Mavis.

'Irmgard isn't a proper au pair girl. She's renting the top-floor flat and says she'll help around the house whenever she can.'

'Which, if the Everards' experience with their Finn is anything to go by, will be never. She stayed in bed till twelve and practically ate them out of house and home.'

'Finns are different,' said Eva. 'Irmgard is German. I met her at the Van Donkens' World Cup Protest Party. You know they raised nearly a hundred and twenty pounds for the Tortured Tupamaros.'

'I didn't think there were any Tupamaros in Argentina any more. I thought they had all been killed off by the army.'

'These are the ones who escaped,' said Eva. 'Anyway I met Miss Mueller and mentioned that we had this top flat and she was ever so eager to have it. She'll do all her own cooking and things.'

'Things? Did you ask her what things she had in mind?'

'Well, not exactly, but she says she wants to study a lot and she's very keen on physical fitness.'

'And what does Henry have to say about her?' asked Mavis moving closer to her real concern.

'I haven't told him yet. You know what he's like about having other people in the house, but I thought if she stays in the flat in the evenings and keeps out of his way ...'

'Eva dear,' said Mavis with advanced sincerity, 'I know this is none of my business but aren't you tempting fate just a little?'

'I can't see how. I mean it's such a good arrangement. She can baby-sit when we want to go out, and the house is far too big for us and nobody ever goes up to the flat.'

'They will with her up there. You'll have all sorts of people coming through the house and she's bound to have a record player. They all do.'

'Even if she does we won't hear it. I've ordered rush matting from Soales and I went up the other day with the transistor and you can hardly hear a thing.'

'Well, it's your affair, dear, but if I had an au pair girl in the house with Patrick around I'd want to be able to hear some things.'

'I thought you said you'd told Patrick he could do what he liked?'

'I didn't say in my house,' said Mavis. 'He can do what he likes elsewhere but if I ever caught him playing Casanova at home he'd live to regret it.'

'Well, Henry is different. I don't suppose he will even notice her,' said Eva complacently. 'I've told her he's very quiet and home-loving and she says all she wants is peace and quiet herself.'

With the private thought that Miss Irmgard Mueller was going to find living in the same house as Eva and the quads neither peaceful nor quiet, Mavis finished her coffee and got up to go. 'All the same I would keep an eye on Henry,' she said. 'He may be different but I wouldn't trust a man further than I could throw him. And my experience of foreign students is that they come over here to do a lot more than learn the English language.'

She went out to her car and drove home wondering what there was about Eva's simplicity that was so sinister. The Wilts were an odd couple, but since their move to Willington Road Mavis Mottram's dominance had diminished. The days when Eva had been her protégée in flower-arranging were over and Mavis was frankly jealous. On the other hand Willington Road was definitely in one of the best neighbourhoods in Ipford and there were social advantages to be gained from knowing the Wilts.

At the corner of Regal Gardens her headlights picked Wilt out as he walked slowly home and she called out to him. But he was deep in thought and didn't hear her.

As usual Wilt's thoughts were dark and mysterious and made the more so by the fact that he didn't understand why he had them. They had to do with strange violent fantasies that welled up inside him, with dissatisfactions which could only be partly explained by his job, his marriage to a human dynamo, the dislike he felt for the atmosphere of Willington Road where everyone else was something important in high-energy physics or low-temperature conductivity and made more money than he did. And after all these explicable grounds for grumbling there was the feeling that his life was largely meaningless and that beyond the personal there was a universe which was random, chaotic and yet had some weird coherence about it which he would never fathom. Wilt speculated on the paradox of material progress and spiritual decadence and as usual came to no conclusion except that beer on an empty stomach didn't agree with him. One consolation was that now Eva was into Alternative Gardening he was likely to get a good supper and the quads would be fast asleep. If only the little buggers didn't wake in the night. Wilt had had his fill of broken sleep in the early years of breast-feeding and bottle-warming. Those days were largely over now and, apart from Samantha's occasional bout of sleepwalking and Penelope's bladder problem, his nights were undisturbed. And so he made his way along under the trees that lined Willington Road and was greeted by the smell of casserole from the kitchen. Wilt felt relatively cheerful.

He left the house next morning in a far more despondent mood. 'I should have been warned by that casserole that she had some bloody ominous message to impart,' he muttered as he set off for the Tech. And Eva's announcement that she had found a lodger for the top flat had been ominous indeed. Wilt had been alert to the possibility ever since they had bought the house but Eva's immediate enthusiasms – gardening, herbalism, progressive playgrouping for the quads, redecorating the house and designing the ultimate kitchen – had postponed any decision about the top flat. Wilt had hoped that the matter would be forgotten. Now she had let the rooms without even bothering to tell him Wilt felt distinctly aggrieved. Worse still, he had been outwitted by the decoy of that splendid stew. When Eva wanted to cook she could, and Wilt had finished his second helping and a bottle of his better

Spanish burgundy before she had announced this latest disaster. It had taken Wilt several seconds before he could focus on the problem.

'You've done what?' he said.

'Let it to a very nice young German girl,' said Eva. 'She's paying fifteen pounds a week and promises to be very quiet. You won't even know she's there.'

'I bloody well will. She'll have lovers fumbling their lascivious way up and down stairs all night and the house will reek of sauerkraut.'

'It won't. There's an extractor fan in the kitchenette up there and she's entitled to have boyfriends so long as they behave themselves nicely.'

'Nicely! Show me some loutish lover behaving nicely and I'll show you a camel with four humps. . . .'

'They're called dromedaries,' said Eva using the tactic of muddled information that usually distracted Wilt and lured him into correcting her. But Wilt was too distracted already to bother.

'They're not. They're called fucking foreigners and I'm using fucking properly for once and if you think I want to lie in bed every night listening to some ruddy Latin prove his virility by imitating Popocatepetl in eruption on an inner sprung mattress eight feet above my head –'

'Dunlopillo,' said Eva. 'You never get things right.'

'Oh yes I do,' snarled Wilt. 'I knew this was in the wind ever since your bloody aunt had to die and leave you a legacy and you had to buy this miniature hotel. I knew then that you would turn it into some foul commune.'

'It's not a commune and anyway Mavis says the extended family was one of the good things about the old days.'

'She'd know all about extended families, Mavis would. Patrick has been extending his family for as long as I can remember, and into other people's.'

'Mavis has given him an ultimatum,' said Eva. 'She's not putting up with his carryings on any longer.'

'And I'm giving you an ultimatum,' said Wilt. 'One squeak out of those bedsprings up there, one whiff of pot, one twang of a guitar, one giggle on the stairs and I'll extend this family by finding digs in town until Miss Schickelgruber has moved out.'

'Her name itsn't Schickelwhatchamacallit. It's Mueller. Irmgard Mueller.'

'So was one of Hitler's nastier Obergruppenführers and all I'm saying is –'

'You're just jealous,' said Eva. 'If you were a proper man and hadn't got hang-ups about sex from your parents you wouldn't get so hot under the collar about what other people do.'

Wilt regarded her balefully. Whenever Eva wanted to subdue him she launched a sexual offensive. Wilt retired to bed defeated. Discussions of his sexual inadequacies tended to result in his having to prove Eva wrong practically and after that stew he didn't feel up to it.

He didn't feel up to much by the time he reached the Tech. next morning. The quads had fought their usual intersororial war about who was going to wear what dress before being dragged off to playgroup and there had been another letter in *The Times* from Lord Longford demanding the release of Myra Hindley, the Moors murderess, from prison on the grounds that she was now thoroughly reformed, a convinced Christian and a socially valuable citizen. 'In which case she can prove her social value and Christian charity by staying in prison and helping her fellow-convicts,' had been Wilt's infuriated reaction. The other news was just as depressing. Inflation was up again. Sterling down. North Sea gas would run out in five years and the Rhodesians had just massacred fifty more blacks while the blacks had butchered more missionaries. All in all the world was in its usual filthy mess and now he had to listen to Dr Mayfield extol the virtues of the Advanced Course in English For Foreigners for several intolerably boring hours before dealing with complaints from his Liberal Studies lecturers about the way he had done the timetable.

One of the worst things about being Head of Liberal Studies was that he had to spend a large part of his summer vacation fitting classes into rooms and lecturers into classes, and when he had finished and had defeated the Head of Art who wanted Room 607 for Life Studies while Wilt needed it for Meat Three, he was still faced with a hassle at the beginning of the year and had to readjust the timetable because Mrs Fyfe couldn't make Tuesday at 2 with DMT One because her husband ... It was on such occasions that Wilt wished he was back teaching *The Lord of the Flies* to Gasfitters instead of running the department. But his salary was good, the rates on Willington Road were exorbitant, and for the rest of the year he could spend much of his time sitting in his office dreaming.

He could sit through most committee meetings in a coma too but Dr Mayfield's course board was the one exception. Wilt had to stay awake to prevent Mayfield lumbering him with several more lectures in his relative absence. Besides, Dr Board would start the term off with a row.

He did. Mayfield had only just begun to stress the needs for a more student-oriented curriculum with special emphasis on socio-economic awareness when Dr Board intervened.

'Codswallop,' he said. 'The business of my department is to teach English students how to speak German, French, Spanish and Italian, not to explain the origins of their own languages to a whole lot of aliens, and as for socio-economic awareness, I suggest that Dr Mayfield has his priorities wrong. If the Arabs I had last year were anything to go by they were economically aware to the nth degree about the purchasing power of oil and so socially backward that it will take more than a three-year course to persuade the sods that stoning women to death for being unfaithful isn't cricket. Perhaps if we had three hundred years ...'

'Dr Board, this meeting may well last as long if you keep interrupting,' said the Vice-Principal. 'Now if Dr Mayfield will just continue ...'

The Head of Academic Development continued for another hour, and was all set for the entire morning when the Head of Engineering objected.

'I see that several of my staff are scheduled to deliver lectures on British Engineering Achievements in the Nineteenth Century. Now I would like to inform Dr Mayfield and this board that frankly they see no reason why they should be asked to lecture on topics outside their field.'

'Hear, hear,' said Dr Board.

'What is more, I would like to be informed why so much emphasis is being placed on a course for foreigners at the expense of our own British students.'

'I think I can answer that,' said the Vice-Principal. 'Thanks to the cuts that have been imposed on us by the local authority we have been forced to subsidize our existing non-paying courses and staff numbers by expanding the foreign sector where students pay substantial fees. If you want the figures of the profit we made last year ...'

But no one took up the invitation. Even Dr Board was momentarily silenced.

'Until such time as the economy improves,' continued the Vice-Principal, 'a great many lecturers are only going to keep their jobs because we are running this course. What is more, it may well be possible to expand Advanced English for Foreigners into a degree course approved by the CNAA. I think you will all agree that anything which increases our chances of becoming a Polytechnic is to everyone's advantage.' The Vice-Principal stopped and looked round the room but nobody demurred. 'In which case all that remains is for Dr Mayfield to allocate the new lectures to the various departmental heads.'

Dr Mayfield distributed xeroxed lists. Wilt studied his new burden and found that it included the Development of Liberal and Progressive Social Attitudes in English Society, 1688 to 1978, and was just about to protest when the Head of Zoology got in first.

'I see here that I am down for Animal Husbandry and Agriculture with special reference to Intensive Farming of Pigs, Hens, and Stock-Rearing.'

'The subject has ecological significance –'

'And is student-oriented,' said Dr Board. 'Battery Education or possibly Hog Raising by Continuous Assessment. Perhaps we could even run a course on Composting.'

'Don't,' said Wilt with a shudder. Dr Board looked at him with interest.

'Your magnificent wife?' he inquired.

Wilt nodded dolefully. 'Yes, she has taken up –'

'If I may just get back to my original objection instead of hearing about Mr Wilt's matrimonial problems,' said the Head of Zoology. 'I want to make it absolutely clear now that I am not qualified to lecture on Animal Husbandry. I am a zoologist not a farmer and what I know about Stock-Rearing is zero.'

'We must all extend ourselves,' said Dr Board. 'After all if we are to acquire the doubtful privilege of calling ourselves a Polytechnic we must put the College before personal interest.'

'Perhaps you haven't seen what you're down to teach, Board,' Zoology continued, 'Sementic Influences ... shouldn't that be Semantic, Mayfield?'

'Must be the typist's error,' said Mayfield. 'Yes it should read Semantic Influences on Current Sociological Theories. The bibliography includes Wittgenstein, Chomsky and Wilkes ...'

'It doesn't include me,' said Board. 'You can count me out. I don't care if we descend to the level of a primary school but I am not going to mug up Wittgenstein or Chomsky for the benefit of anyone.'

'Well then, don't talk about my having to extend myself,' said the Head of Zoology. 'I am not going into a lecture room filled with Moslems to explain, even with my limited knowledge of the subject, the advantages of raising pigs in the Persian Gulf.'

'Gentlemen, while recognizing that there are one or two minor amendments necessary to the lecture titles I think they can be ironed out –'

'Wiped out more likely,' said Dr Board. The Vice-Principal ignored his interruption. '– and the main thing is to keep the lectures in their present format while presenting them at a level suitable for the individual students.'

'I'm still not mentioning pigs,' said Zoology.

'You don't have to. You can do an elementary series of talks on plants,' said the Vice-Principal wearily.

'Great. And will someone tell me how in God's name I can even begin to talk in an elementary way about Wittgenstein? I had an Iraqi last year who couldn't even spell his own name, so what's the poor bugger going to do with Wittgenstein?' said Dr Board.

'And if I may just bring another subject up,' said a lecturer from the English department rather diffidently, 'I think we are going to have something of a communications problem with the eighteen Japanese and the young man from Tibet.'

'Oh really,' said Dr Mayfield. 'A communications problem. You know, it might be as well to add a lecture or two on Intercommunicational Discourse. It's the sort of subject which is likely to appeal to the Council for National Academic Awards.'

'It may appeal to them but it certainly doesn't to me,' said Board, 'I've always said they were the scourings of the Academic world.'

'Yes, and we've already heard you on the subject,' said the Vice-Principal. 'And now to get back to the Japanese and the young man from Tibet. You did say Tibet, didn't you?'

'Well, I said it, but I can't be too sure,' answered the English lecturer. 'That's what I meant about a communications problem. He doesn't speak a word of English and my Tibetanese isn't exactly fluent. It's the same with the Japanese.'

The Vice-Principal looked round the room. 'I suppose it is too much to expect anyone here to have a smattering of Japanese?'

'I've got a bit,' said the Head of Art, 'but I'm damned if I'm going to use it. When you've spent four years in a Nip prisoner-of-war camp the last thing you want is to have to talk to the bastards in later life. My digestive system is still in a hell of a mess.'

'Perhaps you could tutor our Chinese student instead. Tibet is part of China now and if we include him with the four girls from Hong Kong ...'

'We'll be able to advertise Take-Away Degrees,' said Dr Board and provoked another acrimonious exchange which lasted until lunchtime.

Wilt returned to his office to find that Mrs Fyfe couldn't take Mechanical Technicians at 2 on Tuesday because her husband had ... It was exactly as he had anticipated. The Tech.'s year had begun as it always did. It continued in the same trying vein for the next four days. Wilt attended meetings on Interdepartmental Course Collaboration, gave a seminar to student teachers from the local training college on The Meaning of Liberal Studies, which was a contradiction in terms as far as he was concerned, was lectured by a Sergeant from the Drug Squad on Pot Plant Recognition and Heroin Addiction and finally managed to fit Mrs Fyfe into Room 29 with Bread Two on Monday at 10 a.m. And all the time he brooded over Eva and her wretched lodger.

While Wilt busied himself lethargically at the Tech., Eva put her own plans implacably into operation. Miss Mueller arrived two mornings later and installed herself inconspicuously in the flat; so inconspicuously that it took Wilt two more days to realize she was there, and then only the delivery of nine milk bottles where there were usually eight gave him the clue. Wilt said nothing but waited for the first hint of gaiety upstairs before launching his counter-offensive of complaints.

But Miss Mueller lived up to Eva's promise. She was exceedingly quiet, came in unobtrusively when Wilt was still at the Tech. and left in the morning after he had begun his daily walk. By the end of a fortnight he was beginning to think his worst fears were unjustified. In any case, he had his lectures to foreign students to prepare and the teaching term had finally started. The question of the lodger receded into the background as he tried to think what the hell to tell Mayfield's Empire, as Dr Board called it, about Progressive Social Attitudes in English Society since 1688. If Gasfitters were any indication there had been a regression, not a progressive development. The bastards had graduated to queer-bashing.

But if Wilt's fears were premature they were not long being realized. He was sitting one Saturday evening in the Piagetory, the purpose-built summerhouse at the bottom of the garden in which Eva had originally tried to play conceptual games with the 'wee ones', a phrase Wilt particularly detested, when the first blow fell.

It was less a blow than a revelation. The summerhouse was nicely secluded, set back among old apple trees with an arbour of clematis and climbing roses to hide it from the world and Wilt's consumption of homemade beer from Eva. Inside, it was hung with dried herbs. Wilt didn't approve of the herbs but he preferred them in their hung form rather than in the frightful infusions

Eva sometimes tried to inflict on him, and they seemed to have the added advantage of keeping the flies from the compost heap at bay. He could sit there with the sun dappling the grass around and feel at relative peace with the world, and the more beer he drank the greater that peace became. Wilt prided himself on the effect of his beer. He brewed it in a plastic dustbin and occasionally fortified it with vodka before bottling it in the garage. After three bottles even the quad's din somehow receded and became almost natural, a chorus of whines, squeals and laughter, usually malicious when someone fell off the swing, but at least distant. And even that distraction was absent this evening. Eva had taken them to the ballet in the hope that early exposure to Stravinsky would turn Samantha into a second Margot Fonteyn. Wilt had his doubts about Samantha and Stravinsky. As far as he ws concerned his daughter's talents were more suitable for an all-in wrestler, and Stravinsky's genius was overrated. It had to be if Eva approved it. Wilt's own taste ran to Mozart and Mugsy Spanier, an eclecticism Eva couldn't understand but which allowed him to annoy her by switching from a piano sonata she was enjoying to twenties jazz which she didn't.

Anyway, this evening there was no need to play his tape-recorder. It was sufficient to sit in the summerhouse and know that even if the quads woke him at five next morning he could still stay in bed until ten, and he was just uncorking his fourth bottle of fortified lager when his eye caught sight of a figure on the wooden balcony outside the dormer window of the top-floor flat. Wilt's hand on the bottle loosened and a moment later he was groping for the binoculars Eva had bought for bird-watching. He focused on the figure through a gap in the roses and forgot about beer. All his attention was riveted on Miss Irmgard Mueller.

She was standing looking out over the trees to the open country beyond, and from where Wilt sat and focused he had a particularly interesting view of her legs. There was no denying that they were shapely legs. In fact they were startlingly shapely legs and her thighs ... Wilt moved up, found her breasts beneath a cream blouse entrancing, and finally reached her face. He stayed there. It wasn't that Irmgard – Miss Mueller and that bloody lodger were instantaneously words of the past – was an attractive young woman. Wilt had been faced by attractive young women at the Tech. for too many years, young women who ogled him and sat with their legs distractingly apart, not to have built up sufficient sexual antibodies to deflect their juvenile charms. But Irmgard was not a juvenile. She was a woman, a woman of around twenty-eight, a beautiful woman with glorious legs, discreet and tight breasts, 'unsullied by suckling' was the phrase that sprang to Wilt's mind, with firm neat hips, even her hands grasping the balcony rail were somehow delicately strong with tapering fingers, lightly tanned as by some midnight sun. Wilt's mind spun into meaningless metaphors far removed from Eva's washing-up mitts, the canyon wrinkles of her birth-pocked belly, the dugs that haunched her flaccid hips and all the physical erosion of twenty years of married life. He was swept into fancy by this splendid creature, but above all by her face.

Irmgard's face was not simply beautiful. In spite of the beer Wilt might have withstood the magnetism of mere beauty. He was defeated by the intelligence of her face. In fact there were imperfections in that face from a purely physical point of view. It was too strong for one thing, the nose was a shade retroussé to be commercially perfect, and the mouth too generous but it was individual, individual and intelligent and sensitive and mature and thoughtful and ... Wilt gave up the addition in despair and as he did so it seemed to him that Irmgard was gazing down into his two adoring eyes, or anyway into the binoculars, and that a subtle smile played about her gorgeous lips. Then she turned away and went back into the flat. Wilt dropped the binoculars and reached trancelike for the beer bottle. What he had just seen had changed his view of life.

He was no longer Head of Liberal Studies, married to Eva, the father of four quarrelsome replusive daughters, and thirty-eight. He was twenty-one again, a bright, lithe young man who wrote poetry and swam on summer mornings in the river and whose future was alight with achieved promise. He was already a great writer. The fact that being a writer involved writing was wholly irrelevant. It was being a writer that mattered and Wilt at twenty-one had long since settled his future in advance by reading Proust and Gide, and then books on Proust and Gide and books about books on Proust and Gide, until he could visualize himself at thirty-eight with a delightful anguish of anticipation. Looking back on those moments he could only compare them to the feeling he now had when he came out of the dentist's surgery without the need for any fillings. On an intellectual plane, of course. Spiritual, with smoke-filled, cork-lined rooms and pages of illegible but beautiful prose littering, almost fluttering from, his desk in some deliciously nondescript street in Paris. Or in a white-walled bedroom on white sheets entwined with a tanned woman with the sun shining through the shutters and shimmering on the ceiling from the azure sea somewhere near Hyères. Wilt had tasted all these pleasures in advance at twenty-one. Fame, fortune, the modesty of greatness, bons mots drifting effortlessly from his tongue over absinthe, allusions tossed and caught, tossed back again like intellectual shuttlecocks, and the intense walk home through dawn-deserted streets in Montparnasse.

Sense of Humour

Damon Runyon

One night I am standing in front of Mindy's restaurant on Broadway, thinking of practically nothing whatever, when all of a sudden I feel a very terrible pain in my left foot.

In fact, this pain is so very terrible that it causes me to leap up and down like a bullfrog, and to let out loud cries of agony, and to speak some very profane language, which is by no means my custom, although of course I recognize the pain as coming from a hot foot, because I often experience this pain before.

Furthermore, I know Joe the Joker must be in the neighbourhood, as Joe the Joker has the most wonderful sense of humour of anybody in this town, and is always around giving people the hot foot, and gives it to me more times than I can remember. In fact, I hear Joe the Joker invents the hot foot, and it finally becomes a very popular idea all over the country.

The way you give a hot foot is to sneak up behind some guy who is standing around thinking of not much, and stick a paper match in his shoe between the sole and the upper along about where his little toe ought to be, and then light the match. By and by the guy will feel a terrible pain in his foot, and will start stamping around, and hollering, and carrying on generally, and it is always a most comical sight and a wonderful laugh to one and all to see him suffer.

No one in the world can give a hot foot as good as Joe the Joker, because it takes a guy who can sneak up very quiet on the guy who is to get the hot foot, and Joe can sneak up so quiet many guys on Broadway are willing to lay you odds that he can give a mouse a hot foot if you can find a mouse that wears shoes. Furthermore, Joe the Joker can take plenty of care of himself in case the guy who gets the hot foot feels like taking the matter up, which sometimes happens, especially with guys who get their shoes made to order at forty bobs per copy and do not care to have holes burned in these shoes.

But Joe does not care what kind of shoes the guys are wearing when he feels like giving out hot foots, and furthermore, he does not care who the guys are although many citizens think he makes a mistake the time he gives a hot foot to Frankie Ferocious. In fact, many citizens are greatly horrified by this action, and go around saying no good will come of it.

This Frankie Ferocious comes from over in Brooklyn, where he is considered a rising citizen in many respects, and by no means a guy to give hot foots to, especially as Frankie Ferocious has no sense of humour whatever. In fact, he is always very solemn, and nobody ever sees him laugh, and he certainly does not laugh when Joe the Joker gives him a hot foot one day on Broadway when Frankie Ferocious is standing talking over a business matter with some guys from the Bronx.

He only scowls at Joe, and says something in Italian, and while I do not understand Italian, it sounds so unpleasant that I guarantee I will leave town inside of the next two hours if he says it to me.

Of course Frankie Ferocious's name is not really Ferocious, but something in Italian like Feroccio, and I hear he originally comes from Sicily, although he lives in Brooklyn for quite some years, and from a modest beginning he builds himself up until he is a very large operator of merchandise of one kind and another, especially alcohol. He is a big guy of maybe thirty-odd, and he has hair blacker than a yard up a chimney, and black eyes, and black eyebrows, and a slow way of looking at people.

Nobody knows a whole lot about Frankie Ferocious, because he never has much to say, and he takes his time saying it, but everybody gives him plenty of room when he comes around, as there are rumours that Frankie never likes to be crowded. As far as I am concerned, I do not care for any part of Frankie Ferocious, because his slow way of looking at people always makes me nervous, and I am always sorry Joe the Joker gives him a hot foot, because I figure Frankie Ferocious is bound to consider it a most disrespectful action, and hold it against everybody that lives on the Island of Manhattan.

But Joe the Joker only laughs when anybody tells him he is out of line in giving Frankie the hot foot, and says it is not his fault if Frankie has no sense of humour. Furthermore, Joe says he will not only give Frankie another hot foot if he gets a chance, but that he will give hot foots to the Prince of Wales or Mussolini, if he catches them in the right spot, although Regret, the horse player, states that Joe can have twenty to one any time that he will not give Mussolini any hot foots and get away with it.

Anyway, just as I suspect, there is Joe the Joker watching me when I feel the hot foot, and he is laughing very heartily, and furthermore, a large number of other citizens are also laughing heartily, because Joe the Joker never sees any fun in giving people the hot foot unless others are present to enjoy the joke.

Well, naturally when I see who it is gives me the hot foot I join in the laughter, and go over and shake hands with Joe, and when I shake hands with him there is more laughter, because it seems Joe has a hunk of Limburger cheese in his duke, and what I shake hands with is this Limburger.Furthermore, it is some of Mindy's Limburger cheese, and everybody knows Mindy's Limburger is very squashy, and also very loud.

Of course I laugh at this, too, although to tell the truth I will laugh much more heartily if Joe the Joker drops dead in front of me, because I do not like to be made the subject of laughter on Broadway. But my laugh is really quite hearty when Joe takes the rest of the cheese that is not on my fingers and smears it on the steering-wheels of some automobiles parked in front of Mindy's, because I get to thinking of what the drivers will say when they start steering their cars.

Then I get talking to Joe the Joker, and I ask him how things are up in Harlem where Joe and his younger brother, Freddy, and several other guys have a small organization operating in beer, and Joe says things are as good as can be expected considering business conditions. Then I ask him how Rosa is getting along, this Rosa being Joe the Joker's ever-loving wife, and a personal friend of mine, as I know her when she is Rosa Midnight and is singing in the old Hot Box before Joe hauls off and marries her.

Well, at this question Joe the Joker starts laughing, and I can see that something appeals to his sense of humour, and finally he speaks as follows:

'Why,' he says, 'do you not hear the news about Rosa? She takes the wind on me a couple of months ago for my friend Frankie Ferocious, and is living in an apartment over in Brooklyn, right near his house, although,' Joe says, 'of course you understand I am telling you this only to answer your question, and not to holler copper on Rosa.'

Then he lets out another large ha-ha, and in fact Joe the Joker keeps laughing until I am afraid he will injure himself internally. Personally, I do not see anything comical in a guy's every-loving wife taking the wind on him for a guy like Frankie Ferocious, so when Joe the Joker quiets down a bit I ask him what is funny about the proposition.

'Why,' Joe says, 'I have to laugh every time I think of how the big greaseball is going to feel when he finds out how expensive Rosa is. I do not know how many things Frankie Ferocious has running for him in Brooklyn,' Joe says, 'but he better try to move himself in on the mint if he wishes to keep Rosa going.'

Then he laughs again, and I consider it wonderful the way Joe is able to keep his sense of humour even in such a situation as this, although up to this time I always think Joe is very daffy indeed about Rosa, who is a little doll, weighing maybe 90 pounds with her hat on and quite cute.

Now I judge from what Joe the Joker tells me that Frankie Ferocious knows Rosa before Joe marries her and is always pitching to her when she is singing in the Hot Box, and even after she is Joe's ever-loving wife, Frankie occasionally calls her up, especially when he commences to be a rising citizen of Brooklyn, although of course Joe does not learn about these calls until later. And about the time Frankie Ferocious commences to be a rising citizen of Brooklyn, things begin breaking a little tough for Joe the Joker, what with the depression and all, and he has to economize on Rosa in spots, and if there is one thing Rosa cannot stand it is being economized on.

Along, about now, Joe the Joker gives Frankie Ferocious the hot foot, and just as many citizens state at the time, it is a mistake, for Frankie starts calling Rosa up more than somewhat, and speaking of what a nice place Brooklyn is to live in – which it is, at that – and between these boosts for Brooklyn and Joe the Joker's economy, Rosa hauls off and takes a subway to Borough Hall, leaving Joe a note telling him that if he does not like it he knows what he can do.

'Well, Joe,' I say, after listening to his story, 'I always hate to hear of thse little domestic difficulties among my friends, but maybe this is all for the best. Still, I feel sorry for you, if it will do you any good,' I say.

'Do not feel sorry for me,' Joe says. 'If you wish to feel sorry for anybody, feel sorry for Frankie Ferocious, and,' he says, 'if you can spare a little more sorrow, give it to Rosa.'

And Joe the Joker laughs very hearty again and starts telling me about a little scatter that he has up in Harlem where he keeps a chair fixed up with electric wires so he can give anybody that sits down in it a nice jolt, which sounds very humorous to me, at that, especially when Joe tells me how they turn on too much juice one night and kill Commodore Jake.

Finally Joe says he has to get back to Harlem, but first he goes to the telephone in the corner cigar store and calls up Mindy's and imitates a doll's voice, and tells Mindy he is Peggy Joyce, or somebody, and orders fifty dozen sandwiches sent up at once to an apartment in West 72nd Street for a birthday party, although of course there is no such number as he gives, and nobody there will wish fifty dozen sandwiches if there is such a number.

Then Joe gets in his car and starts off, and while he is waiting for the traffic lights at Fiftieth Street, I see citizens on the sidewalks making sudden leaps, and looking around very fierce, and I know Joe the Joker is plugging them with pellets made out of tin foil, which he fires from a rubber band hooked between his thumb and forefinger.

Joe the Joker is very expert with this proposition, and it is very funny to see the citizens jump, although once or twice in his life Joe makes a miscue and knocks out somebody's eye. But it is all in fun, and shows you what a wonderful sense of humour Joe has.

Well, a few days later I see by the papers where a couple of Harlem guys Joe the Joker is mobbed up with are found done up in sacks over in Brooklyn, very dead indeed, and the coppers say it is because they are trying to move in on certain business enterprises that belong to nobody but Frankie Ferocious. But of course the coppers do not say Frankie Ferocious puts these guys in the sacks, because in the first place Frankie will report them to Headquarters if the coppers say such a thing about him, and in the second place putting guys in sacks is strictly a St Louis idea and to have a guy put in a sack properly you have to send to St Louis for experts in this matter.

Now, putting a guy in a sack is not as easy as it sounds, and in fact it takes quite a lot of practice and experience. To put a guy in a sack properly, you first have to put him to sleep, because naturally no guy is going to walk into a sack wide awake unless he is a plumb sucker. Some people claim the best way to put a guy to sleep is to give him a sleeping powder of some kind in a drink, but the real experts just tap the guy on the noggin with a blackjack, which saves the expense of buying the drink.

Anyway, after the guy is asleep, you double him up like a pocketknife, and tie a cord or a wire around his neck and under his knees. Then you put him in a gunny sack, and leave him some place, and by and by when the guy wakes up and finds himself in the sack, naturally he wants to get out and the first thing he does is to try to straighten out his knees. This pulls the cord around his neck up so tight that after a while the guy is all out of breath.

So then when somebody comes along and opens the sack they find the guy dead, and nobody is responsible for this unfortunate situation, because after all the guy really commits suicide, because if he does not try to straighten out his knees he may live to a ripe old age, if he recovers from the tap on the noggin.

Well, a couple of days later I see by the papers where three Brooklyn citizens are scragged as they are walking peaceably along Clinton Street, the scragging being done by some parties in an automobile who seem to have a machine gun, and the papers state the citizens are friends of Frankie Ferocious, and that it is rumoured the parties with the machine gun are from Harlem.

I judge by this that there is some trouble in Brooklyn, especially as about a week after the citizens are scragged in Clinton Street, another Harlem guy is found done up in a sack like a Virginia ham near Prospect Park, and now who is it but Joe the Joker's brother, Freddy, and I know Joe is going to be greatly displeased by this.

By and by it gets so nobody in Brooklyn will open as much as a sack of potatoes without first calling in the gendarmes, for fear a pair of No. 8 shoes will jump out at them.

Now one night I see Joe the Joker, and this time he is all alone, and I wish to say I am willing to leave him all alone, because something tells me he is hotter than a stove. But he grabs me as I am going past, so naturally I stop to talk to him, and the first thing I say is how sorry I am about his brother.

'Well,' Joe the Joker says, 'Freddy is always a kind of a sap. Rosa calls him up and asks him to come over to Brooklyn to see her. She wishes to talk to Freddy about getting me to give her a divorce,' Joe says, 'so she can marry Frankie Ferocious, I suppose. Anyway,' he says, 'Freddy tells Commodore Jake why he is going to see her. Freddy always likes Rosa, and thinks maybe he can patch it up between us. So,' Joe says, 'he winds up in a sack. They get him after he leaves her apartment. I do not claim Rosa will ask him to come over if she has any idea he will be sacked,' Joe says, 'but,' he says, 'she is responsible. She is a bad-luck doll.'

Then he starts to laugh, and at first I am greatly horrified, thinking it is because something about Freddy being sacked strikes his sense of humour, when he says to me, like this:

'Say,' he says, 'I am going to play a wonderful joke on Frankie Ferocious.'

'Well, Joe,' I say, 'you are not asking me for advice, but I am going to give you some free, gratis, and for nothing. Do not play any jokes on Frankie

Ferocious, as I hear he has no more sense of humour than a nanny goat. I hear Frankie Ferocious will not laugh if you have Al Jolson, Eddie Cantor, Ed Wynn and Joe Cook telling him jokes all at once. In fact,' I say, 'I hear he is a tough audience.'

'Oh,' Joe the Joker says, 'he must have some sense of humour somewhere to stand for Rosa. I hear he is daffy about her. In fact, I understand she is the only person in the world he really likes, and trusts. But I must play a joke on him. I am going to have myself delivered to Frankie Ferocious in a sack.'

Well, of course I have to laugh at this myself, and Joe the Joker laughs with me. Personally, I am laughing just at the idea of anybody having themselves delivered to Frankie Ferocious in a sack, and especially Joe the Joker, but of course I have no idea Joe really means what he says.

'Listen,' Joe says, finally. 'A guy from St Louis who is a friend of mine is doing most of the sacking for Frankie Ferocious. His name is Ropes McGonnigle. In fact,' Joe says, 'he is a very dear old pal of mine, and he has a wonderful sense of humour like me. Ropes McGonnigle has nothing whatever to do with sacking Freddy,' Joe says, 'and he is very indignant about it since he finds out Freddy is my brother, so he is anxious to help me play a joke on Frankie.

'Only last night,' Joe says, 'Frankie Ferocious sends for Ropes and tells him he will appreciate it as a special favour if Ropes will bring me to him in a sack. I suppose,' Joe says, 'that Frankie Ferocious hears from Rosa what Freddy is bound to tell her about my ideas on divorce. I have very strict ideas on divorce,' Joe says, 'especially where Rosa is concerned. I will see her in what's-this before I ever do her and Frankie Ferocious such a favour as giving her a divorce.

'Anyway,' Joe the Joker says, 'Ropes tells me about Frankie Ferocious propositioning him, so I send Ropes back to Frankie Ferocious to tell him he knows I am to be in Brooklyn tomorrow night, and furthermore, Ropes tells Frankie that he will have me in a sack in no time. And so he will,' Joe says.

'Well,' I say, 'personally, I see no percentage in being delivered to Frankie Ferocious in a sack, because as near as I can make out from what I read in the papers, there is no future for a guy in a sack that goes to Frankie Ferocious. What I cannot figure out,' I say, 'is where the joke on Frankie comes in.'

'Why,' Joe the Joker says, 'the joke is, I will not be asleep in the sack, and

my hands will not be tied, and in each of my hands I will have a John
Roscoe, so when the sack is delivered to Frankie Ferocious and I pop out
blasting away, can you not imagine his astonishment?'

Well, I can imagine this, all right. In fact when I get to thinking of the
look of surprise that is bound to come to Frankie Ferocious's face when Joe
the Joker comes out of the sack I have to laugh, and Joe the Joker laughs
right along with me.

'Of course,' Joe says, 'Ropes McGonnigle will be there to start blasting
with me, in case Frankie Ferocious happens to have any company.'

Then Joe the Joker goes on up the street, leaving me still laughing, from
thinking of how amazed Frankie Ferocious will be when Joe bounces out of
the sack and starts throwing slugs around and about. I do not hear of Joe
from that time to this, but I hear the rest of the story from very reliable
parties.

It seems that Ropes McGonnigle does not deliver the sack himself, after
all, but sends it by an expressman to Frankie Ferocious's home. Frankie
Ferocious received many sacks such as this in his time, because it seems that
it is a sort of passion with him to personally view the contents of the sacks
and check up on them before they are distributed about the city, and of
course Ropes McGonnigle knows about this passion from doing so much
sacking for Frankie.

When the expressman takes the sack into Frankie's house, Frankie
personally lugs it down into the basement, and there he outs with a big John
Roscoe and fires six shots into the sack, because it seems Ropes McGonnigle
tips him off to Joe the Joker's plan to pop out of the sack and start blasting.

I hear Frankie Ferocious has a very strange expression on his pan and is
laughing the only laugh anybody ever hears from him when the gendarmes
break in and put the arm on him for murder, because it seems that when
Ropes McGonnigle tells Frankie of Joe the Joker's plan, Frankie tells Ropes
what he is going to do with his own hands before opening the sack. Naturally,
Ropes speaks to Joe the Joker of Frankie's idea about filling the sack full of
slugs, and Joe's sense of humour comes right out again.

So, bound and gagged, but otherwise as right as rain in the sack that is
delivered to Frankie Ferocious, is by no means Joe the Joker, but Rosa.

Death of a Goldfish

Auberon Waugh

Last week my pet goldfish was found floating upright in her tank. Marigold had shown no sign of illness the night before and ate her chopped mosquito larvae without complaint. No noise escaped from the kitchen where she slept and no ripple was left on the surface of the water to mark any death struggle. She was a blameless fish and died as she had lived, giving a minimum of trouble.

America, I have been told by a friend, is stuffed with books called *How to Cope with your Grief Reactions* and titles in a similar vein. The stages of grief are carefully listed, with hints about how to progress through them in an approved and healthy way: first, bereavement is met by a refusal to accept it; then by a bitter wish that it had not happened; then extravagant sorrow and self-pity, possible touched with guilt. Finally, there comes a settled acceptance, when the bereaved person is ready to return to society free of the emotional instability which might, uncorrected, lead him to antisocial attitudes and behaviour.

I find myself stuck in the guilt stage. We discussed raising a monument over Marigold's grave, but this seemed an unworthy way of coping with our grief reactions. Can storied urn or animated bust back to its mansion call the fleeting breath? Instead we buried her with minimum fuss – no useless coffin enclosed her breast – but this, too, seemed somehow rat-like and furtive. She lay like a warrior taking her rest with her golden scales around her, but her dignity rebuked us. There was no explicit reproach in her eye as we steadfastly gazed on the face that was dead and we bitterly thought of the morrow. The guilt was in our own hearts.

For more than six years that goldfish had lived with us and shared our fortunes, ever since my wife had won her by throwing hoops at the Mop Fair in Marlborough, Wiltshire. In all that time I never introduced Marigold to another goldfish. Probably, in the course of the six and a half years she spent swimming backwards and forwards in her tank, she lost any memory that other fishes existed. It is true that she always had plenty to eat and was kept cold and wet in well-ventilated conditions. Her water was changed and her tank decorated with semi-precious stones – amethystine, quartz, fool's gold, agate and chalcedony. But she never knew the meaning of companionship, laughter and the love of friends – or, indeed, the pleasures of sex.

Sex. Beyond one cursory glance at where I imagined her private parts would be if she had any (she did not appear to) I never made any serious attempt to discover whether Marigold was a male or a female goldfish. I never spared a thought about how she coped with her libido, if she had any. Quite possibly, she never learned about such things, never associated any strange bodily urges which may have visited her with anything but indigestion. Do female goldfish have monthly troubles? Do lonely male goldfish experience nocturnal emissions and if so, how do they distinguish wet dreams from any other type of dreams in the encircling wetness?

Stricken be remorse after her death, I have taken to reading all I can find in the house on the subject of goldfish. It would have been quite easy, I learn, to decide whether she was male or female. Spawning occurs in spring and as the season approaches the female's colours grow brighter while the male may develop pin-head-sized tubercles (or shagspots) on his gills.

This only makes me feel guiltier. The thought of Marigold blushing brightly in her prettiest colours every spring (or growing fine, manly tubercles on his gills, as the case might be) strikes me as unbearably poignant in light of the fact that nobody ever noticed:

> *Full many a flower is born to blush unseen*
> *And waste its sweetness on the desert air.*

I know, I know. It is all very beautiful and poetic. But I do feel we might have *looked*.

It may be possible to live a full and satisfactory life without any experience of sex. Many monks and nuns achieve it and quite a few secular priests, I dare say, but they at least have the consolation that they are storing up riches in Heaven. A hairy young monk at the establishment where I received my education (it did not prepare me to look after goldfishes properly) used to invite his Religious Instruction class to think of Heaven as a perpetual experience of sexual intercourse. Being a callow fifteen-year-old I took him at his word. Then I thought I understood why that pungent monk was so unswerving in his fidelity to the vows of poverty, chastity and obedience. It is only as I get older than I am less tempted by the thought of perpetual intercourse, more by Sydney Smith's notion of eating *pâté de foie gras* to the sound of trumpets. Perhaps this preference is something to do with the air at Combe Florey, where Sydney Smith lived 135 years before me.

But even if Combe Florey water has the same properties, there is no reason to suppose that goldfish like *pâté de foie gras* and every reason to think they detest the sound of trumpets. A thoughtless guest once put Marigold on an organ in my house and then played *Faith of Our Fathers* simultaneously on the dulcet, diapason, sub-bass and vox humana. Her resulting agitation marked only the second dramatic event in her life, the first being when the cat decided to try his luck at gaff-hook fishing about a year before. On that occasion – how the guilty memories torment me now – I tended to take the cat's side. What cat's averse to fish, I argued, and what pleasures could possibly await Marigold in the year ahead which would compare with the cat's pleasure in eating her?

Next I begin to reflect that Marigold was almost certainly so stupid that she never even noticed when she died, like certain chickens I have seen senselessly trying to fly after their heads have been cut off. If an animal is too stupid even to notice whether it is alive or dead there can be no sense in shedding intelligent human tears for it. Why, for that matter, should one goldfish occupy so much valuable space in a serious weekly magazine when hundreds of thousands of goldfish die every week unwept, unhonoured and unsung?

But then I think of the tender sight of her little corpse. It would have been an act of unspeakable callousness to recycle that innocent thing into cat-protein. Like the Tomb of the Unknown Soldier, there must always be privileged exceptions from which everyone else can draw comfort and inspiration. Now I feel I have passed through all the stages of my grief reaction and am ready to return to normal society.

The Great Savings Swindle

Auberon Waugh

Searching for a birth certificate this week in a neglected corner of the house I came upon a Post Office Savings book in my name whose last entry – a withdrawal of £1 – is dated 21 April 1954. In those days I did not possess a calculator, but I now see that the account (No. 124 at Stinchcombe post office in Gloucestershire) is two shillings in credit, and has been for the last twenty years. I shall probably never know how I came to overlook this sum at the age of fourteen when it would have bought ten Players Medium or six Mars Bars. Nowadays I couldn't buy a single cigarette, since shops have stopped selling them singly, and only one Mars Bar for the money. Moreover, the Mars Bar of 1954 was a great deal bigger than the one today. Its size as brilliantly calculated to make any child feel slightly sick if he ate a whole one himself. Today I could probably eat three of the new ones, if I had a mind to, without any problem.

As a child, one knew instinctively that Post Office Savings were a fraud. Like obligatory offerings in the church box, they were a sort of Morality Tax, a system of confiscation by grown-ups apparently in the interests of character improvement but almost certainly dictated by envy of our simple pleasures and jealousy of our youth. Among the lies told to encourage this form of thrift (or promote this form of theft) was a preposterous statement which I believed until half an hour ago when I began to think about it, that a penny invested at compound interest in Julius Caesar's time would now be worth the world's weight in gold. Quite apart from the fact that since the world is not made of gold your thrift would simply have resulted in a bad debt, it must be obvious to the meanest intelligence that the other party to the deal would rat on it long before. There is no remotely secure way of investing money at the present time – or so I have been told – where interest is greater than the rate of inflation. A penny invested not at compound interest would be worth infinitely less than a hundredth part of a grain of sand in 2,000 years time – always assuming, as life insurance brochures stipulate, that current trends are maintained.

This unexpected windfall of two shillings in the Post Office Savings Bank in fact represents my entire investment portfolio, the sum total of my stake in the usury system. It promises $2\frac{1}{2}$ per cent per annum interest, and I spent a happy hour with my computer working out the compound interest on two shillings for twenty years at $2\frac{1}{2}$ per cent before coming up with the amount of 40.332135 old pence, being the principal plus accrued interest. It was the work of a second to convert this into 16.805056 new pence, still not enough to buy three of the new, small Mars Bars at 6p each. Whereas, as I never tire of pointing out, I could have bought six of the large ones for my original two shillings in 1954.

In fact, it looks as if I may never get this interest, as I see I should have been sending the book to head office on the anniversary of my opening the account (29 July 1953) every year for the past twenty years in order to have the interest entered in it. Probably this is intended as a protection against would-be Julius Caesars, but it seems a little hard on small savers like myself who can only hope for two fifths of a penny by way of interest this year. I only want my Mars Bars back.

Post Office Savings have always been the most notorious of the many methods employed by government to rob the poor of their savings. The amazing thing is that the poor have never twigged. Interest rates have gone up but so, of course, has the general level of inflation and it is truer today than ever before that anyone who saves money is losing it. Yet from his earliest days every citizen is subjected to a barrage of propaganda from parents and teachers as well as from politicians and crooks, all urging him to save money. Between them, inflation, hire purchase and personal taxation have removed every rational argument which ever existed for saving and we are left with nothing but irrational, atavistic terrors as our individual inducement to the one activity which holds the entire economy together.

It was Len Murray who produced what is surely the most significant quotation on the subject, when talking to Michael Leapman of *The Times*. 'We've got to stop worrying about inflation and learn to love it,' he said. Obviously, this pronouncement holds the key to everything that has been puzzling the rest of the world about Britain's attitude to inflation. The great problem is where to start. Children must be taught the simple proposition that saving equals waste. No doubt teachers can illustrate this with ingenious coloured charts but parents, too, can play their part by confiscating any pocket money which has not been spent by bed-time. The only thing which nobody can hope to do at the present time is to make any financial provision for his old age.

Logically, perhaps, I should welcome Mrs Castle's catastrophic increase in social security payments for the self-employed next April. The idea of her scheme is apparently to provide a pension which will be related to the cost of living around the year 2000 – just when I shall be applying for it. But a certain peasant caution creeps into my calculations, derived, no doubt, from the biblical injunction: 'O put not your trust in princes nor in any child of man; for there is no help in them.' I can see it will be very nice for Mrs Castle and her successors in office to receive my huge payments until the year 2000; but also that it will be rather less agreeable for them when it comes to paying out. And it is a feature of government that it can simply pass a law whenever it likes to rid itself of these tiresome obligations.

My own policy has been to shower my poor wife with useless but possibly saleable objects – ancient Greek coins, china boxes, harpsichords with the innards removed – and encourage her to cultivate the vegetable garden. We now have 14 cwt of potatoes in store against the hard winter and enough bric-a-brac to stock the entire Portobello Road for a month against our old age.

Darrowby Show

James Herriot

During the early days of his veterinary practice in the Yorkshire village of Darrowby James Herriot was prepared to undertake with equanimity any task delegated to him by his senior partner, Siegfried Farnon. Caution was learnt only through bitter experience....

'How would you like to officiate at Darrowby Show James?' Siegfried threw the letter he had been reading on to the desk and turned to me.

'I don't mind, but I thought you always did it.'

'I do, but it says in that letter that they've changed the date this year and it happens I'm going to be away that weekend.'

'Oh well, fine. What do I have to do?'

Siegfried ran his eye down his list of calls. 'It's a sinecure, really. More a pleasant day out than anything else. You have to measure the ponies and be on call in case any animals are injured. That's about all. Oh and they want you to judge the Family Pets.'

'Family Pets?'

'Yes, they run a proper dog show but they have an expert judge for that. This is just a bit of fun – all kinds of pets. You've got to find a first, second and third.'

'Right,' I said. 'I think I should just about be able to manage that.'

'Splendid.' Siegfried tipped up the envelope in which the letter had come. 'Here are your car park and luncheon tickets for self and friend if you want to take somebody with you. Also your vet's badge. OK?'

The Saturday of the show brought the kind of weather that must have had the organizers purring with pleasure; a sky of wide, unsullied blue, hardly a whiff of wind and the kind of torrid, brazen sunshine you don't often find in North Yorkshire.

As I drove down towards the show ground I felt I was looking at a living breathing piece of old England; the group of tents and marquees vivid against the green of the riverside field, the women and children in their bright summer dresses, the cattle with their smocked attendants, a line of massive Shire horses parading in the ring.

I parked the car and made for the stewards' tent with its flag hanging limply from the mast. Tristan parted from me there. With the impecunious student's unerring eye for a little free food and entertainment he had taken up my spare tickets. He headed purposefully for the beer tent as I went in to report to the show secretary.

Leaving my measuring stick there I looked around for a while.

A country show is a lot of different things to a lot of different people. Riding horses of all kinds from small ponies to hunters were being galloped up and down and in one ring the judges hovered around a group of mares and their beautiful little foals.

In a corner four men armed with buckets and brushes were washing and grooming a row of young bulls with great concentration, twiddling and crimping the fuzz over the rumps like society hairdressers.

Wandering through the marquees I examined the bewildering variety of produce from stalks of rhubarb to bunches of onions, the flower displays, embroidery, jams, cakes, pies. And the children's section; a painting of 'The Beach at Scarborough' by Annie Heseltine, aged nine; rows of wobbling copperplate handwriting – 'A thing of beauty is a joy for ever', Bernard Peacock, aged twelve.

Drawn by the occasional gusts of melody I strolled across the grass to where the Darrowby and Houlton Silver Band was rendering *Poet and Peasant*. The bandsmen were of all ages from seventies down to one or two boys of about fourteen and most of them had doffed their uniform tunics as they sweated in the hot sun. Pint pots reposed under many of the chairs and the musicians refreshed themselves frequently with leisurely swigs.

I was particularly fascinated by the conductor, a tiny frail man who looked about eighty. He alone had retained his full uniform, cap and all, and he stood apparently motionless in front of the crescent of bandsmen, chin sunk on chest, arms hanging limply by his sides. It wasn't until I came right up to him that I realized his fingers were twitching in time with the music and that he was, in fact, conducting. And the more I watched him the more

fitting it seemed that he should do it like that. The Yorkshireman's loathing
of exhibitionism or indeed any outward show of emotion made it unthinkable
that he should throw his arms about in the orthodox manner; no doubt he
had spent weary hours rehearsing and coaching his players but here, when
the results of his labours were displayed to the public he wasn't going to
swank about it. Even the almost imperceptible twitching of the finger-ends
had something guilty about it as if the old man felt he was being caught out
in something shameful.

But my attention was jerked away as a group of people walked across on
the far side of the band. It was Helen with Richard Edmunson and behind
them Mr Alderson and Richard's father deep in conversation. The young
man walked very close to Helen, his shining, plastered-down fair hair hovering
possessively over her dark head, his face animated as he talked and laughed.

There were no clouds in the sky but it was as if a dark hand had reached
across and smudged away the brightness of the sunshine. I turned quickly
and went in search of Tristan.

I soon picked out my colleague as I hurried into the marquee with
'Refreshments' over the entrance. He was leaning with an elbow on the
makeshift counter of boards and trestles chatting contentedly with a knot of
cloth-capped locals, a Woodbine in one hand, a pint glass in the other. There
was a general air of earthy bonhomie. Drinking of a more decorous kind
would be taking place at the president's bar behind the steward's headquarters
with pink gins or sherry as the main tipple but here it was beer, bottled and
draught, and the stout ladies behind the counter were working with the fierce
concentration of people who knew they were in for a hard day.

'Yes, I saw her,' Tristan said when I gave him my news. 'In fact there she
is now.' He nodded in the direction of the family group as they strolled past
the entrance. 'I've had my eye on them for some time – I don't miss much
from in here you know, Jim.'

'Ah well.' I accepted a half of bitter from him. 'It all looks pretty cosy.
The two dads like blood brothers and Helen hanging on to that bloke's arm.'

Tristan squinted over the top of his pint at the scene outside and shook
his head. 'Not exactly. He's hanging on to HER arm.' He looked at me
judicially. 'There's a difference, you know.'

'I don't suppose it makes much difference to me either way,' I grunted.

'Well don't look so bloody mournful.' He took an effortless swallow which
lowered the level in his glass by about six inches. 'What do you expect an

attractive girl to do? Sit at home waiting for you to call? If you've been pounding on her door every night you haven't told me about it.'

'It's all right you talking. I think old man Alderson would set his dogs on me if I showed up there. I know he doesn't like me hanging around Helen and on top of that I've got the feeling he thinks I killed his cow on my last visit.'

'And did you?'

'No, I didn't. But I walked up to a living animal, gave it an injection and it promptly died, so I can't blame him.'

I took a sip at my beer and watched the Alderson party who had changed direction and were heading away from our retreat. Helen was wearing a pale blue dress and I was thinking how well the colour went with the deep brown of her hair and how I liked the way she walked with her legs swinging easily and her shoulders high and straight when the loudspeaker boomed across the show ground.

'Will Mr Herriot, Veterinary Surgeon, please report to the stewards immediately.'

It made me jump but at the same time I felt a quick stab of pride. It was the first time I had heard myself and my profession publicly proclaimed. I turned to Tristan. He was supposed to be seeing practice and this could be something interesting. But he was immersed in a story which he was trying to tell to a little stocky man with a fat, shiny face, and he was having difficulty because the little man, determined to get his full measure of enjoyment, kept throwing himself into helpless convulsions at the end of every sentence, and the finish was a long way away. Tristan took his stories very seriously; I decided not to interrupt him.

A glow of importance filled me as I hurried over the grass, my official badge with 'Veterinary Surgeon' in gold letters dangling from my lapel. A steward met me on the way.

'It's one of the cattle. Had an accident, I think.' He pointed to a row of pens along the edge of the field.

A curious crowd had collected around my patient which had been entered in the in-calf heifers class. The owner a stranger from outside the Darrowby practice came up to me, his face glum.

'She tripped coming off the cattle wagon and went 'ead first into the wall. Knocked one of 'er horns clean off.'

The heifer, a bonny little light roan, was a pathetic sight. She had been washed, combed, powdered and primped for the big day and there she was with one horn dangling drunkenly down the side of her face and an ornamental fountain of bright arterial blood climbing gracefully in three jets from the broken surface high into the air.

I opened my bag. I had brought a selection of the things I might need and I fished out some artery forceps and suture material. The rational way to stop haemorrhage of this type is to grasp the bleeding vessel and ligate it, but it wasn't always as easy as that. Especially when the patient won't cooperate.

The broken horn was connected to the head only by a band of skin and I quickly snipped it away with scissors; then, with the farmer holding the heifer's nose I began to probe with my forceps for the severed vessels. In the bright sunshine it was surprising difficult to see the spurting blood and as the little animal threw her head about I repeatedly felt the warm spray across my face and heard it spatter on my collar.

It was when I was beginning to lose heart with my ineffectual groping that I looked up and saw Helen and her boyfriend watching me from the crowd. Young Edmundson looked mildly amused as he watched my unavailing efforts but Helen smiled encouragingly as she caught my eye. I did my best to smile back at her through my bloody mask but I don't suppose it showed.

I gave it up when the heifer gave a particularly brisk toss which sent my forceps flying on to the grass. I did what I should probably have done at the beginning – clapped a pad of cotton wool and antiseptic powder on to the stump and secured it with a figure of eight bandage round the other horn.

'That's it, then,' I said to the farmer as I tried to blink the blood out of my eyes. 'The bleeding's stopped, anyway. I'd advise you to have her properly dehorned soon or she's going to look a bit odd.'

Just then Tristan appeared from among the spectators.

'What's got you out of the beer tent?' I inquired with a touch of bitterness.

'It's lunch time, old lad,' Tristan replied equably. 'But we'll have to get you cleaned up a bit first. I can't be seen with you in that condition. Hang on, I'll get a bucket of water.'

The show luncheon was so excellent that it greatly restored me. Although it was taken in a marquee the committee men's wives had somehow managed to conjure up a memorable cold spread. There was fresh salmon and home fed ham and slices of prime beef with mixed salads and apple pie and the big brimming jugs of cream you only see at farming functions. One of the ladies was a noted cheese maker and we finished with some delicious goat cheese and coffee. The liquid side was catered for too with a bottle of Magnet Pale Ale and a glass at every place.

I didn't have the pleasure of Tristan's company at lunch because he had strategically placed himself well down the table between two strict Methodists so that his intake of Magnet was trebled.

I had hardly emerged into the sunshine when a man touched me on the shoulder.

'One of the dog show judges wants you to examine a dog. He doesn't like the look of it.'

He led me to where a thin man of about forty with a small dark moustache was standing by his car. He held a wire-haired fox terrier on a leash and he met me with an ingratiating smile.

'There's nothing whatever the matter with my dog,' he declared, 'but the chap in there seems very fussy.'

I looked down at the terrier. 'I see he has some matter in the corner of his eyes.'

The man shook his head vigorously. 'Oh no, that's not matter. I've been using some white powder on him and a bit's got into his eyes, that's all.'

'Hmm, well let's see what his temperature says, shall we?'

The little animal stood uncomplaining as I inserted the thermometer. When I took the reading my eyebrows went up.

'It's a hundred and four. I'm afraid he's not fit to go into the show.'

'Wait a minute.' The man thrust out his jaw. 'You're talking like that chap in there. I've come a long way to show this dog and I'm going to show him.'

'I'm sorry but you can't show him with a temperature of a hundred and four.'

'But he's had a car journey. That could put up his temperature.'

I shook my head. 'Not as high as that it couldn't. Anyway he looks sick to me. Do you see how he's half closing his eyes as though he's frightened of the light? It's possible he could have distemper.'

'What? That's rubbish and you know it. He's never been fitter!' The man's mouth trembled with anger.

I looked down at the little dog. He was crouching on the grass miserably. Occasionally he shivered, he had a definite photophobia and there was that creamy blob of pus in the corner of each eye. 'Has he been inoculated against distemper?'

'Well no, he hasn't but why do you keep on about it?'

'Because I think he's got it now and for his sake and for the sake of the other dogs here you ought to take him straight home and see your own vet.'

He glared at me. 'So you won't let me take him into the show tent?'

'That's right. I'm very sorry, but it's out of the question.' I turned and walked away.

I had gone only a few yards when the loudspeaker boomed again.

'Will Mr Herriot please go to the measuring stand where the ponies are ready for him.'

I collected my stick and trotted over to a corner of the field where a group of ponies had assembled; Welsh, Dales, Exmoor, Dartmoor – all kinds of breeds were represented.

For the uninitiated, horses are measured in hands which consist of four inches and a graduated stick is used with a cross piece and a spirit level which rests on the withers, the highest point of the shoulders. I had done a fair bit of it in individual animals but this was the first time I had done the job at a show. With my stick at the ready I stood by the two wide boards which had been placed on the turf to give the animals a reasonably level standing surface.

A smiling young woman led the first pony, a smart chestnut, on to the boards.

'Which class?' I asked.

'Thirteen hands.'

I tried the stick on him. He was well under.

'Fine. next please.'

A few more came through without incident then there was a lull before the next group came up. The ponies were arriving on the field all the time in their boxes and being led over to me, some by their young riders, others by the parents. It looked as though I could be here quite a long time.

During one of the lulls a little man who had been standing near me spoke up.

'No trouble yet?' he asked.

'No, everything's in order,' I replied.

He nodded expressionlessly and as I took a closer look at him his slight body, dark, leathery features and high shoulders seemed to give him the appearance of a little brown gnome. At the same time there was something undeniably horsy about him.

'You'll 'ave some awkward 'uns,' he grunted. 'And they allus say the same thing. They allus tell you the vet at some other show passed their pony.' His swarthy cheeks crinkled in a wry smile.

'Is that so?'

'Aye, you'll see.'

Another candidate, led by a beautiful blonde, was led on to the platform. She gave me the full blast of two big greenish eyes and flashed a mouthful of sparkling teeth at me.

'Twelve two,' she murmured seductively.

I tried the stick on the pony and worked it around, but try as I might I couldn't get it down to that.

'I'm afraid he's a bit big,' I said.

The blonde's smile vanished. 'Have you allowed half an inch for his shoes?'

'I have indeed, but you can see for yourself, he's well over.'

'But he passed the vet without any trouble at Hickley.' She snapped and out of the corner of my eye I saw the gnome nodding sagely.

'I can't help that,' I said. 'I'm afraid you'll have to put him into the next class.'

For a moment two green pebbles from the cold sea bed fixed me with a frigid glare then the blonde was gone taking her pony with her.

Next, a little bay animal was led on to the stand by a hard faced gentleman in a check suit and I must say I was baffled by its behaviour. Whenever the stick touched the withers it sank at the knees so that I couldn't be sure whether I was getting the right reading or not. Finally I gave up and passed him through.

The gnome coughed. 'I know that feller.'

'You do?'

'Aye, he's pricked the pony's withers with a pin so many times that it drops down whenever you try to measure 'im.'

'Never!'

'Sure as I'm standing here.'

I was staggered, but the arrival of another batch took up my attention for a few minutes. Some I passed, others I had to banish to another class and the owners took it in different ways – some philosophically, a few with obvious annoyance. One or two of the ponies just didn't like the look of the stick at all and I had to dance around them as they backed away and reared.

The last pony in this group was a nice grey led by a bouncy man wearing a great big matey smile.

'How are you, all right?' he inquired courteously. 'This 'un's thirteen two.'

The animal went under the stick without trouble but after he had trotted away the gnome spoke up again.

'I know that feller, too.'

'Really?'

'Not 'alf. Weighs down 'is ponies before they're measured. That grey's been standing in 'is box for the last hour with a twelve stone sack of corn on 'is back. Knocks an inch off.'

'Good God! Are you sure?'

'Don't worry, I've seen 'im at it.'

My mind was beginning to reel just a little. Was the man making it all up or were there really these malign forces at work behind all this innocent fun?

'That same feller,' continued the gnome. 'I've seen 'im bring a pony to a show and get half an inch knocked off for shoes when it never 'ad no shoes on.'

I wished he'd stop. And just then there was an interruption. It was the man with the moustache. He sidled up to me and whispered confidentially in my ear.

'Now I've just been thinking. My dog must have got over his journey by now and I expect his temperature will be normal. I wonder if you'd just try him again. I've still got time to show him.'

I turned wearily. 'Honestly, it'll be a waste of time. I've told you, he's ill.'

'Please! Just as a favour.' He had a desperate look and a fanatical light flickered in his eye.

'All right.' I went over to the car with him and produced my thermometer. The temperature was still a hundred and four.

'Now I wish you'd take this poor little dog home,' I said. 'He shouldn't be here.'

For a moment I thought the man was going to strike me. 'There's nothing wrong with him!' he hissed, his whole face working with emotion.

'I'm sorry,' I said, and went back to the measuring stand.

A boy of about fifteen was waiting for me with his pony. It was supposed to be in the thirteen two class but was nearly one and a half inches over.

'Much too big, I'm afraid,' I said. 'He can't go in that class.'

The boy didn't answer. He put his hand inside his jacket and produced a sheet of paper. 'This is a veterinary certificate to say he's under thirteen two.'

'No good, I'm sorry,' I replied. 'The stewards have told me not to accept any certificates. I've turned down two others today. Everything has to go under the stick. It's a pity, but there it is.'

His manner changed abruptly. 'But you've GOT to accept it!' he shouted in my face. 'There doesn't have to be any measurements when you have a certificate.'

'You'd better see the stewards. Those are my instructions.'

'I'll see my father about this, that's what!' he shouted and led the animal away.

Father was quickly on the scene. Big, fat, prosperous-looking, confident. He obviously wasn't going to stand any nonsense from me.

'Now look here, I don't know what this is all about but you have no option in this matter. You have to accept the certificate.'

'I don't, I assure you,' I answered. 'And anyway, it's not as though your pony was slightly over the mark. He's miles over – nowhere near the height.'

Father flushed dark red. 'Well let me tell you he was passed through by the vet at....'

'I know, I know,' I said, and I heard the gnome give a short laugh. 'But he's not going through here.'

There was a brief silence then both father and son began to scream at me. And as they continued to hurl abuse I felt a hand on my arm. It was the man with the moustache again.

'I'm going to ask you just once more to take my dog's temperature,' he whispered with a ghastly attempt to smile. 'I'm sure he'll be all right this time. Will you try him again?'

I'd had enough. 'No, I bloody well won't!' I barked. 'Will you kindly stop bothering me and take that poor animal home.'

It's funny how the most unlikely things motivate certain people. It didn't seem a life and death matter whether a dog got into a show or not but it was to the man with the moustache. He started to rave at me.

'You don't know your job, that's the trouble with you! I've come all this way and you've played the dirty on me. I've got a friend who's a vet, a proper vet, and I'm going to tell him about you, yes I am. I'm going to tell him about you!'

At the same time the father and son were still in full cry, snarling and mouthing at me and I became suddenly aware that I was in the centre of a hostile circle. The blonde was there too, and some of the others whose ponies I had outed and they were all staring at me belligerently, making angry gestures.

I felt very much alone because the gnome, who had seemed an ally, was nowhere to be seen. I was disappointed in the gnome; he was a big talker but had vanished at the first whiff of danger. As I surveyed the threatening crowd I moved my measuring stick round in front of me; it wasn't much of a weapon but it might serve to fend them off if they rushed me.

And just at that moment, as the unkind words were thick upon the air, I saw Helen and Richard Edmundson on the fringe of the circle, taking it all in. I wasn't worried about him but again it struck me as strange that it should be my destiny always to be looking a bit of a clown when Helen was around.

Anyway, the measuring was over and I felt in need of sustenance. I retreated and went to find Tristan.

The atmosphere in the beer tent was just what I needed. The hot weather had made the place even more popular than usual and it was crowded; many of the inhabitants had been there since early morning and the air was thick with earthy witticisms, immoderate laughter, cries of joy; and the nice thing was that nobody in there cared a damn about the heights of ponies or the temperatures of dogs.

I had to fight my way through the crush to reach Tristan who was leaning across the counter in earnest conversation with a comely young barmaid. The other serving ladies were middle-aged but his practised eye had picked this one out; glossy red hair, a puckish face and an inviting smile. I had been hoping for a soothing chat with him but he was unable to give me his undivided attention, so after juggling with a glass among the throng for a few minutes I left.

Out on the field the sun still blazed, the scent of the trampled grass rose into the warm air, the band was playing a selection from *Rose Marie* and peace began to steal into my soul. Maybe I could begin to enjoy the show now the pinpricks were over; there was only the Family Pets to judge and I was looking forward to that.

For about an hour I wandered among the pens of mountainous pigs and haughty sheep; the rows of Shorthorn cows with their classical wedge-shaped grace, their level udders and dainty feet.

I watched in fascination a contest which was new to me; shirt-sleeved young men sticking a fork into a straw bale and hurling it high over a bar with a jerk of their thick brown arms.

Old Steve Bramley, a local farmer, was judging the heavy horses and I envied him his massive authority as he stumped, bowler-hatted and glowering around each animal, leaning occasionally on his stick as he took stock of the points. I couldn't imagine anyone daring to argue with him.

It was late in the afternoon when the loudspeaker called me to my final duty. The Family Pets contestants were arranged on wooden chairs drawn up in a wide circle on the turf. They were mainly children but behind them an interested ring of parents and friends watched me warily as I arrived.

The fashion for exotic pets was still in its infancy but I experienced a mild shock of surprise when I saw the variety of creatures on show. I suppose I must have had a vague mental picture of a few dogs and cats but I walked round the circle in growing bewilderment looking down at rabbits – innumerable rabbits of all sizes and colours – guinea pigs, white mice, several budgerigars, two tortoises, a canary, a kitten, a parrot, a mynah bird, a box of puppies, a few dogs, and cats and a goldfish in a bowl. The smaller pets rested on their owners' knees, the others squatted on the ground.

How, I asked myself was I going to come to a decision here? How did you choose between a parrot and a puppy, a budgie and a bulldog, a mouse and a mynah? Then as I circled it came to me; it couldn't be done. The only way was to question the children in charge and find which ones looked after their pets best, which of them knew most about their feeding and general husbandry. I rubbed my hands together and repressed a chuckle of satisfaction; I had something to work on now.

I don't like to boast but I think I can say in all honesty that I carried out an exhaustive scientific survey of that varied group. From the outset I adopted an attitude of cold detachment, mercilessly banishing any ideas of personal preference. If I had been pleasing only myself I would have given first prize to a gleaming black Labrador sitting by a chair with massive composure and offering me a gracious paw every time I came near. And my second would have been a benevolent tabby – I have always had a thing about tabby cats – which rubbed its cheek against my hand as I talked to its owner. The pups, crawling over each other and grunting obesely, would probably have come third. But I put away these unworthy thoughts and pursued my chosen course.

I was distracted to some extent by the parrot which kept saying 'Hellow' in a voice of devastating refinement like a butler answering a telephone and the mynah which repeatedly adjured me to 'Shut door as you go out,' in a booming Yorkshire baritone.

The only adult in the ring was a bosomy lady with glacial pop eyes and a white poodle on her knee. As I approached she gave me a challenging stare as though defying me to place her pet anywhere but first.

'Hello, little chap,' I said, extending my hand, The poodle responded by drawing its lips soundlessly back from its teeth and giving me much the same kind of look as its owner. I withdrew my hand hastily.

'Oh you needn't be afraid of him,' the lady said frigidly. 'He won't hurt you.'

I gave a light laugh. 'I'm sure he won't.' I held out my hand again. 'You're a nice little dog, aren't you?' Once more the poodle bared his teeth and when I persevered by trying to stroke his ears he snapped noiselessly, his teeth clicked together an inch from my fingers.

'He doesn't like you, I can see that. Do you, darling?' The lady put her cheek against the dog's head and stared at me distastefully as though she knew just how he felt.

'Shut door as you go out,' commanded the mynah gruffly from somewhere behind me.

I gave the lady my questionnaire and moved on.

And among the throng there was one who stood out; the little boy with the goldfish. In reply to my promptings he discoursed knowledgeably about his fish, its feeding, life history and habits. He even had a fair idea of the common diseases. The bowl, too, was beautifully clean and the water fresh; I was impressed.

When I had completed the circuit I swept the ring for the last time with a probing eye. Yes, there was no doubt about it; I had the three prize winners fixed in my mind beyond any question and in an order based on strictly scientific selection. I stepped out into the middle.

'Ladies and gentlemen,' I said, scanning the company with an affable smile.

'Hellow,' responded the parrot fruitily.

I ignored him and continued. 'These are the successful entrants. First, number six, the goldfish. Second, number fifteen, the guinea pig. And third, number ten, the white kitten.'

I half expected a little ripple of applause but there was none. In fact my announcement was greeted by a tight-lipped silence. I had noticed an immediate change in the atmosphere when I mentioned the goldfish. It was striking – a sudden cold wave which swept away the expectant smiles and replaced them with discontented muttering.

I had done something wrong, but what? I looked around helplessly as the hum of voices increased. 'What do you think of that, then?' 'Not fair, is it?' 'Wouldn't have thought it of him?' 'All them lovely rabbits and he hardly looked at them.'

I couldn't make it out, but my job was done, anyway. I pushed between the chairs and escaped to the open field.

'Shut door as you go out,' the mynah requested in deepest bass as I departed.

I sought out Tristan again. The atmosphere in the beer tent had changed too. The drinkers were long since past their peak and the hilarious babel which had met me on my last visit had died to an exhausted murmur. There was a general air of satiation. Tristan, pint in hand, was being addressed with great solemnity by a man in a flat cap and braces. The man swayed slightly as he grasped Tristan's free hand and gazed into his eyes. Occasionally he patted him on the shoulder with the utmost affection. Obviously my colleague had been forging deep and lasting friendships in here while I was making enemies outside.

I sidled up to him and spoke into his ear. 'Ready to go soon, Triss?'

He turned slowly and looked at me. 'No, old lad,' he said, articulating carefully. 'I'm afraid I shan't be coming with you. They're having a dance here on the showfield later and Doreen has consented to accompany me. He cast a loving glance across the counter at the redhead who crinkled her nose at him.

I was about to leave when a snatch of conversation from behind made me pause.

'A bloody goldfish!' a voice was saying disgustedly.

'Aye, it's a rum 'un, George,' a second voice replied.

There was a slurping sound of beer being downed.

'But tha knows, Fred,' the first voice said. 'That vet feller had to do it. Didn't 'ave no choice. He couldn't pass over t'squire's son.'

'Reckon you're right, but it's a bugger when you get graft and corruption in t'Family Pets.'

A heavy sigh, then 'It's the way things are nowadays, Fred, Everything's hulterior.'

'You're right there, George. It's hulterior, that's what it is.'

I fought down a rising panic. The Pelhams had been Lords of the Manor of Darrowby for generations and the present squire was Major Pelham. I knew him as a friendly farmer client, but that was all. I'd never heard of his son.

I clutched at Tristan's arm. 'Who is that little boy over there?'

Tristan peered out glassily across the sward. 'The one with the goldfish bowl, you mean?'

'That's right.'

'It's young Nigel Pelham, the squire's son.'

'Oh Gawd,' I moaned. 'But I've never seen him before. Where's he been?'

'Boarding school down south, I believe. On holiday just now.'

I stared at the boy again. Tousled fair hair, grey open-necked shirt, sunburned legs. Just like all the others.

George was at it again. 'Lovely dogs and cats there was, but squire's lad won it with a bloody goldfish.'

'Well, let's be right,' his companion put in. 'If that lad 'ad brought along a bloody stuffed monkey he'd still 'ave got fust prize with it.'

'No doubt about it, Fred. T'other kids might as well 'ave stopped at 'ome.'

'Aye, it's not like it used to be, George. Nobody does owt for nowt these days.

'True, Fred, very true.' There was a gloomy silence punctuated by noisy gulpings. Then, in weary tones: 'Well you and me can't alter it. It's the kind of world we're living in today.'

I reeled out into the fresh air and the sunshine. Looking round at the tranquil scene, the long stretch of grass, the loop of pebbly river with the green hills rising behind, I had a sense of unreality. Was there any part of this peaceful cameo of rural England without its sinister undertones? As if by instinct I made my way into the long marquee which housed the produce section. Surely among those quiet rows of vegetables I would find repose.

The place was almost empty but as I made my way down the long lines of tables I came upon the solitary figure of old John William Enderby who had a little grocer's shop in the town.

'Well how are things?' I inquired.

'Nobbut middlin' lad,' the old man replied morosely.

'Why, what's wrong?'

'Well, ah got a second with me broad beans but only a highly commended for me shallots. Look at 'em.'

I looked. 'Yes, they're beautiful shallots, Mr Enderby.'

'Aye, they are, and nobbut a highly commended. It's a insult, that's what it is a insult.'

'But Mr Enderby ... highly commended ... I mean, that's pretty good isn't it?'

'No it isn't, it's a insult!'

'Oh bad luck.'

John William stared at me wide-eyed for a moment. 'It's not bad luck lad. 'it's nowt but a twist.'

'Oh surely not!'

'Ah'm tellin' you. Jim Houlston got first with 'is shallots and judge is his wife's cousin.'

'Never!'

'It's true,' grunted John William, nodding solemnly. 'It's nowt but a twist.'

'Well I've never heard of such a thing!'

'You don't know what goes on, young man. Ah wasn't even placed with me taties. Frank Thompson got first wi' that lot.' He pointed to a tray of noble tubers.

I studied them. 'I must admit they look splendid potatoes.'

'Aye, they are, but Frank pinched 'em'.

'What?'

'Aye, they took first prize at Brisby show last Thursday and Frank pinched 'em off t'stand.'

I clutched at the nearby table. The foundations of my world were crumbling. 'That can't be true, Mr Enderby.'

'Ah'm not jokin' nor jestin',' declared John William. 'Them's self and same taties, ah'd know them anywhere. It's nowt but a....'

I could take no more. I fled.

Outside the evening sunshine was still warm and the whole field was awash with the soft light which, in the Dales, seems to stream down in a golden flood from the high tops. But it was as if the forces of darkness were pressing on me; all I wanted was to get home.

I hurried to the steward's tent and collected my measuring stick, running a gauntlet of hostile stares from the pony people I had ousted earlier in the day. They were still waving their certificates and arguing.

On my way to the car I had to pass several of the ladies who had watched me judge the pets and though they didn't exactly draw their skirts aside they managed to convey their message. Among the rows of vehicles I spotted the man with the moustache. He still hadn't taken his terrier away and his eyes, full of wounded resentment, followed my every step.

I was opening my door when Helen and her party, also apparently on the way home, passed about fifty yards away. Helen waved. I waved back, and

Richard Edmundson gave me a nod before helping her into the front seat of a gleaming, silver Daimler. The two fathers got into the back.

As I settled into the seat of my Austin, braced my feet against the broken floor boards and squinted through the cracked windscreen I prayed that just this once the thing would go on the starter. Holding my breath I pulled at the knob but the engine gave a couple of lazy turns then fell silent.

Fishing the starting handle from under the seat I crept out and inserted it in its hole under the radiator; and as I began the old familiar winding the silver monster purred contemptuously past me and away.

Dropping into the driver's seat again I caught sight of my face in the mirror and could see the streaks and flecks of blood still caked on my cheek and around the roots of my hair. Tristan hadn't done a very good job with his bucket of cold water.

I looked back at the emptying field and at the Daimler disappearing round a distant bend. It seemed to me that in more ways than one the show was over.

Ephraim's Undoing

H. F. Ellis

Chapter I

At the 'Bull and Scissors'

The little hamlet of Clodbury lay basking in the warm sunlight of a bright May morning. Butterflies flitted from flower to flower in the colourful cottage-gardens, rooks cawed in the distant elm-trees, and by the trim white-painted bridge a gentle gurgling showed that Ebenezer Truelove was taking his midday beer. The village street wore a deserted air and the old man, seeing little chance of getting any more, drank slowly as he listened with grave politeness to the girl who sat beside him at the door of the 'Bull and Scissors'. A stranger approaching more closely (for no one who knew Ebenezer would do such a foolhardy thing) would have seen at a glance that here, if anywhere, was the heroine of the kind of story upon which we are now embarked. The roses in her cheeks and also (I regret to say) in her hair, the freckles on her nose, and the dimple at the side of her enormous mulberry-coloured mouth all marked her out as the best type of simple English girlhood. Beneath her simple muslin frock – but I am forgetting; this is not a war-book. Beneath her simple muslin hat two eyes of cornflower-blue looked out with frank directness, and in their limpid depths one might see reflected not only Ebenezer's mug of beer but the purity and sweet simplicity of her beautiful character. Wherever she went she seemed to carry with her the scent of new-mown hay. A very child of Nature, men called her; though she was, as a matter of fact, the daughter of Simon Earwhacker, one of the hardest-bitten farmers in all the countryside and the kind of father that only a girl like Prudence could possibly be saddled with. She was speaking of him at this very moment to Ebenezer.

'Father is determined to engineer a matrimonial alliance between myself and Ephraim Mathers, and threatens to excoriate my name from the Family Bible if I oppose his wishes,' she said, speaking with the quaint adorable accent of the B.B.C.

'Owd slubberdegullion!' said Ebenezer, who had no wireless-set. 'And doan't 'ee loike Ephraim then, Miss Prue?'

'I detest him, the gurt – great toad! but father is such a cruel hard man, and says he is the wealthiest farmer in the whole district and worth fifty Mr Williamses. And, oh, Mr Truelove, I *do* love Mr Williams so!'

'Be that the poet-chap from Lunnon town yew du mean?' asked Ebenezer, more for the convenience of the reader than because he was in any real doubt about the matter. 'Gentleman-born 'e be – ah, an' wunnerful clever tu, so I've 'eerd tell; though not so big and strong as Ephraim, no, not be a hubbock[1] or more. But 'twill arl cum right i' the end, so doan't 'ee fret theeself, lass.'

'It cannot, it cannot!' cried the unhappy girl, and great tear-drops splashed on the gravel path as she told of the unfair test by which her father had decided to select her mate.

'If yon numskull,' he had said, alluding to Aubrey Williams in his rough unkindly way, 'be a better man than Ephraim here, an' kin beat him at ploughing an' milking – Ah, an' win t' prize for t' best beetroot at t' Flower-Show into t' bargain – y shall have him an' welcome.' And then and there he had drawn up the rules for the triple contest, which was to begin without delay.

'But my Aubrey has never even seen a plough, Mr Truelove, and cows offend his sense of artistic values, so whatever shall I do? It du seem as I mun wed Ephraim – I mean, it looks as if I shall have to marry Ephraim Mathers after all.'

'It be main late for ploughin' sartinly.' Ebeneezer's answer was a little vague. He was wondering whether an offer of a hundred to one against Williams for the triple event would find any takers.

A few moments later he entered the tap-room to make sure, and Prudence, gathering up her basket of eggs, and tucking a cauliflower under her arm, strode sadly home to lunch.

*

[1] A kind of three-handled trowel, now obsolete.

Chapter II

The Milking Contest

The day of the opening contest dawned bright and clear, with just enough wind to make conditions ideal, and a goodly crowd assembled at Earwhacker Farm to see the sport. Conspicuous among them all was Simon Earwhacker himself as he moved from place to place setting everything to rights, now whispering to the judges, now ordering the lines of cows, and ever and anon turning to glance with lowered brows at the corner by the pig-sties where Prudence, her fair head close to Aubrey's, read him hurried extracts from *The Dairyman's Guide*. To tell the truth, Simon was uneasy. Already his gigantic watch pointed six minutes to the hour, and by the rules of the competition either competitor failing to appear by ten o'clock was automatically disqualified. Yet Ephraim Mathers was nowhere to be seen. Minute by minute his agitation grew, until at last a fast-driven gig was reported approaching rapidly from Middle Hutchley. On the very stroke of ten it drew up with a clatter before the gate, and a foul green hat came skimming over the heads of the people into the byre, to be followed a moment later by Ephraim himself, looking fit and well in purple corduroys.

'Ephraim! Ephraim!' shouted the onlookers in a frenzy of excitement, some of them even taking the straws out of their mouths in their enthusiasm, for public sympathy was on the side of the local champion. Outside the milking-shed the rivals met, and a great silence fell upon all as Aubrey spun a bright new sixpence (borrowed from Prudence) high into the air. It fell on a pig, and a mighty roar greeted the announcement that Ephraim had won the toss and would go in first.

Ephraim Mathers came of a long line of skilful milkers, but on this occasion at least he surpassed them all. He was brilliant. Experienced cowherds in the company said that never had they seen a man milk as Ephraim Mathers milked that day. A brindled shorthorn of proved capacity accompanied him to the stool, but in less than two minutes he was calling for another cow. And so it went on, until at the end of the allotted half-hour seventeen empties stood lowing in the yard and as many brimming pails were ranged against the wall. 'A phenomenal display,' as Prudence observed with grudging admiration.

And now it was Aubrey's turn. A man of extreme delicacy, his whole being shrank from contact with an animal with four stomachs; but, reminding himself that it was for Miss Earwhacker's sake, he shook back his long dark curls and plunged boldly into the shed.

Half an hour later, when the officials entered the building, they found him sketching on the back of an old envelope.

'Where be t'milk?' asked Simon roughly.

'What milk?' said Aubrey.

'Why, t' milk as was to help thee win my darter's hand.'

'Dear me! I must have forgotten. I have been doing a little still-life work. but I will begin at once.'

' 'Tis too late, lad,' said Simon triumphantly; and so indeed it was. Already the judges had begun their announcement: 'We hereby proclaim Ephraim Mathers the winner by seventeen clear –'

'Hold!' cried a voice in bell-like tones, and Prudence, leaping upon a wheelbarrow, waved aloft the envelope which she had snatched from Aubrey's unresisting hand. 'By the rules of the contest the winner was to be he who in the space of thirty minutes drew the greater amount of milk. Ephraim Mathers has drawn seventeen pails. Now let *these* be counted,' and with a gesture of defiance she hurled the paper at the feet of the judges.

Aubrey Williams had drawn twenty-three!

In an instant all was confusion. Men shouted, dogs barked and horses swooned. Two Buff Orpingtons were so affected that they never laid again; and amid the tumult Aubrey, with his head in the clouds and his feet in a bucket of pig-wash, clasped the radiant Prudence to his breast.

'Prue!' he whispered.

'Aubrey!' she murmured.

'Dang it!' said Simon Earwhacker.

Chapter III

The Ploughing-Match

The milking contest had ended in an unexpected and glorious victory, but the heart of Prudence Earwhacker grew heavy within her as the date of the ploughing-match drew near. Every evening she took Aubrey down to the Five-Acre to practise, but, do what she would, she could not keep him on his course. Sometimes he would be straight for forty, fifty, sixty yards, and then that old dreamy look would come back and away he would go in great sweeping curves, carolling blithely as he went.

'It is the creative spirit,' he would say when she chided him, and would point out to her the nobility and grace of his twining furrows.

Once, when his whirling share had marked out a pattern of almost unearthly beauty – a thing of curves and loops and complex involutions, he turned to her and, falling on his knees before her in an ecstasy of love, cried, 'It is yours, Prue – all yours! I dedicate this work to you!' And she, poor girl, though her heart was breaking, only reproved him gently, saying, 'Oh, Aubrey, you have made the horses giddy!' and then, turning away to hide her heaving cheeks, went lumbering home to supper.

She was a difficult girl at times, thought Aubrey sadly.

The tale of the match itself – a single-furrow affair over Simon's Ten-acre – is soon told. Ephraim, ploughing with less than his usual care, developed a nasty kink two furlongs from home which marred an otherwise tidy furrow; but even so no one, not even loyal little Prudence, could doubt that the effort was good enough to beat so unworldly a ploughman as Aubrey. Indeed, for all her courage the girl's hopes had sunk to zero, and as she knelt to tie the string below her sweetheart's knees unbidden tears fell thick and fast upon the big boots he had borrowed from Ebenezer.

'Remember what it says in *How to Plough*, beloved,' she faltered as she rose; and for answer he pressed into her hand some verses on the Infinite, then, without word or glance, sprang lightly to the plough handles. Next instant he had burst into song.

Old men in Clodbury still speak with reverence of the sight they saw that day. Forward at a tremendous pace dashed the two great horses, spurred by the sweet sad music, and behind them, running easily over the clods, went Aubrey Williams, the light of genius in his eyes. And when it was all over and the three of them stood sweating at the farther end, a great shout of wonder arose from the spectators. It was the straightest furrow ever seen in Clodbury!

'Good lad! good lad!' said Squire Aitchbone heartily, wringing our hero's hand.

Simon and Ephraim were biting their nails.

'What about they boots?' said Ebenezer.

Prudence had fainted with joy.

But Aubrey, who had read Sneebohl on *The Beauty of the Straight Line* the night before, cared for none of these things. He was seeking a rhyme for 'tilth'.

Chapter IV

A Hopeless Dawn

May passed into June and June into July; the corn ripened, hollyhocks burst into bloom, and Ephraim Mathers grew steadily hotter and hotter under his ill-fitting collar. Twice he had been baulked of victory, and now, on the eve of the Flower-Show, he brooded darkly on the fateful issues of the morrow. Prudence was *his*; he loved her madly, fiercely. The very thought of her in another's keeping set his teeth on edge and sent the dark blood surging into his ears. At all costs Aubrey Williams must not win the Beetroot Cup, and he, Ephraim, could alone prevent it! Not a man save himself was willing to oppose him, so completely had the debonair young poet, dang him! won all hearts by his gallant bearing at the ploughing-match. Once more it was a straight fight between them, but this time, by gubber! the result should be different. With the fearful oath on his lips Ephraim went out to look at his beet.

Night found him still standing among the roots, turning over in his mind the details of a monstrous plan. He had some lovely beet, but what if Aubrey had some lovelier? He must take no risks – must make sure in time. . . .

Half an hour later he was on his way to Aubrey's garden, a tape-measure clasped firmly in his huge right hand. To such lengths will the evil passion of jealousy drive its frenzied victims.

'I give you good day, Miss Prudence,' said Aubrey in his courtly way at five o'clock the following morning. The girl was on her way back from somewhere or other, and he hailed her as she passed his gate.

'Good morning, Aubrey,' she flashed back at him, her face shining from the effects of too much soap and water. 'May I come in?'

Together they walked in silence through the kitchen-garden, and Prue's heart sank within her for about the fifth time since the beginning of May as she surveyed the bedraggled beetroot. She could not conceal from herself the fact that it was wretched stuff, unfit even for the basest cow; but her lover was smiling happily and she said no word.

Outside the tool-shed he took her in his arms. 'Prudence,' he said, 'I have been keeping something from you all these months. Inside this shed lies the Queen of the West, thirty-three inches round the waist, and the finest, handsomest –'

'Beast! Roué! Deceiver!' she cried, the tears starting to her eyes as she flung herself in a frenzy of despair on to an onion-bed. 'That you of all men should treat me so!'

Aubrey was puzzled. He had meant to surprise her, but not to this extent. 'Come, come,' he said sternly – 'the shock has been too much for you. I should have broken it more gently. But what, after all, is a beetroot? In the great harmony of the universe –'

'A beetroot?' she gasped, looking positively hideous in her relief.

'Certainly – a champion beetroot.'

'Oh, Aubrey – and I doubted you! Forgive me.'

'With all my heart.'

'Will you show it to me, dearest?' She was all leaf-mould and contrition.

Proudly he threw open the door of the tool-shed. 'Look!' he cried – and gave a shuddering gasp of dismay.

The Queen of the West had gone!

Chapter V

The Flower-Show

The grounds of Biggeley Manor, the old-world residence of Colonel Harry ('Squire') Aitchbone, were ablaze with life and colour. On the spacious lawns some of the best people in the neighbourhood strolled to and fro, halting now and again to exchange a greeting or to watch the finish of the Mothers' Sack-race. Admiral Fluke was there in full-dress uniform; Lord Isinglass had brought his stupid daughters; in the refreshment tent Lady Ipswich was cracking jokes with the Duchess of Havant and Hook. From the distance came the haunting strains of a roundabout. Clodbury's Annual Fête and Flower-Show was at its height.

There were many lovely faces and expensive frocks to be seen that afternoon, but none looked sweeter than Prudence in her simple white organdie with the crimson sash, and more than one baronet turned to glance at her as she made her way towards the vegetable tent on Aubrey's arm.

'Dashed pretty girl, that – what?' said Sir Archibald Crawshay, M.F.H., cracking his whip to emphasize the words.

'You're right, by gad!' It was the Vicar of Minchin-under-Tapley who so readily expressed his agreement with his companion's views.

Meanwhile Prudence, unconscious of the interest she was exciting, had passed with her escort beneath the flap of the giant marquee, and now stood gazing with lack-lustre eyes at a highly-commended carrot. The judging was over, but the disappointed lovers had little or no interest in the results. The mysterious disappearance of the Queen of the West had been a crushing blow, and, though Aubrey had sent in the best beetroot left in the garden, it was without hope that he did so. Probably it would not even be commended.

A surprise awaited them when they came at last, via the cauliflowers and sea-kale, to the beetroot stall. There were only two, and the second prize, in the absence of any other entries, had gone to Aubrey! Upon the winning exhibit, a veritable monster, were pinned two cards – a red one which said:

First Prize

and a white one on which was written:

Special Prize
For the Best Vegetable in the Show

Prudence regarded its great empurpled sides with awe. 'Oh, Aubrey,' she asked wistfully, 'was the Queen of the West as big as that?'

'That *is* the Queen of the West,' he said fairly quietly. 'There has been dirty work.'

'But who –?'

Their eyes met.

'You must denounce him, Aubrey. You must – you shall!'

'Leave this to me,' he said with a compelling gesture that brought half-a-hundredweight of potatoes about their ears. 'I go to find a hammer.'

We will not attempt to describe in any detail the emotions that racked poor Prudence's bosom as she sat beside her father at the prize-giving some two hours later. The situation seemed indeed a desparate one. What could Aubrey do, even if he found a hammer, to prove the guilt of Ephraim Mathers? Mere violence would not suffice. To add to her misery Ephraim was trying to hold her hand. Would Aubrey never come?

Ephraim himself was at the top of his form. He had certainly stolen the beetroot which now reposed in a place of honour on the judges' table, but who would believe the charge if it were made? Nary a one. It was his hour of triumph.

'We come now,' Squire Aitchbone was saying, 'to the award of the Beetroot Cup, which goes this year, very deservedly in my opinion, to – Well, well, my boy, what is it?'

A slim figure had pushed its way through the throng and now stood in a graceful attitude before them.

'I wish to show you something,' said Aubrey, and, taking a hammer from his pocket caught the Queen of the West a savage wallop in the middle.

She burst into a thousand fragments.

'What is the meaning of this?' roared the Squire.

'Plaster-of-Paris, I fancy,' said Aubrey, and there were tears in his eyes as he spoke. After all, she had been one of his noblest creations.

In the silence that followed all eyes were turned upon Ephraim, who sat as though thunderstruck in his seat. How could he reveal the real author of this false fruit without admitting his own guilty deed? Twice he rose to speak and twice thought better of it. And then:

'I claim the Beetroot Cup,' said Aubrey Williams.

The honeymoon will be spent at Uggely Parva.

Life With Father

John Mortimer

John Mortimer's father was an eminent and eccentric barrister. Although completely blind, he continued to practise at the bar and to take pleasure in unusual and, sometimes embarrassing, exploits ...

'Mr Justice Cunningham gave custody of the two children to the father. It was proved to his satisfaction that the mother went out to tea dances.'

'That's terrible!'

'Well, I was extremely angry at first. You never like to go down in a case, but you'll find this when you're at the bar. You'll have forgotten all about it by the time you slide the tape off your next brief.'

'I mean, it's terrible to lose your children, just for going to tea dances.'

'She went on her own, you see. I suppose the implication was, she danced with gigolos.'

'What's a gigolo?'

'I don't think,' my mother said, 'that's very suitable.'

'Mr Justice Cunningham didn't think it was suitable either.' My father shook his head sadly.

'That Judge sounds an absolute swine. He ought to be locked up. Taking away people's children. Just for dancing!'

'Mr Justice Cunningham is a hard man, old boy,' my father agreed. 'But it's just part of the rough and tumble in the Probate, Divorce and Admiralty Division. No real fun in winning if it's all too easy. You'll find that.'

'I'm not sure I want to. Go to the bar, I mean.'

'How is the viburnum fragrans, Kath? Paint me the picture.'

How many choices do we make in a lifetime? Even the selection of a wife or a lover is severely limited by the number of people of a vaguely appropriate age, sex and physical appearance you happen to meet at a given moment who may possibly fancy you, a field, as far as most marriages are concerned, of three or four possible candidates. If I had been born into one of those solidly conservative criminal families of London burglars I was later to defend, my career would have been mapped out for me by a father when he was home from the Nick. He would have planned an apprenticeship in Takings and Drivings Away, a little minor Warehouse Breaking and finally the responsibility of Look-out Man for a firm of bank robbers. Was my life decided when I was a child, bathed and put to bed by the wife of a lawyer's clerk, given bedtime stories from the Divorce Court? I could have chosen not to be a barrister, but every time my father changed the subject I remained on my predetermined path. If I'm still an agnostic on the subject of Free Will, it operates, I am sure, within the narrowest of limits. We spend our time punishing criminals or rewarding heroes, not for the great decisions they have taken for good or evil but for proceeding, with more or less dedication, in the direction in which they were pointed. At the time my father told me about the custody case and the *thé dansants* my cards had no doubt been dealt, a mixed hand adding up to a bid as a barrister and a writer. Flat-footed and tone deaf, the choice of becoming a second Jack Buchanan, deftly tip-tapping up to the footlights with a silver-topped cane twirling under my arm and a silk hat on the side of my head, was never mine.

'I think I'd like to be an actor.'

But my father had turned away, to examine the shrubs in my uncle's Sussex garden, a place full of ornamental ponds and stone walls and wrought-iron gates. Past the rhododendron walks stood the acres of woodland my uncle owned. My Uncle Harold, married to my mother's sister Daisy, was a manufacturer of beds. He was considerably richer than my father and his garden was consequently larger, equipped with waterfalls and even rarer shrubs.

'Not got any lilies out, Harold, have you?' my father asked, knowing that my uncle was deeply superstitious and dreaded the sight of a lily as a symbol of death. When he had his sight my father would try and steer my uncle under ladders or lure black cats across his path. In fact my father treated Uncle Harold with some condescension because he was so superstitious and had so much money.

We usually spent Christmas with Harold and Daisy. My mother drove the Morris Oxford away from our hills and clay soil and beech woods down to the flat, sandy, coniferous country with the ground covered with pine-needles and cones, to the bungalows filled with retired military men and the distant prospect of the sea. When I was young I was regularly sick at Guildford. My Uncle Harold's house was furnished with his expensive thirties' artefacts, white walls and a lot of blue and plum-coloured glass, chromium and mahogany. Bullrushes stood about in tall jars, and Lalique swans held the chocolates on the polished dinner-table. The house, always referred to by my father as the 'North Pole', was not overheated and my aunt had a sort of tweed overcoat made to match her dress for indoor wear. My Uncle Harold designed all his own clothes as he designed his furniture, with a slide-rule and to his own specifications. He wore wide-brimmed sombreros and had invented a sort of padded flap which hung down at the back of his waistcoat to keep his bottom warm. He was a meticulous man and appreciated conformity. At one breakfast he measured his rasher of bacon with his slide-rule and sent it back to the kitchen when he found it too long.

What I remember most clearly about my Uncle Harold's house was the bath water. By a prodigious feat of engineering and much use of the slide-rule he had harnessed a stream to his will. I remember sitting on the edge of the bath, about to climb into my first dinner-jacket for the entirely grown-up Christmas festivities, and turning on the tap. Nothing whatever happened for the first quarter of an hour. Then, on a clear day with the wind in the right direction, from a distant hillside you could hear the mechanical movements as of sluice gates opening. During the next thirty minutes water could be heard approaching and then a dense cloud of stream gushed from the pipe like a triumphant herald announcing the arrival of a thin brownish trickle which dripped disconsolately into a bath-tub which might have been personally designed for Tallulah Bankhead in the heyday of the Savoy Hotel.

On Christmas Day we would go round and deliver biscuit tins, on which were portrayed the unsmiling faces of King George V and Queen Mary, to the gardeners and woodmen in the cottages. On Boxing Day we went into Brighton, a magical place to me, where the trams were decorated with fairly lights and we had seats for the pantomime. My father always joined loudly in the food song, the words of which descended on a song-sheet from the flies, to embarrass the rest of the family.

'When my wife is on a diet
I daren't mention "Fry it"
Wifie would only be mad.'

'I do like a lovely blo-ater
And so do my mater and pater.'

We saw the Crazy Gang whose pale faces, battered hats and sudden cries filled me with unreasoning fear. I remember three black men, in white suits with belted jackets, who tap-danced in a way it was my ambition to achieve.

'What does John think,' my Uncle Harold said at dinner, shocked at the fact that I had wanted a checked sports coat and a silk tie for Christmas and not a catapult or a *Boy's Own Annual,* 'about the jackets of those Negro dancers? Does he admire the half-belt effect on the back, or was it a little too gigolo-like from a design point of view?'

'John's going to Harrow next term,' my mother told them with considerable amusement. 'He'll have to have a tailed coat there and a boater.'

And a silver-topped cane, I thought, for going to Lord's. I would use it, privately, to dance like Fred Astaire.

'They do roast the fags at Harrow, I suppose?' my father asked innocently. 'I don't know what I'm paying all that money out for unless you get roasted occasionally.'

'A great deal of money!' said my uncle. 'I must say, you don't do things by halves, Clifford.' He had been pained by my father's extravagance ever since he heard about a barrel of oysters his clerk had been sent out to buy in Fleet Street.

'I do like a lovely blo-ater.' My father put down his knife and fork and sang very loudly, 'And so do my mater and pater.'

'Whatever made you choose Harrow?' my Aunt Daisy interrupted him to ask. When it had vaguely occurred to my father that the time had come for me to go on to a public school Noah had immediately said 'Harrow', a choice for which he gave no sort of explanation. Which of the old boys of that school I wonder, did he think I might grow up to resemble? Lord Byron, Cardinal Manning, Winston Churchill or the Mayfair playboys who had recently been flogged in prison after a robbery with violence? My father had, in fact, no more chosen Harrow for me than he had chosen to spend Christmas with his superstitious brother-in-law or to suffer from glaucoma. These things happened in the mysterious cause of evolution and at the wayward direction of the Life Force, and that was that. Darwin could probably explain it all.

'When my wife is on a diet
I daren't mention "Fry it"
Wifie would only be mad.'

My father sang loudly, whilst the others peeled their peaches and tried to pretend that he wasn't happening.

The Joy of Mooching

S. J. Perelman

To Mombasa, Mogadishu, and Modesto I have been; to Montecatini, Montenegro, and Monaco; but never, wide-ranging *Wandervogel* though I pride myself on being, have I set foot in Monza. A town northeast of Milan and slightly northwest of Gorgonzola, on the road to Bergamo, Monza has as its chief industry, as far as I can make out, the export of curiosa to the world press. Here are born those strange and often lunatic fillers that piece out the news stories one reads, such as the paragraph that filtered into the *Times* a while ago: 'Monza, Italy (AP) – Ambrogio Bacis, 69 years old, does not like dentists, so to pull an aching tooth he fastened a cord to the tooth and the other end to an automobile bumper, and started the car. Mr Bacis's head collided with the bumper, and he wound up in the hospital, with the tooth still in his mouth.' To my way of thinking, the classical Tom Sawyer extraction – the silk thread tied to the bedstead, the hot coal brandished in the patient's face – remains unsurpassed in home dentistry, but obviously Bacis, in his anxiety to be up to date, opted for a fifteen-hundred-pound Imbroglio. Ah, well, *autres temps, autres mœurs*.

Another and even more seductive item emanating from Monza turned up in *The Jerusalem Post* recently; to wit: 'It must rank as one the strangest cocktail parties ever – and it was thrown by well-dressed Sebastiano Amara, of Monza, Italy, to boost sales of a book he's just published, *How to Make Begging Pay*. The suave author and man-about-town received his guests, doled out liberal Martinis, then begged to be excused. In a few minutes he returned – disguised as a crippled beggar, his face contorted with agony as he hobbled in on crutches. Guests in cars then followed 25-year-old Sebastiano to Monza's main shopping street, watched as he laid his crutches on the pavement and started weeping. In ten minutes he had collected the equivalent of $15. In his book he claims he never collected less than $100 a day, and says, "I did it as a part-time job, mainly for aesthetic pleasure, and only partly for pocket money."'

My initial response to Signor Amara's exploit was, I must confess, one of jealousy. Myself a suave author and man-about-town, I was piqued that I hadn't conceived so original a method of publicizing my own books. As envy subsided, though, one phrase of his kept pestering me like a caraway seed embedded in a tooth (a dental metaphor doubtless arising from Mr Bacis's predicament): that he had acted thus 'mainly for aesthetic pleasure'. Now, among various paragons on whom I have modelled myself from time to time – the Scarlet Pimpernel, the Earl of Rochester, Baruch Spinoza – one of the more influential was Des Esseintes, the hero of Joris Karl Huysmans' *Against the Grain*, who ceaselessly sought artistic stimulus in drugs, perfumes, and vice. Was it possible that this scribbler on the road to Bergamo had experienced in mendicancy a psychic release overlooked by Des Esseintes and me, deftly fattening his royalties meanwhile? Unimaginable, I told myself, but still I ought to lose no time in emulating him, and I fell to work.

As a neophyte in the world of beggary, I decided that the role best suited to me was traditional. Accordingly. I purchased a ragged shawl and a size-12 gingham dress from a pushcart on Rivington Street, and issued invitations to a half-dozen friends for cocktails at my hotel on Gramercy Park. At the height of the party, while my guests were feverishly consuming Martinis and bandying epigrams, I excused myself, retired to the bedroom, and transformed myself into a waif. The conversion was not wholly successful, as the little match girl in the fairy tale of Hans Christian Andersen is rarely depicted with a mustache, but nonetheless I resolved to brazen it out. To my gratification, the effect on the assemblage was volcanic. Everyone literally stood rooted to the floor.

'*Voyons!* A supreme master of illusion!' I heard people exclaiming. 'Another Lon Chaney! Can our eyes be deceiving us? In a few expert strokes, this *arbiter elegantiarum* has, as it were, metamorphosed himself into a vag.'

Like Sebastiano, I would have liked my intimates to follow me in their motors, but, as none of them owned any, I bade them go on drinking – a somewhat empty gesture, since the bottles were exhausted – and took my leave. Crossing to the south side of Gramercy Park, I stationed myself with my tray of matches outside The Players Club. The circumstances, I saw at once, were unpropitious. Ideally, it should have been snowing; instead, it was a hot, sultry evening, beckoning the passerby to Baskin-Robbins for an ice-cream cone rather than to contribute alms. After a while, a gentleman came out of the club, placing his feet with great deliberation, in the manner of one who has dined well on glazed Virginia ham with sweet potatoes.

'Please, sir, buy my matches,' I whined. 'Owing to a conspiracy among the reviewers, my latest book is already on the eighty-nine-cent table at Barnes & Noble. Have pity on me – don't let them recycle it. Also, I write by gaslight, and Consolidated Edison is threatening to cut off the gas. Support the arts, even if, as I suspect, you can barely support yourself.'

My prospect gaped at me incredulously and, muttering to himself, went back into the club. An ashen-haired model in three shades of denim, leading an ashen-haired borzoi, approached; as they neared me, the dog sat down growling and she pulled him past with an apologetic 'Sorry, he hates beggars' that at least certified that my disguise was valid. Then two character actors, their brows furrowed by unemployment, emerged from The Players. Sucking in my cheeks to stimulate the ravages of hunger, I bore down on them.

'"A benison, playgoers, a cornucopia! A feast for the intelligence!"' I snuffled. 'That is what the New York critics wrote about my last play – amateur rights now available from Samuel French, Incorporated. And how many scripts have they sold? Three lousy copies! How am I to sustain myself, to wield my pen in the tradition of Congreve, Sheridan, and Wilde, without your philanthropic assistance? Buy my vestas, I implore you.'

'Beat it, chump,' the elder of the pair countered roughly. 'Save those hard-luck stories for the Bowery. Write yourself a soap for Procter & Gamble, or go on relief, like the rest of us.'

Crestfallen and perspiring from the heat of the shawl, I shambled back to the hotel and sat down to rethink a modus operandi. Could it be, I asked myself, that the persona I had chosen was too depressing, the people would be more generous if the nature of my plight were bizarre or offbeat? To the fiery temperament, decision is consonant with action; in a trice I divested myself of my rags, slipped into a dinner jacket, and, faultlessly arrayed in black silk hose but no slippers, shot uptown in a taxi. Dismounting between two expensive Park Avenue apartments in the Sixties, I took up a stand near the canopy of the more opulent. Several cabs arrived bearing couples and parties, but I ignored them. At length, one discharged a jovial, fortyish individual with a worldly air, smoking a Perfecto. I accosted him furtively.

'Excuse me, friend, but I'm in a bit of a jam. Might we have a word?'

His eyes encompassed my garb, widened at my stockinged feet. 'What is it?'

'Well,' I confided, chuckling in hearty man-to-man fashion, 'the fact is, I was having a slap and a tickle with a certain married lady in this building whose identity must be protected at all costs. I mean, we're all human, what? As the fellow said, who's to cast the first stone?'

'Yes, yes,' he said impatiently. 'So her husband came home unexpectedly and you left just in the nick without your pumps. Where do I fit into this?'

'Wait. I was coming to that.' I swallowed. 'You see, I'm a writer by profession, and I'm supposed to autograph my new best-seller at Doubleday's for admirers, but I can't let them see me like this. Unfortunately, though, I forgot my wallet upstairs, too. If you could lend me the price of a new pair – '

He cut me short with a paternal hand on my sleeve. 'Shape up, brother,' he said. 'You're not a writer – you're a schmo. Anyone that leaves their shoes and their wallet in a lady's boudoir is a butterfingers. Take my advice – if you want to play Lothario, go join the Actors Studio.' He shook his head commiseratingly and melted into the foyer.

Dashed though I was by his rebuff, I was not minded to give up so easily, and I squared my jaw. Of the next two arrivals, the first rejected my appeal on the ground that no shoe stores were open at that hour; the second derisively demanded the name of my inamorata. In nineteen years' residence in the house, he said, he had yet to see a female worthy of pursuit. As if to make matters worse, it shortly came on to rain, and by the time I reached home in my wet socks I had such a cold that laryngologists skyed in from as far away as Mayo to study it.

During the long, slow convalescence that followed, I stewed over my inability to equal Sebastiano's receipts or to glean even a mite of aesthetic pleasure from the process. At last, I hit on the reason. The identities I had chosen, match girl and philanderer, were too foreign to my nature. Temperamentally a dreamer and a rover, I was trying to be a schnorrer, too, which was altogether alien, for *au fond* I was prouder than a Spanish hidalgo and would accept alms from no man. It was out of character – as if Lord Olivier were to impersonate Pecksniff and then pass the hat. Ergo, I must not dissemble; I must boldly admit myself a genius whose wares were unsalable, a drug on the market, and if that shamed an apathetic public into showering me with gold, I could with dignity accept my rightful due. Immediately a weight lifted from my shoulders. Donning the velvet jacket, Windsor tie, and beret I normally wear when writing, I hurried to the Marboro bookshop on West Eighth Street. Rapture – my suspicion was confirmed; and unsold pile of my most recent opus, reduced to fifty-nine cents, loomed up higher than a ziggurat. Folding my arms, I took up a position alongside it and waited to be pitied.

Half an hour passed and nobody appeared – not even a kleptomaniac. Finally, a heavily bearded man in a filthy Confederate tunic, who looked like Colonel Mosby but proved to be a youth of seventeen, materialized and asked the clerk for a primer on flagellation. A couple of teenagers with schoolbags came in, leafed through Eberhard and Phyllis Kronhausen's *Pornography and the Law*, and left, sniffing disappointedly. A stout yenta in picador dress but minus leather chaps exchanged a copy of Sara Kasdan's *Love and Knishes* for a poster of Donatello's David. With that, all activity halted, and I grew hot under the collar. My patience was ebbing fast.

'Hey, General Guderian, what gives here?' I queried the uniformed guard sporting a nightstick. 'Where are the browsers?'

'Nobody gets up before noon in the Village,' he said. 'Takes a while for the marijuana fumes to clear.'

In due course, the pace altered; shoppers, most of them somnambulists, started drifting through the aisles, languidly fingering the bargains and striving to read the erotica sealed in cellophane. Posed by my works, I assumed an expression at once dismal and haughty, insouciant yet despondent, that would have wrung the stoniest heart. But naught booted me, truth to tell, for as the illiterate swine neared my books their faces hardened and they sheared off, burying their noses in the fescennine pages of Harold Robbins and Irving Wallace. Resolved that those who had died for literature should not have fallen in vain, I determined to speak out.

'So the philistines have triumphed again, have they?' I began, raising my voice. 'What price now Kafka in his garret, Melville eking out his days as a customs inspector? Was it for this that Keats –'

Suddenly the words died in my throat; a Lincolnian figure I recognized as – or took to be – Philip Roth's had entered the door and was scanning the counters for remaindered copies of his books. He did not have to scan long, because adjacent to mine stood another ziggurat, even taller and likewise discounted, of *The Great American Novel*. In the same instant, his quick novelist's eye discerned what I was doing and he strode angrily toward me.

'Scab! Cut-rate fink!' he exploded. 'So this is how you dispose of your overstock, by appealing to the sentimental side of your non-readers!'

'For shame, mealymouth!' I flung back. 'Who are you to criticize? You were just sneaking in to push your own remainders. I at least was bent on deriving aesthetic pleasure from my humiliation.'

'Oho!' he jeered. 'Uncontent with being a dreamer and a rover, you're a masochist, too. My psychiatrist has an ugly name for that!'

'You don't say,' I returned, interested. 'What is it?'

'Well, I forget, actually,' he said, 'but I'll give you his phone number – you can ask him.'

'Gee, that's nice of you, Roth,' I said. 'Look here, I'd like to inscribe one of my books for you.'

'And I for you,' he said, doing so and handing it to me. 'Listen, if you're going uptown, why don't we split a cab? After all, between us we sold a couple of books this afternoon.'

And that, plus a talk we had about girls over a glass of tea at the Belmore Cafeteria, is the sum total of what I gleaned from patterning myself on the author of *How to Make Begging Pay*. Well, I hope his manual sells like hotcakes in Monza and never gets remaindered. Because if the silly beggar comes around to me for sympathy, I'll tell him a thing or two.

The Great Sea Saga of Photocopier III

Miles Kington

Reports received from on board Photocopier III, our entry in The Observer Transatlantic Boat Race.

June 9 Conditions are very difficult at the moment. In these Force 8 winds I find it extremely hard to type, as the motion of the boat often sends the carriage of the machine to the end of the line before I have started it. I have rigged up a temporary self-righting gear for it, but it breaks down two or three times a day.

I am also doubting the wisdom of taking an electric typewriter with us, as salt crystals are perpetually forming on the golf ball and I have to stop after every paragraph to remove them. In addition, the small generator which runs the typewriter broke down this morning, and only prompt action by 'Evoe' Knox-Johnston, my crew, got it going again. The next time I write the day-to-day account of a voyage like this, I think I shall prefer an old-fashioned manual machine. The photocopier, though, is working absolutely tremendously and there have been no problems at all.

The worse problem about a long sea voyage such as this, I think, is the lack of loneliness. I am constantly being interrupted by the crew with queries about navigation and the set of the sails, as they are called. He does not seem to realize that it is the captain's job to write a lucid, powerful and bestselling journal of the voyage, not to get bogged down in details which he is perfectly capable of working out for himself. How can I work out alternatives for clichés like 'towering waves' and 'scudding clouds' if people are always coming to me with moans about spinnakers being swept away? Next time I shall have a cabin with a lock.

This morning we sighted a waterlogged copy of a Naomi James paperback, presumably jettisoned by some other yacht. We left it in the water.

Two boxes of A4 paper were washed overboard last night but the other 92 are safe, thank God. I have given orders for it to be lashed more firmly, to avoid a repetition of this near-disaster.

The only craft we sighted today was a Liberian oil tanker going the other way. We tried to hail it in order to get them to take my first two completed chapters back to London, but they did not understand us and failed to stop. Neither of us speaks Liberian, unfortunately. I have given orders for photocopies of the chapters to be thrown overboard in the empty bottles so kindly provided for the purpose by the Scotch industry, in case the unthinkable should happen.

The bundles of last Sunday's *Observer* are safe in the hold, if a little damp. The management presumably knows best, but I cannot help thinking every time I look at them that it's hardly surprising the English Sunday papers get to New York so late.

June 16 Dawn in the Atlantic is a truly breathtaking spectacle, or so I am informed by my crew, 'Evoe' Knox-Johnston, who is always up at some unearthly hour crashing around on the deck upstairs with brooms and buckets and God knows what. As I have to be up very late in the evening correcting my typescript for my book, *Before Me The Ocean*, I find this totally lacking in any kind of consideration.

Back home in London there is a woman in the flat above me who gets up way before breakfast and makes a terrible racket with her cleaning, which is one of the reasons I came to sea in the first place. To find that even in mid-Atlantic I have the clatter of housework going on upstairs is almost more than I can bear. I am only thankful that 'Evoe' did not bring a vacuum cleaner.

Our morning routine changes little. At about nine Knox-Johnston brings me coffee in bed, and we work out the day's tasks. He looks after what little navigation and sailing there is to be done, while I try to get out of him whether it will be fine enough for me to type in the open, or whether I should stay in bed away from the elements. His forecasting is not always, I am afraid, very reliable.

Yesterday he assured me that it would stay dry until lunch, yet no sooner had he brought me elevenses in the cockpit than it came on to drizzle. Seeing the paper go to shreds as I type is bad enough; being put in mortal danger by sparks from my electric typewriter is altogether something else.

June 17 Today I find a terrible thing has happened. By now we should be entering warmer climes, with flying fish alongside and friendly dolphins basking near by. I asked Knox-Johnston if we would soon be near the Equator. To my amazement he said that not only were we not near the Equator, but that we should go nowhere near it on a transatlantic race.

'Transatlantic?' I said. 'But we are going round the world!' He then informed me with ill-concealed satisfaction that we were going no further than North America. I find this news incredible. How can one write a classic of the sea by merely popping across the Atlantic? These days the public will settle for nothing less than a circumnavigation, and by a woman if possible.

I have issued an ultimatum to Knox-Johnston to go right round the world, but he says nothing. I can, however, hear him muttering on deck to himself. I fear I may have a mutiny on my hands.

June 30 More mechanical trouble to report, I'm afraid. My job as captain – to write a best-selling account of the voyage entitled *Before Me The Ocean* – could not be done satisfactorily without a constant supply of hot coffee, and after much consultation with several loud round-the-world typists, I decided to install a constant percolating machine. I now think that was a mistake. In high winds the coffee slops over the top and burns on the electric element; the resultant noxious smell is hardly disguised by my Gauloises and I am driven up on deck where I am naturally sea-sick. Next time I shall take an electric kettle and a big tin of instant.

My crew, 'Evoe' Knox-Johnston, who spends most of the day and night idly at the helm, is a non-smoker. That probably explains why, when courteously asked to empty my ashtray, he tends to throw ash and tray overboard together. Luckily, I found a large brass ashtray screwed to the deck upstairs, which I have taken into my study and keep hidden from him.

Later. An interesting talk with 'Evoe'. It appears that his uncle was Mgr Ronnie Knox-Johnston, a member of the Crazy Gang.

Later still. I am worried about 'Evoe'. He stood behind me for two hours as I typed, then suddenly said: 'There are two r's in coruscating.' I went to look for my dictionary, but it was nowhere to be seen.

July 1 I retrieved a book from the sea which came floating past us. It was my dictionary. I firmly suspect 'Evoe' of having just thrown it overboard, but he denies it utterly. The ocean can do strange things to a man.

Later. Land! At last, after nearly three weeks, we are in sight of the end. The United States is a green, soft place, not at all full of sky-scrapers as I had been led to expect.

Even later. Having put ashore, we accosted a man working in the fields. 'Sure,' he said, 'this is not America at all, at all. This is the Emerald Isle. But keep going west and you can't be missing it.'

I berated 'Evoe' bitterly for his navigation, but he was recalcitrant. How could he be expected to steer straight, he wanted to know, if some idiot had removed the binnacle from the cockpit. I fail to understand what he means, unless he is referring to the simple transfer of a brass ashtray downstairs. I fear this may prove to be a long and arduous journey.

July 9 We have been becalmed off Ireland for several days now, so I would imagine that our chances of winning the race, even on handicap, are slim. But the weather is beautiful and the object is not to win but to write a book, so I am not unhappy.

I wish I could say the same for my crew, 'Evoe' Knox-Johnston. We both miss the morning papers very much, I as a writer because it means I have to get straight to work after breakfast, he because he needs the weather forecast and in the absence of a paper has to rely on a short-wave radio. This morning he picked up the news that 'Tiny' Rowland has been allowed to buy *The Observer*. Apparently the Monopolies Commission decided it was all right for him to sponsor *The Observer* Race, which now constitutes virtually the whole British naval deterrent. 'Evoe' is upset because, he says, Lonrho will insist on the Race starting from Africa in future and he is very subject to heat rash. Well, I have never met 'Tiny' Rowland but I am glad for him. Dwarfs have a hard enough time without the Monopolies Commission gunning for them.

'How's the book coming on, Thor Heyerdahl?' said 'Evoe' jokingly this morning. I could have hit him. Heyerdahl and Severin and that lot are not real writers. It's all very well building boats out of rice paper and proving that chefs could have sailed from Hong Kong to London in 1066, but what's the point if you take modern typewriters to write the book?

Of course, I have all the modern aids, but I also have below decks Susie, a goose, who keeps me supplied with quills. Only by using truly authentic writing tools can I prove that Tudor seamen could have written books during their voyage. So far, I have found that in some ways quill and parchment is superior to typewriting. If a wave breaks over a quill, you just shake the water off. If it breaks over the typewriter, you get a blinding flash and 300 volts coursing through you.

Later. 'Evoe' has some very interesting relations. He told me at dinner that he is the nephew of 'Groucho' Knox-Johnston, the wit and prelate. Apparently 'Groucho' was once offered a cardinal's hat but turned it down saying: 'I wouldn't believe in any god who was prepared to forgive me.'

'Evoe' is coming on as a cook. For dinner he served an extremely tasty casserole swimming in garlic and tomato. When I complemented him he said. 'Yes, usually they're too rich and oily, but this one was fine.'

Later still. I have just realized what he meant. I rushed downstairs, but Susie is no more. I instantly dismissed 'Evoe' from my service, but in mid-Atlantic this is harder than it sounds, and I have reluctantly reinstated him. I fear trouble lies ahead, though.

November 10 This is my first dispatch to you since July 9. To those of my readers who had given me up for lost, and to those of my sponsors who had given me up as unviable, may I just say this: I have been held totally incommunicado by my captors.

Yes. You have read correctly. For the last four months I have been in the hands of the Irish Secret Police. You may remember that on July 1, thanks to the total incompetence of my crew 'Evoe' Knox-Johnston, we made landfall on what I hoped would be in America but turned out to be Ireland, and were subsequently becalmed just off shore. A quarter of an hour after telephoning to *The Times* another instalment in my forthcoming book *Before Me The Ocean*, I was arrested and taken before two Irish policemen.

'So, it's a spy you are, is it?' said one roughly.

Appalled, I realized that they suspected me of the kind of activity that Russian submarines have recently popularized off Sweden.

'Certainly not,' I said. 'I am a writer aboard *Photocopier III*, sponsored by Wizzamatic the machine that solves *all* your office problems. Why not ask for a free demo ...'

'A *writer*, is it?' said the second policeman, cutting short my nautical explanation.

'By God, you're in trouble now. You'll soon wish you were a spy.'

Not ten minutes after he had made a hurried phone call, the door burst open and in walked the man I came to know as Flynn.

'Irish Secret Police,' he said, flashing a badge.

'Begob,' said one of the policemen. 'I never knew we had a Secret Police.'

'Sure,' said the second, 'and what would be the point of having one if people knew about it?'

'Out of here, you two stage Irishmen,' said Flynn angrily. 'Leave me to interrogate this man.'

I thought I would be ready for any kind of interrogation, being a writer and therefore used to lying. One lies mostly to publishers who ring up and ask questions like, 'How is the book coming along' or, 'How do you justify a further advance?' But Flynn put me through an ordeal which called on my deepest resources.

It seems that writers are allowed to live in Ireland tax-free, if permitted to enter. Those not permitted to enter often try to sneak into the country by small boat and go to ground. Flynn thought I was one of those. He therefore put me through a series of tests designed to see if I were a genuine writer or not.

He filled me full of Guinness, with a stopwatch in his hand.

He gave me five new novels and demanded a review within 24 hours.

He took me on all-night literary pub-crawls round Dublin.

He made me give ten reasons why I could have written *Ulysses* better than James Joyce.

He challenged me to get advances from five different publishers for the same book.

He got me to destroy the reputations of ten writers I secretly admired.

And after four months of this non-stop ruthless examination he declared that I would now be permitted to take up residence in Ireland. He was, I think, nonplussed for the first time when I declared that I wanted nothing of the sort and would sail straight on to New York, as soon as they had released Knox-Johnston.

'Oh, your fellow Knox-Johnston has been at liberty all this time,' he said. 'We never suspected him of authorship. He has many relations here, with whom he has been having a rare old time. Apparently his fore-fathers went over on the *Mayflower*.'

'That doesn't explain why he has relations here,' I said icily.

'Apparently they didn't like the look of the place and came straight back.'

So now I am ready to sail on, as soon as 'Evoe' has properly installed the cask of stout his relations insist on giving him. I shall not, I think, now win the race, but what a chapter in my book it will all make! Now for the open sea, at last.

April 7 One of the last things you expect to see in the southern Atlantic is a British submarine, so I and my crew, 'Evoe' Knox-Johnston, were taken aback when a huge sub emerged in front of us this morning. We knew it was British because of the Union Jack painted on the conning tower and 'Come On You Spurs!' scrawled on the side.

'I wonder if you could tell us the way to the Falkland Isles?' said the very polite officer who eventually appeared.

'Straight on,' I said.

'*Immer geradeaus,*' said Evoe.

The officer looked very curiously at Evoe. I thought it would take too long to explain that he has been learning German from the BBC World Service, and insisted on speaking nothing else before lunch; anyway, there were more important matters.

'Do you think you could pop over and have a look at our radio?' I said.

'Delighted, old boy.'

The trouble with the radio is that ever since we left Ireland four or five months ago it has been receiving but not transmitting, which explains why *Times* readers have not heard from me, nor have been told about our decision to give America a miss and go round the world. There are very few records left to break, and one of them is to be the first boat to go round the world during a transatlantic race.

Everything is going beautifully. The weather is so good that Evoe has given up wearing clothes and goes around with only a huge pair of field-glasses round his neck. He is the only man I know with a bathing suit mark in the middle of his chest.

'What's your business in the Falklands?' I said, when the man had fixed the radio for us. He put his finger to his lips, and looked round to see if anyone was listening.

'Very hush hush,' he said.

People go rather odd when they sign the Official Secrets Act, I find.

'My God, look at that!' he said suddenly. He had just noticed the Spurs graffiti on his sub.

'A bit bad form,' I said.

'It certainly is,' he said furiously. 'I'm a QPR supporter, always have been. Heads will roll for this. Well, goodbye.'

'*Hasta la vista,*' I said. He looked at me curiously before he, and then the sub, vanished. I suppose I ought to have explained that I have been learning Spanish from the BBC World Services. Evoe and I sometimes have long chats without a single word of English appearing.

'*Entonces,*' I said, 'let's make for the Falkland Isles and do some restocking. It'll be nice to spend an hour or two on shore in absolute peace and quiet. The Falklands must be the most off-the-beaten-track place possible for an undisturbed weekend. OK, *amigo?*'

'*Ausgezeichnet,*' says Evoe.

Our next report will be from the sleepy Falklands, then. *Hasta luego, mis lectors amados!*

April 14 I wish someone would explain to me what is going on.

As I reported last week, we had intended to put in at the Falkland Islands for a quiet weekend. There is nowhere quieter in the world than the Falklands, unless perhaps it's the Foreign Office at weekends, or so I was once told by a friend who works at the Foreign Office at weekends. (He works in the section which is trying to phase out what's left of the Empire – he himself is in charge of getting rid of the Falklands, though he says it's a hopeless task.)

Anyway, I was bowling along through the south Atlantic yesterday – my crew 'Evoe' Knox-Johnston, has the technical details if you're interested – when a huge aircraft carrier came out of nowhere, towards us. I was idly watching it through binoculars when to my amazement a plane took off from it, circled towards us and peppered the sea around us with what I can only imagine were bullets.

'What on earth was that?' said Evoe popping up from downstairs, where he'd been poring over what he calls charts, though they look just like maps to me.

'We're being attacked,' I said. 'Stand by to repel jet fighter aircraft.'

'Oh ha, bloody ha,' said Evoe. Then the plane did another sweep over us. 'I take it all back,' said Evoe. 'What do we do now?'

'As captain of this vessel,' I said importantly, 'I order you to take over and do what you think fit.'

Evoe immediately changed course to head straight for the aircraft carrier, explaining that the safest place is right next to it, where they can't attack you and often can't even see you. Soon we were close enough to see that it was called *Invincible*, which I guessed from my World Service Spanish lessons was Spanish for invincible. It was clearly an Argentinian ship.

'Leave this to me, Evoe,' I said, and in my best Spanish I announced through the loud-hailer that steam gives way to sail, and would he kindly move over. Somewhat to my surprise, we were answered in British through what sounded like a 20-ton disco system: 'This is a Battle Zone – Kindly Keep 200 Miles From Port Stanley!'

Five minutes later the ship was a smoking dot on the horizon, and we two, rather shaken, were discussing what it all might mean. Evoe was sure it was a British ship but I have a friend who works in the Admiralty at weekends, in the section which is trying to phase out the Navy, and I am sure we have nothing that big left.

'Well, somebody is at war with somebody, that's for sure, and we're in the middle of it,' said Evoe. 'If you ask me, Britain and Argentina are fighting each other, and that can mean only one thing: the World Cup has started.'

'There'll be trouble in the Middle East, mark my words,' I said. 'I have a friend who works in the Israeli army at weekends, and he says that whenever there's a big international hoo-ha such as Poland or Afghanistan, they always undertake some unnoticed offensive.'

'That, if I may say so, is neither here nor there. Look, the next ship that comes may take offence at being addressed in either Spanish or English, so let me use my German, OK?'

'How many Argentinians understand German, for heaven's sake?'

'More than you might think,' said Evoe mysteriously.

He got his chance sooner than we expected. Not two hours later a submarine surfaced silently beside us and three officers emerged on deck, though whether British or Latin American I could not tell. Evoe shouted to them in his best German that we came in peace, that we were unarmed and that nuclear power gave way to sail. The officers conferred, and then shouted back something also in German.

'Oh my God,' groaned Evoe. 'Sometimes I wish I'd never learned German.'

'Why, for heaven's sake?'

'It's an Israeli sub,' said Evoe. 'Apparently the war isn't hotting up as they'd like, and they've been sent to cause an incident.'

'What sort of incident?'

'As far as I can gather, they intend to blast us out of the water.'

I will relate the sequel to all this in my next dispatch. Meanwhile, as I think I may have said already, I wish someone would explain to me what is going on.

The Ceremonial Tasting of the First Potato

Caryl Brahms and S. J. Simon

It is Elizabethan England and intense excitement has been
caused by news of an exotic plant brought back from the
New World by Sir Walter Raleigh. A magnificent banquet
is organized to celebrate the first tasting and the hopes of
many rest upon its outcome ...

All over London there was only one topic of conversation. It was not the
unrest in Ireland – the public was tired of that. It was not the rebellion in
Scotland, for was not the Crown practically secured for their James VI, still
hiding in France in case it wasn't? It was not the rumour that Spain was
trying to build a new Armada. It was not that the plotting Walsingham had
over-reached himself in Holland – they had been waiting for that from the
moment they heard he went there. It was not even the whisper that Bacon,
having by skilled legal circumnavigation saved the Crown an annuity on a
citizen since beheaded, was going to get a Bed at last. No, it was none of
these things that had caused heads to nod, mouths to water and a crowd to
gather outside the Guildhall.

It was, in fact, the Ceremonial Tasting of the First Potato.

The entire capital was one vast stomach. It was rumoured that after the
Flower of England had been regaled, Sir Walter Raleigh was going to release
some supplies to the poor outside the gates. Optimists had even brought their
platters with them.

It would not be long now.

Since early morning idlers had been arriving in ones and twos, by afternoon
the trickle had become a torrent and now it had congealed into a rabble.

Even Gloriana's progress to Tilbury had hardly brought out a greater company.

In a candle-lit room in the Guildhall, before a great mirror, a famous figure was being arrayed and raised all hell about it.

'Where is my rouge pot?' called a querulous voice.

There was a patting-in of too high a colour, a wiping-off of too much cream, and a starting all over again.

'Fetch me my busks. Lace me into them. Not so tight, you fool!'

The servant fumbled.

'Fetch me my robe. Hurry, you sluggard!'

The servant scuttled into the cupboard. A pantoble followed him.

The figure before the mirror threw up its arms.

'Why does everyone conspire against my looking my best tonight?' it demanded of the frescoed ceiling.

The candles guttered.

The servant came timidly back with an embroidered garment over his arm.

'Not that one, you fool,' screamed the figure beside itself. 'My robe of Hercolas.'

The servant sighed. Only last week he had been a hauler of cannons for Philip Henslowe and here he was, promoted to be manservant to his son-in-law.

'My pantoble,' screamed Edward Alleyn. 'I've only got one on.'

Sighing heavily, the manservant went back into the cupboard. Promotion – yes, but he was not at all sure he was going to be able to hold this job down.

The door opened. Philip Henslowe came lovingly in. On his face was an encouraging smile and his whole bearing was redolent of an impresario's idea of a bedside manner. He looked at Edward Alleyn. His hands flew out in an ecstasy of admiration.

'Charming,' he said. 'Very charming.'

'I'm not dressed yet,' snapped Edward Alleyn. 'Can't find my pantoble. Hurry!' He cursed the wobbling behind that could be seen jutting out of the cupboard.

The behind wobbled more furiously.

'How are you feeling?' asked Henslowe, trying his hardest not to smile at the scene.

'Frightful,' said Edward Alleyn. 'Look at the material I have to put across tonight before the Flower of England and the Queen herself.'

'The Masque,' said Henslowe stiffly. 'Do not tell me that you are dissatisfied with that – it was at your request that I paid Master Jonson thirty shillings to devise it.'

Edward Alleyn waved the thirty shillings aside. 'Look at the supporting cast,' he grumbled.

Henslowe sought to change the subject. 'Burbage,' he said, 'would give his ears to play before the audience you will have tonight.'

'Burbage,' retorted Edward Alleyn sulkily, 'has a very nice new theatre.'

'He has no audience,' said Henslowe. 'It is too far for them to go. And the plague draws nearer and nearer to it. Only yesterday the Master of the Revels was telling me that if his returns do not improve he might have to consider taking away his patent.'

'Hold this candle,' said Edward Alleyn. 'I think my wig is awry.'

'Further,' said Philip Henslowe, holding up the candlestick, 'I have this day arranged with a gang of cut-throats to waylay and rob such hardy spirits as might venture on the journey to the Whitefriars Theatre. Take my word for it,' said Philip Henslowe complacently, 'Burbage is finished.'

The manservant emerged with a pantoble. Edward Alleyn slipped it on. He stood back. He wrapped the robe of Hercolas around him. He admired himself.

'How do I look?' he gloated.

Henslowe examined him.

'Marvellous,' he said. 'But your pantobles don't match.'

'How do I look?' asked Elizabeth of England.

Lady Meanwell looked at the bald head, the scraggy neck, the blackened teeth, the grim shoulder-blades.

'Wonderful,' she said.

Elizabeth of England picked up a pantoble and threw it at her.

'Fool,' she screamed, 'do you think you can deceive me with your sweet-tongued flattery? I know that I am an old hag, that none of you loves me, that you are all afraid.'

Lady Meanwell caught back a sob. She held out a whale-bone stomacher. 'See,' she said, 'the waist of a stripling lad.' She laced the Queen in.

Elizabeth of England smoothed her hips.

'Not bad, Meanwell,' she said. 'Not at all bad for a woman of – ah well, no matter.'

'And now for the cheeks,' said Lady Meanwell. Deftly she patted on the rouge. 'It is not every skin,' she admired, 'that can stand this exotic colour.'

Queen Elizabeth peered into the candle-lit mirror. 'You are right there, Meanwell,' she said. 'My colouring has always been good.'

'And now the frock,' said Lady Meanwell. 'White silk with pearls,' she fondled them, 'the size of beans – a present from your beloved pirate.'

'Ah, Drake,' said Queen Elizabeth. 'My thoughtful Drake. There, Meanwell, is one who really does love me. He shall have his victuals. I shall speak to Burghley tonight – or maybe tomorrow. Come, Meanwell, help me into it.'

'And now,' said Lady Meanwell some ten minutes later, 'the coiffure.'

'I am a little doubtful about this,' admitted Elizabeth. 'Is bright red really suitable, do you think?'

For once Lady Meanwell dared to speak the truth.

'Suitable, no, M'am,' she said. 'But entirely lovable.'

Queen Elizabeth patted her on the shoulder.

'Meanwell, you whore,' she said affectionately, 'you flatter me.'

Lady Meanwell turned away to pick up a pantoble. She was crying.

'How do I look?'

The Master of the Revels woke up with a jerk. Viola Compton, the lad's disguise discarded, was dancing round the room in skirts.

'Dear me,' said the Master of the Revels, 'you remind me of pretty little Kitty Howard the night Hal asked her to dance.'

Viola took off her pantoble and threatened him with it.

'I believe,' she said, 'you are as old as the devil himself.'

'Older,' said the Master of the Revels sadly. 'Much older.'

From the banqueting kitchens of the Guildhall arose a smell. A smell unlike any of the smells known to Londoners. And Londoners were connoisseurs of smells. It was a soggy smell, a flat and depressed smell, a smell that was trying to warn you not to expect too much.

The quick-witted in the crowd nudged one another.

'The potato,' they said. 'Delicious,' they added loyally.

Sir Philip Sidney riding into the courtyard turned to Sir Christopher Hatton.

'Do you smell anything, Kit?' he asked.

Sir Christopher Hatton sniffed. He shook his head. 'I have a cold,' he explained.

The crowd cheered. Sir Philip Sidney waved a hand. He was gone.

The crowd shifted to another foot and settled down to await the next comer.

Now the guests began to arrive more quickly, the flower of the land with their women-folk beside them. Drake came with Grenville, Leicester with the Earl of Surrey, and the Earl of Southampton, elegant and scowling and alone.

And now the crowd became jocular. For here, asked at the last moment, but assuring each other that no one would realize this, came the Bacon brothers.

'Greetings, Master Robert,' they shouted. 'How goes the law?'

'Greeting, Master Francis. How goes the bed?'

Sir Francis Bacon tried to look confident. It was a sorry effort. He essayed a cheerful smile.

But the crowd had lost interest in him. For here was old Father Burghley, who had England in his care and loved every mother's son of them, clad as usual in a cloak not one of them would be seen dead in. Beside him the Master of the Revels, by contrast, was a figure of splendour. As usual they were deep in conversation. What grave secrets of State occupied their attention?

'For my part,' Burghley was saying, 'I intend to bite my potato most carefully.'

But now the crowd took a deep breath. The Queen was coming.

First came the gentlemen, barons, earls, knights of the Garter, all richly dressed and bare-headed. Next came the Chancellor, bearing the seals in a red-silk purse, walking between two stalwarts, one of whom carried the Royal Sceptre, the other the sword of State, in a red scabbard studded with golden fleurs-de-lis, point upwards.

Next, borne high on a palanquin by ten bearded pirates, came Elizabeth of England, proud and glorious, surrounded by her attendants, twenty ladies of the Court, very handsome and well-shaped and dressed in white. The Queen's bosom was uncovered, as all the English ladies had it till they married, and she had on a necklace of exceedingly fine jewels. She had in her ears two pearls with very rich drops. She had red hair. Upon her head she had a small crown. She was dressed in white silk, bordered with pearls the size of beans, and over it a mantle of black silk, shot with silver threads; instead of a chain she had an oblong collar of gold and jewels.

What a Queen! How they loved her! How they would die for her!

The crowd let out a roar.

In his tiring room at the Guildhall, Edward Alleyn was fuming. He had put on his cloak of Hercolas four times and taken it off five and still the backing behind in the cupboard had been unable to produce his pantoble. True, he had produced a pair of fur-lined boots, an armoured knee-cap, and a warrant for the execution of ... with the name left blank, but none of these seemed to be quite suitable to adorn his other foot.

'Hurry,' fretted Edward Alleyn, 'or I shall be late for my first entrance.'

He need not have worried. Before a Prince of England, balanced on plots and surrounded by jealousies, conspiracies and the bitterly smarting Spain, could eat, there were certain ceremonials, founded on common sense and heavily disguised with Court regalia, to be observed – no matter how hungry the Monarch or how appetizing the tit-bit.

First a gentleman had entered the banqueting hall bearing a rod, and along with him another who had with him a small army bearing a giant table-runner, which, after they had all knelt three times with the utmost veneration, they spread on the long banqueting table and, after kneeling again, they all retired from the empty room.

Then came two others, one with a rod again, the other with a salt cellar, a plate and bread. This was for the Queen. When they had knelt as the others had done and placed what was brought upon the table they, too, retired with the same ceremonies as performed by the first.

With less ceremony, but quicker, an army of salt cellars appeared on the long table. These were for the Flower of England. It seemed unlikely that anyone should wish to poison them all and the seating order had been kept a secret, not so much for reasons of State, but because the hard-pressed Sir Walter had only just worked it out. He hoped it would turn out all right.

Last came an unmarried lady, we are told she was a countess, and with her a married one, we feel sure it was Lady Meanwell, bearing a tasting fork. The former was dressed in white silk, who, when she had prostrated herself three times in the most graceful manner, approached the table and rubbed the plate with bread and salt with as much awe as if the Queen had been present and not peering at her through the curtains.

When they had waited there a little while the Yeomen of the Guard entered, bare-headed and clothed in scarlet, with a golden rose upon their backs, bringing in at each turn a course of twenty-four dishes, served on plate most of it gilt – the Spanish galleon had sunk too quickly for Drake's pirates to salvage the lot.

These dishes were received by a gentleman in the same order as they were brought – he very seldom got muddled – and placed upon the table. Lady Meanwell gave to each of the guards a mouthful to eat of the particular dish he had brought for fear it should be poisoned. Lady Meanwell, who had a private feud, waited hopefully as the seventeenth guard from the left munched his tit-bit. She was ever hopeful when the seventeenth guard munched the Queen's dishes, but, as usual he obstinately remained alive.

During the time the guard, which consisted of the tallest and stoutest men that could be found in all England (being carefully selected for this service), were bringing dinner, twelve trumpets and two kettle-drums were making the hall ring for half an hour together. Through this heartening fanfare, the Flower of England, hungrily waiting in the ante-room, bawled small-talk at one another.

'I always say half an hour is too long,' shouted Burghley. 'Five minutes would be more than enough.'

'In Harry Tudor's time,' said the Master of the Revels, 'it was an hour and a half. Sometimes,' he remembered, 'Hal would get impatient and would pick up a fowl and start.'

'No manners,' said Burghley.

'Ah,' said the Master of the Revels, 'but a fine musician.'

The drums and trumpets modulated themselves into a boastful triumph.

Decoratively disposed about the ante-room, in attitudes originally learnt from posing to exigent painters, the Flower of England was chatting affably in loud tones.

The potato, exciting and unknown, was the main source of discussion, but one or two scandalous sidelines were developing quite promisingly.

'I wonder,' said Sir Philip, in a loud aside to the Earl of Southampton, 'what has happened to my Lord Essex?'

'He isn't coming,' announced the well-informed Master of the Revels.

'Essex isn't coming!' The news sped round the room. Heads nodded, knowing smiles flickered from face to face, and in the corner farthest from Gloriana winks were openly exchanged.

Essex was out of favour. Gloriana was definitely displeased with him.

As the trumpeters blew themselves into a martial air, everyone was busy passing on rumours.

'Scolded like a naughty boy!'

'Banished from Court!'

'No potato for him!'

'Answered her back!'

'Beheaded if he isn't careful.'

'She's confined him to his room,' the Master of the Revels told the sulking Earl of Southampton. 'Alone.'

The Earl of Southampton scowled heavily. He was very cross about this. He and Essex were the closest of friends. They had arranged to taste the potato together and later to compose sonnets to one another to commemorate the occasion. The Earl of Southampton had cheated slightly and commissioned his in advance. Even at this moment Will Shakespeare, invited by the Earl's influence to represent the Arts, was showing his gratitude by taking himself to a corner, ignoring the Flower of England milling around and staring with concentrated intensity at a piece of parchment. The Earl of Southampton hoped that the blare of the trumpets would not disturb the imagery of the final couplet.

He need not have worried. The milling of the aristocracy and the roll of the kettle-drums were sheer seclusion to Shakespeare accustomed to working in repertory. Besides, the sheet at which he was staring was headed:

'*Love's Labour Won*. Act I. Scene I. A Banqueting Hall. Blare of Trumpets.'

'Gloriana,' said the Earl of Southampton, after a hurried glance to make certain she was nowhere near him, 'is intolerable. It is never safe these days to make a private engagement for fear of State displeasure. I had arranged to sing madrigals with Essex tonight after this bear fight was over,' he finished wistfully.

'You should concentrate on a tenor less high in the Queen's favour,' said Sir Philip Sidney blandly. 'Master Bacon, for instance,' he suggested.

'He is a treble,' said the Earl of Southampton stiffly.

The trumpets embarked on a new composition by Master Purcell. One of them developed a wobble. The Flower of England were too finely mannered to notice this, but from the ladies of the Court came a giggle.

The Queen turned and eyed them sharply. The Compton chit, of course!

Her anger vanished. She smiled happily to herself. What a cunning old bitch she was. She had silenced the ugly rumours of jealousy and spite that Viola's absence from Court could not fail to cause by producing her for this great occasion, but she had safeguarded herself by sending Essex out. She cackled. Poor Robert Devereux – how bewildered he had looked! But it would do the Lordling no harm to spend an evening in meditation. No doubt he would pen a sonnet to her.

She warmed to the thought.

'How well the Compton chit looks tonight,' she told Lady Meanwell.

'Her rest in the country has done her good,' said Burghley tactfully.

'It is a pleasure to have her with us again,' said Francis Drake, smoothing his beard.

'Make the most of it,' snapped the Queen. 'The wench leaves tomorrow.' She spat.

'Ah,' said Burghley. He changed the subject. 'Raleigh is very late.'

Raleigh, indeed, was very late. It was a matter of comment throughout the whole hungry room. Some, in fact, were in favour of starting without him.

'Doubtless,' sneered Bacon, 'he is standing in front of a mirror admiring himself in his new cloak.'

Standing in front of a mirror, wrapped in a cloak, trying to subdue his fretfulness and his fuming by the sustaining image of his reflection, stood a commanding figure. It had a beautiful silky wig, a pistol and a prompt copy, but its pantobles did not match.

The backing behind undoubled itself and hopefully offered a Venice goblet.

'Look what I've found,' he said.

Edward Alleyn threw it at him.

'I hear,' said Philip Sidney, 'he brought it from a sailor, and the material is of a shade and texture never before seen in this great kingdom.'

'He can carry his cloak,' admitted the Earl of Southampton, as one wearer of cloaks to another. With a motion of his shoulders he displayed his own gold brocade and looked meaningly at Burghley.

Burghley twitched peevishly at his mildewed emerald velvet. No help for it – he would have to get it re-lined.

'There is no one in the land can wear a cloak better than Raleigh,' acknowledged Sidney handsomely. 'I am looking forward to seeing his new one – I admit it.'

'It is no small accomplishment to wear a cloak with an air,' said the Master of the Revels profoundly. 'How many royal princes have there been who could do it? Hal Eight.' He began to count them on his fingers. 'Richard of Bordeaux. Ethelred the Unready.' He babbled himself into silence.

For in the doorway stood Sir Walter Raleigh.

His hat was plumed. His breeches took your breath away. His pantobles matched perfectly. But his cloak – his magnificent cloak – was a pale, drained, shrunken beetroot with the dye in runnels.

Lord Burghley might have come in out of the rain in it.

The Flower of England was silent. No one quite knew what to say as he hastened to the side of Elizabeth to make his apologies.

But Elizabeth of England had no manners. She slapped her knees in unholy glee.

'Your cloak, Walter,' she cackled. 'What's happened to your cloak?'

Raleigh breathed heavily.

'They boiled it,' he said.

To Elizabethan England all was clear. It might have happened to any one of them. Raleigh's tailor had gone down with the plague.

Unlucky!

'Poor Walter,' said Queen Elizabeth. 'Never mind, you shall sit beside me and teach me how to eat the potato.'

Tears came into Sir Walter Raleigh's eyes. His Queen had understood his tragedy. He knelt and kissed her hand.

'It would have been such a lovely cloak,' he murmured sadly.

Sir Walter Raleigh had planned his banquet with an eye for dramatic effect. Naturally it must consist of the two classic great courses – the problem facing him, therefore, was where he could most effectively serve his fascinating new root. After deep deliberation, and much putting in and taking out again, he had decided to serve it, dramatically but quite simply, between the two great courses.

At the moment a regiment of waiting men were bearing in the first course. This ran along the traditional lines of costly viands and in Henslowe's diary would have been entered as follows:

Banquette fore to taste th Poetatoe per hedde.

1st Course

	s.	d.
Caviare	1	1
Cheate and mancheate	0	8
Bere and ale	0	10½
Wine	3	6
Mutton boylde	1	0
Capon gr. boylde	2	0
Chickens boylde	1	2
Larks boylde	0	9
Partridges boylde	1	8
Mutton Pr.	0	7
Beafe boylde	6	8
Beafe boylde dim surloyne	1	8
Signett	7	0
Capon gr.	4	0
Veale	5	0
Mutton for allower	1	0
Chines of beafe rost	2	0
Cocks	3	6
Chickens	2	7½
Plovers	3	9
Veale pies	2	6
Custird	1	4

'Personally,' said Burghley, waving aside a boylde signett and a veale pie and helping himself delicately to boylde lark, 'I shall bite my potato most carefully and I advise you, my Lord Leicester, to do the same.'

'Tcha,' said the Earl of Leicester. He reached out and grabbed a connye.

From her position as maid of honour Viola could see Master Will quite clearly. He seemed abstracted but not a bit overawed, and he did not snatch or grab at the dishes as they circulated past him. She must tell him that this would never do at Court, where you would never get anything to eat at all if you merely waited for it to arrive. Suddenly she remembered her frock, her position, her duties, her secret. He must not recognize her here. She tried to shrink behind Lady Meanwell. It was like a sparrow hiding behind an angry pigeon.

Shakespeare was looking at her with a deep reflective look. Would the potato taste like an apricok? he was wondering.

Always thinking of his art, thought Viola. She must tell him if you thought about your art at Court you would never get anything to eat.

The Master of the Revels was helping himself largely from a dish of caviare. He was fond of caviare; he could remember the first time it had been served in England and they had put sugar on it, poor souls.

'Ah,' he said, and swallowed a large spoonful. 'Leicester,' he called, 'pass the cream.'

'What are you eating?' called the Earl of Leicester.

'The roe of the sturgeon,' said the Master of the Revels. 'Delicious.' He poured cream over the plate and stirred vigorously.

The Earl of Leicester looked puzzled.

'Try some,' said the Master of the Revels. He hailed a serving man and handed him the plate he had so carefully prepared.

'Caviare,' he said. 'To the General.'

Shakespeare looked up. The Master of the Revels wagged a finger at him.

'Now, now,' he said. 'No quotations.'

Shakespeare blushed. He put away his pencil.

At the head of the table Queen Elizabeth laid down the skeleton of a chicken and slapped her thighs.

'And that reminds me, Raleigh,' she said. 'Are you good at riddles?'

'Well,' said Raleigh cautiously.

'What is it,' asked Elizabeth of England, 'that stands on the roof at midnight and crows like a cock?'

Beads of sweat stood out on Raleigh's brow. If he didn't guess right it might cost him a monopoly.

He concentrated.

In the tiring room the wobbling behind came up with a suggestion.

'How would it be,' he asked, 'if I went back and brought another pair of pantobles from your wardrobe?'

An idea, by God!

'Post haste,' said Edward Alleyn.

The wobbling behind streaked away.

And now the great moment had come. The remnants of the first course had been carried off, and the clean plates placed carefully before each guest with an implement to match, and the chef had taken up his position in the doorway, staggering under an enormous tray.

He was doomed to stagger for a long time, for before the tray could be triumphantly trundled in the Master of the Revels had to make a speech.

He had promised Raleigh faithfully that, on this occasion, he would try to remember not to remember too much. But somehow or other, after a brisk and confident start, he found himself remembering the new French chef at the marriage feast of Anne of Cleves.

'Polonius,' said Elizabeth warningly.

The Master of the Revels pulled himself together.

'Um, ah,' he said guiltily. 'What was it I stood up to tell you? Ah, yes.'

From his pocket he pulled out a sheet of parchment.

'I have here,' he said, 'some verses written by the Earl of Essex.'

Elizabeth of England sighed. She settled herself more comfortably.

The Master of the Revels unrolled his parchment. He studied it. He put his head on one side.

' 'Tis good,' he said. ' 'Tis very good.'

'Read it, you fool,' said Elizabeth of England.

The Master of the Revels read.

> 'Happy were he could furnish forth his fate
> In some unhaunted desert, most obscure
> From all societies, from love and hate
> Of worldly folk; then might he sleep secure;
> Then wake again and give God ever praise,
> Content with hips and haws and bramble-berry;
> In contemplation spending all his days,
> And change of holy thought to make him merry,
> Then, when he dies, his tomb may be a bush
> Where harmless robin dwells with gentle thrush.'

Elizabeth of England was weeping. ' 'Tis piteous,' she said.

She wiped her eyes. 'Bring on the potatoes,' she ordered.

The Flower of England was looking at its plates with a mixture of doubt tinged with awe. In front of each one of them lay a soggy island of white mush, shaped rather like a warped egg, only larger.

The potato!

This was it!

'Well, well, well,' said the Master of the Revels, in a resigned voice.

Sir Philip Sidney would not permit his doubts to show on his face. He was making up his mind not to let old Walter down. 'Delicious,' he was going to say, whatever it tasted like.

The Earl of Southampton picked his up and experimented. The potato turned over quite easily, and seemed to be the same on the other side.

In spite of the evidence of his eyes, Burghley showed no relaxation of his vigilance. He had picked up a knife, and was pricking delicately.

'I shall bite it most carefully,' he asserted stubbornly.

But Elizabeth of England showed no such daintiness. Forthright and purposeful, she dug her spoon into the potato, collected half of it, and carried it firmly to her mouth.

The Flower of England waited.

Sir Walter Raleigh gripped his seat under the table. He had sailed halfway round the world to find this root, he had faced great perils to bring it back, he had withstood the blandishments of the most expert cajolers at Court, and had not even hinted at the secret of its flavour, he had changed his chef six times, and now Elizabeth of England was tasting it.

He looked at her.

Elizabeth of England spat.

'Not enough salt,' she said

In the tiring room Edward Alleyn was doing a one-footed morris of impatience. If his servant did not return with those pantobles inside one hundred and sixty hops he'd scream the Guildhall down. Already the muscles of his throat were tightening.

The door opened. The wobbling behind trundled in, his hands coyly folded behind him.

'I've got it,' he panted triumphantly.

'Good,' said Edward Alleyn, and held out a foot.

Beaming all over his face, the wobbling behind produced a soggy island of white mush shaped rather like a warped egg, only larger.

'The potato,' he said ecstatically. 'I got one for you.'

Edward Alleyn scooped it up and threw it at him.

Outside the Guildhall the rabble was fast becoming festive. The bright lights of candles twinkling out at them through the windows fired their imagination. The snatches of gay music and the glimpses of famous faces as the dance swung them past the casements tempted them to shuffle clumsily themselves. Great barrels of ale, set out by the benevolent Sir Walter, and now empty, had quenched their thirst, and since it was so late already – let it get later.

A hefty fellow had tilted over one of the great barrels, hoping in vain to squeeze out another drop. The crowd gathered round him and shouted encouragement, and some sailors helped him along with a hauling song.

Soon the crowd had picked up the chorus and, when they had tired of this and the hefty fellow had gone thirsty away, they sang snatches to one another till the City rang with their hearty voices and put the lute boys inside the Guildhall out of time.

Till suddenly there was an ill-tempered slam of the Guildhall great door and Sir Walter Raleigh came striding out.

A reveller detached himself from the crowd and came staggering towards him. He doffed his cap and essayed a bow.

'How does it go?' he asked, as one host to another.

Sir Walter Raleigh looked at him.

'Not enough salt,' he said bitterly, and strode into the night.

Ride With Olympy

James Thurber

Olympy Sementzoff called me '*Monsieur*' because I was the master of the
Villa Tamisier and he was the gardener, the Russian husband of the French
caretaker, Maria. I called him '*Monsieur*', too, because I could never learn
to call any man Olympy and because there was a wistful air of *ancien régime*
about him. He drank Bénédictine with me and smoked my cigarettes; he
also, as you will see, drove my car. We conversed in French, a language alien
to both of us, but more alien to me than to him. He said '*gauche*' for both
'right' and 'left' when he was upset, but when I was upset I was capable of
flights that put the French people on their guard, wide-eyed and wary. Once,
for instance, when I cut my wrist on a piece of glass I ran into the lobby of
a hotel shouting in French, 'I am sick with a knife!' Olympy would have
known what to say (except that it would have been his left wrist in any case)
but he wouldn't have shouted: his words ran softly together and sounded
something like the burbling of water over stones. Often I did not know what
he was talking about; rarely did he know what I was talking about. There
was a misty, faraway quality about this relationship, in French, of Russia
and Ohio. The fact that the accident Olympy and I were involved in fell
short of catastrophe was, in view of everything, something of a miracle.

Olympy and Maria 'came with' the villa my wife and I rented on Cap
d'Antibes. Maria was a deep-bosomed, large-waisted woman, as persistently
pleasant as Riviera weather in a good season; no mistral ever blew in the
even climate of her temperament. She must have been more than forty-five
but she was as strong as a root; once when I had trouble getting a tough
cork out of a wine bottle she took hold and whisked it out as if it had been
a maidenhair fern. On Sundays her son came over from the barracks in
Antibes and we all had a glass of white Bordeaux together, sometimes the
Sementzoffs' wine, sometimes our own. Her son was eighteen and a member
of the Sixth Regiment of Chasseurs Alpins, a tall, somber boy, handsome in

his uniform and cape. He was an *enfant du premier lit*, as the French say. Maria made her first bed with a sergeant of the army who was *cordonnier* for his regiment during the war and seemed somehow to have laid by quite a little money. After the war the sergeant-shoemaker resigned from the army, put his money in investments of some profoundly mysterious nature in Indo-China, and lost it all. '*Il est mort*,' Maria told us, '*de chagrin.*' Grief over his ill-fortune brought on a decline; the *chagrin*, Maria said, finally reached his brain, and he died at the age of thirty-eight. Maria had to sell their house to pay the taxes, and go to work.

Olympy Sementzoff, Maria's second husband, was shy, not very tall, and wore a beard; in his working clothes you didn't notice much more than that. When he was dressed for Sunday – he wore a fine double-breasted jacket – you observed that his mouth was sensitive, his eyes attractively sad, and that he wore his shyness with a certain air. He worked in a boat factory over near Cannes – Maria said that he was a *spécialiste de bateaux*; odd jobs about the villa grounds he did on his off days. It was scarcely light when he got up in the morning, for he had to be at work at seven; it was almost dark when he got home. He was paid an incredibly small amount for what he did at the factory and a handful of sous each month for what he did about the grounds. When I gave him a hundred francs for some work he had done for me in the house – he could repair anything from a drain to a watch – he said, '*Oh, monsieur, c'est trop!*' '*Mais non, monsieur*,' said I. '*Ce n'est pas beaucoup.*' He took it finally, after an exchange of bows and compliments.

The elderly wife of the Frenchman from whom we rented the villa told us, in a dark whisper, that Olympy was a White Russian and that there was perhaps a *petit mystère* about him, but we figured this as her own fanciful bourgeois alarm. Maria did not make a mystery out of her husband. There was the Revolution, most of Olympy's brothers and sisters were killed – one knew how that was – and he escaped. He was, of course, an exile and must not go back. If she knew just who he was in Russia and what he had done, she didn't make it very clear. He was in Russia and he escaped; she had married him thirteen years before; *et puis, voilà!* It would have been nice to believe that there was the blood of the Czars in Olympy, but if there was anything to the ancient legend that all the stray members of the Imperial House took easily and naturally to driving a taxi, that let Olympy out. He was not a born chauffeur, as I found out the day I came back from our automobile ride on foot and – unhappily for Maria – alone.

Olympy Sementzoff rode to and from his work in one of those bastard agglomerations of wheels, motor and superstructure that one saw only in France. It looked at first glance like the cockpit of a cracked-up plane. Then you saw that there were two wheels in front and a single wheel in back. Except for the engine – which Maria said was a 'Morgan *moteur*' – and the wheels and tires, it was handmade. Olympy's boss at the boat factory had made most of it, but Olympy himself had put on the *ailes*, or fenders, which were made of some kind of wood. The strange canopy that served as a top was Maria's proud handiwork; it seemed to have been made of canvas and kitchen aprons. The thing had a right-hand drive. When the *conducteur* was in his seat he was very low to the ground: you had to bend down to talk to him. There was a small space beside the driver in which another person could sit, or crouch. The whole affair was not much larger than an overturned cabinet victrola. It got bouncingly under way with all the racket of a dog fight and in full swing was capable of perhaps thirty miles an hour. The contraption had cost Olympy three thousand francs, or about a hundred dollars. He had driven it for three years and was hand in glove with its mysterious mechanism. The gadgets on the dash and on the floorboard, which he pulled or pushed to make the thing go, seemed to include fire tongs, spoons, and doorknobs. Maria miraculously managed to squeeze into the seat beside the driver in an emergency, but I could understand why she didn't want to drive to the Nice Carnival in the 'Morgan'. It was because she didn't that I suggested Olympy should take her over one day in my Ford sedan. Maria had given us to understand that her *mari* could drive any car – he could be a chauffeur if he wanted to, a *bon* chauffeur. All I would have to do, *voyez-vous*, was to take Olympy for a turn around the Cap so that he could get the hang of the big car. Thus it was that one day after lunch we set off.

Half a mile out of Antibes on the shore road, I stopped the car and changed places with Olympy, letting the engine run. Leaning forward, he took a tense grip on a steering wheel much larger than he was used to and too far away from him. I could see that he was nervous. He put his foot on the clutch, tentatively, and said, '*Embrayage?*' He had me there. My knowledge of French automotive terms is inadequate and volatile. I was forced to say I didn't know. I couldn't remember the word for clutch in any of the three languages, French, Italian and German, in which it was given in my 'Motorist's Guide' (which was back at the villa). Somehow '*embrayage*' didn't sound right for clutch (it is, though). I knew it wouldn't do any good for an American writer to explain in French to a Russian boat specialist the purpose that particular pedal served; furthermore, I didn't really know. I compromised by putting my left foot on the brake. '*Frein,*' I said. '*Ah,*' said Olympy, unhappily. This method of indicating what something might be by demonstrating what it wasn't had a disturbing effect. I shifted my foot to the accelerator – or rather pointed my toe at it – and suddenly the word for that, even the French for gasoline, left me. I was growing a little nervous myself. '*Benzina,*' I said, in Italian finally. '*Ah?*' said Olympy. Whereas we had been one remove from reality to begin with, we were now two, or perhaps three, removes. A polyglot approach to the fine precision of a gas engine is roundabout and dangerous. We both lost a little confidence in each other. I suppose we should have given up right then, but we didn't.

Olympy decided the extra pedal was the *embrayage*, shifted into low from neutral, and the next thing I knew we were making a series of short forward bounds like a rabbit leaping out of a wheat field to see where he is. This form of locomotion takes a lot out of man and car. The engine complained in loud, rhythmic whines. And then Olympy somehow got his left foot on the starter and there was a familiar undertone of protest; this set his right foot to palpitating on the accelerator and the rabbit-jumps increased in scope. Abandoning my search for the word for starter, I grabbed his left knee and shouted '*Ça commence!*' Just what was commencing Olympy naturally couldn't figure – probably some habitual and ominous idiosyncrasy of the machinery. He gave me a quick, pale look. I shut off the ignition, and we discussed the starter situation, breathing a little heavily. He understood what it was finally, and presently we were lurching ahead again, Olympy holding her in low gear, like a wrestler in a clinch, afraid to risk shifting into second. He tried it at last and with a jamming jolt and a roar we went into reverse: the car writhed like a tortured leopard and the engine quit.

I was puzzled and scared, and so was Olympy. Only a foolish pride in masculine fortitude kept us going. I showed him the little jog to the right you have to make to shift into second and he started the engine and we were off again, jolting and lurching. He made the shift, finally, with a noise like lightning striking a foundry – and veered swoopingly to the right. We barely missed a series of staunch granite blocks, set in concrete, that mark ditches and soft shoulders. We whisked past a pole. The leaves of a vine hanging on a wall slapped at me through the window. My voice left me. I was fascinated and paralyzed by the swift passes disaster was making at my head. At length I was able to grope blindly toward the ignition switch, but got my wrist on the klaxon button. When I jerked my arm away, Olympy began obediently sounding the horn. We were riding on the edge of a ditch. I managed somehow to shut off the ignition and we rolled to a stop. Olympy, unused to a left-hand drive, had forgotten there was a large portion of the car to his right, with me in it. I told him, *'A gauche, à gauche, toujours à gauche!'* *'Ah,'* said Olympy, but there was no comprehension in him. I could see he didn't know we had been up against the vines of villa walls: intent on the dark problem of gearshifting, he had been oblivious of where the car and I had been. There was a glint in his eye now. He was determined to get the thing into high on his next attempt; we had come about half a mile in the lower gears.

The road curved downhill as it passed Eden Roc and it was here that an elderly English couple, unaware of the fact that hell was loose on the highway, were walking. Olympy was in second again, leaning forward like a racing bicycle rider. I shouted at him to look out, he said *'Oui'* – and we grazed the old man and his wife. I glanced back in horror: they were staring at us, mouths and eyes wide, unable to move or make a sound. Olympy raced on to a new peril: a descending hairpin curve, which he negotiated in some far-fetched manner, with me hanging onto the emergency brake. The road straightened out, I let go the brake, and Olympy slammed into high with the desperate gesture of a man trying to clap his hat over a poised butterfly. We began to whiz: Olympy hadn't counted on a fast pickup. He whirled around a car in front of us with a foot to spare. *'Lentement!'* I shouted, and then *'Gauche!'* as I began to get again the whimper of poles and walls in my ears. *'Ça va mieux, maintenant,'* said Olympy, quietly. A wild thought ran through my head that maybe this was the way they used to drive in Russia in the old days.

Ahead of us now was one of the most treacherous curves on the Cap. The road narrowed and bent, like a croquet wicket, around a high stone wall that shut off your view of what was coming. What was coming was usually on the wrong side of the road, so it wouldn't do to shout *'Gauche!'* now. We made the turn all right. There was a car coming, but it was well over on its own side. Olympy apparently didn't think so. He whirled the wheel to the right, didn't take up the play fast enough in whirling it back, and there was a tremendous banging crash, like a bronze monument falling. I had a glimpse of Olympy's right hand waving around like the hand of a man hunting for something under a table. I didn't know what his feet were doing. We were still moving, heavily, with a ripping noise and a loud roar. *'Poussez le phare!'* I shouted, which means 'push the headlight!' *'Ah-h-h-h,'* said Olympy. I shut off the ignition and pulled on the hand brake, but we had already stopped. We got out and looked at the pole we had sideswiped and at the car. The right front fender was crumpled and torn and the right back one banged up, but nothing else had been hurt. Olympy's face was so stricken when he looked at me that I felt I had to cheer him up. '*Il fait beau*,' I announced, which is to say that the weather is fine. It was all I could think of.

I started for a garage that Olympy knew about. At the first street we came to he said '*Gauche*' and I turned left. '*Ah, non*,' said Olympy. '*Gauche*,' and he pointed the other way. 'You mean *droit*?' I asked, just that way. '*Ah!*' said Olympy. '*C'est bien ça!*' It was as if he had thought of something he hadn't been able to remember for days. That explained a great deal.

I left Olympy and the car at the garage; he said he would walk back. One of the garage men drove me into Juan-les-Pins and I walked home from there – and into a look of wild dismay in Maria's eyes. I hadn't thought about that: she had seen us drive away together and here I was, alone. '*Où est votre mari?*' I asked her, hurriedly. It was something of a failure as a reassuring beginning. I had taken the question out of her own mouth, so I answered it. 'He has gone for a walk,' I told her. Then I tried to say that her husband was *bon*, but I pronounced it *beau*, so that what I actually said was that her husband was handsome. She must have figured that he was not only dead but laid out. There was a *mauvais quart d'heure* for both of us before the drooping figure of Olympy finally appeared. He explained sadly to Maria that the mechanism of the Ford is strange and curious compared to the mechanism of the Morgan. I agreed with him. Of course, he protested, he would pay for the repairs to the car, but Maria and I both put down that suggestion. Maria's idea of my work was that I was paid by the City of New York and enjoyed a tremendous allowance. Olympy got forty francs a day at the boat factory.

That night, at dinner, Maria told us that her *mari* was pacing up and down in their little bedroom at the rear of the house. He was in a state. I didn't want an attack of *chagrin* to come on him as it had on the *cordonnier* and perhaps reach his brain. When Maria was ready to go we gave her a a handful of cigarettes for Olympy and a glass of Bénédictine. The next day, at dawn, I hear the familiar *tintamarre* and *hurlement* and *brouhaha* of Olympy's wonderful contraption getting under way once more. He was off to the boat factory and his forty francs a day, his dollar and thirty cents. It would have cost him two weeks' salary to pay for the fenders, but he would have managed it somehow. When I went down to breakfast, Maria came in from the kitchen

with a large volume, well fingered and full of loose pages, which she handed
to me. It was called *Le Musée d'Art* and subtitled *Galerie des Chefs-d'oeuvre et
Précis de l'Histoire de l'Art au XIXᵉ Siècle, en France et à l'Etranger (1000 gravures,
58 planches hors texte)*. A present to *Monsieur* from Olympy Sementzoff, with
his compliments. The incident of the automobile was thus properly rounded
off with an exchange of presents: cigarettes, Bénédictine, and *Le Musée d'Art*.
It seemed to me the way such things should always end, but perhaps Olympy
and I were ahead of our day – or behind it.

The Love-Philtre Of Ikey Schoenstein

O. Henry

The Blue Light Drug Store is downtown, between the Bowery and First Avenue, where the distance between the two streets is the shortest. The Blue Light does not consider that pharmacy is a thing of bric-à-brac, scent and ice-cream soda. If you ask it for pain-killer it will not give you a bonbon.

The Blue Light scorns the labor-saving arts of modern pharmacy. It macerates its opium and percolates its own laudanum and paregoric. To this day pills are made behind its tall prescription desk – pills rolled out on its own pill-tile, divided with a spatula, rolled with the finger and thumb, dusted with calcined magnesia and delivered in little round pasteboard pill-boxes. The store is on a corner about which coveys of ragged-plumed, hilarious children play and become candidates for the cough drops and soothing syrups that wait for them inside.

Ikey Schoenstein was the night clerk of the Blue Light and the friend of his customers. Thus it is on the East Side, where the heart of pharmacy is not glacé. There, as it should be, the druggist is a counsellor, a confessor, an adviser, an able and willing missionary and mentor whose learning is respected, whose occult wisdom is venerated and whose medicine is often poured, untasted, into the gutter. Therefore Ikey's corniform, bespectacled nose and narrow, knowledge-bowed figure was well known in the vicinity of the Blue Light, and his advice and notice were much desired.

Ikey roomed and breakfasted at Mrs Riddle's two squares away. Mrs Riddle had a daughter named Rosy. The circumlocution has been in vain – you must have guessed it – Ikey adored Rosy. She tinctured all his thoughts; she was the compound extract of all that was chemically pure and officinal – the dispensatory contained nothing equal to her. But Ikey was timid, and his hopes remained insoluble in the menstrum of his backwardness and fears. Behind his counter he was a superior being, calmly conscious of special knowledge and worth; outside he was a weak-kneed, purblind, motorman-cursed rambler, with ill-fitting clothes stained with chemicals and smelling of socotrine aloes and valerianate of ammonia.

The fly in Ikey's ointment (thrice welcome, pat trope!) was Chunk McGowan.

Mr McGowan was also striving to catch the bright smiles tossed about by Rosy. But he was no out-fielder as Ikey was; he picked them off the bat. At the same time he was Ikey's friend and customer, and often dropped in at the Blue Light Drug Store to have a bruise painted with iodine or get a cut rubber-plastered after a pleasant evening spent along the Bowery.

One afternoon McGowan drifted in in his silent, easy way, and sat, comely, smooth-faced, hard, indomitable, good-natured, upon a stool.

'Ikey,' said he, when his friend had fetched his mortar and sat opposite, grinding gum benzoin to a powder, 'get busy with your ear. It's drugs for me if you've got the line I need.'

Ikey scanned the countenance of Mr McGowan for the usual evidence of conflict, but found none.

'Take your coat off,' he ordered. 'I guess already that you have been struck in the ribs with a knife. I have many times told you those Dagoes would do you up.'

Mr McGowan smiled. 'Not them,' he said. 'Not any Dagoes. But you've located the diagnosis all right enough – it's under my coat, near the ribs. Say! Ikey – Rosy and me are goin' to run away and get married tonight.'

Ikey's left forefinger was doubled over the edge of the mortar, holding it steady. He gave it a wild rap with the pestle, but felt it not. Meanwhile Mr McGowan's smile faded to a look of perplexed gloom.

'That is,' he continued, 'if she keeps in the notion until the time comes. We've been layin' pipes for the getaway for two weeks. One day she says she will; the same evenin' she says nixy. We've agreed on tonight, and Rosy's stuck to the affirmative this time for two whole days. But it's five hours yet till the time, and I'm afraid she'll stand me up when it comes to the scratch.'

'You said you wanted drugs,' remarked Ikey.

Mr McGowan looked ill at ease and harassed – a condition opposed to his usual line of demeanor. He made a patent-medicine almanac into a roll and fitted it with unprofitable carefulness about his finger.

'I wouldn't have this double handicap make a false start tonight for a million,' he said. 'I've got a little flat up in Harlem all ready, with chrysanthemums on the table and a kettle ready to boil. And I've engaged a pulpit pounder to be ready at his house for us at 9.30. It's got to come off.

And if Rosy don't change her mind again!' – Mr McGowan ceased, a prey to his doubts.

'I don't see then yet,' said Ikey, shortly, 'what makes it that you talk of drugs, or what I can be doing about it.'

'Old man Riddle don't like me a little bit,' went on the uneasy suitor, bent upon marshalling his arguments. 'For a week he hasn't let Rosy step outside the door with me. If it wasn't for losin' a boarder they'd have bounced me long ago. I'm makin' $20 a week and she'll never regret flyin' the coop with Chunk McGowan.'

'You will excuse me, Chunk,' said Ikey. 'I must make a prescription that is to be called for soon.'

'Say,' said McGowan, looking up suddenly, 'say, Ikey, ain't there a drug of some kind – some kind of powders that'll make a girl like you better if you give 'em to her?'

Ikey's lip beneath his nose curled with the scorn of superior enlightenment; but before he could answer, McGowan continued:

'Tim Lacy told me he got some once from a croaker uptown and fed 'em to his girl in soda water. From the very first dose he was ace-high and everybody else looked like thirty cents to her. They was married in less than two weeks.'

Strong and simple was Chunk McGowan. A better reader of men than Ikey was could have seen that his tough frame was strung upon fine wires. Like a good general who was about to invade the enemy's territory he was seeking to guard every point against possible failure.

'I thought,' went on Chunk, hopefully, 'that if I had one of them powders to give Rosy when I see her at supper tonight it might brace her up and keep her from reneging on the proposition to skip. I guess she don't need a mule team to drag her away, but women are better at coaching than they are at running bases. If the stuff'll work just for a couple of hours it'll do the trick.' 'When is this foolishness of running away to be happening?' asked Ikey.

'Nine o'clock,' said Mr McGowan. 'Supper's at seven. At eight Rosy goes to bed with a headache, at nine old Parvenzano lets me through to his backyard, where there's a board off Riddle's fence, next door. I go under her window and help her own the fire-escape. We've got to make it early on the preacher's account. It's all dead easy if Rosy don't balk when the flag drops. Can you fix me one of them powders, Ikey?'

Ikey Schoenstein rubbed his nose slowly.

'Chunk, said he, 'it is of drugs of that nature that pharmaceutists must have much carefulness. To you alone of my acquaintance would I intrust a powder like that. But for you I shall make it, and you shall see how it makes Rosy to think of you.'

Ikey went behind the prescription desk. There he crushed to a powder two soluble tablets, each containing a quarter of a grain of morphia. To them he added a little sugar of milk to increase the bulk, and folded the mixture neatly in a white paper. Taken by an adult this powder would insure several hours of heavy slumber without danger to the sleeper. This he handed to Chunk McGowan, telling him to administer it in a liquid if possible, and received the hearty thanks of the backyard Lochinvar.

The subtlety of Ikey's action becomes apparent upon recital of his subsequent move. He sent a messenger for Mr Riddle and disclosed the plans of Mr McGowan for eloping with Rosy. Mr Riddle was a stout man, brickdusty of complexion and sudden in action.

'Much obliged, he said, briefly, to Ikey. 'The lazy Irish loafer! My own room's just above Rosy's. I'll just go up there myself after supper and load the shot-gun and wait. If he comes in my backyard he'll go away in a ambulance instead of a bridal chaise.'

With Rosy held in the clutches of Morpheus for a many-hours deep slumber, and the blood-thirsty parent waiting, armed and forewarned, Ikey felt that his rival was close, indeed, upon discomfiture.

All night in the Blue Light Drug Store he waited at his duties for chance news of the tragedy, but none came.

At eight o'clock in the morning the day clerk arrived and Ikey started hurriedly for Mrs Riddle's to learn the outcome. And, lo! as he stepped out of the store who but Chunk McGowan sprang from a passing street car and grasped his hand – Chunk McGowan with a victor's smile and flushed with joy.

'Pulled it off,' said Chunk with Elysium in his grin. 'Rosy hit the fire-escape on time to a second, and we was under the wire at the Reverend's at $9.30\frac{1}{4}$. She's up at the flat – she cooked eggs this mornin' in a blue kimono – Lord! how lucky I am! You must pace up some day, Ikey, and feed with us. I've got a job down near the bridge, and that's where I'm heading for now.'

'The – the – powder?' stammered Ikey.

'Oh, the stuff you gave me!' said Chunk, broadening his grin; 'well, it was this way. I sat down at the supper table last night at Riddle's, and I looked at Rosy, and I says to myself, 'Chunk, if you get the girl get her on the square – don't try any hocus-pocus with a thoroughbred like her.' And I keeps the paper you give me in my pocket. And then my lamps fall on another party present, who, I says to myself, is failin' in a proper affection toward his comin' son-in-law, so I watches my chance and dumps that powder in old man Riddle's coffee – see?'

Growing Pains

Kenneth Robinson

I don't have green fingers, but I do have black thumbs. By which I mean that they are often soiled, not by gardening but by the print from books *about* gardening.

Especially since the vandalizing of my willow tree.

It's true there are straggling remnants of it, hovering over what we laughingly refer to as the lawn. Though on a closer look it resembles a mutilated hatstand hung about with random houseplants. And it's no good my wondering why it wasn't completely destroyed. I know very well.

'If that tree goes,' I had said to my wife, 'then I shall go too.'

So she merely had the twelve finest branches lopped off, leaving me not knowing how much of my promise I ought to keep. I mean, do I go away for just a night or two each week? I find I'm rather like the man in Clarence Day's *Life with Father*. Whenever I pack my bags, I'm always back in time for tea.

My wife says it wasn't her fault. It seems she was approached by a local tree butcher with no soul and less skill, who said I had sent him to do the job. I'm not suspicious by nature, but it was pretty clever of him to pick the hour in the week when I was busy helping to address the nation on Radio 4.

But I digress. In fact, I don't know why I'm telling you any of this. Except that is does explain what I said earlier about getting black thumbs from all those printed words on gardening.

You see, I simply had to buy all the likeliest books and get some advice on wounded willow trees. The way I was behaving, it wouldn't have been long before the neighbours arranged for me to be put away. I kept patting the gaping scars on the tree trunk, saying, 'There, there,' and discussing with anyone passing the chance of grafting with some plastic boughs. But a friend who knows about such things told me a willow tree always responded to kindness. And that's how I got on to reading, not everyday nature study books, but a collection of folklore. Leafing, if that's the word I want, through page after page about the archaic beliefs that persist in the countryside.

Did you *know* that a freshly picked onion stuffed into the ear 'can do wonders for earache'? Like giving it to you, I shouldn't wonder. Or that if you've got a spare onion, and don't fancy it down the earhole, you could put it under your rose trees? This, they say in Dorset, brings out the colour. What's more, they say irrelevantly, if you wash your cat and sprinkle the dirty water on the garden this will keep away mice.

Moles, if you're interested, are not so easy to get rid of. One author recommends a team of boys playing football in the garden to give the ground a good shaking. And if you're short of boys you could offer the moles a red herring.

Which is what I seem to be offering to you. I mean, you're eager, I know, to hear the truth about willow trees. Though I always feel there's no harm in passing on *any* useful information casually acquired. After all, some of you may be having trouble with your sprouts. To grow these vegetables, country folklore suggests the planting of mothballs or ladies' underwear. And one American woman, it seems, got very excited about burning her undies every day, until she found they were not the sort of fertility symbol she had in mind.

But if you are wanting offspring from a marriage, says my folk literature, you need a mandrake. You should be careful how you pick it, because it is said to shriek and send you mad. This is why dogs were once trained to do the uprooting and go mad *for* you. To save any inconvenience.

This all sounds a bit eccentric. There's the belief, for instance, about only a well-endowed man being fit to sow cucumbers. And there's a tip from South America that peppers should be planted either by a lunatic or by a man in a hot temper. I could easily have qualified for that job on the day the willow wept.

When I *did* come across the bit about willow trees, I found that not only do they reach out their fronds to sympathizers, but they die if their owners leave them. So it looks as if I must stay and watch my tree and my wife growing old and gnarled together.

In the meantime, you may care to know that in Oxfordshire people have a habit of leaving parcels of bacon at crossroads. I'm told this never fails. Whoever picks up the parcel comes out in warts. It wouldn't be a very nice thing to do, would it?

Even to somebody who had dismantled your willow tree?

The Cricket Team

John Moore

Brensham is a village in the heart of England's rural West
Country, and John Moore described life here, and in the
neighbouring village of Elmbury, between the wars. It is a
world full of much-loved traditions — not least, of course,
the village cricket team.

The Cricket-Ground

I used to think that the cricket-field at Brensham, on a blue afternoon in
May, must surely be one of the pleasantest places in the world; and certainly,
when I travelled about the world, I found fewer places pleasanter. About
the time of the first match, the apple-blossom came out, and the willows put
on their young green. The first cuckoo arrived and started calling from the
small adjacent meadow which was appropriately named Cuckoo Pen. There
were cuckoo-flowers in this meadow too, a silver-lilac carpet of them, so that
we did not know whether it was called after the bird or the flower. Lapwings
had their nests there, and sometimes we found the mottled eggs when we
were looking for a ball which had been skied, Brensham-fashion, right over
the tops of the willow-trees.

To match the newness of the Spring, Mr Chorlton had repainted the
pavilion in green-and-white. Against the very fresh green of the pitch – the
floods had lain on it for weeks at midwinter – the white lines of the creases
showed sharp and clear. And how white in the Spring sunshine were the
flannels well-creased after months in bottom-drawers, the umpires' coats, the
new-blanco'd pads and cricket-boots! How bright were the many-coloured
blazers, and Mr Chorlton's Harlequin cap, and Mr Mountjoy's I. Zingari!
(Where else had I seen those colours? Why, round the battered straw hat

which the Hermit wore when he showed visitors up to the roof of the Folly on high days and holidays. Mr Mountjoy must have given it to him!)

Smells and sounds: the sweet linseed-smell of bat-oil, and an indefinable clean smell (waterweed and foam?) which came from the weir and the lock just up-river. The gillyflower smell which blows in little brief gusts all over Brensham when there is a wind. The satisfying smack of a well-oiled bat hitting a ball during a knock-up before the game. The first bees buzzing in the apple-blossom. And in the willow-branches ubiquitous the endlessly repeated *chiff-chaff, chiff-chaff, chiff-chaff, chiff,* of the little yellow-olive bird from across the sea.

Clatter of plates in the lean-to hut behind the pavilion: the Helpers were already preparing the tea. These Helpers were a personable lot: Mrs Doan's daughter Sally, the young wife of the landlord of the Adam and Eve, and two merry little blondes, Mimi and Meg, from the Horse Narrow. We were proud of them, because they always excited the wonder and admiration of visiting teams. We were also proud of their teas, which were not teas in the sedate drawing-room sense, but were more like Hunt Breakfasts, for they consisted of home-made meat pies, wonderful salads – lettuces, tomatoes, spring onions, watercress from the same stream in which we sometimes lost our cricket-balls – and generally a ham, home-smoked at the Adam and Eve and decorated with paper frills and parsley so that it looked like a picture out of Mrs Beeton. The tea interval was always a long one at Brensham.

And now the captains have tossed and Sammy Hunt leads us out to field. Sammy has a completely bald head, which at the beginning of the season appears startlingly white; but he scorns to wear a hat, and as the season progresses his pate becomes rubicund, and then gradually goes brown, until by mid-August it is the colour of an overwintered russet apple. Mr Chorlton, of course, wears his Harlequin cap, the gayest cap in cricket, but it's old and faded and it's the very same cap, he tells us, in which he ran about the field for hours, in 1895, chasing the ball which Archie Maclaren hit so mercilessly when he scored 424 against Somerset. Mr Mountjoy, who wears his I. Zingari cap, must have been a useful cricketer too in his young days; but he can't run very fast or bend very quickly, and his old eyes – so sharp at spotting the chiff-chaff in the willow-tree – are too slow to follow the ball which comes quick off the pitch and breaks away. Therefore his innings generally end with a loud *snick* and a yell of 'How's that?' from the delighted wicket-keeper; and as the umpire's finger goes up Mr Mountjoy mutters sadly: 'Oh Lord, that awful noise again!'

Sammy begins to arrange his field, doing so with humanity and a sense of the fitness of things. Thus Mr Mountjoy, since he can't run far, goes to mid-off and to save him walking between overs takes point when the bowling is from the other end. Mr Chorlton, who can't or won't run at all, keeps wicket; and another elderly member of the team, a retired engineer called Hope-Kingley, alternates between mid-on and square leg. But Briggs the blacksmith, who has huge horny hands with which he sometimes bends a six-inch nail for fun, must stand at forward short-leg or in the deep, and take what's coming to him; the village policeman goes in the slips, because, says Sammy, that's a suitable place for a bobby – 'they catch you out when you're not looking.' Billy Butcher, who is the village ne'er-do-weel and drunkard, is sent to long-leg in the hope that a bit of running about will do him good; and the 'boys', a collective term for any youths whom the secretary has roped in at the last moment to make up the team, are distributed round the boundary where with luck some high hits will harden up their palms. As for Sammy himself, he will be anywhere and everywhere, wherever the catches come low and hard, wherever the new red ball races towards the boundary there will be Sammy's bald head bobbing after it; for he is like a good general who turns up unexpectedly wherever the fight is hottest.

Our Secretary, a small wiry market-gardener called Alfie, takes the ball for the first over. Joe Trentfield, our umpire and the landlord of the Horse Narrow, counts his six pennies and drops them one by one into the pocket of his smock. Dai Roberts the postman opens his score-book at the pavilion window and licks the point of his pencil.

'Play!' says Joe: and the season begins.

The Captain

Sailors hardly ever take to cricket; they don't get the chance to practise, for one thing, and for another, I think cricket is a game of people who have roots, it is a territorial game, in which men really do bowl and bat with greater satisfaction when they do so for the place they belong to. It is an expression of parochialism; and even the County sides, which play for money, would scorn to buy and sell their players as footballers do, dealing in men as stockbrokers deal in shares. Thus if you should meet, say, the Lancashire side and the Gloucestershire side together in a pub you could easily differentiate them by their accents; and when Somerset or Yorkshire go on tour they take the speech of Somerset and Yorkshire with them. This territorial aspect of the game is even more evident in village cricket; and people were sometimes quite shocked that I should be allowed to play for Brensham, although I lived only four miles away. Peripatetic cricketers, who hawk their batsmanship or their fast bowling round all the teams in the district and change sides as often as Warwick the King-Maker are rare and generally disapproved of; certainly Brensham would have nothing to do with them. For cricket, as I have said, is somehow mixed up with our vigorous parochialism; and when Brensham goes out to field on Saturday afternoon, it is Brensham going to war.

Therefore it was curious that Sammy Hunt should be our captain; for he was one of the rootless, heartless ones, a sailor, and hadn't had the opportunity, during his wandering life, to learn that absurd loyalty to a piece of well-kept turf. It was curious of course, that he should have settled down at Brensham at all, to 'muck about with little boats,' as he put it, 'on a piddling little river.' I suppose all sailors carry with them about the world, in addition to that small green kit-bag of their personal possessions, a dream of green fields; and for most of them the dream fades or the salt water tarnishes it; but somehow or other Sammy managed to keep his fresh and bright so that when the time came for him to reitre he knew exactly what kind of a cottage he wanted, knew all about the green-sprouting osiers and the slow winding river, bent like a bow as it runs round the hill, and the water-meadows where in June the wind-waves trouble the mowing-grass as if it were the sea.

However, Sammy never forgot that he was a sailor; and he often enlivened the cricket-matches with great sea-oaths or astonished the opposing team by shouting to his bowler: 'Pitch the beggar one on the starboard side!' or commanding a fieldman to 'move round a couple of points to port.' In the pub afterwards he would sooner or later launch himself into one of his long salty tales, about how he ran out of coal during a storm in the Bay of Biscay, or how he dealt with a mutiny at Tiensin, or how he nearly married a geisha girl in Japan; but although we knew these tales so well, and loved to hear Sammy telling them, we never learned what happened in the end: closing time always came too soon, leaving Sammy's tramp-steamer drifting helplessly towards Vigo, Sammy driving the mutineers into the fo'c'sle with his bare fists, or Sammy and his geisha girl locked in a timeless embrace on the sea-front of Yokohama.

The Blacksmith

Jeremy Briggs, who helped Mr Chorlton to make our pitch one of the best in the West Country, was another craftsman. At his blacksmith's forge, when he was not shoeing horses, he would contrive you almost anything from a cigarette-lighter to a set of fire-irons or a pair of wrought-iron gates. On the cricket-field he lumbered about rather like one of those great slow farm-horses whose enormous hairy hoofs he cared for. Between matches he often mowed the ground for us, or patiently dragged the heavy roller to and fro, to and fro between the creases while Mr Chorlton with a pocket-knife dug up the daisies, and filled in the holes. These two, as they worked together, carried on an argument which never ended; for Briggs was a Socialist and Mr Chorlton, whose wide classical reading had persuaded him that the political troubles of Athens and Rome were much the same as ours, believed that mankind was incapable of improvement and that no doctrine could save it from damnation. The argument continued from week to week and was abandoned in September only to be resumed in the following April. When Briggs' rolling took him down the pitch away from the crease where Mr Chorlton knelt before a daisy, Briggs began to shout; and Mr Chorlton shouted back, so that you could hear them in Magpie Lane, the one quoting Marx, the other Pericles. Our nearly-perfect cricket-pitch was really a by-product of their differences; for if they hadn't enjoyed arguing we should not have had two good groundsmen for nothing.

Briggs' smithy was next door to the Adam and Eve. There was no spreading chestnut tree, only a heap of old iron in the yard, with some broken carts, rusty farm implements and dismantled motor-cars. A notice-board announced: 'J. Briggs, Shoeing Etc, Smith. Contracts Undertook. Odd Jobing.' I once asked him what Contracts he Undertook; and it turned out that he had an arrangement with a market-gardener to shoe his pony all round twice a year in return for four bundles of asparagus and a pot of plums.

There was plenty of work for Briggs in Brensham. Most of the farmers' sons had their hunters and Point-to-pointers, the district abounded with children's ponies, there was a riding-school at Elmbury, and the Hunt stables were only five miles away. Briggs, for whom the colour red had a very different connotation from that of pink coats, shod these Hunt horses somewhat reluctantly, pointing out to the Whips and Second Horsemen who brought them to his smithy that Hunt Servants were merely the misguided flunkeys of the idle rich. The Whips, secure in their certainty that jumping a stiff blackthorn or hollering a fox away as he crept down the winter covertside was a very different thing from flunkeydom, merely smiled and wondered how a man who could handle horses so confidently came to believe in Labour. There was a close association, in their minds, between horseflesh and Conservatism.

But when it came to a question of working for the Syndicate, Briggs stuck his toes in. The Syndicate kept horses for hacking; they did not hunt. They liked, we thought, to have their photographs taken on horseback when they came down from town for the week-end. Briggs, who merely disapproved of the Hunt, really hated the Syndicate. The Hunt, after all, performed its wicked Capitalist actions openly, publicly and indeed ostentatiously, with shiny top-hats and red coats and polished top-boots. It galloped over your holding and broke down your fences with a hurrah and a holloa. If you got in the way, and General Bouverie cursed you, you could curse him back; you could scowl at the elegant gentlemen and the great ladies and the fat smug farmers and the feckless farmers' sons and pleasantly contemplate stringing them up to the lamp-posts in the fullness of time. But the Syndicate worked in darkness and in disguise: it was the kind of Capitalism which pulled the invisible wires and made poor men dance to its tune. It was part of the monstrous mysterious Thing which sent up the rent of cottages and sent down the miner's wage; which contrived a glut of coffee in Brazil or a rice famine in Bengal by fiddling about in some unexplained way with Foreign Exchange. In some unspecified fashion, Briggs was sure of it, the Syndicate was associated with the terrible, powerful, nameless people whom he thought of as 'They'. 'They' had their offices in London and New York and Amsterdam; 'They' were supernational; 'They' played with Governments as if Governments were pawns, stood above Prime Ministers and Kings, and laughed cynically at revolutions, being confident that 'They' could easily corrupt the revolutionaries with the gift of a little illusory power. 'They' was invisible, anonymous, unidentified; you couldn't curse them, break their windows, imprison them or hang them. Briggs had serious doubts whether even the Russian Communists had effectively got rid of Them.

Seeing in the Syndicate's workings a trivial, fragmentary manifestation of Their power, Briggs stoutly refused to shoe their horses and assaulted their Head Groom who apparently 'called him names'. For this he was bound over by the Justices of the Peace for Elmbury. 'What did he actually call you?' asked General Bouverie, who was Chairman of the Bench.

'A bloody Bolshie, your Worship,' said Briggs.

'Very provocative. I should have hit him myself,' said General Bouverie, who knew all about Briggs' politics. 'In the circumstances I shall refrain from imposing a fine.'

Of course, Briggs could easily afford to refuse the custom of the Syndicate; he was an extremely prosperous tradesman. There is a mistaken notion that the blacksmith's is a dying trade; and those who are always moaning and mourning the departure of Ye Olde things, the William-Morrissy-arty-crafty people, will tell you that the village smith is disappearing, another craftsman-victim of 'the thing we miscall Progress'. In fact I believe that Jeremy Briggs made a good deal more money than James Briggs his father, who owned the smithy before him. It is true that there were not so many farm horses in 1930 as there were in late Victorian times (although there were more hunters); but the 'odd-jobbing' which he so proudly advertised more than redressed the balance. If there were fewer horses, there were more farm-machinery; and when the binder or the haysweep went wrong it was generally the blacksmith's job to put it right. Again, fewer horses meant more motor-cars; and these motor-cars from time to time ran into each other head-on. When the drivers had been taken to hospital, and the vehicles had been towed to the garage, and the doctors, the motor manufacturers and the garagemen had all levied their dues upon the insurance company, there often remained a kind of residue in the shape of two bent front-axles which found their way to Briggs' forge. Besides, being a skilled worker in most metals, Briggs made a good many profitable odds-and-ends in his spare time; the local builder alone gave him enough work to pay for the beer which he drank in enormous quantities. He certainly didn't deserve the pity of the arty-crafty crowd who went in for folk-dancing and played upon pan-pipes and taught long-suffering villagers to make useless things out of raffia.

Like most blacksmiths, Briggs possessed notable biceps, forearms and hands. When he was a young man he could tear a pack of cards in two. His palms were criss-crossed with old calloused scars, which were the consequence of his youthful foolishness in bending six-inch nails for the entertainment of the company at the Adam and Eve. In later years, becoming less reckless, he wrapped handkerchiefs round his hands before starting his demonstration.

At one time he was the terror of travelling showmen at the local fairs; for whether it was a matter of bending pokers or lifting weights, Briggs could always do it better than they could. When the Strongest Man in the World with painful effort and streams of perspiration had managed to give a slight twist to an iron bar, Briggs, pleading with affected innocence 'Let me try that, Mister! Let me have a go!' would mount the rostrum and without apparent exertion bend the bar almost double. All the Strongest Men in the World hated and feared him.

At Elmbury Mop he elected one night to try his strength upon one of those machines which you smite with a mallet. He had had a great deal of beer, and what happened would have served as a good advertisement for the brewery. With his first shot, being as he freely admitted a bit unsteady on his pins, he missed altogether. The showman laughed; and this annoyed him. He took a lot of trouble over his next shot, his great hands which had clamped in their awful grip the kicking hoof of an angry stallion clasped the handle of the mallet, the muscles of his forearms stood out like the roots of an old tree, and Briggs smote. He hit the machine fair and square with such force that it fell apart; the head of the mallet flew off into the crowd. Satisfied, he shrugged his shoulders and walked away.

Yet at cricket he hardly ever hit sixes, but batted with a huge stolidity which would have done credit to a Lancashire stonewaller; his favourite stroke was what he imagined to be a neat and professional cut through the slips, off which he was generally caught in the gulley. And at darts he had a most curious style which seemed to be a flat contradiction of his great size and strength: he threw rather like a girl. He possessed a set of darts of his own, very tiny and, as one might say, sissy darts, which he picked up deliberately between his enormous fingers (which weren't half as clumsy as they looked) and propelled very neatly and primly into the particular double or treble he wanted.

The 'Boys'

The last five or six places in our cricket-team were filled, generally at the last moment, by various unreliable and often unwilling youths whom Alfie impressed out of the pubs: labouring boys, farmers' sons and so on. The former, who toiled all the week in the fields and market-gardens, found no enjoyment whatever in chasing a cricket-ball in the hot sun upon their afternoon off; the latter, whose interest lay chiefly in fiery horses and powerful motor-bikes, had little enthusiasm for a game which offered no prospect of a broken neck. However, Alfie by his press-gang methods usually captured a few of them; and some, especially the farmers' sons, often slogged happily and heartily or took a few wickets with their murderous fast bowling.

We included in the category of 'the boys', because they were equally unreliable, Billy Butcher the village ne'er-do-weel and Banks, the village policeman. We could not count on either: the former because he was almost always drunk and the latter because he was often on duty. On one occasion we lost both players through the same cause: Billy Butcher chose a Saturday afternoon to go roaring round the village merrily breaking windows, and Banks was called out to arrest him.

That must have been the only arrest Banks made in his first five years at Brensham. He arrived, as all our village policemen do, as a young, efficient and rather officious constable, eager for promotion, willing to go out of his way to look for trouble, and inclined to hang about in the neighbourhood of the pubs at closing-time. He had succeeded an elderly, easy-going fellow who knew our ways; and at first we regarded Banks with suspicion and dismay. But Joe Trentfield, the landlord of the Horse Narrow, who'd seen village policemen come and go for twenty years, laughed at our fears and said philosophically: ''Tis allus the same with new brooms. Wait a bit, and you'll see we'll tame him. Be they real tigers, Brensham allus tames 'em in the end.'

And sure enough, we tamed Banks. We married him off, for one thing, to Joe Trentfield's daughter. We persuaded him to play for us at cricket and darts. Sammy Hunt built him a boat and taught him to fish for chub. Soon he learned that the business of a village constable was concerned, not with criminals and crooks, but with Foot and Mouth Disease and Swine Fever, Straying Animals and Lost Dogs: and that the nearest he was likely to get to dealing with a murder was his annual duty of quelling a row between the Fitchers and the Gormleys about a murder which had happened fifty years ago. He discovered (Joe Trentfield's daughter may have had something to do with the discovery) that the best way of making sure that the pub closed at ten was to drop in for a quiet drink with the landlord at ten-thirty. He found out that prosecuting people for having no dog licence or riding a bicycle without lights was not, after all, a short cut to promotion; and before very long the dream of quick promotion faded, and a different dream took its place: he began to save up towards buying a cottage with perhaps a little orchard and a couple of pigstyes, so that he could still live in the shadow of Brensham Hill when he retired.

The Match Against Woody Bourton

It was delightful to watch these three extraordinary and lovable spectators sitting together on the bench that was only just long enough for them: Goaty Pegleg with his impressive white beard and his wooden peg held out straight in front of him, looking extremely salty and piratical although he'd never seen the sea, nor, in fact, travelled more than twenty miles from Brensham; the Colonel in his green tweeds which merged into the leafy background so that his figure lacked definition and you only noticed the fire-red, gnome-like face, the badger-grizzled moustache, the bright humorous blue eyes; and the scarecrow lord whose panama hat had not worn as well as the Colonel's deerstalker, so that he gave the impression of having, literally, straws in his hair.

I remember a match at which I too was a spectator, and sat on the grass at the feet of these three, because I had sprained my ankle in a fall from my motor-bike. I remember it better than all the other matches, perhaps because the looker-on sees most of the game, or perhaps because it had such a comic and glorious ending, or perhaps again because it happened on the loveliest June day you could possibly imagine, a day of blue and green and gold, and of light breezes, gillyflower-scented, and lullaby sounds of bees, wood-pigeons and far-away cuckoos. The sky was immaculate, hedge-sparrow-egg-blue; the mowing-grass rippled in all the water-meadows along the river and like green foam were the leafy orchards on the lower slopes of the hill. Buttercups along the unmown edges of our ground were a frieze of gold which gilded white cricket boots and the turn-ups of flannel trousers.

The match was against a team called Woody Bourton and it was a match we particularly wanted to win; for the plain reason that we detested Woody Bourton, whose captain was a dull humourless stone-waller, whose one-eyed umpire had never been known to give an l.b.w. against his own side, and whose wicket-keeper appealed almost ceaselessly in a cracked voice like that of a raven prophesying doom. Do not let yourself be misled by romantic writers into the belief that village cricket is played in a cheerful, 'sporting' spirit of 'Never mind who wins.' I have said that when we took the field we were Brensham going to war. Therefore we minded very much who won. And especially we should mind if we were defeated by Woody Bourton who were known to us as Bloody Bourton. They had beaten us (or, as some said, their umpire had beaten us) the previous year; and we thirsted for revenge.

But from the first ball, which took Mr Chorlton's off stump out of the ground, things went ill with us. Sir Gerald Hope-Kingley, who was next in, ran out Mr Mountjoy, who shortly afterwards ran out himself. ('Like two old hens scampering up and down the wicket they are,' commented Dai.) Sammy Hunt batted for a while with the heroic determination of one who maintains a crumbling citadel against an innumerable enemy; then the wicket-keeper appealed for a catch and up went the loathed umpire's cigarette-stained finger. Sammy walked slowly back, his bald head bright scarlet, which meant, we rightly guessed, that he was furious about the verdict. Alfie went out, had his stumps knocked flying, and returned to spread alarm and despondency among 'the boys'. 'He's bowling helluva fast,' said Alfie, who frequently employed this curious adjective. Banks, who batted next, was so cast down by Alfie's report that he jumped out of the way of his first ball, which took the bails off.

So far we had lost five wickets for thirty runs, most of which were byes off the fast bowler. Then there was a brief gallant stand by Briggs and Billy Butcher. Briggs for once in a way forgot his ambition to chop every ball County-fashion between the slips; he threw caution to the winds, took hold of his bat by the top of the handle as one would hold a sledge-hammer – and used it as a sledge-hammer. He had a private reason for disliking the Bloody Bourton captain: the man was Conservative Agent for the constituency. So when Briggs smote the ball, he felt that he was smiting the Tories. Thus inspired he walloped it three times to the boundary and once over the willow-trees: three fours and a six, twenty-four runs for Brensham, four hearty blows struck for the proletariat.

Billy, as it happened, was suffering from an appalling hangover: he'd had a bad bout which had lasted three days and hadn't yet, we suspected, come to an end. But he cocked his cap at a defiant angle and jauntily took his guard, brandished his bat at the first ball in a devil-may-care gesture, missed it altogether, and received the ball on the inside of his thigh. It came quick off the pitch, and it must have hurt badly; but Billy only grinned, pointed his bat at the fast bowler, and called out: 'Hey, mind my courting tackle, if you please!' This made the bowler laugh, and brought a faint smile even to the sombre face of the Bloody Bourton captain. The next ball was a loose one, and Billy cut it over the slip's head for an accidental four. Encouraged, he began to play the fool, and his clowning provoked, irritated and thoroughly put off the opposing players, who dropped him twice and let him make several runs from overthrows. Then, unexpectedly in the middle of his clowning, the poetry appeared. Billy would have been a very fine batsman indeed if he could only have achieved the necessary co-ordination between hand and eye; the whisky got in the way of that. Today, however, he suddenly pulled himself together and made three successive strokes in which the timing was quite perfect. They were sublime: they were a poet's strokes. The first was a drive through the covers which flowed like a slow river with lovely, lazy grace. The next was a cheeky glance to leg carried out as casually as if it had been an impertinent aside during a serious conversation. The third was a glorious pull off his middle stump made with a sort of despairing gaiety, a laughing challenge to the gods, a wild unorthodox defiant shot which you realized, if you knew him well, was Billy cocking a snook at the world. The ball went sailing over the brook and into the buttercups beyond. 'Oh, lovely, lovely, lovely!' cried Lord Orris, clapping his thin pale hands. The Colonel, wiping the mouth of his flask, muttered: 'By God, I'll have a drink on that one,' and did so. A full half-minute later Goaty Pegleg, travelling slowly in the Fourth Dimension, declared loudly: 'He's hit a six.'

But the effort of co-ordination had been too much for Billy. He failed to see the next ball until it hit his pads, which were plainly in front of the wicket. 'Howzat?' croaked the Raven, and Joe after a moment's hesitation to show Bloody Bourton that he could have got even with their umpire if he had liked, reluctantly gave Billy out. After that the innings soon ended; three hobbledehoys, unlucky victims of Alfie's press-gang, made three runs between them and Briggs, trying to hit another six for Labour, was caught in the deep. Brensham was all out for seventy-nine and the teams came in to tea.

I remember the cuckoo which called all tea-time from a willow-tree in Cuckoo Pen; and the background of bees and woodpigeons and gillyflower sent on the soft light airs. I remember the Colonel's Ionian laughter at some remark of Billy Butcher's, and old Orris' gentle manners and gentle smile. I remember Mrs Hatley's ham with the golden breadcrumbs on it, and a ridiculous garden-party hat which Mimi wore, and Meg confiding her film-ambitions to Mr Chorlton who listened gravely and didn't smile even when she said: 'They told me I was ever so photogenic.' I remember Sally Doan plying Billy with meat-pies and whispering to him urgently: 'Now you must *eat*' – and I remember wondering if she were in love with him. How absurd and disastrous if she were! But then Joe Trentfield, who'd been a Sergeant-Major before he took the Horse Narrow, looked at his watch and said: 'Come along, boys! Late on parade!' and Sammy led our team out into the field.

Now Bloody Bourton had an hour and a half in which to score eighty runs. They could have done it easily; but being Bloody Bourton they scratched and scraped and niggled and fiddled about, as Dai put it, so that by half-past five – we drew stumps at six, which was opening-time – they had only scored forty for the loss of four wickets. The game looked like ending in a dreary draw; but Bloody Bourton, realizing too late that they would have to score much faster in order to have a chance of winning, suddenly began to hit; and hitting was not in their nature. After Mr Mountjoy had missed an easy catch, because he was listening to the curlews and the drumming snipe in the meadows beyond Cuckoo Pen, Alfie Perks took two wickets in the same over. And still the Bloody Bourton batsmen went out for the runs. A curious sort of desperation had overtaken them; for they delighted as a rule to make little pernickety shots along the ground, to score in singles, and to keep their opponents running about in the hot sun for two or three hours while they enjoyed themselves in their prim puritanical cautious way. But now they waved their bats wildly at every ball and called each other frantically for short runs. I heard Mr Chorlton say to Mr Mountjoy between overs: *Quem Deus vult perditur, prius dementat*; and sure enough next ball he was able to stump a batsman who had run half-way down the pitch to one of Alfie's leg-breaks and missed it altogether.

Six wickets for fifty-one, and twenty minutes to go! Sammy, who must be in the forefront of the battle always, put himself on to bowl, pounded down to the wicket with his bald head flaming, and yorked his man with the last ball of the over. Then Billy missed a catch; and our hearts sank. 'It iss the whisky and the pubs and the profane goings-on,' said Dai primly, 'that iss the ruination of cricket in Brensham!' We suffered another set-back a moment later, when Mr Chorlton appealed for a catch and the one-eyed umpire (who might have been blind in both eyes, and stone-deaf as well, for all the notice he took of our appeals) remained motionless as if rooted to the ground, stared stonily in front of him, and took no notice. The Bloody Bourton captain, taking heart, scored a couple of fours, and sixty went up on the score-board. Things looked bad; but a few minutes later Sammy took another wicket for a yorker and at twenty past six the ninth man was stumped by Mr Chorlton. The last man walked out to the wicket as slowly as he dared and as eagerly as if he went blindfold towards the scaffold, snicked a two and a four off Sammy, and got a present of another four from one of Sir Gerald's overthrows. The score was seventy-two when Alfie bowled a long hop to the Bloody Bourton captain, who astonished even himself by hitting it for six.

This was the last over, and Bloody Bourton wanted two runs to win. Even the Colonel sat up tensely and put his flask away in his pocket. Everybody was on his toes with the solitary exception of Briggs, who was standing deep at long-on where for a long time he had had nothing to do. I noticed a faint blue haze hanging about him in the still evening air; I looked again, and perceived that Briggs was lighting his pipe.

Alfie came up to the wicket with his familiar hop, skip and jump, tousled fair hair falling into his eyes. The Bloody Bourton captain, whose success in hitting a six had gone to his head, ran down the pitch and hit the ball a full toss. He caught it awkwardly high up on the splice of the bat but it was a hefty clout all the same, and the ball flew high towards long-on. Everybody looked at Briggs; but Briggs, with his big hands cupping a match, was still puffing away at his pipe. The whole team yelled at him. Sammy shouted terrible sea-oaths at the top of his voice. I shouted, the Colonel shouted, even Lord Orris shouted in his small piping voice. Only goaty Pegleg, who had not yet tumbled to what was happening, remained silent. At last Briggs looked up, and saw the ball falling towards him. He did not move. Without hurry he put the box of matches into his left pocket and the pipe into his right pocket. Then, as one who receives manna from heaven he extended his enormous hands in front of him. The ball fell into them, the strong fingers closed as if they would squeeze it out of shape. Finally, still without hurry, he removed his pipe from his pocket lest it burn his trousers.

When the cheering was over there was a little silence while Joe Trentfield pulled up the stumps and the team came back towards the pavilion. Then Goaty Pegleg announced in a loud voice *urbi et orbi*: 'He's caught it! We've won!' as if he were an astronomer who watches the stars through a telescope and sees, a hundred light-years after the event, the flaming destruction of a far-distant sun which, at the moment of earth-time when he witnesses it, has long been black and dead.

So off go Bloody Bourton with perfunctory handshakes and insincere smiles and with black hatred in their hearts. 'It was a good game,' we say, rubbing it in. 'Just the right sort of finish,' they agree without enthusiasm. Mr Mountjoy hurries off to his Evening Service – he's two minutes late already. The Colonel mounts his motor-bike and chugs off towards the Swan. Lord Orris untethers from the gate Tom Pearce's grey mare and rides slowly back towards his ruined mansion. Goaty Pegleg stumps away, the girls wash up the tea-things, Mrs Hartley puts back her ham in its muslin bag. The persistent cuckoo, whose voice is breaking already, calls his last throaty cuck-cuck-cuck-oo from the top of the willow-tree.

'And now,' says Sammy Hunt, wiping the sweat-beads off his bald head, 'now for a pint at the Adam and Eve, and a game of darts!'

Acknowledgements

The Publishers wish to thank the following for permission to reprint copyright material: Roald Dahl, Jonathan Cape Ltd and Penguin Books Ltd for 'The Hitch-hiker' from *The Wonderful World of Henry Sugar*; Clive James and A. D. Peters & Co. Ltd for 'Postcard from Biarritz' from *Flying Visits*; Fran Lebovitz and Sidgwick & Jackson Ltd for 'Travel Hints' from *Social Studies*; Miles Kington and Anthony Sheil Associates for 'Kington's Book of Lists' and 'Growing Pains' from *Miles and Miles*, and 'The Great Sea Saga of *Photocopier III*' from *Moreover*; David Niven and Hamish Hamilton Ltd for an extract from *The Moon's a Balloon*; Alan Coren and Robson Books Ltd for 'Let Us Now Phone Famous Men' and 'All You Need to Know About Europe' from *The Best of Alan Coren*; Barry Took, Marty Feldman and The Woburn Press for an episode from *Round The Horne*; The Executors of the Estate of W. Somerset Maugham and William Heinemann Ltd for 'The Luncheon' and 'The Verger' from *The Complete Stories of W. Somerset Maugham*; A. D. Peters & Co. Ltd for 'Life at Boulton Wynfevers' and 'Trousers over Africa' from *The Best of Beachcomber* by J. B. Morton; Douglas Dunn and Punch Publications Ltd for 'Do It Yourself'; Hamish Hamilton Ltd for 'The Secret Life of Walter Mitty', 'The Dog that Bit People' and 'Ride with Olympy' from *Vintage Thurber* by James Thurber; Alan Melville and William Heinemann Ltd for 'Showing Round' from *The Gnomes' Guide to Gardening*; Penguin Books Ltd for 'The Pope's Mule' from *Letters From My Windmill* by Alphonse Daudet, translated by Leonard Tancock; Tom Sharpe and Martin Secker & Warburg Ltd for 'Too Much of a Good Thing' from *Porterhouse Blue* and 'Foreign Affairs' from *The Wilt Alternative*; Jilly Cooper and Methuen Publishers Ltd for 'The Cruel C. E.' from *Jolly Marsupial*; Richard Ingrams, John Wells and Private Eye Ltd for 'A Flying Visit' from *Dear Bill*; The Trustees of the Wodehouse Trust No. 3 and Century Hutchinson Ltd for 'Rodney Fails to Qualify' from *The Heart of a Goof* by P. G. Wodehouse; Richard Gordon and

Curtis Brown Ltd for 'Barnsfather's Syndrome' and an extract from *Doctor in Clover*; Robin Clark Ltd for 'Mipsie' from *Lady Addle Remembers* by Mary Dunn; Simon & Schuster Inc. for 'Letters to Warner Brothers' by Groucho Marx, © 1967 by Groucho Marx; Bernard Levin and Jonathan Cape Ltd for 'The Luck of the Irish' from *Conducted Tour*; David Godine Publishers Inc. for 'Henry VIII' and 'Elizabeth' from *The Decline and Fall of Practically Everybody* by Will Cuppy. Copyright 1950 by Fred Feldkamp; Paul Theroux and Hamish Hamilton Ltd for 'The Direct-Orient Express' from *The Great Railway Bazaar*; Little, Brown & Co. Inc. for 'Vignettes of Travel' from *The Dog Who Wouldn't Be* by Farley Mowat; Bob Larbey and Severn House Publishers Ltd for an extract from *A Fine Romance*; Joyce Grenfell and Macmillan Publishers Ltd for 'Going Home Time' and 'Opera Interval' from *Turn Back the Clock*; Stephen Leacock and The Bodley Head for 'Soaked in Seaweed' from *Nonsense Novels* and 'The Dentist and the Gas' from *Behind the Beyond*; A. D. Peters & Co. Ltd for 'Animals at Alconleigh' from *The Pursuit of Love* by Nancy Mitford; Arthur Marshall and Hamish Hamilton Ltd for 'Behind the Scenes' and 'Oh I Say Thanks Awfully' from *I'll Let You Know*; Graham Greene and The Bodley Head Ltd for 'A Trip to Brighton' from *Travels with My Aunt*; Kenneth Williams and J. M. Dent & Sons Ltd for 'Pages from a Private Diary' from *Back Drops*; J. H. Irving and Virgin Books Ltd for an extract from *The Killjoy's Book of the Cinema*; A. D. Peters & Co. Ltd for 'A Love-Match' from *The Spanish Pistol* by A. G. Macdonnell; Gerald Duckworth Co. Ltd for 'The Standard of Living' and 'The Waltz' by Dorothy Parker; Christopher Matthew and Pavilion Books Ltd for 'Office Parties' from *How to Survive Middle Age*; Dodd Mead & Co. Inc. for 'Bonny Boating Weather' and 'The Skin-Game' from *Dithers and Jitters* by Cornelia Otis Skinner. Copyright 1937, 1938 by Cornelia Otis Skinner. Copyright renewed 1965, 1966 by Cornelia Otis Skinner Blodget; Gerald Durrell and Grafton Books for 'An Entertainment with Animals' from *My Family and Other Animals*; Richard Stilgoe and Allen & Unwin Ltd for 'Col. Tiger Rashid' from *The Richard Stilgoe Letters*; Richard Briers and J. M. Dent Ltd for 'Oops! Conversations of a Delicate Nature' from *Natter, Natter*; Curtis Brown Ltd for 'Climbing Napes Needle' from *It's Never Too Late* by A. A. Milne; Basil Boothroyd and A. P. Watt Ltd for 'No Man is an Island' from *Let's Move House*; 'Butch Minds the Baby' and 'Sense of Humour' by Damon Runyon from *Runyon on Broadway*, reprinted by permission of Constable Publishers and by special arrangement with Raoul Lionel Felder Esq. and the American Play Company. Copyright by Damon Runyon September 13th 1930.

Renewed 1957 by Damon Runyon Jnr and Mary Runyon McCann; A. D. Peters & Co. Ltd for 'Men in Fiction' by E. M. Delafield; Peter Tinniswood and Century Hutchinson Ltd for 'The Groundsman's Horse' from *Tales from the Long Room*; Jonathan Lynn, Anthony Jay and BBC Publications for 'Equal Opportunities' from *Yes, Minister*, volume 3; A. P. Watt Ltd for 'Lucia and the Garden Fete' from *Mapp and Lucia* by E. F. Benson; The Hogarth Press for 'Village School' from *Cider with Rosie* by Laurie Lee; Victoria Wood and Methuen Publishers Ltd for 'Cleaning' from *Victoria Wood, As Seen on TV*; Douglas Sutherland and Debretts Peerage Ltd for 'Conversation Abroad' from *The English Gentleman Abroad*; Auberon Waugh and A. D. Peters & Co. Ltd for 'The Great Savings Swindle' and 'Death of a Goldfish' from *In the Lion's Den*; James Herriot and Michael Joseph Ltd for 'The Darrowby Show' from *Let Sleeping Vets Lie*; Curtis Brown Ltd for 'Ephraim's Undoing' by H. F. Ellis; John Mortimer and George Weidenfeld & Nicholson Ltd for 'Life with Father' from *Clinging to the Wreckage*; A. D. Peters & Co. Ltd for 'The Joy of Mooching' from *The Last Laugh* by S. J. Perelman; Curtis Brown Ltd for 'The Ceremonial Tasting of the First Potato' from *No Bed for Bacon* by Caryl Brahms and S. J. Simon © 1941 by Caryl Brahms and S. J. Simon; Kenneth Robinson and Century Hutchinson Ltd for 'Growing Pains' from *On the Offensive*; A. D. Peters & Co. Ltd for 'The Cricket Match' from *Brensham Village* by John Moore.

Every effort has been made to trace the owners of the copyright material in this book. In the case of any question arising as to the use of any such material, the Publishers would be pleased to receive notification of this.